BIOLOGY AND THE EXPLORATION OF MARS

BIOLOGY AND THE EXPLORATION OF MARS

Report of a Study Held under the Auspices of the
SPACE SCIENCE BOARD
NATIONAL ACADEMY OF SCIENCES   NATIONAL RESEARCH COUNCIL
1964-1965

Edited by
COLIN S. PITTENDRIGH, WOLF VISHNIAC, AND J. P. T. PEARMAN

Publication 1296
NATIONAL ACADEMY OF SCIENCES   NATIONAL RESEARCH COUNCIL
WASHINGTON, D. C.   1966

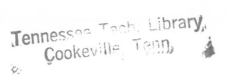
Copies of this publication are available from
Printing and Publishing Office
National Academy of Sciences
2101 Constitution Avenue, N. W.
Washington, D. C. 20418

Library of Congress Catalog Card Number 65-60913

FOREWORD

This volume presents the proceedings of the Exobiology Study conducted under the chairmanship of Dean Colin S. Pittendrigh of Princeton University and the co-chairmanship of Professor Joshua Lederberg of Stanford University. The Study was initiated by the Space Science Board of the National Academy of Sciences, at the request of the National Aeronautics and Space Administration. Meetings were held on the campus of Stanford University and at the Rockefeller Institute in New York. These meetings began in the Summer of 1964 and concluded with a session in October 1965.

The present volume consists of a general chapter summarizing the findings of the study, and a series of 29 technical chapters and 2 appendixes by the various participants. A companion volume, in press, provides an anthology and a selected bibliography of some 2,000 references: the study group believed that such a compilation would be useful to their colleagues.

We are grateful to the 66 specialists from many disciplines who have contributed to this study and whose conscientious efforts as participants or correspondents have made this report and its companion volume possible. We are also very much indebted to Dean Colin S. Pittendrigh, whose leadership is most gratefully acknowledged.

HARRY H. HESS, *Chairman*
Space Science Board

v

PREFACE

Until recent years the origin of life and its possible occurrence elsewhere in the universe have been matters for speculation only. The rapid growth of molecular biology since 1940 has, to be sure, made it possible to discuss life's origins in far more precise and explicit terms than was possible earlier; and the subject entered a new experimental phase in the 1950's with successful abiogenic synthesis of important biochemical substances in conditions simulating the presumptive environment of the primitive Earth. But the real transformation that the subject has undergone stems from the spectacular growth of space technology in the last decade. The possibility of life's origin and occurrence on planets other than ours is no longer limited to idle speculation: it has entered the realm of the testable, of science in the strict sense. Given the rockets now available, and especially those available by 1969, it has become fully realistic to consider plans for the biological exploration of Mars.

The study that this report seeks to interpret was initiated in June, 1964, by the Space Science Board of the National Academy of Sciences to examine this possibility. The working group comprised 36 people representing a broad spectrum of scientific interests: evolutionary biology, genetics, microbiology, biochemistry and molecular biology, animal physiology, soil chemistry, organic chemistry, planetary astronomy, geochemistry, and theoretical physics. The participants included some with considerable prior involvement in problems of space exploration and others with none. Advice was also sought outside the group of immediate participants on the potentialities of selected analytical methods for the experimental study of extraterrestrial life and its environment. More than 30 individuals contributed in this fashion written assessments of techniques in which they were particularly well versed.

Our task was to examine the scientific foundations and merits of the proposal to undertake a biological exploration of Mars. What are the potential scientific yields? How valuable, if attained, would they be? What, in fact, is the possibility of life occurring on Mars? And of our detecting it with available and foreseeable technology? What could be achieved by further astronomical work from Earth? by Martian fly-by missions? by Martian orbiters? and Martian Landers? What payloads would we recommend for planetary missions? What timing and over-all strategy would we recommend for Martian exploration were we to consider it worthwhile at all?

In brief, the over-all purpose was to recommend to the government, through the Academy's Space Science Board, whether or not a biological exploration of Mars should be included in the nation's space program over the next few decades; and, further, to outline what that program, if any, should be.

We emphasize that our conclusions were reached on strictly scientific grounds, and that we recognize that a much wider array of considerations bears upon any ultimate decision to undertake Martian exploration. We were not charged with, nor did we attempt, the broad overview that entails these other considerations. We predicated our discussion on the continued vigor of a national space program. We did not, for instance, address ourselves to the question of whether the very large cost of developing the Saturn boosters could be justified on scientific grounds. Nor should we have; the development of the Saturn boosters is already firmly committed for other reasons. The question we faced was whether the application of such boosters to the biological exploration of the solar system—of Mars in particular—can answer well-defined and important scientific questions; and what priority such a question merits within the space program.

The essence of our conclusions (pages 15-18) is that the exploration of Mars—motivated by biological questions—does indeed merit the highest scientific priority in the nation's space program over the next decades. We concluded, further, that the favorable opportunities for exploration between 1969 and 1973 can and should be exploited as vigorously as possible. Considering the diversity of discipline and persuasion represented by so large a group as ours, the unanimity achieved on these basic conclusions itself merits emphasis.

We achieved, understandably, less unanimity on precisely what course the exploration should take. There was a small minority among us that insisted that the first opportunity be taken to land a mission on Mars equipped with even a minimum of analytical devices. The majority view leaned toward a more gradualistic approach. Its foundation was twofold: (1) the tenet that specifically biological questions should be asked in an ordered sequence of exploration whose purpose is to understand the over-all evolution of the planet's crust and atmosphere; and (2) the large amount of work that remains to be done in designing and equipping a lander with the diversity of sensors necessary for study of a life of uncertain characteristics. The program emerging from this approach begins with emphasis on orbiter missions designed to enlarge our knowledge of the astronomical, geophysical, and geochemical features of Mars and its seasonal changes. Such new knowledge of the Martian environment will greatly enhance chances for the success of subsequent landing missions. And, further, it will also permit, prior to landing, a substantial re-evaluation of all those features on which our present judgment of the plausibility of Martian life depends.

This study was prompted by a specific request from the National Aeronautics and Space Administration to the National Academy of Sciences, and was carried out with its support. But it has also been a natural culmination of a discussion of many years in which many of the working group members have participated. Thus, to the extent that it has succeeded in accomplishing its assigned mission, it has depended on the work of several earlier committees and smaller symposia; and the conclusions and recommendations it presents are the product of prolonged deliberation and scrutiny. None of the working group failed to sense the burden of responsibility that such a costly program as Martian exploration entails; and none failed to sense the magnificent challenge and opportunity that is now before scientific man.

The present volume contains the findings of the study, a postscript discussing the significance of the observations obtained during the flight of Mariner IV past Mars, and a collection of the working papers that formed the basis of our discussions. As a guide to the reader, a synopsis of the principal sections is given below.

The conclusions and recommendations arising from the discussions are set forth in *PART I*. These statements express the agreements of the working group of the study and the rationale on which they were based.

PART II. Life: its Nature and Origin. An understanding of the nature of life is a prerequisite to any attempt to find evidence of it, but a concise definition is elusive. The salient properties and characteristics of living organisms are discussed.

Contemporary views on the chemical and physical processes that led to the appearance of life on Earth contribute to an assessment of the probability of finding evidence of biological activity elsewhere. Laboratory syntheses of biologically significant compounds are reviewed in the light of geochemical pertinence.

PART III. The Cosmic Setting. Some astronomical evidence bears on the distribution of environments that may be suitable for life. The planets of the solar system that are, or may become, accessible for closer study are examined as possible sites of biological activity. The reported presence of organic compounds in certain meteorites is discussed in terms of possible origins.

PART IV. Recognition of Life and some Terrestrial Precedents. Systematic problems in the experimental detection of biological activity are reviewed. Optical asymmetry, so characteristic of terrestrial life, is discussed in terms of its diagnostic significance. The special properties of terrestrial soils are reviewed in relation to the problem of detecting biological activity, and the possibility of recognizing terrestrial life by observation of the Earth from a distance is examined.

PART V. Some Extrapolations and Speculations. Synthetic materials and structures produced in the laboratory from amino acids imitate some of the properties of living material. These effects are discussed in connection with the enumeration of tests for living systems. An hypothetical anaerobic ecological system, capable of operating under presumed Martian conditions, is outlined in theoretical fashion. Some speculative possibilities for the existence of biochemical systems radically different from the terrestrial are discussed in relation to adaptation to the environment and implications for experimental procedures for detection of life. The improbability of the existence of higher organisms on Mars is briefly discussed.

PART VI. Approaches to the Exploration of Mars. Practical means for confirming and enlarging our knowledge of Mars by laboratory work, astronomical observation and the use of spacecraft for remote observations, are discussed. The characteristics of space vehicles for planetary exploration are reviewed, together with the limitations and special conditions that govern their use for Martian investigations.

Although unlikely to provide direct detection of life, observations from the Earth and its vicinity, from Martian fly-bys and particularly from orbiters are essential preliminaries to more detailed investigations at the planet's surface. Potentialities of these kinds of observations for aiding the definition of phenomena of biological relevance are discussed.

PART VII. Martian Landings: Unmanned. Precise determination of the Martian environment and the identification and characterization of any living organisms requires that suitable instruments be landed on the surface, after preliminary investigations have identified sites of interest. Special problems attending the design of landers for biological studies are discussed and analytical techniques of potential application are reviewed.

PART VIII. Martian Landings: Manned. If the study of Mars by means of automatic devices obtains evidence of an indigenous biota, the scope of further investigations would be markedly increased by the ability to dispatch manned expeditions and to return samples to Earth. Some current estimates of the prospects of undertaking such flights are outlined and problems of quarantine that might arise are discussed.

PART IX. Avoiding the Contamination of Mars. Preventing the introduction of viable terrestrial microorganisms has been recognized as an essential condition to the experimental study of the Martian environment. The importance of this condition and some possible consequences of violating it are discussed, together with procedures that might be followed if contamination were known to have occurred. Present aims and methods of sterilization are outlined, quantitative standards proposed and the problem of embedded microorganisms reviewed.

A companion volume, *Extraterrestrial Life: Anthology and Bibliography* (National Academy of Sciences—National Research Council Publication 1296A), was prepared on the recommendation of the working group and with its guidance. It contains a selected anthology and bibliography on the origin of life, its possible existence beyond the Earth, and related subjects. A supplementary group of papers on Mariner IV and rocket observations of Mars that were made during 1965 is also included.

The working group of the study acknowledges with gratitude the help it received from the many outside contributors and from the staff of the National Aeronautics and Space Administration and the Jet Propulsion Laboratory. We are grateful also, to the authorities of Stanford University and the Rockefeller Institute for providing facilities for our meetings.

It is a pleasure to express on behalf of the entire working group a special note of thanks to the study's secretariat. The devoted effort and the imagination of Mr. J. P. T. Pearman (Executive Director) carried us over many difficult problems in the course of a long summer's work; and the whole task was made easier by the tireless support of his staff—Dr. E. A. Shneour, Miss A. K. Grittner, Mr. E. Ottesen, Mr. R. A. Fisher, Miss J. A. Durbin, and Mrs. A. E. Carlson. The assistance of Miss Ann Wagoner, of the Space Science Board staff, was invaluable in the final stages of preparation of our report for press.

COLIN S. PITTENDRIGH
Chairman of the Study

CONTENTS

PART I

BIOLOGY AND THE EXPLORATION OF MARS

SUMMARY AND CONCLUSIONS

THE ORIGIN AND NATURE OF LIFE

The modern, naturalistic view of life's origin and evolution dates from the foundations of modern biology a century ago. Implicit in the evolutionary treatment of life is the proposition that the first appearance of organisms was only a chapter in the natural history of the planet as a whole. Oparin later made this notion explicit in his view that the origin of life was a fully natural, perhaps inevitable, step in the ontogeny of the Earth. Systems capable of self-replication and controlled energy transfer —living organisms—had their origin in the sequence of chemical changes that were part of the planet's early history.

The tractability of this great inductive step to further discussion has been enhanced by the progress of terrestrial cellular biology and biochemistry over the last few decades. From that progress has emerged a unified picture of life at the subcellular and chemical levels, underlying the unity at higher levels that so largely influenced Darwin. Not only is there a common pattern to the structure of cellular organelles—membranes, mitochondria, nuclear apparatus—but a still more surprising unity is found in its molecular constituents. Everywhere on Earth the essential catalytic functions are discharged by proteins, energy transfer effected by adenosine triphosphate, and the synthesis of proteins today controlled by an elaborate nucleic acid system. The same enzymatic cofactors are found in organism

3

after organism; particular metabolic pathways recur from cell to cell; and everywhere the fundamental functions of information storage and replication are assigned to the nucleic acids.

To a significant extent the discussion of life's origin must concern the origin of those molecular types that are crucial in cellular organization: the origin of nucleic acids, of proteins, of carbohydrates, and so on.

In the 1950's a series of experiments was initiated in which the synthesis of biologically important compounds was accomplished by application of energy to presumptive primitive environments. The list includes: amino acids and their polymers; carbohydrates and fatty acids; purines and pyrimidines; nucleotides, including adenosine triphosphate, and oligo-nucleotides—every major category of molecular sub-unit of which the cell is built.

The credibility of the naturalistic, evolutionary view of life's origin as an exploitation of previous chemical evolution on a sterile Earth is greatly heightened by these results: the great chemical complexity of its molecular constituents does not, in last analysis, require the intervention of the cell itself.

The general tenet that life involves no qualitative novelty—no *élan vital*—goes hand in hand with the more explicit proposition that it is the molecular organization, as such, of living things that alone distinguishes them from the non-living. The central issue in discussing origins now concerns not so much the prior evolution of complexity in molecular constituents as the development of their organization into a system that is alive. It is here we lack any sure guides—save one—on the contingency involved; on how improbable it all was. That one lead comes from the great and well-known advances of molecular genetics in the past ten years.

The essence of organization in one sense is its improbability, its dependence on specification or information. And the most characteristic feature of living organizations—organisms—is their capacity to store and replicate the evolving information on which their existence depends. The high point of our biochemical advance has been identification of the molecular basis of these defining characteristics. It is astonishing how much we have recently learned about the manner in which the information underlying life's organization is encoded in molecular structure; that we understand how that molecular structure is replicated; and further that simple poly-nucleotides have been synthesized in cell-free systems.

It remains unclear, of course, what precise sequence of events exploited the opportunities afforded by the purely chemical evolution of the Earth's surface and atmosphere. But at some point in the unknown sequence a community of molecules would have been fully recognizable to us as a living as against a non-living thing: it would have been bounded from its environment by a membrane, capable of controlled energy expenditure in fabricating more of itself and endowed with the capacity to store and replicate information.

We cannot fully know the precise course of the Earth's early chemical evolution, and the degree of contingency involved in the subsequent transition to a living organization of molecules; and for these reasons we cannot fully assess just how probable or improbable life's origin was at the outset of our own planet's evolution. Nor can we estimate to what extent the emerging picture of a single chemical basis of life on Earth reflects a physical necessity for living organization as against a mixture of physical sufficiency and historical accident. Can the catalysis essential to biochemical organization be effected only by proteins containing the 20 amino acids we encounter in cells? Are the nucleic acids the only polymers, for physical reasons, that can carry molecular information on satisfactorily? Or are these and other empirical generalizations about life on Earth, such as optical activity, merely reflections of the historical contingency that gave such molecules first access to living organization, thus preempting the field and precluding realization of other physically sufficient molecular foundations for life?

To the extent that we cannot answer these questions, we lack a true theoretical biology as against an elaborate natural history of life on this planet. We cannot prejudge the likelihood of life's appearance on Earth; therefore we cannot confidently take the great inductive step when we are told by astronomers that there may be 10^{20} planetary systems elsewhere in the Universe with histories comparable to our own. One thing is clear: If life is unique to our planet the probability of its origin must be almost unimaginably low. If, on the other hand, the probability is at all appreciable, life must be abundant in the 10^{20} planetary systems that fill the sky.

At stake in this uncertainty is nothing less than knowledge of our place in nature. It is the major reason why the sudden opportunity to explore a neighboring planet for life is so immensely important.

We emphasize that the act of discovery itself would have this great scientific, and for that matter philosophical, impact. But it is also important that discovery would, in another way, be only the beginning. The existence and accessibility of Martian life would mark the beginning of a true general biology, of which the terrestrial is a special case. We would have a unique opportunity to shed new light on the meaning of the astonishing molecular similarity in all terrestrial organisms. Is it there as a physically necessary basis for life? Or is it—physically sufficient but not necessary—a historical accident in the sense that, in another instance of planetary evolution, a different basic chemical complexity could equally well have emerged and preempted the local opportunity for life?

THE POSSIBILITY OF LIFE ON MARS

No thoughtful person will disagree with our assertion on the scientific importance of life elsewhere in the solar system. It is, however, another matter to conclude that search for it should proceed at once. The exploration will be costly in money and other resources. To undertake it we need *some* assurance that it is not folly from the outset.

temp.

Interest immediately focuses on Mars. The nearest and most Earth-like of the planets in the solar system are Mars and Venus, but the surface of Venus has been tentatively excluded as a possible abode of life, because of the probably high surface temperatures. The Martian year is long (687 days), but the length of its day is curiously similar to that of Earth, a fact that to considerable degree ameliorates an otherwise very severe environment.

atmp.

Mars has retained an atmosphere, although it is thin: present estimates of pressure at the surface range from 10 to 80 millibars. The major constituents are unidentified, but are thought to be nitrogen and argon. Carbon dioxide has been identified spectroscopically and its proportion estimated to lie between 5 per cent and 30 per cent by volume. Oxygen has been sought but not detected; the sensitivity of measurement implies a proportion not greater than 0.1 per cent by volume. Water vapor has also been identified spectroscopically as a minor atmospheric constituent in the amount of 2×10^{-3} g cm^{-2}. (For comparison, approximate terrestrial values of the quantities given above are: surface pressure 1,000 millibars; carbon dioxide 0.03 per cent; oxygen 20 per cent; water vapor 3 g cm^{-2}).

The intensity of ultraviolet radiation at the Martian surface may be high by comparison with Earth, but this is not yet certain; some models of the composition of the atmosphere allow for effective shielding.

Surface temperatures overlap the range on Earth: at some latitudes and seasons they have a daily high of $+30°C$ with a diurnal range of about $100°C$.

There are two white polar caps whose composition has been the subject of some controversy. The evidence now is clear that they are ice, in the form of hoar frost. They undergo a seasonal waxing and waning, which is probably accompanied by an atmospheric transfer of water vapor from one hemisphere to another.

Sea "Canals"

Our knowledge of what lies between the polar caps is limited to the distinction between the so-called "dark" and "bright" areas and their seasonal changes. The latter, usually considered "deserts," are an orange-ochre or buff color. The former are much less vividly colored. It is likely that early descriptions of the dark areas as green result from an optical illusion due to contrast with the orange "bright" areas.

Biological interest nevertheless continues to center on the "dark" areas. In several respects they exhibit the kind of seasonal change one would expect were they due to the presence of organisms absent in the "bright" (desert) areas. In spring, the recession of the ice cap is accompanied by development of a dark collar at its border, and as the spring advances a wave of darkening proceeds through the dark areas toward the equator and, in fact, overshoots it 20° into the opposite hemisphere.

Polarimetric studies suggest that much of the Martian surface may be covered with small sub-millimeter-sized particles. The curve on which this inference is based shows a seasonal displacement in the dark areas, but not in the bright. Infrared absorption features have been attributed to the dark areas, suggesting abundant H—C bonds there, but more recent analysis throws great doubt on this interpretation, leaving us with no definite information, one way or the other, about the existence and distribution of organic matter.

Needless to say, none of these inferences about the Martian dark areas *demands* the presence of organisms for their explanation.

Indeed, the question is whether the Martian environment could support life at all; and further, whether its history would have permitted the indigenous origin of life. These are clearly different questions. Our answer to the first question is that we find no compelling evidence that Mars could not support life even of a kind chemically similar to our own. Were oxygen present to the small limiting extent current measurements allow, a fully aerobic respiration would be possible. But even its total absence would not of itself preclude life. One of our more rewarding exercises has been the challenge to construct a Martian ecology assuming the most adverse conditions indicated by present knowledge: it posed no insuperable problem. Some terrestrial organisms have already been shown to survive freeze-thaw cycles of +30° to —70°C. Others are known to cope with extremely low humidities and to derive their water supply metabolically. There are many conceivable ways of coping with a strong flux of ultraviolet (and even of exploiting it as an energy source). The history of our own planet provides plenty of evidence that, once attained, living organization is capable of evolving adjustments to very extreme environments. And, finally, we are reminded that the evidence we have on Martian conditions is very coarse-grained, a sort of average that takes account of almost no local variations dependent on topography. Within the range of conditions represented by our present numerical estimates, it is likely that there exist, perhaps abundantly—as on Earth—places where the extremes of temperature, aridity, and adverse irradiation are markedly ameliorated. Even the presence of water in the liquid phase is perhaps not unlikely, if only transiently, by season, in the subsoil.

A measure of our judgment that niches in the contemporary Martian environment could support life of a sort comparable to that of Earth is provided by our overriding concern with the danger of inadvertently contaminating Mars with terrestrial organisms. We shall return to this problem later.

The other question—whether life in fact *is* there—depends on our judgment of how probable its *origin* on Mars has been. The *a priori* probability of origin we can not assess, even for Earth; it is the principal reason for considering exploration in the first place.

Given all the evidence presently available, we believe it entirely reasonable that Mars is inhabited with living organisms and that life independently originated there. However, it should be clearly recognized that our conclusion that the biological exploration of Mars will be a rewarding venture does not depend on the hypothesis of Martian life. The scientific questions that ought not to be prejudged are:

    a. Is terrestrial life unique? The discovery of Martian life, whether extant or extinct, would provide an unequivocal answer.

    b. What is the geochemical (and geophysical) history of an Earth-like planet undisturbed by living organisms? If we discover that Mars is sterile we may find answers to this alternative and highly significant question.

THE SCIENTIFIC AIMS OF MARTIAN EXPLORATION

We approach the prospect of Martian exploration as evolutionary biologists. The origin of organisms was a chapter in the natural history of the Earth's surface. The hypothesis to be tested is a generalization from that single case: the origin of living organization is a probable event in the evolution of all planetary crusts that resemble ours. We thus conceive the over-all mission as a *systematic study of the evolution of the Martian surface and atmosphere:* has that evolution included, in some niches of the planet, chemical systems with the kind of organization we would recognize as "living"?

Our aims, in summary form, are:

    (1) determination of the physical and chemical conditions of the Martian surface as a potential environment for life,

    (2) determination whether life is or has been present on Mars,

    (3) determination of the characteristics of that life, if present, and

    (4) investigation of the pattern of chemical evolution without life.

This formulation emphasizes that, as biologists, we have as much interest as the planetary astronomers in a thorough study of the meteorology, geochemistry, geophysics, and topography of Mars. Whatever the outcome of a direct search for life, its full meaning will escape us unless the findings can be related to the prevailing environment.

AVOIDING THE CONTAMINATION OF MARS

Before proceeding to the more programmatic aspects of the undertaking, we are concerned to single out the task of spacecraft sterilization from the many and diverse problems that Martian exploration will entail. We believe that many of our nonbiologist colleagues have still not fully grasped either the magnitude or the fundamental importance of this issue.

Contamination of the Martian surface with terrestrial microbes could irreversibly destroy a truly unique opportunity for mankind to pursue a study of extraterrestrial life. Other future uses of Mars are not evident to us now; whatever they are, they may be clumsily destroyed by premature and uninformed mistakes in our program. We are eager to press Martian exploration as expeditiously as the technology and other factors permit. However, our present sure knowledge of Mars is very slim and so our recommendation to proceed is subject to one rigorous qualification: that no viable terrestrial microorganism reach the Martian surface until we can make a confident assessment of the consequences.

In operational context, this means that the probability of a single viable organism reaching the Martian surface be made small enough to meet scientifically acceptable standards. These standards, already established provisionally,* should be continually reexamined in the light of all new information. Moreover, every effort should be made to ensure the continued acceptance by other launching nations of the recommended confidence levels for protection of Mars against contamination. The technical problems precipitated by this demand include the control of trajectories to an accuracy sufficient to prevent the accidental impact of unsterilized payloads, the development of sterilizable spacecraft components for vehicles intended for landing, the development of procedures that will prevent the introduction of microorganisms, and the means for establishing the reliability of the entire program. Since we have not yet succeeded in sterilizing a space vehicle, the problem must be considered unsolved.

An energetic program for the development of procedures for sterilizing space vehicles and their components must be implemented immediately if we are to take advantage of the opportunities that will arise between 1969 and 1973. We must guard not only against accidental neglect of necessary safeguards but also against placing ephemeral considerations of prestige

* Report of COSPAR Seventh Meeting, Florence, Italy, May 1964, Resolution 26.

above enduring scientific significance and utilitarian value in our exploration of space.

AVENUES OF APPROACH TO THE EXPLORATION OF MARS

For convenience, we distinguish four categories of work that can contribute to attaining our goals: (a) laboratory work needed to develop techniques for planetary investigations and the knowledge needed to interpret their findings; (b) Earth-bound astronomical studies of Mars; (c) the use of spacecraft for the remote investigation of Mars; and (d) a direct study of the Martian surface by landing missions.

LABORATORY WORK

The consideration of the evolution of life on Mars raises many problems that can be studied in Earth-based laboratories. Such studies are, in fact, essential to provide the background against which the results of planetary missions must be interpreted. The work includes the chemical analysis of meteorites, especially with respect to their content of organic compounds, and the extension of studies on the spontaneous formation of organic molecules and their aggregation into larger units. These investigations may reveal to us not only the mechanism by which the materials essential for living organisms were first formed, but also the origin of reactions and mechanisms that lead to the formation of organized structures and their self-perpetuation. Other possibly interesting lines of effort include study of alternatives to the carbon-water system of biochemistry and simulations of Martian and other planetary environments. While some of these simulated environments may allow terrestrial microorganisms or enzyme systems to function, others may be more conducive to the activity of reaction systems based on alternative biochemistries.

It will become clear later that considerable work remains to be done in defining schemes for life detection and in developing the instrumentation to exploit them.

EARTH-BOUND ASTRONOMICAL STUDIES OF MARS

The observation of Mars from terrestrial observatories enjoys the advantages of economy, absence of weight and size limitations, and high data rate. It is, however, limited by the terrestrial atmosphere in attainable resolution and spectral range, and further constrained by daylight and weather. Nevertheless, much valuable work could be conducted at a cost that is low compared to that of space programs if the nation's large instruments were made available during prime seeing time for the observation of Mars. The use of 120″ and 200″ optical telescopes and of the largest radio telescopes and interferometers could rapidly extend our knowledge of Mars. We support the recommendations of another committee of the National Academy of Sciences[1] on the need for additional ground-based astronomical facilities. For such facilities to play a significant role in the planning of 1969-73 Mars missions, work on this program must be begun early.

USE OF SPACECRAFT FOR REMOTE OBSERVATION OF MARS

Some of the observational limitations imposed by the terrestrial environment can be overcome by balloon-borne observatories, but, since they are severely restricted in size and observation time, their usefulness is limited; it is also restricted by absorption in the Earth's atmosphere. The projected Earth-orbiting astronomical observatory overcomes some of these limitations, and we believe the observation of Mars, particularly in the ultraviolet, should be included in the plans for its use.

It is, however, from Martian fly-by missions and, in particular, from Martian orbiters that the remote observation of that planet is best undertaken. We hope to obtain our first closeup information on the Martian surface from the video scan to be carried out by Mariner IV, and to gain additional knowledge of atmospheric density by observation of the telemetry signals during occultation of the spacecraft.

Fly-by missions are, however, severely limited in the time available for observation; they provide at best a fleeting glimpse of the planet.

Martian orbiters will be technically possible for the opportunities of 1969 and thereafter. They offer an unparalleled opportunity to scrutinize the planet at comparatively short range. Potential orbiter payloads have been examined by another group, and compositions of such payloads have been suggested for a range of instrument weights up to 200 lbs (which is within the capability of the Saturn IB-Centaur). For example, a modest payload that any of several vehicles could place in orbit could include instruments for (1) infrared and television mapping; (2) microwave radiometry and bistatic radar; (3) infrared spectrometry; and (4) optical polarimetry. These sensors would yield information on temperatures, surface and atmospheric composition, topography, certain characteristics of surface

[1] *Ground-Based Astronomy, A Ten-Year Program,* National Academy of Sciences Publication No. 1234, 1964.

structure, and, most important of all, permit a sustained scrutiny through a full cycle of seasonal change and over a major fraction of the Martian surface.

MARTIAN-LANDING MISSIONS: ABL'S SMALL AND LARGE

While it is conceivable that the findings of a Martian orbiter could establish the presence of life on the planet, we are in any case convinced that landing missions are essential for adequate Martian exploration. The definition of lander payloads is a complex and demanding task that we have only begun to explore.

Their design is to some extent dependent on our knowledge of the structure of the Martian atmosphere. The size of the payload that can be deposited depends, for instance, on whether the use of a parachute is feasible or whether the density of the atmosphere is so low as to require the use of retrorockets; this is especially critical for small payloads. In this connection, we note the possibility that the density profile of the Martian atmosphere will be determined by astronomical means, or by Mariner IV, with sufficient precision for the purpose of designing a landing system. A more direct method for studying the Martian atmosphere involves the use of nonsurvivable atmospheric-entry probes that could transmit information on atmospheric density, structure and composition. Such probes could be launched from either fly-bys or orbiters. Since their design is not dependent on atmospheric density, these are useful devices for obtaining advance information, if needed, for the survivable landing of an instrument package. The view has also been presented that a small surviving capsule would have even more value, in that it might determine not only the density profile of the atmosphere, but also its composition at the surface, wind velocity, and other data that would enhance the probability of success of a large lander.

However, if we had complete knowledge of these prerequisites for a successful survivable lander, our principal design difficulty would remain: it concerns the problem of life detection. *What minimal set of assays will permit us to detect Martian life if it does exist?* A debate on this question for the past several years has yielded a variety of competing approaches. Each of these is directed to some manifestation of life according to the cues of terrestrial biology. Needless to say, visual reconnaissance, from microscope to telescope, is one of the most attractive of these, for it offers the expectation that many recognizable hints of life would immediately attract our attention. However, we can easily imagine circumstances in which this type of observation would be inconclusive. Many other suggested procedures are designed to identify, at the outset, the more fundamental biochemical structures and processes that we would, in any case, explore in depth. No one of these analyses, however—whether photosynthesis or respiration, DNA or proteins, growth, enzymes or metabolism, or, in a figurative sense, fleas or elephants—can be sure of finding its target and reliably reporting on it under all circumstances, nor would any single approach satisfy all the particular interests that motivate different investigators in their search.

We cannot recount here all our deliberations on the life-detection problem. We have sought the most generalized criteria; among these is net optical activity, which is almost surely the result of steric restrictions imposed by a historical accident in the origin of life. Another is the presence in assays of exponential features that can be ascribed only to growth and reproduction. And we have reconciled ourselves to the fact that early missions should assume an Earth-like carbon-water type of biochemistry as the most likely basis of any Martian life. On that assumption, enzymes that should be widespread can be sought and growth may be demonstrated by the use of generalized media.

The fact remains, and dominates any attempt to define landers for detecting life, that no single criterion is fully satisfactory, especially in the interpretation of some negative results. To achieve the previously stated aims of Martian exploration we must employ as mixed a strategy as possible.

Discussion throughout our study has returned repeatedly to the conclusions that we would not be convinced by negative answers from single "life detectors"; that, given the hazards of any chemical or metabolic assay, we should ensure some direct visual inspection by television, and that the lander program must ultimately involve an Automated Biological Laboratory (ABL). The ABL concept is not fully defined: it involves provision for the multiplicity and diversity of chemical analytical techniques and biological assays that our aims call for; it involves, too, the idea of an onboard computer by means of which a variety of programmed assay sequences can be initiated contingently on the results of prior steps; it also involves the idea of a sustained discourse between the computer and investigators on Earth. It is, in short, an ambitious concept. But our preliminary scrutiny of the ABL idea suggests that, though ambitious, it is, in principle, realizable with current technology.

In the long run, we believe that manned expeditions and the return of Martian samples to the Earth will be part of the exploration of the planet. Neither of these is imminent, but some of our readers will be as surprised as we were to discover that manned Martian missions will probably be feasible in the 1980's. Certainly neither the return of samples nor the sending of men to Mars will be scientifically justifiable until unmanned landings have prepared the way.

THE TIMING AND OVER-ALL STRATEGY OF EXPLORATIONS

In principle, all of us would prefer a gradualistic approach to the ultimate goals of landing a large ABL on Mars and, eventually, of returning samples for study here. It is clear on all grounds—of economy, and scientific prudence—that we should exhaust the possibilities of further progress using Earth-based observations and non-landing missions to Mars.

For instance, a strong majority of the working group believes a successful orbiter program should precede a landing. The orbiter promises an immense extension of our knowledge of the atmosphere (its density and chemical composition) and surface of Mars. Its capability for sustaining seasonal observation and extensive topographic mapping will permit a thorough re-evaluation of the several Martian features that have been considered suggestive of life. And it will permit a far-better-informed selection of landing site for the ultimate ABL missions. It has the further merit of effecting this substantial step forward with minimum risk of contaminating the surface.

Constraints to proceeding in a completely unhurried, step-by-step fashion arise from several sources, however. They are a combination of celestial mechanics and the operational realities of space research. Any space experiment takes years of preparation and budgetary commitment; the preliminaries to actual flight involve years of experimental design, spacecraft development, and the coordination of effort among large numbers of people in a wide range of disciplines. The scientific investigator no longer has the total freedom he usually enjoys to make tentative starts, to explore hunches without full commitment, to stop and follow another course. He is further plagued by the prospect of investing years of work only to encounter a mission failure or cancellation in which it is all lost—at least until a new opportunity arises, perhaps years hence. He may chafe under these circumstances but he must accept them if he wishes to proceed at all. The kind of Martian lander that we visualize will be a most complex and difficult spacecraft to build and will require the combined efforts of many different scientific specialists. For these reasons, its development will be most costly and time-consuming. A Martian orbiter is also a much larger undertaking than any scientific spacecraft yet flown. The point is that we are confronted with the necessity of near-commitment many years ahead of flight time; and the opportunities for flights to Mars are by no means always at hand. The orbits of Earth and Mars are such that these opportunities are now limited to brief windows that recur about every second year but undergo a further, approximately 17-year cycle of favorableness. Our attempt to develop a systematic and gradualistic program is thus constrained to some extent by the fact that, while favorable opportunities occur in the 1969-1973 period, they will not return before 1984-1985.*

We have concluded that the 1969-1973 opportunities can be and should be exploited for a substantial program of planetary missions. By that time, the Saturn booster system will be available, and a four- to five-year lead time is evidently adequate for the development of initial spacecraft.

The more detailed planning of planetary missions for 1969-1973 is for the most part outside the scope of this working group's competence and commission: the decisions concerned involve engineering and many other elements with which we did not cope.

CONCLUSIONS AND RECOMMENDATIONS

THE BIOLOGICAL EXPLORATION OF MARS RECOMMENDED

The biological exploration of Mars is a scientific undertaking of the greatest validity and significance. Its realization will be a milestone in the history of human achievement. Its importance and the consequences for biology justify the highest priority among all scientific objectives in space —indeed in the space program as a whole.

THE SCIENTIFIC AIMS OF THE EXPLORATION

We approach the prospect of Martian exploration not only as biologists but as scientists interested in evolutionary processes over the broadest range. Living systems have emerged as a chapter in the natural history of the Earth's surface. We wish to test the hypothesis that the origin of life is a probable event in the evolution of all planetary environments whose histories resemble ours.

We thus conceive the over-all mission as a systematic study of the evolution of the Martian surface and atmosphere: has that evolution in-

---

*For these reasons an alternative strategy has been discussed: it would allow the early use of landing probes, always providing that reliable decontamination systems will have been developed and authenticated. A minority opinion holds that small landers may provide environmental information useful in the design of other spacecraft and may succeed more readily than orbiters. According to this view, the way should be left open to their use even though the results obtained may well be less comprehensive.

cluded, in some niches of the planet, chemical systems with the degree of complexity, organization, and capacity for evolution we would recognize as "living"? Our specific aims are:

(1) determination of the physical and chemical conditions of the Martian surface as a potential environment for life,

(2) determination whether life is or has been present on Mars,

(3) determination of the characteristics of that life, if present, and

(4) investigation of the pattern of chemical evolution without life.

AN IMMEDIATE START TO EXPLOIT THE 1969-1973 OPPORTUNITIES

A major effort should be initiated immediately to exploit the particularly favorable opportunities of 1969-1973.

We are here concurring with the Space Science Board's views that planetary exploration should be the major aim of the nation's space science efforts in the 1970's and 1980's; and, further, that the biological exploration of Mars should be the primary focus of the program.

AVOIDING THE CONTAMINATION OF MARS: A MAJOR MISSION CONSTRAINT

Before proceeding to other aspects of the undertaking, we are concerned to single out the task of prevention of contamination from the many and diverse problems that Martian exploration will entail.

Contamination of the Martian surface with terrestrial microbes could irrevocably destroy a truly unique opportunity for mankind to pursue a study of extraterrestrial life. Thus, while we are eager to press Martian exploration as expeditiously as the technology and other factors permit, we insist that our recommendation to proceed is subject to one rigorous qualification: that no viable terrestrial microorganisms reach the Martian surface until we can make a confident assessment of the consequences.

PROGRAMMATIC RECOMMENDATIONS

Every opportunity for remote observation of Mars by Earth-bound or balloon- and satellite-borne instruments should be exploited. A vigorous program here can yield a very substantial increase in our knowledge of

Mars before the major program of planetary missions begins in 1969.

It has become evident that an adequate program for Martian exploration cannot be achieved without using scientific payloads substantially larger than those currently employed in our unmanned space research program. Although predominantly engineering considerations may incline to early use of smaller payloads, we see very substantial advantages in the use, from the outset, of the new generation of large boosters that are expected to become operational toward the end of the present decade. These advantages include: the possibility of avoiding spacecraft obsolescence due to a change in booster; the potential for growth in the versatility of scientific payloads and the relief of pressure on the engineer to design spacecraft to the limit of booster capacity.

We deliberately omit an explicit recommendation in favor of any fly-by missions in addition to those already executed or planned for the 1964 (and possibly 1966) opportunities. They yield at best a fleeting glimpse of the planet, and unless they are already so large that they could as well have been orbiters, the array of sensors they carry is small. Given the booster power adequate to deliver it, an orbiter is overwhelmingly preferable. It may well be, however, that strictly engineering considerations will demand some preliminary flights in 1969 and, if these are undertaken, their exploitation as fly-bys could yield worthwhile information.

Every effort should be made to achieve a large orbiting mission by 1971 at the latest. This mission should precede the first lander. (A dissenting minority view supports the simultaneous use of small landing probes.) By "large" we mean a scientific payload that would include instrumentation for (a) infrared and television mapping; (b) microwave radiometry and bistatic radar; (c) infrared spectrometry; and (d) optical polarimetry. The success of this mission will depend on the availability of a large booster and a substantial improvement in currently available communications facilities.

The first landing mission should be scheduled no later than 1973, and by 1971 if possible.

We have not yet outlined what the contents of a large lander should be in terms so specific as those used to describe the orbiter. The central point on which all agree is that the mission ultimately demands a large lander, which we have come to call an ABL (Automated Biological Laboratory). What is unclear at present is how fast such a large lander can be designed and developed from biological and engineering viewpoints. It is clear, however, that the development, both as to conceptual design and as to engineering, will go through several generations. It is hoped that the first generation of an ABL could be used for the 1971 opportunity.

The lander we are recommending for 1971 is something short of what is ultimately possible and necessary, but could have a sufficiently diverse array of instrumentation to answer some of the scientific questions we have posed.

The task of designing an ABL should be initiated immediately as a continuing project. The contents of landers in 1971 and 1973 will be products of this continuing undertaking.

The problems associated with the biological exploration of Mars are diverse, and the task of implementation raises challenges in many respects wholly novel. Orbiter and lander missions alike will involve many different experimenters. The evolution of an optimum scientific payload will require a continuing dialogue among all potential investigators and the engineers responsible for implementing their scientific goals. The undertaking we are recommending cannot proceed without some provision for organizing and sustaining that dialogue on a continuing basis. As the program develops other devices may become more appropriate, but at the outset we believe a standing committee of the Space Science Board will be a useful provision. It should be charged with: (1) a continuing surveillance of progress from a scientific viewpoint; and (2) the responsibility of giving advice to the National Aeronautics and Space Administration.

POSTSCRIPT: OCTOBER 1965

During the interval between publication in March 1965 of the Summary and Conclusions of our Study and the appearance of this volume, our knowledge of Mars has been raised to an entirely new level by the success of the Mariner IV mission. On July 15 of this year a spacecraft encountered Mars, passed at 6118 miles, and succeeded in taking twenty-two pictures of its surface that were subsequently transmitted back to Earth. Those pictures represent a major technical and scientific achievement.

Our Study began in the summer of 1964. By the time of the 1965 Spring Meeting of the Academy it was possible to present a summary of our general findings to the scientific community. This permitted us to take cognizance of the reactions of our colleagues while work progressed on the various topical chapters of the Study. The time required for the latter has also permitted us to take cognizance of the new information from Mariner IV at a session of the study participants at Stanford on October 24 and 25, 1965.* This meeting formed the basis for this postscript. One of its two

* Participants in this session were: K. C. Atwood, R. M. Bock, A. H. Brown, A. L. Burlingame, H. Fernández-Morán, H. Gaffron, D. A. Glaser, J. Gross, H. K. Hartline, T. Jukes, H. P. Klein, J. Lederberg, E. C. Levinthal, J. McCarthy, A. D. McLaren, S. L. Miller, M. Minsky, J. Oró, G. C. Pimentel, C. S. Pittendrigh, D. C. Rea, A. Rich, C. E. Sagan, E. A. Shneour, L. Stryer, and W. Vishniac. Participants invited specifically to present the results of Mariner IV included R. B. Leighton, V. R. Eshleman, and G. Fjeldbo.

19

purposes is to answer the question: Do the results of Mariner IV change
our earlier conclusions and recommendations? The other is to re-emphasize some salient features of those conclusions which public reaction to our
summary indicates were largely ignored or misunderstood.

The essence of our position was, and still is, the immense scientific
importance of evaluating the uniqueness of life on Earth; of discovering
facts that will permit more valid inference on its abundance in the Universe;
and the fact that the new space technology allows us to obtain empirical
evidence on the frequency with which living organization and its precursors
emerge in the evolutionary history of planets.

Given the importance of discovering life there, our judgment was that
the exploration of Mars—biologically oriented—was not only fully justified
but, given further the opportunity of the space program, it was a clear
national goal of the highest scientific merit. To escape that conclusion, we
would have had to conclude first that the possibility of Martian life was
negligibly low. The decision rests, as it were, on the product of the importance of the discovery and the possibility of attaining it, not on the latter
alone. What we concluded on examination of the facts then available was
that life, even in essentially terrestrial form, could very well have originated
on Mars and have survived in some of its contemporary micro-environ-
ments. And the facts revealed by Mariner IV have not changed that
judgment.

It is, however, important to re-emphasize here a major aspect of our
position that critics have unaccountably missed; we sought to emphasize
"that our conclusion that the biological exploration of Mars will be a
rewarding venture does not depend on the hypothesis of Martian life."
Throughout our deliberations we have treated the issues at stake as questions about the general evolutionary processes in nature: in exploring Mars,
as biologists, what we are seeking to clarify is the probability of living
organization emerging in the sequence of chemical change inherent in a
planet's history. It is clear that the positive result of discovering Martian
life would be the greatest clarification, empirically demonstrating the
probability to be high. But it is not the only result that would be useful.
Any knowledge of the history of Martian chemical evolution will contribute
to our total understanding of the fundamental issues involved. The origin
of terrestrial life was a feature in the evolution of one planet; our attempt
to estimate the prevalence of life in nature as a whole hinges precisely on
our understanding of planetary evolution in general; and the exploration
of Mars is the surest way in the present context to enlarge that understanding.

Our position is then, that Martian exploration, biologically motivated,
is fully justified even if life has not emerged there; but we will again be

misunderstood if that emphasis is taken to mean we believe the chance of discovering fully fledged life to be negligible. The arguments offered by critics reduce to three categories: (1) life can only exist as we know it; (2) the existing Martian environment is too hostile for life, in essentially terrestrial form to be present; and (3) conditions essential to its origin have never existed on Mars. None of these arguments was valid before the Mariner IV results were known and none is compelling now.

The biologist is aware of and impressed by the incredible resourcefulness of living systems on Earth. In their evolutionary history they have found ways to exploit the pages of library books, the near boiling water of hot springs, saline pools on the polar ice caps, the bottom of the ocean, and the exposed rocks at over 6,000 m. We cannot conclude that on Mars the temperature range, the low water content, the very low oxygen tension, or even the high ultraviolet flux necessarily create a challenge that defeats the resourcefulness of self-replicating systems. Even before the Mariner pictures were available we were wary of taking the average measurements available to us as a guide to the range of microclimates present and the Mariner pictures only reinforced that caution. They reveal differences in elevation of at least 3,000 m; they contain features we cannot exclude as frost on the highlands; they show many features that defy any certain explanation; and, in particular, they raise questions about erosion mechanisms we cannot answer as yet; and to that extent they warn strongly against any premature inference on the contemporary environment in general let alone that of the past.

The inference from the Mariner pictures that Mars is currently very dry only reinforces what we already knew. The only novel feature they might imply is that extensive drought has prevailed for a very long time. But even here caution is needed. An initial suggestion that present surface features are about 2 to 5 billion years old has already been challenged by other estimates an order of magnitude smaller. The general and more important point is that analyses of these new and complex data will continue for many years before their full meaning becomes clear. The specific and more urgent *Contemptory* point is that they do not prove that Mars is lifeless now and certainly do *results.* not prove that its early history was incompatible with life's origin.

It is appropriate here to re-emphasize that the central issues at stake are issues of past history; issues on which our inference even for the terrestrial case is uncertain. That very uncertainty is what prompts us to extend our knowledge of life and its chemical precursors to other planets. We cannot conclude that a current absence of hydrogen on Mars means it was always absent and biogenesis therefore impossible. We cannot on the basis of its escape velocity and the absence of a magnetic field conclude that hydrogen escaped in the early history of the planet so rapidly as to preclude at least transiently the existence of sufficiently reducing conditions to permit the origin of life. More generally we cannot without an unwarranted lack of humility pretend we understand life sufficiently to infer from the meager facts available that it is absent on Mars now. Neither the advocate nor the critic of Martian exploration can rest his case on purely empirical and inferential certainty; the judgment for or against the mission rests largely on other grounds. We have deliberately limited ourselves to issues of science not because we think fiscal policy and allocation of the society's resources are irrelevant but because they are clearly different issues on which we have no special wisdom. It is clear that any final decision on the merits of Martian exploration will devolve strongly on these issues— indeed, they will surely play the major role; but we would insist that in public debate of the venture the distinction between them and the scientific merits of the case be more clearly distinguished than they seem to have been so far.

PART II

LIFE: ITS NATURE AND ORIGIN

CHAPTER 1

WHAT IS LIFE?

DANIEL MAZIA

We do not seek to evade the question of the nature of life, but perhaps we should, with stricter discipline, speak rather of living things, organisms, biological objects or the like. For these things exist and they are distinctive among things in general. Biology, in common sense and in formal science, may be unrigorous but it is not imbecilic. It is not trivial that we distinguish corals from rocks, babies from dolls, know when to call the doctor and when to call the undertaker. To say that we cannot answer the question "What is Life?" may imply only that we have no simple predicate for the sentence beginning "Life is . . .". That may be a statement of fact, namely that we now believe that the intuitive hypotheses that life is a special "something," a special force or a magic substance, are scientifically incorrect. This experience is not unique in science; the discrediting of the phlogiston theory wiped out the pat definitions of fire and heat, but we did not for that reason deny fire and heat. Perhaps we should not speak of a definition at all. Our task is rather to identify those properties—forms, substances, processes—that are comprehended in the idea of life. The longer the statement, the better, if length is a measure not of prolixity but of the number of features common to living things and distinguishing them from other kinds of things. Such an experimental approach—it is an experiment to see whether the facts of life define life—cannot pretend to satisfy the desire for a more analytical and purely logical approach, but at

25

least it can make precise what we mean when we talk about living things
and what we look for when we examine them.

The question "What is Life?" begins to acquire newer implications in
a time when the exploration of space is beginning. Whatever the probability of life in other worlds, the possibility of an answer turns old philosophical exercises on the definition of life into a concrete observational
problem: What criteria are significant, what observations would be practicable, what does this or that kind of measurement or observation tell us
about living things, what observations of non-living things could confuse
us, what exotic departures from the kind of life we know could go un-
recognized? The same questions concern both the advocates of the explorations and their critics.

We begin, then, with the modest affirmation that the world of things
in general—the domain of physics—includes a class of things that are
highly distinctive—the domain of biology. As we shall see, the question
of a blurring of the boundaries between the two is far from damaging in
an evolving universe; on the contrary, we think we could recognize the
transitional stages and learn much about living things from them. Though
we seek the distinctiveness of living things by studying them as things, we
do not deny alternative approaches to the distinctiveness of life: through
instinct, poetry or religion. The present discussion, however, conforms
to the limitations of science and exploration.

A measure of the distinctiveness of the living world is that it confronts
us with phenomena, principles and values that are essential to itself but
not to the physical world as a whole. If in the end we must investigate
living things as things having a special—a very special—material organization, we begin by noting that the values that govern the investigation are
also distinctive. Put more plainly, living things are characterized by the
kinds of questions we put to them—or more simply, *by what is interesting
about them*. It is important that the scientific investigation of rock and of
cells gives different answers, but just as important that it asks quite different questions.

What is interesting about living things—and the focus of all questions
about them—is contained in the idea of *survival*. Survival contains the
idea of an *organism*. The living world thwarts time by survival, all the
rest combats time by endurance. An organism lives; its fossil relic endures.
Survival contains the idea of an *organism,* an individual that can change
and replace its atoms and molecules without loss of identity. Survival contains a special version of the idea of a *species;* in the living world the
similarity of members of a species derives from common descent and from
no other cause. Survival implies a particular version of *purpose* and *value,*
although these philosophical swear-words are usually concealed prudishly
in the term *function*. There is no biologist, whether he be a biochemist

who discovers some small molecule in a microorganism, or a student of behavior examining the social organization of apes, who does not seek, in his observations, for purpose and value in relation to survival.

Thus we approach living things as things designed for survival. Our observations and measurements concern the things; our judgments of what we seek, observe and measure concern survival. All this would be rather abstract and, perhaps, marginal to the practice of science, if the world we know contained a great variety of things designed for survival, sharing only the characteristic that they *are* designed for survival. But that is not the case. The most important fact of the biology that we know is that living things are profoundly similar, and the most important deduction from this fact is that the similarities represent true relationship by common descent. The wonderful thing about evolution on the Earth is that it can produce such a beauty of variety and variety of beauty among things that are fundamentally the same. It is by virtue of that fundamental sameness that we can surely identify living things on Earth, as well as things that were once alive and (would that we could find them!) things in the process of evolution toward life, if only we are given the means to make a sufficient number of observations. It is the general principles of operation of living things on Earth, as well as the general principles of their material organization, that permit us to make judgments about the biological exploration of other worlds.

Survival of living things on Earth is observed on two scales of time, and the time itself is biological time (the unit of which is a generation), not clock time. The smaller scale contains those attributes that govern the survival of the individual. Otherwise expressed it contains all the attributes of the individual, judged by the values of survival. It includes the form, organization and anatomy, that identify the individual visibly as the thing that survives. It includes his developmental history, for we are interested in eggs as well as chickens. It includes all the flow of matter through the individual, all the self-sustaining transformations of the invariably simple substances of the non-living world into the often-complex substances making up the fabric of living bodies. It includes the flow of energy by which all the improbable operations of living things become possible operations. It includes all the movement, responses and behavior of the organism, for all of these may be interpreted as purposeful, once we recognize purpose as survival. It includes behavior of organisms in relation to other organisms; not only competition, but also social behavior and co-operation for no inference from natural selection is more obsolete than the idea that survival means only tooth-and-claw conflict.

The individual on the smaller scale of time is a self that is self-making and self-sustaining at the expense of the world outside.

The larger time-scale of survival is imposed by the physical fact of death. Organisms are not very durable; neither are they immune to fatal accident. Any static population of organisms would be destroyed in time or, if aging is an intrinsic property, by time. The means of survival over an indefinite time-span is reproduction: replacement and increase of individuals of a kind by more of the same kind. Most descriptions of life include reproduction as the most important attribute, and correctly so. Other activities that contribute to survival would be futile if organisms could not reproduce; indeed the survival of the individual is often sacrificed to the propagation of the kind. Reproduction itself allows for indefinite survival of a species so long as the external conditions permit survival at all. Species are, however, not absolutely stable, but change in time, for organisms are subject to alterations (mutations) that are propagated by reproduction. The survival and accumulation of inheritable changes are governed by their value for the survival of the reproducing individuals; thus viewed the fruit of Darwin's genius becomes a truism. It has been said that living things are *things that can reproduce, mutate and reproduce mutations.* We are fairly sure that this statement covers all the living things in nature on this planet and that it is free from ambiguity so far as natural objects are concerned. (We would want such a distinction to apply only to natural objects. The invocation of man-made models that imitate the formal attributes of living things is irrelevant; who would desire a conception of an organism so strict that men could not aspire to imitate it? If we are horrified by imitations of life, it is because the imagination of science fiction and cybernetics seems to run to intelligent machines with obscurely malevolent intentions; most of us would be less horrified by nice, soft, synthetic arteries to replace our sclerosing plumbing, or synthetic yeasts that would produce superior beer.)

If an object is most satisfactorily identified as a living thing by showing it to be capable of self-replication, mutation and replication of mutation, that is not necessarily the only or the most practical expedient. It certainly would not be the best means of attributing life to an elephant; it takes much enterprise to observe the reproduction of elephants and excessive patience to demonstrate their mutations. On the other hand, it is easy to demonstrate reproduction of a bacterium (and almost as easy to demonstrate mutation).

In practice, we would seldom be mistaken in assuming that an elephant is alive because he is wagging his tail, but it takes a good microscopist to observe a bacterium waving its tail. In fact, there has been considerable debate as to whether a bacterium moves its flagellum or whether the flagellum moves the bacterium. The admission that we cannot always appeal to the ideal criteria of an organism—reproduction and mutation—

is inconvenient, but not very damaging. We are assisted by recognizing that the processes of organisms are so interlocked that the observation of any one of them leads to inferences about the survival of individuals and species. If we are assured that the elephant wagging his tail is a living thing, we will not doubt that it can be shown that the wagging of the tail serves some purpose, however minor, in improving the elephant's chances of surviving to produce more elephants. There is small hazard in assuming that a microscopic object that beats a flagellum will produce a colony of descendants if placed in a suitable nutrient medium.

Organisms are surviving things: self-making, self-sustaining, kind-conserving things. And it is as things in the ordinary sense, as objects defined by their *form,* that we commonly identify them among things in general and classify them among themselves. The forms of organisms are hardly the sole basis for discriminating decisions about living things, as we shall see, but they can be the most immediate and most subtle ones. We may resist them in scientific principle—while never failing to resort to them in practice—because the judgments are inherently subjective and qualitative, difficult to express and impossible to measure. The values and the pitfalls of morphology have the same cause: our total perceptions are far more subtle and discriminating than are readings of meters, but harder to describe and agree upon. (Thus a romantic poet can charm by his efforts to assert that one girl is exceptional among girls in general, describing her form by surface anatomy and by analogies to astronomical objects, flowers, jewels and the more attractive fauna. We share his feelings, but would not recognize that girl from his description, and if we did we might not think she was so very different from girls in general.)

In appealing to morphology as a criterion of living things, we are in that ever-embarrassing position of feeling confident that we could recognize something though we are unable to state with great precision what we are looking for. We want a language, a mathematics of form. What we can say is that the organization of living things is expressed in complex form, in form-within-form. The forms are plastic, topological in spirit, recognizable and functional despite distortion. (When Donald Duck is flattened by a steamroller, he is still Donald Duck; the plasticity of living form can be a source of naive humor.) Most important, because deriving from the survival principles themselves, is the generic character of biological form; identification is not based solely on the finding of one individual with a given complex form but on the fact that there will be many individuals with *similar* form.

Part of our sense of biological form is its contrast with inorganic form. Crystals are the structures in the non-living world that have regular and repetitive forms. If we had no preconceptions about the structure of crystals, we might perhaps confuse some of them with some biological forms. But we *do* know a good deal about crystals, have many ways of identifying them and are not likely to be confused.

The appeal of morphology in the identification of living things rests on the multiplicity of clues rather than the precision of single criteria. A common paradigm of scientific insight—and one of considerable literary appeal—is our ability to deduce from fossil shadows the forms and ways of life of organisms that have long ago surrendered survival to durability. It is a true paradigm. Complex forms are always taken seriously as signs of living things. We can be moved by fossil forms and find a singular beauty in form that is congealed in time.

If seeing is at least a strong invitation to believing, it goes without saying that seeing is not limited to naked vision. The clues of complex form hold good for all levels of "seeing," not only for the smallest organisms, but for the smallest parts of organisms. If biological science admitted its dogmas, "function goes with form" would stand high on the list. We have a rather good historical test in the work of the early microscopists: old Leeuwenhoek, an uneducated man who made crude microscopes in the 17th century, had no hesitation in identifying "animalcules" in the world he found beyond the limits of the unaided eye and he did not make many mistakes.

In our own world, there are few organisms that cannot be seen with the ordinary light microscope, and there is a good reason for this: even simple surviving things require a considerable number of large molecules for their minimum functions and the smallest living thing is bound to be rather large. There are some forms whose dimensions are just beyond the power of the optical microscope—for example the so-called PPLO (pleuromonia-like) organisms. Their existence tells us that the search is not ended at the limits of the light microscope, but no change of principle is called for: such organisms have regular and complex form, not easily confused with that of any known natural non-biological system when viewed with the electron microscope. We do not think that much smaller, still-undiscovered organisms exist in our world.

Viruses are a little aside from the point. They do have complex form but generally are recognized either by chemical criteria (which we shall discuss later) or by the fact that they reproduce in larger organisms. The very idea of a virus implies the existence of larger and more complex organisms; if we were to find something with a virus-like chemistry we would strongly suspect that cellular organisms were also present.

The great generalization of morphology is the cell theory, which states that organisms are either cells or societies of cells. Despite the myriad variations of cells, ranging from relatively large and elaborately equipped protozoa to degenerate forms such as red blood cells, the microscopist can identify cell structure with reliability and certainly will not confuse it with anything belonging to the inorganic world. He has an abundance of criteria and does not need a full-fledged "typical" cell in order to know that he is observing a cell.

The prevalence of morphology does not end there. Cells are composed of sub-units: walls, nuclei, various particles, *all* of which are recognizable as having consistent forms, which is only to say that the principle of survival is a very strict one and that all the finer details of the organization of the living things we know are preserved and propagated.

Thus, as a naturalist exploring a strange world, I think I would recognize a cow as a living thing, but if I were not permitted to see the cow but could examine a sample of hamburger with an ordinary microscope I would have little difficulty in knowing that I was observing the vestiges of an animal and might be able to say something about the animal. If the hamburger were so finely ground that I could no longer see cells, I would see nuclei, mitochondria, membranes, etc., all of them bodies of characteristic form. Even small pieces of these pieces would be identifiable with the electron microscope. It is difficult to see how one could be deceived.

True, there are imaginable simplicities of biological form that might call for some reservations. The simplest imaginable cell would be a membrane-enclosed sphere in which the macromolecules responsible for life-processes would not be organized into formed "organs," but would be dispersed in a liquid internal medium. If one found a population of such limp bags, all very much alike, he would strongly suspect that they had significance for biological evolution, though he could not be so sure he was dealing with an organism as if he had found a cow. Such a discovery would excite us greatly; it would be an ambiguity, but one that could be resolved by appeal to the molecular properties of living things. We are not restricted to morphology.

All this appeal to form in perception of the character of living things may be a little embarrassing to the Laputan in us. Facing toward immediate experience, it weds the scientific self to the self that responds unthinkingly to nature and to natural beauty, that loves flowers because they are lovely and delights in the curiousness of the shells of sea animals.

Yet we can turn our consideration of biological form in a more analytical direction. We do not think that structure in organisms is ever a play of nature; it is always valuable and meaningful for survival. We think this is so for the gayest plumage of birds, the most sumptuous coloring of flowers, the most exquisite or barbaric sculpturing of molluscan shells, the lace-patterns of diatom shells, the strange forms of fish or insects, sometimes charming, sometimes nightmarish. Even when we find our explanations of these forms inadequate, we are not prepared to deny their significance for survival.

The maxim that relates form to function holds at the deepest analytical level. The cell, the fundamental unit, is both the unit of biological form and the atom of survival. Its own form, and the form of its parts, can be understood as a device for maintaining a rather precisely defined population of molecules and maintaining these molecules in proper—for survival—spatial relationships to each other. Conversely, the maintenance of these spatial relations of molecules is the ultimate source of all biological form.

Thus we arrive at the idea of a Molecular Biology: namely that the form of living things and the operations that produce and are produced by that form are reflections of a definite and definable organization of matter. The molecular approach to biology is not the only one, but it needs no justification. We study Life as a molecular operation because it *is* a molecular operation.

It would be unfortunate if this outlook seemed to arouse archaic misgivings about "materialism." The whole point is that molecular biology discovers in organisms potentialities, subtleties, values and purposes in the organization and operation of matter that are not disclosed in the elementary properties that are the domain of physics; we could not know, but had to discover, that matter is not necessarily undignified dirt.

We are allowed to make rather firm general statements about the organization of the living things we know by the *fact* that they are so much alike in so many ways. It is a fact that we can explain on evolutionary grounds. We may even think that they are too much alike for the purposes of a still more general understanding. Natural Selection could tend to eliminate alternatives that would be viable under other conditions; that is one reason why concern about life in other worlds is as relevant to our own biology as it is to a fundamental curiosity about the universe.

Let us consider some of the ways in which all the cells we know are fundamentally alike.

THE CELL AS AN ENCLOSED AQUEOUS SYSTEM

Cells contain water, usually more than 50 per cent by volume, and cease to operate when the water content falls too low. This inability to operate without an ample amount of liquid water is not necessarily fatal; there is the fascinating possibility of dormant life-processes that resume when the liquid water is restored. An ordinary seed is an example of this.

The cell is bounded by a membrane that separates the inside aqueous solution from the outside aqueous medium. The membrane is a lipid-protein complex about 50-100 Å thick and is rather similar in form in every kind of cell. The similarities extend to fine details, which will not be described here.

A living system does not conform even in its simple internal chemistry to the chemistry of its surroundings, but selects and rejects among even the simplest components of its world. The chief constituent of the internal solution is the potassium ion. This ion is relatively scarce in the environment and the internal concentration of potassium is almost invariably higher than that in the medium. Other ions are either concentrated or excluded and it can be said that the composition of the internal solution is invariably different from that of the bathing environment.

ENZYME PRINCIPLE

The entire chemistry of the cell is governed by the principle that all reactions are catalyzed by enzymes and that each reaction is catalyzed by a different enzyme. This principle, exceptions to which are rare, sets biochemistry apart from the natural chemistry of the non-living world and even from chemical technology, which may employ catalysts but does not possess such a variety and specificity of catalysts. (The enzyme principle is seldom named as such in the biological literature, apparently because it developed gradually and is not associated with a single sensational discovery.) In our own world, all the enzymes are proteins. In any other world in which the principle applies, they would have to be a class of molecules with the same possibility of variety. The fundamental meaning of the enzyme principle is not merely that life-processes are very rapid, even though they take place at low temperatures, but that their rates are governed and balanced by the nature of the enzymes and are not at the mercy of their spontaneous rates. Sometimes we exaggerate when we say that the life of a cell could be completely described if we knew enough about its enzymes, but it is not an outrageous exaggeration.

FLOW OF MATTER AND ENERGY

The conservation principle of living things is different from, in fact opposite to, the main conservation principles of physics. Survival is a synonym for the "conservation of individual and kind" and it takes place by an expenditure of both matter and energy by the individual and the kind. (Only if we had some quantitative expression for what is conserved in survival would biology cease to be an essentially qualitative science.)

The flow of matter in living systems in our world is ultimately governed by the capture of simple constituents of the Earth and its atmosphere, such as carbon dioxide, nitrogen or its simpler compounds, water and a small number of inorganic elements. These are built into molecules much more complex than any that exist in the non-living world itself and if we find complex molecules outside organisms we always assume that they were put there by organisms. The life-death cycle returns matter to the non-biological world, so that the total flow of matter is describable in terms of cycles. It is, of course, incorrect to say that living things consume matter; what we mean is that their mere survival demands an enormous flow of matter through them.

The source of energy for the transformations of matter in our kind of living things is chemically reduced molecules and the energy is made available by catalyzed oxidation of reduced molecules. The major ultimate source of energy is sunlight, which is used in photosynthesis to reduce carbon compounds. But there are other sources available to specialized organisms, such as reduced inorganic elements. It is also postulated in contemporary discussion that the early history of our planet, and perhaps of others, included the production of reduced organic compounds by processes not requiring organisms, so that a ready source of energy and of prefabricated organic molecules could have been available at primitive stages of evolution (cf., Chapter 2).

The fundamental principles of our biological energetics may first be stated in negative form by contrasting organisms with familiar engines: organisms cannot use directly the energy released by oxidation, nor can they exploit temperature differences to perform work. They employ what may be called a principle of chemical energy coupling, a two-step process. Energy is "stored" in so-called *high-energy* compounds and "used" by breaking down these compounds, much as an old-fashioned submarine burned fuel in its engines to charge its batteries on the surface, then used the stored energy to propel it under water. In cells, the energy made available by oxidation of food (reduced compounds) is used to form high-energy compounds. The latter supply energy to the systems of the cell, where it is expended in many ways: synthesis, "pumping" of matter, movement, production of electricity, production of light, communication, etc. All the organisms we know use the same high-energy compound for carrying out most of their work—adenosine triphosphate, familiarly called ATP. Thus living things are quite different kinds of machines from those made for us by our engineers. An automobile is a device for oxidizing reduced compounds by combustion, using the heat to drive pistons. A horse is a cool device in which the muscles oxidize sugar without combustion, storing the chemical energy (originally solar energy) in ATP. The ATP then reacts with a system of molecular fibers in the muscle, causing motion as the ATP is broken down.

We would expect the principle of chemical energy coupling to apply to any form of life; to imagine surviving systems that solve their energetic problems in any other way is to appeal to an extreme of science fiction that is beyond the asymptotes of our knowledge. Still, the details we know about such systems are not so demanding. We cannot say why ATP in particular was chosen during evolution of life on our world, since chemical considerations suggest that many kinds of compounds may be suitable for energy storage.

THE DESIGN FOR SURVIVAL

Survival, both of the individual and of its kind, implies a conservation of *character* in the face of a continuous flux of matter. Stability of the matter itself is secondary to the character by which we acknowledge the individual or species; whether this dog is still the same dog named Igor or whether he is a descendant or an ancestor of dogs, does not depend at all on whether he still has any of the atoms he was born with. (The conservation of self and of kind is most vividly expressed in consciousness; conversely, the temptation to impute consciousness to dogs or to bacteria comes from the evidence of behavior that can be explained only in terms of survival of self and kind.)

Modern biology has accepted the task of accounting for what is conserved, and for the means of conserving it, in terms of the molecules of which living things are made. It is superfluous to say that living systems *are* molecular systems; the objective of molecular biology is to translate the meanings of survival into molecular terms. The skeleton of the design is now perceived; the cardinal intellectual sin is to think the story complete. The essential points are these:

(1) The unit organism, the biological atom capable of surviving in a non-living environment, is the cell. If we abstract to the essentials, all cells are the same.

(2) The two main domains of action in the cell are what we may call, loosely, a *genome* and a *cytoplasm.* The *genome* embodies the hereditary material. It is the embodiment of conservation and survival, that part of the organism which remains constant in character and is transmitted from generation to generation. The replication of genomes is the ultimate basis of

survival, for so long as exact copies of the genome can be made and exact copies of the copies can be made, survival becomes independent of the flux of matter.

(3) The replication of genomes is an extraordinarily exact process, but mistakes can be made. The mistakes are then replicated indefinitely. These are the hereditary changes or *mutations*, that are thought to be the sources of variation at the disposal of the evolutionary process.

(4) The cytoplasm—all the structure and working-equipment of the cell —forms itself and grows under the government of the genome. Its constancy is a reflection of the constancy of the genome; its ability to vary in a consistent way is a reflection of the versatility of the genome. The genome seems to be programmed to give a consistent pattern of instructions over the life of the organism, yet also is responsible in its commands to "needs" of the organism.

(5) The molecular basis of the genome is deoxyribonucleic acid (DNA); the inherited instructions to the organism are coded by the sequence of subunits (nucleotides) in DNA as letters of a language are coded by their sequence in words and sentences. DNA is the self-replicating molecule, and many of the chemical principles of its replication are known.

(6) The main molecular basis of the form and functions of the cytoplasm —both factory and machinery—is expressed in protein molecules, whose individual character depends on a sequence of small component molecules, the amino acids. This is clearer in the chemical operations of the cell which, as we have seen, are governed by the amounts and kinds of enzymes. All known enzymes are proteins. The genome determines the character of the cell as a machine for capturing and transforming matter by determining the kinds of enzymes, the amounts of enzymes, and the time when each enzyme is made.

(7) The instructions in the genome, which is DNA, are translated into the formation of proteins by a system of molecular transcription, many of whose features are known.

Thus, the minimum design for survival can be expressed in the proposition that the cell is a device for maintaining and propagating a genome. The genome determines the structures and the operations of a cytoplasm which in turn provides the genome with all the goods and services it needs for its maintenance and propagation. The genome makes only two things: copies of itself and copies of commands to the cytoplasm. The cytoplasm makes everything else, structures, enzymes, ATP, etc., carries on the business with the outside world and plays peasantry and proletariat to the autocratic (and parasitic) dynasties of the genome.

These features of the living things we know are common to all of them, and each contains details that are equally common. We may repeat once more that in the life we know it is not only the principles that are shared, but the material embodiments of the principles. Instead of stating principles we could list the corresponding substances: water, potassium and other characteristic elements, the molecules of cell membranes, ATP and lesser high-energy compounds, an immense number of protein catalysts (all of which we would expect to find in every cell), DNA, the chemical constituents involved in the replication of DNA, the substance ribonucleic acid (RNA) into which the messages of the genome are transcribed, the chemical machinery of genome-directed protein synthesis . . . and the list would go on with molecules we have not mentioned. If we think of living things as chemical systems, evolution, which has produced such a vast variety of forms, has been rather conservative in the kinds of molecules it seems to have used from the first. It is not that there has been no molecular evolution, but that molecular evolution leaves its imprint mainly in the finer details of molecules and in those molecules (the pigments of flowers, for example) that are significant to the special problems of survival of special organisms, but are not fundamental to the state-of-being-a-living-thing. Anyone can observe the difference between a man and a chimpanzee, but it takes rather clever chemistry to establish the fact that the molecules of the two are different. On the other hand, it takes only very simple chemistry to decide that both are organisms.

If we contemplate living things over the longest time scale, we will not confine our thoughts to self-maintaining, kind-maintaining organisms. We will acknowledge that something came before them, and find force for that opinion in the very fact that existing organisms have so much in common. For the quintessential point of evolutionary reasoning is that similarity implies common descent and, if that point has sometimes been misleading, we still are inclined to think that the common material features of living things imply common descent beginning with a common supply of molecules out of which the first organisms were made.

Therefore, an evolutionary frame of thought leads to the conclusion that a biological exploration of this world at one time would have been a search for the molecular features of a planet on its evolutionary way to the production of full-fledged organisms. Some of these features are contained in a familiar word that has lost some of its original implications but not all of them: the term *organic chemistry.* Originally implying that certain kinds of molecules could be produced only by the action of living things, it lost its vitalistic meaning when the chemist in his laboratory began to learn how to make similar molecules and so became an organic chemist. In a way, that event which was so portentous in the history of science and technology seems rather insignificant from our immediate standpoint; it merely says that one kind of organism, which we call an organic chemist, is capable of imitating in the laboratory the molecules made by other organisms. But evolution gives it a deeper meaning: that there must have been a time in this world when molecules now made in nature by organisms (which have a sumptuous battery of enzymes at their disposal) were made directly and without the guidance of enzymes by natural processes of the planet itself.

Organic chemistry defines itself as the study of that immense class of compounds that is made possible by the ability of carbon atoms to bond to other carbon atoms in a great variety of linear and cyclic forms. On the planet Earth, the presence of such molecules can be taken as traces of life: signs of living things, the remains of living things that have lost their investment in survival, or products made and cast off by living things. But the chemical traces of life can be much more definite than the mere presence of organic compounds and more compelling as evidence of the presence or transit of organisms. If we limit our consideration of biochemistry only to that chemistry which is characteristic and indispensable to all the organisms we know, we can appeal to distinct classes of carbon compounds, to extraordinarily important linkages of carbon to nitrogen or to phosphorus or to sulfur, can search for those vital complexes of organic molecules with metals, iron or magnesium or others, that play such a part in the energetics of organisms. We need not be more specific here; any elementary text of biochemistry lists dozens of compounds that belong only to the world of organisms in the world we know.

Another general principle of the chemistry of biological systems is that of polymerization. We have seen that the design for survival and reproduction calls for operations of very large molecules; all the naturally occurring molecules at the long end of the chemists' size-spectrum are products of organisms. The crucial classes of such large molecules are the nucleic acids, by which the genetic record is coded, replicated and translated, and the proteins, whose subtle and varied chemical shapes are adapted to recognizing particular molecules, combining with those molecules, and catalyzing their transformations. The nucleic acids are the genes, the regulators of the genes, the messengers of the genes; the proteins are the enzymes. This variety of immense molecules is made by stringing together smaller molecules. In the case of nucleic acids the huge molecules represent merely permutations of the sequence of four kinds of small molecules called nucleotides. In the case of the proteins, the variety and subtlety is achieved by the patterned folding of chains that themselves comprise permutations of the sequence of about 20 types of smaller molecules, the amino acids, molecules of the same kind but different in important ways. Thus, all the variety of living things as we know them is derived essentially from four kinds of nucleotides (or 8 kinds by a different reckoning that is mainly of technical interest), and from 20 kinds of amino acids. The trick lies in how they are lined up, much as all the meanings and operations of all the languages using our alphabet depend on the ordering of 26 or so letters.

The spoor of life is in such chemical traces, and the means for observing them are powerful and objective. It makes sense to think that instruments detecting the constellations of atoms that go with living things could give us news about life, though it might say very little about organisms. The chemical traces would be expected in a world at the early stages of biological evolution, before organisms; according to prevailing ideas, the molecules might be accumulated in even greater abundance than in an evolved biological world, precisely because of the absence of reproducing organisms to "eat them up." The traces might be found in a world in which organisms were now extinct; we do not always think of an oil well as a trace of life, though we know it is.

To think of a universal biology is to test the generality of propositions that apply to our own biological world. A basic example is a question that has often been discussed since it can be approached through theoretical chemistry: must organic chemistry be a chemistry of carbon, or can one think of a comparable variety of biochemical compounds and reactions that is based on some other element? (cf., Chapter 14.) For example, could a comparable chemistry be achieved with the silicon atom? The answer generally has been negative, although such questions will continue to be asked. At an even more fundamental level, it has been asked whether water should be regarded as a unique medium for organic reactions, or whether other solvents (for example, liquid ammonia) might not serve the same purpose in another world. Again, the answer has seemed dubious, yet no one would exclude categorically the possibility of other solvents though we probably would insist that biological systems would have to be liquid systems. As we turn to molecules with a more particular significance for survival, the estimates of their universality are even less certain. In principle, a biological system will require "high-energy compounds" but how similar to ATP would they have to be? Heredity would require a coded replicable polymer (unless governed by a principle not yet imagined); what properties of DNA could be embodied in a polymer that was quite different from DNA—so different that it would not give any of the chemical tests for a DNA-like molecule? What kinds of large molecules that did not test as proteins could have the same versatility of catalytic powers? Perhaps theory can expose possibilities and probabilities; the explorer will make the tests.

We ask "What is Life?" but find that we can define only the attributes and material traces of living things. The definition is not succinct, for it comprehends all the principles and material facts that distinguish the life we know, and gains precision from the specification of additional detail.

Nevertheless, the distinction between the living and the non-living is no less real because the boundary seems blurred. Indeed, the evolutionary approach to biology implies that we should expect the boundary to be diffuse (in the past, if not now), though the domains on either side are quite different. The problem is not that our conception of a living thing is vague; on the contrary, our concern is that it is too definite because it is too provincial.

It may seem curious that the biologist has so little to say about death in his talk about life, but he has his reasons. The failures of individual survival are determined by a multitude of causes: caprices of the environment, accident and predation, excessive fecundity, and senescence in those few individuals that can enjoy the luxury of old age. There is no common denominator. The powers of reproduction are so efficacious that death seldom leads to the extinction of species unless it is assisted by the singular lethality of the most advanced of species. Death is a private affair; the poet and the prophet have more to tell us about it than does the biologist.

CHAPTER 2

THE ORIGIN OF LIFE*

S. L. MILLER and N. H. HOROWITZ

INTRODUCTION

To modern scientists, the origin of life seems one of the most difficult of all problems. This was not always so. From classic Greek times until the middle of the 19th century it was generally accepted that living organisms could originate spontaneously, without parents, from non-living material. Thus, for centuries it was believed that insects, frogs, worms, etc. were generated spontaneuosly in mud and decaying matter. This notion was experimentally disproved in 1668 by Redi, who showed that larvae did not develop in meat if adult insects were prevented from laying their eggs on it; but it was revived again following the discovery of microorganisms by Leeuwenhoek in 1675. Since bacteria, yeasts and protozoa were much smaller and apparently simpler than any previously known living things, Redi's disproof did not seem to apply to them, and the possibility of their spontaneous origin became a matter of controversy for nearly 200 years. We know today that these organisms, despite their small size, are enormously complex—as complex as the cells of higher organisms—and the possibility that they could originate spontaneously from non-living material is as remote as it is for any other cells. In a series of brilliant ex-

* Parts of this paper are taken with permission from the review by N. H. Horowitz and S. L. Miller, "Current theories on the origin of life," which appeared in *Fortschritte der Chemie organischer Naturstoffe, 20*, 423 (1962), edited by L. Zechmeister (Springer-Verlag).

periments, *Pasteur* [1922] in 1861 finally overcame the technical difficulties that had prevented solution of the problem and demonstrated, by logically the same argument that Redi had used, that microorganisms arise only from pre-existing microorganisms. The genetic continuity of living organisms was thus established for the first time.

Shortly before, in 1858, Darwin and Wallace had published, simultaneously and independently, the theory of evolution by natural selection. This theory could account for the evolution from the simplest single-celled organism to the most complex plants and animals, including man. Therefore, the problem of the origin of life involved no longer how each species developed, but only how the first living organism arose.

To most scientists, Pasteur's experiments demonstrated the futility of inquiring into the origin of life. It was even suggested that life had no origin, but, like matter, was eternal. *Arrhenius* [1908] proposed that life-bearing seeds (panspermia) are scattered throughout cosmic space and that they fall on the planets and germinate wherever conditions are favorable. Concern with the origin of life thus faded into the background, while biologists applied themselves to the more profitable task of investigating the nature of living matter. As a result of these investigations, carried out over the last 100 years, the problem can be viewed today in a new light. Biologists have come to realize that life is a manifestation of certain molecular combinations. The origin of life concerns the origin of these molecular combinations, not of the mysterious properties of growth, irritability, metabolism, etc. Since, according to cosmologists, not even the elements have existed forever, it is impossible to believe that life has always existed. Biology is therefore faced again with the question of how life arose (cf. *Oparin* [1957, 1959]).

'One of the reasonably well established facts that we have to start with is that life did originate on the Earth at some time in the distant past. We shall therefore first consider the nature of living matter from a general point of view and show in what essential properties it differs from inanimate matter. Next, we will examine the chemical basis for these special properties. We will then turn to the chemistry of the primitive Earth and describe the conditions that are believed to have been present during prebiotic times. We will finally discuss experiments dealing with the production of biologically interesting compounds under primitive Earth conditions.

THE NATURE OF LIVING ORGANISMS

Some biologists and biochemists regard the question of how life started as essentially meaningless. They view living and non-living matter as forming a continuum, and the drawing of a line between them as arbitrary. Life, in this view, is associated with the complex metabolic apparatus of the cell—enzymes, membranes, metabolic cycles, etc.—and the point at which such a system becomes "alive" is undefinable [*Pirie, 1937*]. Most biologists, however, are agreed that living matter is uniquely defined by its genetic properties. According to this view, the feature that above all others distinguishes living matter is its mode of duplication. The reproduction of living things differs from the self-propagation that is found in many nonliving systems (e.g., the multiplication of crystals, the autocatalytic increase of certain enzymes in the presence of their proenzymes, the growth of a flame) in that it is basically a process of *copying*. Like the non-living examples mentioned, living organisms select appropriate materials from their environment and transform them into (usually) accurate replicas of themselves. Kinetically, the reproduction of living organisms is indistinguishable from the autocatalysis of non-living systems; both processes lead to the same mathematical law of autocatalytic increase. They differ fundamentally, however, in that the self-replication of living systems extends to the occasional accidental variants (mutants) which appear from time to time in populations. The mutants copy themselves when they replicate; they do not copy the parental type from which they originated. This remarkable property, which is found only in systems that we call living, is what makes organic evolution possible. Combined with natural selection, it underlies the seemingly infinite capacity of organisms to adapt themselves to the needs of their existence. *In other words, an organism, to be called living, must be capable of both replication and mutation; such an organism will evolve into higher forms.*

The concept that the essential attributes of living matter are reproduction with mutation derives principally from the discoveries that have been made in genetics since 1900. Its most cogent expression has been given by *Muller* [*1922, 1929*]. One of the most far-reaching genetic discoveries was that the properties of self-replication and mutation (henceforth called *genetic* properties) are associated with a material substance of the cell which is confined largely to the chromosomes.

One of the major accomplishments of biochemistry and genetics has been the identification of the genetic material in cells as deoxyribonucleic acid (DNA). The genetic material of a number of bacterial viruses (bacteriophages) has also been shown to be DNA. In many plant and animal viruses the genetic material is not DNA but ribonucleic acid (RNA).

It is now generally agreed that the structure of DNA, as isolated from a variety of cells, is that proposed by *Watson and Crick* [*1953*].

The investigations of *Kornberg* and his associates [*1960*] on the enzymatic synthesis of DNA *in vitro* furnish the most important evidence for

TABLE 1. Polymerization of DNA.

m AdRPPP + m TdRPPP + n GdRPPP + n CdRPPP
$$\downarrow \uparrow \qquad \text{DNA} + \text{Polymerase} + \text{Mg}^{++}$$
$(AdRP)_m(TdRP)_m(GdRP)_n(CdRP)_n + 2(m + n)PP$

A = adenine.	C = cytosine.	P = phosphate.
T = thymine.	dR = deoxyribose.	PP = pyrophosphate.
G = guanine.		

the self-replication of DNA. These workers have obtained an enzyme from bacterial cells that polymerizes the 5′-triphosphates of the four constituent nucleosides of DNA to produce DNA and inorganic pyrophosphate. This polymerization takes place only in the presence of DNA as a catalyst or primer (Table 1).

The DNA formed in this reaction is indistinguishable in physical properties from natural, two-stranded, high-molecular weight DNA. Chemical evidence shows that the two strands are anti-parallel, as predicted by the Watson-Crick model. The absolute requirement for a DNA primer and for all four deoxynucleoside triphosphates indicates that the reaction involves the copying of the primer. This is further strengthened by the observation that the base composition of the product is the same as that of the primer for a variety of different DNA's, and is independent of the initial concentrations of substrates.

It is believed at the present time that the heterocatalytic activity of the genes can be accounted for entirely on the basis of their role in the synthesis of enzymes and other proteins.

Considerable progress has been made in recent years in elucidating the synthesis of proteins in cell-free systems, despite difficulties owing to the complexity and lability of the systems. It has been established that the major site of protein synthesis in the cell is in submicroscopic ribonucleoprotein particles of the cytoplasm, the ribosomes. It is believed that genetic information from the nucleus is contained in these particles in the form of RNA and that the latter determines the sequence of amino acids in the synthesized protein. Considerable attention has been paid to the mode of activation of the amino acids and to their mode of transfer to the ribosomes. It has been established that activation and transfer require a specific enzyme and a specific ribonucleic acid for each amino acid.

It has recently been found that synthetic polyribonucleotides can act as "messenger" RNA *in vitro*. Thus, when polyuridylic acid is added to a ribosomal preparation from *E. coli*, it stimulates the system to produce polyphenylalanine [*Nirenberg and Matthaei*, 1961]. This discovery has

TABLE 2.   DNA Replication and Control of Protein Synthesis.

$$\text{DNA} + \text{deoxyribonucleoside triphosphates} \xrightleftharpoons{\text{DNA polymerase}} 2\ \text{DNA}$$

$+$

Ribonucleoside triphosphates

$\downarrow\uparrow$

"Messenger" RNA   Amino acid $+$ ATP $+$ specific "transfer" RNA

$\downarrow$ RNA polymerase $\downarrow$ specific activating enzyme

Ribosome $\leftarrow$ Amino acid $\cdot$ RNA

$\downarrow$

Protein

made it possible to assign trinucleotide code words to most of the amino acids [*Speyer et al.,* 1962; *Matthaei et al.,* 1962].

The similarity between the reactions of gene duplication and of "messenger" RNA synthesis is striking. Both involve base pairing and polymerization of nucleoside triphosphates. It is likely that base pairing also operates in the alignment of amino acids in polypeptide synthesis [*Hoagland,* 1960].

Table 2 summarizes schematically the autocatalytic and heterocatalytic reactions of DNA.

The view adopted here is that the unique attribute of living matter from which all of its other remarkable features derive, is the capacity for self-duplication with mutation. Genetic studies on a variety of organisms have shown that this capacity is confined to material that is largely localized in the chromosomes. Besides directing its own synthesis, the genetic material induces the synthesis of proteins in the cell, including the catalysts that make available the energy and the precursors needed for the perpetuation of the system. *The central problem in the origin of life is to account for the origin of material combining these properties.*

The genetic material of living organisms has been identified as nucleic acid. Of the two nucleic acids, DNA appears to be the principal genetic substance of bacterial viruses, bacteria, and higher plants and animals. RNA is the genetic substance of many plant and animal viruses, and it is not excluded that it has a genetic role in higher organisms.

The molecular structure of DNA is such as to suggest a simple mechanism for its replication. This mechanism is supported by experiments *in vivo* and *in vitro.* The latter show that replication of DNA can occur in a system containing activated precursors and a single enzyme. The structure of DNA also suggests a molecular basis for mutation, and this, too, is supported by experimental findings.

The heterocatalytic action of DNA is mediated by a specific RNA which is synthesized in a DNA-dependent reaction which appears to be very similar in mechanism to the reaction by which DNA itself is replicated. The RNA enters the ribosomes, where it determines, in an unknown manner, the amino acid sequence of a specific polypeptide chain.

The system described above fulfills the minimal requirements for a living system, as defined earlier. Its discovery and elaboration, starting from the observations of Mendelian genetics, is surely the major accomplishment of twentieth century biology to date. The system is relatively simple, compared to a whole cell, and to this extent it brings us closer to an understanding of the origin of life. Yet it is undoubtedly still too complex and too efficient to have originated spontaneously by random chemical reactions. It is almost certain that this system is itself the product of a long evolution.

It can be argued that the present genetic system has evolved so far from the original, primitive genetic system that it bears little resemblance to it. Thus the first genetic system might have utilized nucleic acids with different sugars and different purines and pyrimidines; it might not even have contained a sugar-phosphate backbone. It is obvious that other self-replicating polymers might be possible but until specific models are proposed and their plausibility examined relative to the DNA model, the simplest assumption is that the first genetic material was closely related to DNA but probably not identical to it. The answer to this problem may become apparent when we know more about the reactions that took place in the primitive oceans.

It is tempting to speculate—and many authors have done so—that the first living organism consisted of a polynucleotide which produced or was associated with a polymerase. Such an entity would be capable of performing only one function—self-replication at the expense of preformed organic compounds (nucleotides) in its environment—but it would have the capability of evolving, by known mechanisms, into a highly complex organism. Crow [1959] has pointed out that the primitive organism need not have functioned very efficiently. Replication need only have been accurate enough to prevent the system from mutating itself out of existence. Natural selection would lower the mutation rate by favoring those mutants whose ratio of correct to wrong copies was greatest. Replication may also have been slow, with perhaps a small polypeptide performing the role of polymerase. Here, too, selection would favor the discovery of more effective catalysts.

The polynucleotide hypothesis is attractive, but it is not so simple as it appears. It is by no means clear how even such a simple organism as a self-duplicating polynucleotide was produced by random chemical combinations. To obtain a polynucleotide of the required specificity implies that random polymerization of mononucleotides occurred on the primitive

Earth on a large scale. This would require the presence of catalysts in the environment to guide the reactions of the activated monomers in the direction of polymer synthesis, as against hydrolysis and other degradations which would otherwise predominate. To obtain these specific catalysts, it might be supposed that catalytically active polypeptides (primitive enzymes) were formed from the amino acids which there is reason to believe were abundant on the primitive Earth.

It is not necessary to assume that these primitive enzymes were as specific or as efficient as modern enzymes; neither is it necessary to assume that they were as large. Recent work has shown that the entire structure of some enzymes is not needed for their activity [*Anfinsen,* 1959] and it is possible that even a small polypeptide can manifest some catalytic activity.

Some authors consider it more likely that the first organisms were not individual molecules, but polymolecular aggregates of one kind or another, separated from the surrounding medium by a definite phase boundary. Thus, *Oparin* [1957] assumes the formation in the primitive ocean of coacervate droplets containing proteins and other high-molecular weight compounds. These are assumed to have carried out a kind of primitive metabolism, accumulating proteins and other substances from the environment, growing in size, and finally fragmenting into smaller droplets which repeated the process. The coacervate concept is not useful as a model for the first living organism, because no detailed mechanism has been proposed by which coacervates can replicate, mutate, and therefore evolve. The DNA mechanism is the only one for which we have both direct evidence and a satisfactory theoretical model at the present time. For reasons stated earlier in this article, we believe that any model of primitive life which neglects to account for the genetic properties of living matter is doomed to failure. The coacervate concept may, however, provide a possibly useful means for concentrating specific substances in a small volume, thus increasing their opportunities for interaction.

THE ORIGIN OF LIFE ON THE EARTH

The Geological Record

It is estimated from various methods of dating rocks and meteorites that the Earth was formed about 4.5 to 5.0 billion years ago (4.5×10^9). The first fossils of hard shelled animals occur in the Cambrian which begins about 0.6 billion years ago. Structures that have been found in Precambrian rocks are the fossil remains of algal colonies. A number of Precambrian coals are known, and it likely that they are of biological origin. (For further discussion, see *Barghoorn and Tyler* [1963]; *Barghoorn* [1957]).

The oldest known fossils are the remains of algal colonies found in Southern Rhodesia. Their age is at least 2.7 billion years [*Holmes*, 1954; *Macgregor*, 1940]. It is likely that life was present before this, but so far no geological evidence is available. Many of the Precambrian rocks have been metamorphosed, and the heat has destroyed most of the fossils that may have been present. However, there are some Precambrian sediments that have not been heated and recrystallized, and these offer a rich field for investigation.

There is a period of about 2 billion years, between the origin of the Earth and the occurrence of the first algal fossils, during which the origin and early evolution of life took place. This is almost half of geological time. We are without any knowledge of the biological events that occurred during this period.

There is little in the geological record that indicates what the conditions were in the very early Precambrian. The temperatures are not known, but are frequently assumed to be close to the present temperatures. The principal problem is the composition of the primitive atmosphere. Proposals have been made that the atmosphere was strongly reducing, strongly oxidizing, and every variation in between. It is generally agreed that free oxygen was absent. The principal disagreement is whether the carbon in the atmosphere was methane, carbon dioxide or carbon monoxide, and the nitrogen was N_2 or ammonia. It has been claimed that the presence of large deposits of ferric iron in the Precambrian demonstrates the presence of oxidizing conditions, but this iron may have been oxidized after it was deposited by oxygen in ground waters. The ferric iron might also have been formed by iron bacteria or by non-biological processes, even though the thermodynamically stable species would presumably be ferrous.

Since the geological record tells us very little about the conditions on the primitive Earth and when life arose, we must approach this problem from the standpoint of the origin of the Earth.

The Formation of the Earth

It is presently held that the planets and Sun were formed at the same time from a cloud of cosmic dust at low temperatures. This spherical cloud of dust and gas collapsed into a round disk due to the forces of rotation and gravitation. The disk, in turn, broke up into sections or rotating segments, and the particles of dust and gases in these cells were pulled together by gravitational attraction until they became solid bodies. The central portion became the Sun, while the sections farther out became the planets. It is clear that most of the gaseous material, particularly the hydrogen, helium, nitrogen (as ammonia), carbon (as methane) and oxygen (as water) escaped before the Earth was formed. This is true because the Earth contains very much less of these elements relative to a non-volatile element such as silicon than does the Sun. In the case of Jupiter and Saturn more of these elements were retained when these planets formed because of the lower temperatures at that distance from the Sun.

After the mass of dust and gas becomes dense enough, it acquires a gravitational field that slows up or prevents the escape of the gases in its atmosphere. In the case of the Earth only the two lightest elements, hydrogen and helium, can escape. The rate of escape is strongly dependent on the temperature and the gravitational field, so that in the case of Jupiter and Saturn, their low temperatures and high gravitational fields make the escape of hydrogen and helium very slow. Therefore, the present atmospheres of these planets are probably not much different from the atmospheres they had when they were formed. The atmospheres of Jupiter and Saturn are observed to contain methane and ammonia, and the presence of hydrogen and helium has been observed indirectly. For a discussion of the formation of the Earth that emphasizes the chemical aspects, see *Urey* [1952a] and for atmospheres, *Urey* [1959].

The Primitive Atmosphere

It is reasonable to expect that the Earth possessed initially an atmosphere similar to that of Jupiter and Saturn since the Earth was formed from the same dust cloud, but with much less hydrogen and helium. In the case of Venus, Earth and Mars, this atmosphere has been altered by the escape of hydrogen. These planets, smaller and closer to the Sun than the major planets, lose their hydrogen rapidly enough to change the nature of the atmosphere in geological times.

The loss of hydrogen results in the production of carbon dioxide, nitrogen, nitrate, sulfate, free oxygen and ferric iron. The over-all change has been oxidation of the reducing atmosphere to the present oxidizing atmosphere. Many complex organic compounds would have been formed during the overall change, thereby presenting a favorable environment for the formation of life.

The idea that organic compounds were produced on the primitive Earth under reducing conditions was first clearly stated by *Oparin* [1937] in his book, *The Origin of Life. Urey* [1952a, 1952b] gave a more detailed statement of the reasons for a reducing atmosphere, and showed by thermodynamic analysis that so long as molecular hydrogen is present, methane and ammonia will be the stable forms of carbon and nitrogen.

The equilibrium constant (at 25°C in the presence of liquid water) for the reaction

$$CO_2 + 4 H_2 = CH_4 + 2 H_2O$$

is 8×10^{22}, and therefore any pressure of hydrogen greater than about 10^{-4} atm. will reduce carbon dioxide to methane. The same is true for graphite. Carbon monoxide is unstable relative to carbon dioxide, hydrogen, and methane in the presence of water. The carbon dioxide in the atmosphere is kept low by absorption in the oceans to form HCO_{-3}, H_2CO_3 and $CO_{=3}$. The carbon dioxide also reacts with silicates, to form limestones, for example

$$CaSiO_3 + CO_2 = CaCO_3 + SiO_2 \quad K_{25} = 10^8$$

The equilibrium constant for the reaction

$$\tfrac{1}{2} N_1 + \tfrac{3}{2} H_2 = NH_3$$

is 7.6×10^2. Ammonia is very soluble in water and therefore would displace the above reaction toward the right, giving

$$\tfrac{1}{2} N_2 + \tfrac{3}{2} H_2 + H^+ = NH_4^+$$

$$(NH_4^+)/P_{N_2}^{1/2} \quad P_{H_2}^{3/2} = 8.0 \times 10^{13} \, (H^+),$$

where P = partial pressure. This equation shows that most of the ammonia would have been present in the ocean instead of the atmosphere. The ammonia in the ocean would have been stable until the pressure of hydrogen fell below about 10^{-5} atm., assuming the pH of the ocean was 8, i.e., the present value.

From these equilibria it is seen that so long as there is an appreciable amount of molecular hydrogen present, we can say that the atmosphere will consist of methane, ammonia, nitrogen, and water vapor. Carbon monoxide is unstable under these conditions. Carbon dioxide dissolves in the ocean, and it also reacts with silicates to form limestones ($CaCO_3$). As the hydrogen escapes, the methane and ammonia are dehydrogenated, and this hydrogen also escapes. In the end this results in the oxidation of the methane and ammonia to carbon dioxide and nitrogen. Finally, the water is photochemically dissociated to oxygen and hydrogen. This hydrogen escapes, and free oxygen appears in the atmosphere resulting in a highly oxidizing atmosphere. This does not mean that thermodynamically unstable gases were entirely absent from the primitive atmosphere, but that they were present only to the extent of a few parts per million.

It is asserted by *Rubey* [1955] that surface carbon of the Earth came from the outgassing of the interior, the carbon being in the form of carbon monoxide and carbon dioxide. This may well have been an important source of the surface carbon, but the more oxidized carbon would be converted to methane so long as molecular hydrogen was present.

For a more detailed discussion of the equilibria in the primitive atmosphere, see *Miller and Urey* [1959].

It has been recently proposed by *Lederberg and Cowie* [1958], by *Fowler, Greenstein and Hoyle* [1961] and by *Oró* [1961], that the synthesis of organic compounds took place before the Earth was formed. Organic compounds have been synthesized at low temperatures from a mixture of methane, ammonia and water under conditions possibly present in comets. These compounds include acetylene, ethane, propane and several other hydrocarbons [*Glasel,* 1961]; and urea, acetamide and acetone [*Berger,* 1961]. It is quite probable that such syntheses took place in the primitive dust cloud and that much of the carbon was retained on the Earth in this form. Most of these organic compounds were probably destroyed by heating during the formation of the Earth. The organic compounds thus destroyed would eventually form methane, carbon dioxide and hydrogen, and the surviving organic compounds would undergo further transformations. Therefore the form in which the carbon was retained does not appreciably affect the conditions in the atmosphere and hydrosphere of the primitive Earth. This point is discussed further by *Miller and Urey* [1964].

The idea that the Earth had a reducing atmosphere is at first difficult to accept, since it is so different from what is now present. It would probably not be necessary to accept the hypothesis of the reducing atmosphere if organic compounds could be synthesized under oxidizing conditions (that is, from carbon dioxide and water) and thereby provide favorable conditions for the origin of life.

Numerous attempts have been made to synthesize organic compounds under oxidizing conditions. Ultraviolet light and electric discharges do not give organic compounds except when contaminating reducing agents are present [*Rabinowitch,* 1945]. If a mixture of hydrogen, carbon dioxide and water is used, then organic compounds will be obtained, but only very small amounts of hydrogen could be present under oxidizing conditions. Formic acid and formaldehyde have been synthesized from carbon dioxide and water by using 40 million electron volt helium ions from a 60 inch cyclotron as a source of energy. However, only 10^{-7} molecules of formaldehyde were synthesized per ion pair [*Garrison et al.,* 1951]. Although the simplest organic compounds were indeed synthesized, the yields were so small that this experiment can best be interpreted to mean that it would not have been possible to synthesize organic compounds non-biologically as long as the Earth had oxidizing conditions. This experiment is important in

TABLE 3.   Present Sources of Energy Averaged Over the Earth
[*Miller and Urey*, 1959; *Horowitz and Miller*, 1962]

Source	cal per cm^{-2} $year^{-1}$
Total radiation from sun	260,000
Ultraviolet light	
<2500 Å	570
<2000 Å	85
<1500 Å	3.5
Electric discharges	4.0[a]
Cosmic rays	0.0015
Radioactivity (to 1.0 km depth)	0.8[b]
Volcanoes	0.13[c]

[a] Includes 0.9 cal cm^{-2} $year^{-1}$ from lightning and about 3 cal cm^{-2} $year^{-1}$ due to corona discharges from pointed objects.
[b] The value 4×10^9 years ago was 2.8 cal cm^{-2} $year^{-1}$.
[c] Calculated assuming the emission of 1 km^3 of lava per year at 1000°.

that it induced a re-examination of Oparin's hypothesis of the reducing atmosphere; and subsequent experiments have shown the ease with which organic compounds can be synthesized under reducing conditions.

Energy Sources on the Primitive Earth

Table 3 gives a summary of the sources of energy in the terrestrial surface regions. It is evident that sunlight is the principal source of energy, but only a small fraction of this is in the wavelengths below 2000 Å which can be absorbed by CH_4, H_2O, NH_3, CO_2, etc. If more complex molecules were formed, the absorption could move up to the 2500 Å region (or longer wavelengths) where substantial energy is available. Visible light would be ineffective in the synthesis of organic compounds in the atmosphere, but it might have been important in the oceans for organic transformations not requiring large amounts of energy; a possible example is the formation of a peptide bond.

Although probable, it is not certain that the large amount of energy from ultraviolet light would make the principal contribution to the synthesis of organic compounds. Most of the photochemical reactions at these short wavelengths would take place in the upper atmosphere. The compounds so formed would absorb at longer wavelengths and therefore might not reach the oceans before they were decomposed by the ultraviolet light. The question is whether the rate of decomposition in the atmosphere is higher or lower than the rate of transport to the oceans.

Next in importance as a source of energy are electric discharges which, as lightning and corona discharges, occur closer to the Earth's surface, and hence more efficient transfer to the oceans would have taken place.

Cosmic ray energy is negligible at present, and there is no reason to assume it was greater in the past. The radioactive disintegration of uranium, thorium and potassium was more important 4.5×10^9 years ago, but still the energy was largely expended on the interior of the solid material of the rocks, and only a very small fraction of the total energy was available in the oceans and atmosphere. The energy from volcanoes is small at the present time. If volcanic activity were much greater on the primitive Earth, this source of energy could play a significant but not dominant role in the synthesis of organic compounds.

Synthetic Processes

Amino Acids

A considerable amount of experimental work has been carried out on the synthesis of organic compounds under possible primitive Earth conditions. These experiments are based either directly or indirectly on the assumption that reducing conditions were present during the early history of the Earth.

The first experimental work on the synthesis of organic compounds under reducing conditions was performed using electric discharges as a source of energy. These experiments showed that milligram quantities of glycine, α-alanine, β-alanine and α-amino-n-butyric were produced when methane, ammonia water and hydrogen were subjected to a high-frequency spark [*Miller, 1953*]. A more complete analysis of the amino acids as well as other products give the results shown in Table 4 [*Miller, 1955, 1957a, 1957b*]. The compounds in the table account for 15 per cent of the carbon added as methane, with the yield of glycine alone being 2.1 per cent. Indirect evidence indicated that polyhydroxyl compounds (possibly sugars) were also synthesized. These compounds were probably formed from condensation of the formaldehyde that was produced by the electric discharge. The alanine was demonstrated to be racemic as would be expected in a system which contained no asymmetric reagents. It was shown that the syntheses were not due to bacterial contamination, since the yields were the same as when the autoclaving was omitted. This experiment has been repeated and confirmed by *Abelson* [1956], *Pavlovskaya and Pasynskii* [1959] as well as by *Heyns, Walter and Meyer* [1957]. Various mixtures of H_2, CH_4, CO, CO_2, NH_3, N_2, H_2O, and O_2 have been used, and

TABLE 4. Yields in moles ($\times 10^5$) from Sparking a Mixture of CH_4, NH_3, H_2O, and H_2 (710 mg of carbon was added as CH_4)

Glycine	63	Succinic acid	4
Glycolic acid	56	Aspartic acid	0.4
Sarcosine	5	Glutamic acid	0.6
Alanine	34	Iminodiacetic acid	5.5
Lactic acid	31	Iminoacetic-propionic acid	1.5
N-Methylalanine	1	Formic acid	233
α-Amino-n-butyric acid	5	Acetic acid	15
α-Aminoisobutyric acid	0.1	Propionic acid	13
α-Hydroxybutyric acid	5	Urea	2
β-Alanine	15	N-Methyl urea	1.5

amino acids were obtained when conditions were reducing—i.e., H_2, CH_4, CO, or NH_3 were present in excess. No amino acids were obtained under oxidizing conditions. Several of these mixtures are unstable and could not have constituted an atmosphere of the primitive Earth.

The action of electric discharges on a mixture of CH_4, NH_3, H_2O and H_2S gave approximately the same yields of amino acids as obtained in the absence of H_2S. In addition ammonium thiocyanate, thiourea and thioacetamide were synthesized [*Heyns et al., 1957*].

Oró [1963*b*] used mixtures of CH_4, C_2H_6, NH_3 and H_2O with electric discharges. Glycine, alanine, considerable yields of aspartic acid, and asparagine were obtained. Isoleucine and proline were tentatively identified. A number of the precursor nitriles and amides of these compounds were also obtained.

The mechanism of the amino acid synthesis is of interest if we are to extrapolate the results in this simple system to the primitive Earth. It would be possible for the amino and hydroxy acids to be synthesized near the electrodes from the ions and free radicals produced by the electric discharge. However, the major products of the electric discharge are aldehydes and hydrogen cyanide. These react in the aqueous phase of the system to give amino and hydroxy nitriles, which are hydrolyzed to the amino and hydroxy acids (Strecker and cyanohydrin syntheses). The reactions for the amino acid syntheses are

$$RCHO + NH_3 + HCN \rightleftarrows RCH(NH_2)CN + H_2O$$
$$RCH(NH_2)CN + 2H_2O \rightarrow RCH(NH_2)COOH + NH_3$$

and similar reactions for the hydroxy acid syntheses

$$RCHO + HCN \rightleftarrows RCH(OH)CN$$
$$RCH(OH)CN + 2H_2O \rightarrow RCH(OH)COOH$$

The β-alanine was not formed by this mechanism, but probably by the addition of ammonia to acrylonitrile, followed by hydrolysis to β-alanine. Similarly, the addition of hydrogen cyanide to acrylonitrile would give the succinic acid on hydrolysis.

This mechanism accounts for the fact that most of the amino acids produced were α-amino acids. As is well known, the amino acids in proteins are α-amino acids; and this raises the question whether the enzymatic and structural functions of proteins can be constructed only with α-amino acids. The answer to this question is not known, but it is possible that α-amino acids are present in protein because they were the only amino acids available for use when the origin of life took place, and they have persisted in proteins ever since.

It is clear from Table 3, that the greatest source of energy on the primitive Earth would have been ultraviolet light. The effective wavelengths are $CH_4 < 1450$ Å, $H_2O < 1850$ Å, $NH_3 < 2250$ Å, $CO < 1545$ Å, $CO_2 < 1960$ Å, $N_2 < 1100$ Å and $H_2 < 900$ Å. These short wavelengths are difficult to work with in the laboratory, and hence less work has been done with this source of energy. One would expect that the results of the ultraviolet light experiments would be similar to the electric discharge experiments since similar free radicals would be formed.

Groth and v. Weyssenhoff [1957, 1960] synthesized glycine from a mixture of methane, ammonia and water using the 1470Å and 1295 Å lines of xenon. Glycine, alanine, α-aminobutyric acid, formic acid, acetic acid and propionic acid were synthesized from ethane, ammonia and water. *Terenin* [1959] has obtained several amino acids from a mixture of methane, carbon monoxide, ammonia and water using the short wavelengths from a hydrogen lamp.

The yields from these syntheses were low. The mechanism of synthesis was not investigated, but it is possible that it is by a Strecker synthesis as in the case of the electric discharge experiments. The low yields may be due to the small yield of hydrogen cyanide by ultraviolet light in contrast to electric discharges.

The experiments on the mechanism of the electric discharge synthesis indicate that a special set c⸱ conditions or type of electric discharge is not required to obtain amino acids. Any process or combination of processes that yielded both aldehydes and hydrogen cyanide would have contributed to the amount of α-amino acids in the ocean of the primitive Earth. Therefore, it is not fundamental whether the aldehydes and hydrogen cyanide came from ultraviolet light or from electric discharges, since both processes would contribute to the result. Possibly, the electric discharges were the principal source of hydrogen cyanide and ultraviolet light was the principal source of aldehydes, so that the two processes complemented each other.

Good yields of amino acids have been obtained by *Palm and Calvin* [1962] using electron irradiation on a mixture of CH_4, NH_3 and H_2O. The results are similar to the electric discharge experiments. Electron irradiation experiments on CH_4, NH_3 and H_2O mixtures in the solid, liquid and gas phases have also been carried out by *Oró* [1963c].

Amino acids have been synthesized in two laboratories by heating CH_4, NH_3 and H_2O to 900–1200°C in silica and other tubes [*Oró*, 1964b; *Harada and Fox*, 1964a, 1964b]. Silica gel and alumina were used as catalyst beds in these tubes, and the contact time of the heated gases in the tubes was very short. The major amino acids synthesized were glycine and alanine, but small quantities of most of the amino acids which occur in proteins were also reported. The identification of the minor components needs further attention. The yields in these experiments are very low, approximately 10^{-3} per cent based on the CH_4 [*Oró*, 1964b]. The very low yields do not rule out this type of process since only a single pass system was used, and the yields could undoubtedly be improved in a multipass system. The mechanism was not investigated, but it may also be a Strecker synthesis since a considerable amount of HCN was synthesized.

There are a number of experiments using x rays, electrons and other sources of high-energy radiation to synthesize amino acids in aqueous solutions. These experiments will not be reviewed here, because of the small amount of high-energy radiation that would have been present on the primitive Earth, even though some of these experiments claim to simulate primitive Earth conditions.

There are several amino acid syntheses that use reasonable organic compounds as starting materials. *Bahadur et al.* [1954, 1958, 1959] have reported the synthesis of amino acids by the action of sunlight on concentrated paraldehyde solutions containing ferric chloride and nitrate or ammonia as the source of nitrogen. *Pavlovskaya and Pasynskii* [1959] have synthesized a number of amino acids by the action of ultraviolet light on a 2.5 per cent solution of formaldehyde containing ammonium chloride. Such high concentrations of formaldehyde could not have been present on the primitive Earth. If such syntheses could work with 10^{-4} or 10^{-6} M formaldehyde, then this type of synthesis might have been important, since formaldehyde would have been synthesized in the atmosphere by ultraviolet light and electric discharges.

The synthesis of glycine, alanine and aspartic acid from the polymerization of concentrated NH_4CN was reported by *Oró and Kamat* [1961]. Their experiments were extended by *Lowe et al.* [1963] in which a number of the amino acids formed in smaller yield were identified. The concentrations of ammonium cyanide ($> 0.9\ M$) used in these experiments are probably too high to have occurred on the primitive Earth. It would be desirable to perform these experiments at lower concentrations of reactants.

Amino acids have also been synthesized from paraformaldehyde and hydroxylamine [*Oró et al., 1959*] under relatively concentrated conditions ($0.25\ M$). It is not clear how hydroxylamine could have been formed in large yield on the primitive Earth.

The synthesis of amino acids under primitive Earth conditions is on a relatively firm foundation. It appears to have involved a Strecker synthesis. This synthesis can take place at high dilutions of the aldehyde and cyanide [*Miller, 1957b*], but the limit of dilution has not been demonstrated experimentally.

It is also to be noted that while amino acids are synthesized, only the simplest ones are obtained in these experiments in significant yield. The syntheses of histidine, phenylalanine, tyrosine, tryptophane, etc. have not been properly demonstrated. It is evident that further experiments in this area are needed.

Purines and Pyrimidines

The first synthesis of purines under primitive Earth conditions was carried out by *Oró* [1960; *Oró and Kimball, 1961, 1962*] who demonstrated that adenine was synthesized from concentrated ammonium cyanide ($> 0.9\ M$). The reaction is

$$NH_3$$
$$5\ HCN \rightarrow Adenine$$

This synthesis has been confirmed by *Lowe et al.* [1963]. It was shown [*Oró and Kimball,* 1962] that 4-amino imidazole-5-carboxamidine and formamidine were probably intermediates in this reaction. The plausible mechanism of this synthesis was given as

NH₂

Hypoxanthine would be obtained by the hydrolysis of amino imidazole carboxamidine to the amide followed by closure of the ring with formamidine. Guanine and xanthine have been synthesized by heating aqueous solutions of amino imidazole carboxamide at 100–140° C [*Oró*, 1963*a*, 1964*a*]. Yields of 1.5 per cent were obtained for both purines.

It is likely that this remarkable synthesis discovered by Oró was the reaction by which purines were synthesized on the primitive Earth. However, it is unlikely that such high concentrations of NH_4CN occurred, at least on an extensive scale, and it would be desirable to determine the scope of these reactions at lower concentrations of reactants.

Ponnamperuma et al. [1963] synthesized adenine by electron irradiation of CH_4, NH_3 and H_2O. The yields are substantial, about 0.01 per cent of the carbon added as methane. The mechanism of this synthesis is probably similar to Oró's synthesis although there may be differences in detail. The concentration of NH_4CN was not determined, but it was probably less than 0.9 *M,* and this implies that some "catalyst" facilitated the synthesis of adenine.

Guanine has been synthesized by *Ponnamperuma et al.* [1964] from the heating for six hours at 190°C of a mixture of the amino acids that usually occur in proteins. The yield (gm guanine/gm of amino mixture) was 2×10^{-3} per cent. No other purines or pyrimidines were formed in significant yield.

A preliminary report by *Ponnamperuma and Mariner* [1963] states that both adenine and guanine are formed by the ultraviolet irradiation of a 10^{-3} *M* HCN solution. The yields of adenine and guanine are 0.2 per cent and 0.1 per cent, respectively, based on the HCN. Urea is formed in 1.5 per cent yield. A concentration of 10^{-3} *M* HCN in the oceans of the primitive Earth is in a reasonable range although it may be somewhat high. Subject to a more detailed investigation of the scope and mechanism of the reaction, one can say that the synthesis of purines is on as firm a foundation as that of the amino acids.

The synthesis of pyrimidines is in a less satisfactory state than that of the purines. This is surprising since the pyrimidines would seem to be simpler compounds.

Fox and Harada [1961] have synthesized uracil by heating a mixture of malic acid, urea and polyphosphoric acid to 100–140°C for approximately one hour. This reaction is similar to the well known synthesis of uracil from malic acid, urea and sulfuric acid [*Davidson and Baudisch,* 1926]. These reactions could not have occurred on the primitive Earth since polyphosphoric acid or any other strong acid would not have been present.

Oró [1963a] synthesized uracil from urea and β-amino acrylonitrile (and also from acrylonitrile and from β-amino acrylamide) by heating to 135 °C in aqueous solution. The yields are less than 1 per cent. The limiting step in this reaction is apparently the dehydration of the dihydropyrimidine formed by ring closure. These reactions do not appear to be adequate for the synthesis of pyrimidines in significant quantities on the primitive Earth.

Sugars

The condensation of formaldehyde to sugars in aqueous solution generally catalyzed by $Ca(OH)_2$ has been known for many years [*Butlerow,* 1861; *Loew,* 1886; *Mayer and Jäschke,* 1960; *Pfeil and Ruckert,* 1961]. Hexoses, pentoses, tetroses and trioses can be obtained in these reactions. Indirect evidence was obtained for the synthesis of sugars in the electric discharge experiments [*Miller,* 1955]. These sugars were probably synthesized from the large amount of formaldehyde produced by the spark.

Deoxysugars can reasonably be expected from aldol type condensations. *Oró and Cox* [1962] have synthesized 2-deoxyribose, the pentose of DNA, by the aldol condensation of glyceraldehyde with acetaldehyde.

The problem with the production of sugars on the primitive Earth is not so much that of synthesis, but rather that of decomposition. Sugars decompose relatively rapidly in basic solution and particularly the presence of ammonia [*Evans,* 1942].

These decompositions would be very important in the geological time scale. The same problem is present with amino acids, purines and pyrimidines, but the problem is less acute. Since there are no kinetic data for the decomposition of sugars under the conditions in question, we can only estimate that the steady-state concentrations of sugars on the primitive Earth would be low, the figure being dependent on the rate of synthesis and the rate of decomposition.

Lipids

The simplest fatty acids, formic, acetic and propionic acid, were formed in the electric discharge experiments. There have been no successful experiments in synthesizing fatty acids in the C_{12} to C_{24} range. However, this would not seem to be a particularly difficult problem, except for the complication of getting primarily straight chain fatty acids instead of highly branched isomers.

A mechanism for obtaining straight chain hydrocarbons and fatty acids has been reported by *Johnson and Wilson* [1964]. This method involves crowding the reaction chains of fatty acids on to a surface so that only the ends are available for reaction, thus preventing branching. A mono-molecular layer of palmitic acid (C_{16}) was formed on water and methyl radicals (from the pyrolysis or di-*t*-butyl peroxide) reacted to give the C_{18} and C_{19} straight chain acids. Little or no branched chain acids were formed.

Peptides

Fox has shown that polypeptides can be synthesized by heating various mixtures of amino acids to 150–180°C [*Fox and Harada*, 1958; *Fox et al.*, 1963]. In order to obtain a large yield of polypeptide it is necessary to add an excess of aspartic acid or glutamic acid or both. These experiments have been criticized because amino acids decompose when heated to such temperatures, and it is difficult to envision a process on the primitive Earth that would allow the heating of the dry amino acids for the proper length of time [*Miller and Urey*, 1959; *Horowitz and Miller*, 1962]. The temperature problem has been attacked by using lower temperatures and concentrated phosphoric acid [*Fox and Harada*, 1960], but concentrated phosphoric acid could not have occurred on the primitive Earth.

Oró and Guidry [1961] have synthesized glycine peptides from concentrated glycine solutions in aqueous ammonia at temperatures above 100°C. Peptides are unstable relative to the amino acids in aqueous solution at room temperature, but surprisingly, the peptide bond becomes more stable as the temperature is raised. It is likely that this peptide synthesis is simply an equilibrium process and therefore might not be feasible at lower temperatures and lower concentrations of amino acids. Polyglycine has also been synthesized from glycine amide [*Oró*, 1960], which is the intermediate in the hydrolysis of the amino nitrile to the amino acid. There is no problem with the energetics of peptide bond formation here, but the relative rates of peptide bond formation and hydrolysis of the -amide bond to the amino acid would be dependent on concentration. This aspect has not been investigated.

Lowe et al. [1963] have shown that amino acids can be incorporated into hydrogen cyanide polymers. No evidence was presented that the amino acids were in a peptide linkage. In addition, the incorporation of these amino acids took place in 1.5 *M* NH$_4$CN and such concentrations could not have occurred on the primitive Earth.

It would appear that no satisfactory peptide synthesis under primitive

Earth conditions has yet been demonstrated, although there are differences of opinion on this point. Although this problem is not a simple one, it is reasonable to believe that such synthesis may be forthcoming in the near future.*

Nucleotides and Polynucleotides

Schramm et al. [1962] have reported that nucleosides and nucleotides can be synthesized from the purine or pyrimidine and the pentose by ethyl metaphosphate in anhydrous formamide as solvent. *Ponnamperuma et al.* [1963*b*] have synthesized adenosine, AMP, ADP, ATP and A4P from the same reagent using ultraviolet light as an activator or catalyst for the phosphoryl transfer from the ethyl metaphosphate to the nucleotide. The ethyl metaphosphate is prepared from phosphorus pentoxide, diethyl ether and chloroform. Phosphorus pentoxide does not occur on the Earth at the present time, and since it takes up water so rapidly it could not have occurred on the primitive Earth. Therefore, ethyl metaphosphate is not a suitable model compound for primitive Earth conditions.

Ponnamperuma et al. [1963*a*] have synthesized adenosine from adenine, ribose and phosphate in dilute aqueous solution (10^{-3} M) on irradiation by ultraviolet light. The phosphate acts as a catalyst in this reaction since it does not enter the product. The mechanism of this reaction has not been investigated. *Ponnamperuma et al.* [1964] have synthesized deoxyadenosine by a similar reaction—adenine, deoxyribose and phosphate. Deoxyadenosine can also be synthesized from adenosine, deoxyribose and cyanide. This synthesis takes place both with and without ultraviolet light, the yields being 7 per cent and 1 per cent, respectively. The mechanism of this reaction is not known, but it would appear that this type of reaction may have been an important one for the synthesis of nucleosides on the primitive Earth.

Organic Phosphates and High-Energy Phosphates

Adenosine triphosphate and other nucleotides have been synthesized from ethyl metaphosphate as discussed earlier. The ethyl metaphosphate requires phosphorus pentoxide for its synthesis, and the latter could hardly occur on the primitive Earth.

It would be more plausible to assume the presence of meta- or polyphosphates. These compounds are well known and easily prepared by

* Since this was written, *Ponnamperuma and Peterson* (*Science 147*, 1572, 1965) have reported synthesis of simple dipeptides and a tripeptide by ultraviolet irradiation of 10^{-2} M aqueous solutions of amino acids in the presence of cyanamide. *Steinman, Lemmon, and Calvin* (*ibid.*, 1574) have reported a similar synthesis of peptides using dicyandiamide as a condensing agent.

heating alkali metal and calcium dihydrogen phosphates above $\sim 300\,°C$. However, metaphosphate minerals are not known to occur in nature. This is not surprising since $Ca(H_2PO_4)_2$ which would be the starting material for a thermal dehydration to calcium metaphosphate, is itself not a known mineral. Pyrophosphate could be formed by a thermal dehydration of Brushite $(CaHPO_4 \cdot 2H_2O)$ or Monetite $(CaHPO_4)$, which are relatively rare minerals, but this apparently does not occur since not a single pyrophosphate mineral is known [*Rankama and Sahama*, 1954; *Palache et al.*, 1951].

A low temperature synthesis of pyrophosphate and other high energy phosphates appears to be required. Pyrophosphate has been synthesized from soluble phosphate using cyanamide and its dimer (dicyandiamide) as a source of free energy [*Steinman et al.*, 1964]. The yields were not given. Pyrophosphate has also been synthesized from hydroxy apatite $[Ca_{10}(PO_4)_6(OH)_2]$ and cyanate [*Miller and Parris*, 1964]. The apatites are by far the most abundant form of phosphorus on the Earth. Apatite is insoluble, as is calcium pyrophosphate, and so this synthesis takes place on the surface of the apatite. The yield of pyrophosphate is a maximum of 27 per cent (at $pH = 6.5$) of the cyanate added to the system.

It appears likely that pyrophosphate was synthesized by such processes. There may have been other processes yet to be outlined that also synthesized pyro- and other high-energy phosphates.

Enzymes

There are many small molecules that act as catalysts for various reactions, and in a number of cases coenzymes have catalytic activity in the absence of the protein. There is an extensive literature on these model enzyme reactions [*Westheimer*, 1959]. The primitive enzymes should have more than a simple catalytic activity. These catalysts should be active, they should catalyze one reaction in good yield without a large amount of side reaction, and they should possess some degree of specificity for their substrates. It is quite possible that together these requirements are too restrictive for the primitive catalysts, but some of these requirements would seem to be necessary.

The synthesis of such primitive enzymes has not been accomplished, nor does it appear that this problem will be easy. A scheme for the prebiological synthesis of enzymes has been proposed by *Granick* [1957] and *Calvin* [1956], but no experiments have been carried out. *Fox and Krampitz* [1964] have shown that polypeptides containing large amounts of lysine will catalyze the decarboxylation of glucose or an intermediate in the decomposition of glucose. The catalyzed reaction is a very small side reaction since the yield of CO_2 is about 10^{-2} per cent of the glucose.

However, there may be ways of increasing the yield, specificity, and rate of this catalyst so that it approaches more closely the characteristics apparently needed for prebiological catalysts.

Coacervates and Microspheres

Oparin's model of the first living organism was a coacervate particle that would be able to divide into two or more coacervate particles by absorbing material from the environment [*Oparin, 1957*]. In the course of time these coacervate particles would acquire the ability to accumulate selectively the desired material from the environment and to divide into two particles that were more and more alike. Although not emphasized by Oparin, it is envisioned that in the course of time a genetic apparatus of DNA would be incorporated into this system.

A point of view similar to Oparin's has been expressed by Fox who has synthesized spherical particles about 1 micron in diameter by heating in $1 M$ NaCl solution the polypeptides formed from the thermal polymerization of amino acids [*Fox et al., 1959; Fox, 1960; Fox and Yuyama, 1963; 1964; Fox and Fukushima, 1964*]. Such microspheres may have been formed whether the polypeptides were synthesized by thermal processes or by another mechanism. Fox envisions these microspheres as the precursors to the first living organism. However, the mechanism by which such microspheres could acquire the ability to self-replicate has not been demonstrated experimentally nor even outlined theoretically.

As discussed earlier, modern biological advances in our knowledge of the molecular biology of DNA would indicate that the essential point is that of accurate self-reproduction. There is nothing so far in the area of primitive syntheses to indicate that this point of view is in error.

Synthesis of Polynucleotides Capable of Self-duplication

As indicated earlier, a self-duplicating molecule of DNA would be the first living organism. Kornberg's polymerase enzyme together with the nucleotide triphosphates will carry out this synthesis. Even with the synthesis of such an enzyme on the primitive Earth and the presence of the nucleotide triphosphates, such a system could not continue to operate under geological conditions, principally because of the dilution of the precursors. Some structure or mechanism would be necessary to hold the system together, and to provide for the synthesis of the polymerase. It is reasonable to assume some sort of membrane, presumably lipid, to do this task, but there may be other mechanisms. There are no experiments nor even detailed hypotheses in this area. Therefore, the problems will not be discussed further here.

CONCLUSIONS

The experimental work on the synthesis of organic compounds under primitive Earth conditions is lacking in a number of important areas, and a number of the experiments were not carried out under reasonable conditions. However, these experiments taken together indicate that large quantities of organic compounds were synthesized on the primitive Earth, and that many of these compounds are those that occur in contemporary living organisms. Compounds that do not occur in present living organisms have not usually been sought in such experiments, principally because it is difficult to decide which "nonbiological" compounds might have been synthesized. In spite of this, it is probably the case that a surprisingly large fraction of "biological" compounds is obtained. It will require a great deal of experimental work to justify this statement. If it proves to be true, then this implies that the first living organism was constructed from the predominant organic compounds in the primitive oceans, while the classes of compounds that were not "useful" were excluded from its structure.

This would mean that availability and "usefulness" determined the basic constituents of organisms on the Earth, and that chance did not play the major role in this area.

These considerations, although the answers are not yet known, are important for the design of experiments to detect life on Mars. If we accept the above arguments that the components of life on Mars are the same as those in Earth organisms, then the growth medium should be designed accordingly. It is unlikely (but not impossible) that the organisms on Mars will be identical in their basic components. For example, the biological catalysts may be proteins, but it would be surprising if the Martian proteins had the same 20 amino acids as those in Earth organisms. We can, however, make provision in the experimental procedures to anticipate reasonable differences.

The discussion in this article is based on conditions that are generally believed to have been present on the primitive Earth. It is clear that the same syntheses would have taken place on Mars if the conditions were similar. We have no certain knowledge of the early conditions on Mars, just as we are not certain in the case of the Earth. However, it is quite probable that the conditions were similar in terms of these planets' reducing character since they were formed from the same cosmic dust cloud. The uncertainty is in whether there was sufficient water initially on Mars and whether there was sufficient time available for life to have started before most of this water escaped. There are also the related questions of the time for life to begin under favorable conditions and the ability of life to survive during drastic changes in the environment. All these questions are best answered by conducting a search for life on Mars.

REFERENCES

Abelson, P. H. (1956) Amino Acids Formed in "Primitive Atmospheres." *Science, 124*, 935.

Anfinsen, C. B. (1959) *The Molecular Basis of Evolution.* John Wiley & Sons, New York.

Arrhenius, S. (1908) *Worlds in the Making.* Harper, New York.

Bahadur, K. (1954) Photosynthesis of Amino Acids from Paraformaldehyde and Potassium Nitrate. *Nature, 173*, 1141.

Bahadur, K. (1959) The Reactions Involved in the Formation of Compounds Preliminary to the Synthesis of Protoplasm and Other Materials of Biological Importance. In: A. I. Oparin *et al.*, eds., *Proceeding of the First International Symposium on the Origin of Life on Earth*, p. 140, Pergamon Press, New York.

Bahadur, K., Ranganayaki, S., and Santamaria, L. (1958) Photosynthesis of Amino Acids from Paraformaldehyde Involving the Fixation of Nitrogen in the Presence of Colloidal Molybdenum Oxides, as Catalyst. *Nature, 182*, 1668.

Barghoorn, E. S. (1957) Origin of Life. *Geol. Soc. Amer., Memoirs No. 67*, 2, 75.

Barghoorn, E. S. and Tyler, S. A. (1963) Fossil Organisms from Precambrian Sediments. *Ann. N.Y. Acad. Sci., 108*, 451.

Berger, R. (1961) The Proton Irradiation of Methane, Ammonia, and Water at 77°K. *Proc. Natl. Acad. Sci. U.S., 47*, 1434.

Butlerow, A. (1861) *Compt. Rend., 53*, 145.

Calvin, M. (1956) Chemical Evolution and the Origin of Life. *American Scientist, 44*, 248.

Crow, J. F. (1959) Darwin's Influence on the Study of Genetics and the Origin of Life. In: M. R. Wheeler, *Biological Contributions*, p. 49. Univ. of Texas, Austin.

Davidson, D. and Baudisch, O. (1926) The Preparation of Uracil from Urea. *J. Am. Chem. Soc., 48*, 2379.

Evans, W. L. (1942) Some Less Familiar Aspects of Carbohydrate Chemistry. *Chem. Rev., 31*, 537.

Fowler, W. A., Greenstein, J. L. and Hoyle, F. (1961) Deuteronomy: Synthesis of Deuterons and the Light Nuclei During the Early History of the Solar System. *Am. J. Physics, 29*, 393.

Fox, S. W. and Harada, K. (1958) Thermal Co-polymerization of Amino Acids to a Product Resembling a Protein. *Science, 128*, 1214.

Fox, S. W., Harada, K. and Kendrick, J. (1959) Production of Spherules from Synthetic Proteinoid and Hot Water. *Science, 129*, 1221.

Fox, S. W. (1960) How Did Life Begin? *Science, 132*, 200.

Fox, S. W. and Harada, K. (1960) Thermal Co-polymerization of Amino Acids in the Presence of Phosphoric Acid. *Arch. Biochem. Biophys., 86*, 281.

Fox, S. W. and Harada, K. (1961) Synthesis of Uracil under Conditions of a Thermal Model of Prebiological Chemistry. *Science, 133*, 1923.

Fox, S. W. and Yuyama, S. (1963) Abiotic Production of Primitive Protein and Formed Microparticles. *Ann. N.Y. Acad. Sci., 108,* 487.

Fox, S. W. *et al.* (1963) Amino Acid Compositions of Proteinoids. *Arch. Biochem. Biophys., 102,* 439.

Fox, S. W. and Fukushima, T. (1964) Electron Micrographs of Microspheres from Thermal Proteinoid. In: W. L. Kretovich, ed., *Problems of Evolutionary and Applied Biochemistry,* p. 93. "Nauka" Press, Moscow.

Fox, S. W. and Krampitz, G. (1964) Catalytic Decomposition of Glucose in Aqueous Solution by Thermal Proteinoid. *Nature, 203,* 1362.

Fox, S. W. and Yuyama, S. (1964) Dynamic Phenomena in Microspheres from Thermal Proteinoid. *Compar. Biochem. Physiol., 11,* 317.

Garrison, W. M., Morrison, D. C., Hamilton, J. G., Benson, A. A. and Calvin, M. (1951) Reduction of Carbon Dioxide in Aqueous Solutions by Ionizing Radiation. *Science, 114,* 416.

Glasel, J. (1961) Stabilization of NH in Hydrocarbon Matrices and its Relation to Cometary Phenomena. *Proc. Natl. Acad. Sci. U.S., 47,* 174.

Granick, S. (1957) Speculations on the Origin and Evolution of Photosynthesis. *Ann. N.Y. Acad. Sci., 69,* 292.

Groth, W. and Weyssenhoff, H. v. (1957) Photochemische Bildung von Aminosauren aus Mischungen einfacher Gase. *Naturwiss., 44,* 510.

Groth, W. and Weyssenhoff, H. v. (1960) Photochemical Formation of Organic Compounds from Mixtures of Simple Gases. *Planet. Space Sci., 2,* 79; Also: *Ann. Physik., 4,* 70 (1959).

Harada, K. and Fox, S. W. (1964*a*) Thermal Synthesis of Amino Acids from Simple Gases. In: S. W. Fox, ed., *The Origin of Prebiological Systems,* p. 187. Academic Press, New York.

Harada, K. and Fox, S. W. (1964*b*) Thermal Synthesis of Natural Amino Acids from a Postulated Primitive Terrestrial Atmosphere. *Nature, 201,* 335.

Heyns, K., Walter, W. and Meyer, E. (1957) Modelluntersuchungen zür Bildung organischer Verbindungen in Atmosphären einfacher Gase durch elektrische Entladungen. *Naturwiss., 44,* 385.

Hoagland, M. B. (1960) The Relationship of Nucleic Acid and Protein Synthesis as Revealed by Studies in Cell Free Systems. In: E. Chargaff and J. N. Davidson, eds., *The Nucleic Acids, 3,* p. 349. Academic Press, New York.

Holmes, A. (1954) The Oldest Dated Minerals of the Rhodesian Shield. *Nature, 173,* 612.

Horowitz, N. H. and Miller, S. L. (1962) Current Theories on the Origin of Life. *Progress in the Chemistry of Organic Natural Products, 20,* 423.

Johnson, C. B. and Wilson, A. T. (1964) A Possible Mechanism for the Extraterrestrial Synthesis of Straight Chain Hydrocarbon. *Nature, 204,* 181.

Kornberg, A. (1960) Biologic Synthesis of Deoxyribonucleic Acid. *Science, 131,* 1503.

Lederberg, J. and Cowie, D. B. (1958) Moondust. *Science, 127,* 1473.

Loew, O. (1886) *J. Prakt. Chem., 33,* 321.

Lowe, C. V., Rees, M. and Markham, R. (1963) Synthesis of Complex Organic Compounds from Simple Precursors: Formation of Amino Acids, Amino Acid Polymers, Fatty Acids, and Purines from Ammonium Cyanide. *Nature, 199,* 219.

The Origin of Life   67

MacGregor, A. M. (1940) A Precambrian Algal Limestone in Southern Rhodesia. *Geol. Soc. South Africa, Trans.*, 43, 9.
Matthaei, J. H., Jones, O. W., Martin, R. G., and Nirenberg, M. W. (1962) Characteristics and Composition of Coding Units. *Proc. Natl. Acad. Sci. U.S.*, 48, 666.
Mayer, R. and Jaschke, L. (1960) Conversion of Formaldehyde into Carbohydrates. *Liebigs Ann.*, 365, 145.
Miller, S. L. (1953) A Production of Amino Acids Under Possible Primitive Earth Conditions. *Science*, 117, 528.
Miller, S. L. (1955) Production of Some Organic Compounds Under Possible Primitive Earth Conditions. *J. Am. Chem. Soc.*, 77, 2351.
Miller, S. L. (1957a) The Mechanism of Synthesis of Amino Acids by Electric Discharges. *Biochem. Biophys. Acta*, 23, 480.
Miller, S. L. (1957b) The Formation of Organic Compounds on the Primitive Earth. *Ann. N.Y. Acad. Sci.*, 69, 260.
Miller, S. L. and Urey, H. C. (1959) Organic Compounds Synthesis on the Primitive Earth. *Science*, 130, 245.
Miller, S. L. and Parris, M. (1964) Synthesis of Pyrophosphate under Primitive Earth Conditions. *Nature*, 204, 1248.
Miller, S. L. and Urey, H. C. (1964) Extraterrestrial Sources of Organic Compounds and the Origin of Life. *Problems of Evolutionary and Applied Biochemistry*, "Nauka" Press, Moscow, p. 357.
Muller, H. J. (1922) Variation Due to Change in the Individual Gene. *Amer. Naturalist*, 56, 32.
Muller, H. J. (1929) The Gene as the Basis of Life. *Proc. Intn'l Congr. Plant Science, Ithaca 1*, 897.
Nirenberg, M. W. and Matthaei, J. H. (1961) The Dependence of Cell-free Protein Synthesis in *E. coli* upon Naturally Occurring or Synthetic Polyribonucleotides. *Proc. Natl. Acad. Sci. U.S.*, 47, 1588.
Oparin, A. I., Braunstein, A. E., Pasynskii, A. G., and Pavlovskaya, T. E., eds., Boyd, Edinburgh.
Oparin, A. I., Braunstein, A. E., Pasynskii, A. G., and Pavlovskaya, T. E., eds., (1959) *Proceedings of the First International Symposium on the Origin of Life on the Earth*. Pergamon Press, New York.
Oró, J., Kimball, A., Fritz, R., and Master, R. (1959) Amino Acid Synthesis from Formaldehyde and Hydroxylamine. *Arch. Biochem. Biophys.*, 85, 115.
Oró, J. (1960) Synthesis of Adenine from Ammonium Cyanide. *Biochem. Biophys. Res. Comm.*, 2, 407.
Oró, J. and Guidry, C. L. (1960) A Novel Synthesis of Polypeptides. *Nature*, 186, 156.
Oró, J. (1961) Comets and the Formation of Biochemical Compounds on the Primitive Earth. *Nature*, 190, 389.
Oró, J. and Guidry, C. L. (1961) Direct Synthesis of Polypeptides. I. Polycondensation of Glycine in Aqueous Ammonia. *Arch. Biochem. Biophys.*, 93, 166.
Oró, J. and Kamat, S. S. (1961) Amino Acid Synthesis from Hydrogen Cyanide under Possible Primitive Earth Conditions. *Nature*, 190, 442.
Oró, J. and Kimball, A. P. (1961) Synthesis of Purines Under Possible Primitive Earth Conditions. I. Synthesis of Adenine. *Arch. Biochem. Biophys.*, 94, 217.

Oró, J. and Cox, A. C. (1962) Non-enzymatic Synthesis of 2-deoxyribose. *Federation Proc., 24,* 80.

Oró, J. and Kimball, A. P. (1962) Synthesis of Purines Under Possible Primitive Earth Conditions. II. Purine Intermediates from Hydrogen Cyanide. *Arch. Biochem. Biophys., 96,* 293.

Oró, J. (1963a) Non-enzymatic Formation of Purines and Pyrimidines. *Federation Proc., 22,* 681.

Oró, J. (1963b) Synthesis of Organic Compounds by Electric Discharges. *Nature, 197,* 862.

Oró, J. (1963c) Synthesis of Organic Compounds by High Energy Electrons. *Nature, 197,* 971.

Oró, J. (1964a) Prebiological Synthesis of Nucleic Acid Constitutents. In: W. L. Kretovich, ed., *Problems of Evolutionary and Applied Biochemistry,* p. 63, "Nauka" Press, Moscow.

Oró, J. (1963b) Stages and Mechanisms of Prebiological Organic Synthesis. In: S. W. Fox, ed., *The Origin of Prebiological Systems,* p. 137. Academic Press, New York.

Palache, C., Berman, H., and Frondel, C., eds. (1951) *Dana's System of Mineralogy, 2,* 7th Edition, John Wiley & Sons, New York.

Palm, C. and Calvin, M. (1962) Primordial Organic Chemistry. I. Compounds Resulting from Electron Irradiation of $C^{14}H_4$. *J. Am. Chem. Soc., 84,* 2115.

Pasteur, L. (1922) Mémoire sur les corpuscules organisés qui existent dans l'atmosphère. Examen de la doctrine des générations spontanées. Dans: P. Vallery-Radot, *Oeuvres de Pasteur, 2,* p. 210, Masson et Cie, Paris.

Pavlovskaya, T. E. and Pasynskii, A. G. (1959) The Original Formation of Amino Acids Under the Action of Ultraviolet Rays and Electric Discharges. In: A. I. Oparin, *et al.,* eds., *Proc. 1st Intn'l. Symp. on the Origin of Life on Earth,* p. 151, Pergamon Press.

Pfeil, E. and Ruckert, H. (1961) Formaldehyde Condensations. Formation of Sugars from Formaldehyde by the Action of Alkalies. *Liebigs Ann. 641,* 121.

Pirie, N. W. (1937) The Meaninglessness of the Terms Life and Living. In: J. Needham and D. E. Green, *Perspectives in Biochemistry,* p. 11, Cambridge Univ. Press.

Ponnamperuma, C., Lemmon, R. M., Mariner, R., and Calvin, M. (1963) Formation of Adenine by Electron Irradiation of Methane, Ammonia and Water. *Proc. Natl. Acad. Sci. U.S., 49,* 737.

Ponnamperuma, C. and Mariner, R. (1963) A Possible Prebiotic Synthesis of Purines. *Congress of Pure and Applied Chemistry, London, England, July, 1963* (Abstract).

Ponnamperuma, C., Mariner, R. and Sagan, C. (1963a) Formation of Adenosine by Ultraviolet Irradiation of a Solution of Adenine and Ribose. *Nature, 198,* 1199.

Ponnamperuma, C., Sagan, C., and Mariner, R. (1963b) Synthesis of Adenosine Triphosphate under Possible Primitive Earth Conditions. *Nature, 199,* 222.

Ponnamperuma, C. and Kirk, P. (1964) Synthesis of Deoxyadenosine under Simulated Primitive Earth Conditions. *Nature, 203,* 400.

Ponnamperuma, C., *et al.* (1964) Guanine: Formation during the Thermal Polymerization of Amino Acids. *Science, 143,* 1449.

Rabinowitch, E. I. (1945) *Photosynthesis and Related Processes, 1,* p. 81, Interscience Publ., New York.

Rankama, K. and Sahama, T. G. (1954) *Geochemistry,* p. 454, Oxford Univ. Press, Oxford.

Rubey, W. W. (1955) Development of the Hydrosphere and Atmosphere, with Special Reference to Probable Composition of the Early Atmosphere. *Geol. Soc. Amer., Special Paper No. 62,* 631.

Schramm, G., Grötsch, H. and Pollmann, W. (1962) Non-enzymatic Synthesis of Polysaccharides, Nucleosides and Nucleic Acids and the Origin of Self-reproducing Systems. *Angew. Chem.* (Intern. Ed.), *1,* 1.

Speyer, J. F., Lengyel, P., Basilio, C., and Ochoa, S. (1962) Synthetic Polynucleotides and the Amino Acid Code, IV. *Proc. Natl. Acad. Sci. U.S., 48,* 441.

Steinman, G., Lemmon, R. M., and Calvin, M. (1964) Cyanamide: A Possible Key Compound in Chemical Evolution. *Proc. Natl. Acad. Sci. U.S., 69,* 390.

Terenin, A. N. (1959) Photosynthesis in the Shortest Ultraviolet. In: A. I. Oparin, *et al.,* 1959, eds., *Proc. 1st Intn'l. Symp. on the Origin of Life on Earth,* p. 136, Pergamon Press.

Urey, H. C. (1952*a*) *The Planets: Their Origin and Development.* Yale Univ. Press, New Haven, Conn.

Urey, H. C. (1952*b*) On the Early Chemical History of the Earth and the Origin of Life. *Proc. Natl. Acad. Sci. U.S., 38,* 351.

Urey, H. C. (1959) The Atmospheres of the Planets. In: S. Flügge, ed., *Handbuch der Physik, 52,* p. 363, Springer-Verlag, Berlin.

Watson, J. D. and Crick, F. H. C. (1953) Molecular Structure of Nucleic Acids. A Structure for Deoxyribose Nucleic Acid. *Nature, 171,* 737.

Westheimer, F. H. (1959) Enzyme Models. In: P. D. Boyer, *et al.,* eds., *The Enzymes, 1,* 2nd Edition, p. 259, Academic Press, New York.

PART III

THE COSMIC SETTING

CHAPTER 3

THE SOLAR SYSTEM AS AN ABODE OF LIFE

Carl Sagan

INTRODUCTION

By most astronomical criteria, there seems nothing extraordinary about our corner of the Universe. We live on one of nine planets of a common G dwarf star situated on the outskirts of a typical spiral galaxy. There are some 10^{11} other stars within our Galaxy. A visual impression of the number of stars in a galaxy may be garnered from Figure 1, a photograph of a very small region of our Galaxy, in the constellation Sagittarius. There are at least 10^{10} other galaxies within the presently accessible Universe. The total number may approach 10^{11} or 10^{12} as astronomers probe even further into the recesses of space, especially if—as present radioastronomical evidence suggests—the very distant galaxies are packed relatively closely together. The total number of galaxies may be literally infinite, for we do not know whether our Universe is bounded. Evidence from the rates of stellar rotation, from periodic perturbations of nearby stars, from theories of the origin of our solar system, and the example of our Copernican heritage all suggest that the formation of planets is the rule, rather than the exception, and that the origin of planetary systems is a general occurrence in the course of stellar evolution.

According to present ideas of stellar and planetary cosmogony, the solar system was formed by the gravitational contraction and condensation of a

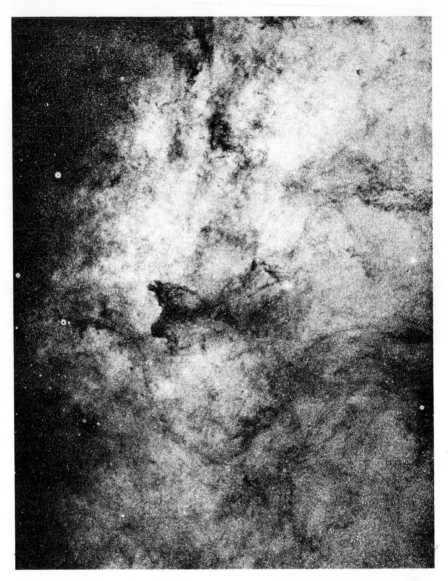

Figure 1.   Photograph of a star cloud in the constellation Sagit-
tarius. Photographed in red light with the 48-inch
Schmidt camera at Mt. Palomar Observatory.
(Courtesy of Mt. Wilson and Palomar Observatories.)

cloud of interstellar gas and dust (see, e.g., *Jastrow and Cameron* [1963]). While the exact details of this condensation are still under discussion, it is quite certain that objects ranging from interstellar grains ($\sim 10^{-5}$ cm in diameter) to supergiant stars ($\sim 10^{13}$ cm in diameter) are being formed today. The prevalence of binary and multiple star systems suggests that many of the larger objects condense collectively. If the condensation has a mass much larger than that of the planet Jupiter, in time the interior temperatures, steadily increasing during the accretion process, become so high that thermonuclear reactions are initiated, and the star reaches the main sequence in the Hertzsprung-Russell diagram. Most stars then radiate quite stably for many billions of years. In the case of an object less massive than Jupiter, the interior temperatures reached are not adequate to permit thermonuclear reactions, and the object may become a non-self-luminous planet, or a black dwarf star.

Many of the nearest stars exhibit periodic perturbations in their proper motions that can best be explained by the presence of a dark companion of mass intermediate between that of the sun and that of Jupiter. For example, Barnard's star, the second nearest star system to us (counting α Centauri A, B, and C as one system), has at least one dark companion of mass 50 per cent greater than that of Jupiter [*van de Kamp*, 1963]. Lalande 21185, the fifth nearest system by the same reckoning, has a companion with a mass about ten times that of Jupiter. The farther these systems are from the Earth, the more difficult it is to detect dark companions by perturbations in the stellar proper motion. A planet with the mass of the Earth could not be so detected, even in the nearest systems. But the statistics are already good enough to imply strongly that the formation of planets is a common, if not invariable, accompaniment to the formation of stars.

If this is so, there must be at least 10^{21} to 10^{23} other planets in the Universe. Thus, if the Earth is the only abode of life, the probability of the origin of life must be as small as 10^{-21} to 10^{-23}. Especially in the context of contemporary experiments on the origin of life (cf., Chapter 2), it seems much more likely that the development of life is a routine accompaniment of the development of planets. This contention is not proved; at the moment, it is at best a likely story. However, just as the finding of dark planetary companions to the nearest stars strengthens the view that most stars have planetary systems, so would the finding of life on a nearby planet strengthen the contention that the origin and evolution of life is a common cosmic occurrence.

In addition to the philosophical excitement that the discovery of even one example of extraterrestrial life would provide, the characterization of any extraterrestrial biological system would provide an ingredient currently lacking in biology: perspective. Since all organisms that the biologist can now study are almost certainly relatives, common descendants from a single instance of the origin of life, it is difficult to determine which biological characteristics are evolutionary accidents and which are necessary for living systems in general. We expect that because of different adaptations to different environmental circumstances, extraterrestrial life forms will differ fundamentally from terrestrial organisms. It is also possible, however, that strong biochemical or even morphological and physiological similarities will be found. Only by investigating extraterrestrial life can we acquire the perspective to separate the accidental from the inevitable in biology.

The quest for life beyond the Earth can be pursued in three ways. First, we may study contemporary terrestrial biology and organic chemistry to approach the problem of the origin of life on Earth. If it appears relatively likely that life emerged in the primitive terrestrial environment, it may follow that the origin of life is a fairly general planetary phenomenon. Second, we can investigate the physical environments of the planets, and determine whether conditions there are so severe that living processes are entirely excluded, even allowing for the adaptability of life. Third, the planets may be studied for direct evidence of indigenous life forms.

All three approaches are beset with uncertainties and it is important to state at the outset that no completely convincing evidence exists for extraterrestrial life. The problem often reduces to probability considerations and estimates of observational reliability. At convenient places in the marshalling of evidence, I shall try to pause and give brief expression to alternative interpretations. In almost all cases, an optimistic view can be found which holds that the evidence is strongly suggestive of, or at worst, not inconsistent with, the existence of extraterrestrial life; and a pessimistic view can be found, which holds that the evidence adduced in favor of extraterrestrial life is unconvincing, irrelevant, or has an alternative, nonbiological explanation. I leave it to the reader to pick his own way among the factions.

THE ORIGIN OF LIFE

The question of the nature of life is relevant to any consideration of its origins. Perhaps remarkably, there is no definition of life that is acceptable to the large majority of biologists. The energetics, homeostasis and relative environmental isolation of many living things have convinced one group of workers that the origin of metabolism is the critical event in the origin of life. They have regarded as significant primitive Earth simulation experiments in which an enclave of the experimental medium is separated from the remainder by a membranous barrier. Such enclaves, including the coacervates of *Oparin* [1957] and the microspheres of Fox [*Fox and Yuyama*, 1963], also provide a local concentration of organic materials. For such workers, the synthesis of something resembling a cell would be required for the laboratory synthesis of life.

In another view, evolution by natural selection is the *sine qua non* of living systems. Without evolution, it is argued, nothing recognizable as living would ever have developed. For natural selection to proceed, a self-replicating, mutating system is required. It then follows that the critical event in the origin of life is the origin of a self-replicating, but not invariably meticulous, molecular system.

The genetic view and the enclave view are not mutually exclusive. It is really not of much operational significance whether some forms of primitive metabolism preceded replication, or whether some form of primitive replication preceded metabolism. It is generally recognized that replication, mutation, metabolism and isolation of the organism from its environment are characteristic features of contemporary organisms, and must have been important in the early development of life.

Self-replication in contemporary terrestrial organisms occurs through the mediation of the nucleic acids. In the now confirmed Watson-Crick model of deoxyribonucleic acid (DNA), two polynucleotide strands are helically wound about each other. Each strand is a nucleotide polymer; each nucleotide is a nucleoside phosphate; and each nucleoside is composed of the five-carbon sugar deoxyribose and one of the four bases adenine, guanine, cytosine and thymine. Replication occurs when the two strands (held together by weak hydrogen bonds) become uncoupled, and each synthesizes its complementary strand from precursors in the cell medium. A good degree of precision in replication is insured by the fact that, for stereochemical reasons, adenine will bond only with thymine; and guanine, only with cytosine.

Cellular metabolism is also controlled by DNA, the information for the entire functioning of the cell being contained in the sequencing of the four kinds of nucleotides along the DNA strand. The information contained in this four-letter code is transcribed on the proteins of the cytoplasm, constructed of approximately 20 different sub-units, the amino acids. This translation of the four-letter DNA code to the 20-letter protein code is mediated by ribonucleic acid (RNA), whose structure is only slightly different from that of DNA. The proteins synthesized according to the nuclear instructions include enzymes that control the rate of chemical reaction in the cytoplasm, and thereby, the metabolism of the cell. The transcription ratio from DNA to RNA is one-to-one, one base of DNA transcribing to one base of RNA. The RNA-protein transcription ratio is three-to-one, three RNA bases carrying the information for the construction of one amino acid, and $3n$ bases carrying the information for the construction of the n-amino acid-containing protein. These transcriptions require a stereochemically and enzymatically sophisticated apparatus in contemporary cells, and it is immediately clear that, at the time of the origin of life, control by the nucleic acids of their immediate environment could not have been nearly so elaborate nor so complete as it is today.

There is no evidence that molecules of such complexity are being produced abiologically on the Earth today. Could the conditions in the early history of the Earth have been more favorable for abiological synthesis of organic molecules?

If planetary systems condense, as we think, from the interstellar medium, they should originally have a so-called "cosmic" distribution of the elements —that is, a distribution characteristic of the interstellar material and of most stars. This composition is outlined in Table 1, where we see that by far the most abundant element in the Universe is hydrogen. The next most abundant chemically reactive elements are oxygen, nitrogen and carbon. Thus we expect that any cold, non-dilute, cosmic environment should have large amounts of the fully saturated hydrides of these elements, i.e., H_2, H_2O, NH_3, and CH_4. Comets and interstellar grains are believed to consist primarily of these compounds, the relative proportions depending on the ambient temperatures and the vapor pressures.

The Earth and the other planets, early in their history, should also have been composed of these substances. We have direct evidence that the early atmosphere of the Earth was lost to space, because the noble gases, which generally remain chemically inactive, have been preferentially fractionated on the Earth (compared to other cosmic material that we can investigate spectroscopically). Such a fractionation may have occurred by thermal escape during the early history of the Earth, when the acceleration due to gravity may have been small, or the exosphere temperature high [*Kuiper*, 1952; *Sagan*, 1966]. Alternatively, the fractionation may be due to ambipolar diffusion in the magnetic field of the condensing solar nebula [*Jokipii*, 1964]. In either case, before fractionation occurred, much precipitation and compound-formation must have occurred in the Earth's primitive reducing atmosphere. This material, sequestered in the forming Earth, must later have been outgassed as the Earth became heated by radioactive decay of now-extinct radionuclides, by gravitational accretion, and by tidal forces. Thus, as the Earth approached its present form, its atmosphere must have retained its reducing character.

The transition from a reducing to an oxidizing atmosphere is attributed to two causes: (1) plant photosynthesis; and (2) ultraviolet photodissociation of water in the upper atmosphere and the preferential gravitational escape of hydrogen. It is not known whether photosynthesis is the main

TABLE 1. Distribution of the Elements

Atom	Relative Atomic Weight	Relative Cosmic Abundance (by number)
Hydrogen	1.0	10,000,000.
Helium	4.0	1,400,000.
Lithium	6.9	0.003
Carbon	12.0	3,000.
Nitrogen	14.0	910.
Oxygen	16.0	6,800.
Neon	20.2	2,800.
Sodium	23.0	17.
Magnesium	24.3	290.
Aluminum	27.0	19.
Phosphorus	31.0	3.
Potassium	39.1	0.8
Argon	40.0	42.
Calcium	40.1	17.
Iron	55.8	80.

cause of the transition [*Sagan,* 1966]. The present atmospheres of the Jovian planets, Jupiter, Saturn, Uranus and Neptune, retain their reducing character; are probably composed primarily of hydrogen, helium, methane, ammonia and water; and therefore are close in composition to the primitive atmosphere of the Earth.

When energy is supplied to a mixture of methane, ammonia, water and hydrogen, in the presence of liquid water—that is, in a laboratory simulation of the primitive environment of the Earth—complex organic compounds of distinctly contemporary biological significance are produced.

A survey of these laboratory experiments is presented in Chapter 2, and in *The Origin of Prebiological Systems,* S. W. Fox, ed. [1965]. Amino acids, pentose and hexose sugars, nucleosides, nucleoside phosphates and polypeptides have all been produced under conditions that resemble, more or less, the primitive terrestrial environment. It has been pointed out independently by *Beadles* [1960] and by *Sagan* [1961*a*, 1964] that spontaneous copolymerization of nucleoside triphosphates may have been a key event in the origin of the first self-replicating system. The picture that emerges of the origin of life is, then, as follows:

The application of energy to the primitive reducing atmosphere causes the efficient production of sugars and bases. Phosphates are presumably present in the primitive oceans. The interaction of sugars, bases and phosphates—especially after ultraviolet irradiation—leads directly to the synthesis of nucleoside triphosphates. In periods of time long compared with the lifetimes of contemporary organisms, but short compared with geological time, reactions among the nucleoside triphosphates lead to the formation of nucleic acids. The nucleic acids then prime the synthesis of identical molecules from the organically rich surrounding waters. Random errors in the replication process lead to occasional deviations in the nucleic acid structure. These deviations precisely reproduce themselves, so that, in the course of time, many varieties of nucleic acids can be found in the primitive oceans.

However, this cannot be the whole story. In our hypothetical reconstruction of the origin of life, natural selection has not yet come into play. For evolution to have proceeded, the nucleic acids must, in some way, have controlled the environment in primitive times. Natural selection operates only on the phenotype and not on the genotype. Something analogous to the nuclear DNA-messenger–RNA-adapter–RNA-enzyme transcription sequence, but much simpler, must be postulated for the primitive oceans; the contemporary triplet code is far too complex [*Rich*, 1962; *Stent*, 1962]. A singlet coding directly between DNA and polypeptides would satisfy this requirement, but it is not known whether such a configuration is sterically feasible. If DNA itself had some weak catalytic properties, or protein some weak self-replicating properties, the difficulties would be alleviated. Alternatively, it is possible that the information content of the first living systems was contained in RNA, and that DNA played no fundamental primitive role. The necessity for a transcription intermediary would thereby be obviated. As time progressed, there may have been a selective advantage to storing the genetic inheritance in a molecule less labile than RNA. DNA admirably serves this function. Such a possibility of a secondary origin of DNA is consistent with *Horowitz'* [1945] hypothesis on the origin of biochemical reaction chains, in which successive members of contemporary enzyme-catalyzed reaction chains arose in a sequence opposite to the one in which they are utilized today. At the present time, this remains one of several major uncertainties faced by the genetic approach to the origin of life.

Another uncertainty concerns the assumption that nucleoside triphosphates will spontaneously polymerize in times short compared with 5×10^9 years. An investigation of these reaction rates would be very useful. Other agents—for example, ultraviolet light—may have been active in accelerating the rate of nucleoside triphosphate polymerization in the primitive synthesis of polynucleotides.

In all primitive Earth simulation experiments, only a few reactants, all of high purity, have been used. However, the primitive terrestrial oceans, or any other hypothetical media for the origin of life, were certainly not composed of these pure substances alone. In the primitive Earth, there must have been major contamination by large numbers of other substances. Some of them would accelerate the production of compounds of biological interest, others would impede their synthesis or destroy them once they had been formed [*Abelson*, 1961; *Horowitz and Miller*, 1962]. Until the immensely difficult task of allowing for all probable contaminants has been made, the successful laboratory synthesis of substances relevant to the origin of life can have only a vague resemblance to the chemical events of primitive times. The striking success of such simulation experiments should not obscure the existence of this complication. Nevertheless, this success itself—the preferential production of just those compounds that are of biological interest—suggests that the contaminants did not entirely alter the course of abiological organic synthesis.

Finally, the question arises whether such complex molecules as the nucleic acids really were implicated in the origin of life. Might they not be a relatively recent evolutionary sophistication? And might the first self-replicating system have been composed of other molecules altogether? Answers to such questions can only be provided experimentally. The success in producing nucleic acid precursors in simulated primitive environments at least suggests that polynucleotides may indeed have been the first self-replicating systems.

It is a logical consequence of the genetic approach to the origin of life that the subsequent development of living systems was an evolutionary attempt at local retention of the primitive environment, so that nucleic acid survival and replication could be maintained. The organism can then be viewed as a temporary repository for the genetic material, a situation aptly summarized in Samuel Butler's aphorism, "The hen is the egg's way of making another egg."

At the turn of the century, when it was much more difficult to imagine how life came into being from inanimate matter than it is today, *Arrhenius* [1903] proposed the panspermia hypothesis. This was a stopgap measure that attributed the origin of life on Earth to the germination of a spore wafted by radiation pressure to the Earth from some other planet. The problem of the origin of life was thereby deferred, but not answered. It is now possible to perform some computations on the panspermia hypothesis. The preliminary results are as follows: Some bacterial and fungal spores are of the proper size range to be driven by solar radiation pressure out of our solar system entirely, if somehow they could first escape from the Earth's gravitational field. However, long before such a spore could reach even the orbit of Mars, it would receive a lethal dose of solar ultraviolet radiation. If we surround the spore with ultraviolet-absorbing protective material, then it does not escape from the solar system at all; because of the increased mass, it falls into the Sun. Particles that successfully enter our solar system must have a different range of sizes from the particles that are driven away from the Sun by radiation pressure. The hotter the star, the more massive the spore that can be driven out by radiation pressure; but also the greater the administered ultraviolet radiation dose. The spore must also survive solar x rays and protons and galactic cosmic rays. The last will be significant for very long journeys. Even if an occasional spore does escape from a planetary system, it is geometrically very unlikely that it will encounter another suitable planet and there initiate life—space is very empty.

These limitations of geometry and radiation damage seem quite general, and make it appear very unlikely that life in our solar system was initiated, through the Arrhenius mechanism, by a spore from some other planetary system.

If the origin of life is a necessary consequence in a relatively short time period of the physics and chemistry of primitive planetary environments, and if, on the average, each star has a planetary system, it follows that life must be pervasive throughout the Universe. Organisms with our level of intelligence and technical civilization have emerged on our planet about midway in the residence time of our Sun on the main sequence. Large numbers of stars within our Galaxy are older than the Sun, and many of them may contain planetary systems on which life is flourishing. We do not know whether the emergence of intelligence and technical civilization, in a variety of local forms, is a necessary eventuality in the evolution of life, or whether it involves a concatenation of many very unlikely circumstances. But the large number of presumptive planets and the belief that there is nothing extraordinary about our sector of the Universe, both argue for the contention that there may be other intelligences and other technical civilizations in our Galaxy. Some of them may be far in advance of ourselves.

Project Ozma, an attempt to listen for radio signals from ϵ Eridani and τ Ceti, two nearby stars of approximately solar spectral type, was conducted unsuccessfully at the National Radio Astronomy Observatory in 1961 [Drake, 1965]. But the search was restricted to a short period of time, a specific frequency and two stars. The potentialities of interstellar communication with other intelligent species are enormous, and further investigations along these lines could be immensely rewarding.

ENVIRONMENTS FOR EXTRATERRESTRIAL LIFE

We wish to inquire whether other bodies in our solar system are capable of supporting indigenous life. Accordingly, we must first attempt to specify the range of planetary parameters consistent with the existence of living systems.

Temperature

For a given molecular system, the temperatures may be too high, in which case thermal degradation will occur; or the temperatures may be too low, in which case the rate of chemical reaction may be biologically insignificant. However, as pointed out in Chapter 12, we must not be too provincial in assessing such temperature ranges. Chemistries are known, or can be anticipated, that utilize conceivably abundant but terrestrially unfamiliar compounds. Such compounds may be stable at several hundred °C or enter into reactions that proceed at substantial rates at −100°C. It is also important to bear in mind that a variety of temperatures may be found on any given planet. As we shall see, the temperatures of the planets in our solar system are such that probably not one can be excluded as a possible abode of life on grounds of temperature alone.

Solvent System

In terrestrial life forms, water serves as the primary solvent system. It functions as an interaction medium and as a thermal reservoir. Water possesses these and other properties of biological significance partly because of hydrogen bonding between adjacent molecules in the liquid state. Water also has the advantage of being a liquid over a fairly wide range of expected planetary temperatures. In eutectic salt solutions, open pools of water can be stable at temperatures several tens of degrees below 0°C, and pure liquid water can be maintained at even lower temperatures in subsurface capillaries.

Other solvents also have large dielectric constants and large thermal inertias. Chief among these are ammonia, hydrogen cyanide and hydrogen fluoride. The possibility that hydrogen fluoride is a significant solvent system on other planets can be excluded on the basis of cosmic abundance. The expected abundance of hydrogen cyanide is greater, but is also probably too low to be of major exobiological significance. Liquid ammonia, however, should be abundant in highly reducing planetary atmospheres. The temperature range over which it maintains liquid properties is, however, small.

As described in Chapter 12, many of the properties of water that we consider essential for living systems are probably not essential. Being composed largely of water ourselves, we may be unjustifiably unsympathetic to other possibilities. For example, mixtures of hydrocarbons have many useful solvent properties, and they also may have high abundances on planets with reducing atmospheres.

Energy Source

An energy source is needed for replication and metabolism. In primitive times on the Earth, the ultimate energy source was very likely sunlight, which, directly or indirectly, produced organic compounds that could be tapped by simple organisms for their free energy. At the present time on the Earth, sunlight is still the ultimate energy source, but an active biological involvement in the form of plant photosynthesis is required to make this energy available to living systems, the plants themselves included. In earlier times, pure heterotrophs could function very nicely; at the present time, extensive autotrophy is essential for life.

In some extraterrestrial environments, we can imagine the origin of life in a subsurface cache of organic substances. However, such a system is inherently limited by the total free energy available in the organic medium and organisms arising in such an environment can be expected, after an initial geometrical increase in numbers, to die of malnutrition.

Atmosphere

The presence of an atmosphere is important for its potentially reactive contents, and for its ultraviolet opacity, but there is no evidence that living systems cannot survive a wide range of ambient pressures. Similarly, a wide range of magnetic field strengths has little influence on biological processes.

Oxygen is not a prerequisite for living systems. Life almost certainly arose in a highly reducing environment, and the production of large amounts of molecular oxygen appears to be only a later development. In fact, there are some respects in which molecular oxygen is a cellular poison, against which the nuclei of contemporary cells must be protected. An oxygen atmosphere does provide one important energetic economy—greater efficiency by an order of magnitude in the extraction of free energy from certain foodstuffs, such as glucose. It is sometimes concluded that free oxygen is therefore necessary for all but the simplest organisms, but a less complete metabolic oxidation coupled with a greater food collection efficiency, or, alternatively, a more sluggish metabolism, would serve as well. The presence of molecular oxygen leads to ozone formation and, therefore, to the essentially complete absorption of ultraviolet light at wavelengths shortward of 3000 Å. Thus, on any particular planet, it is unlikely that organisms have to cope simultaneously with high ultraviolet fluxes and high oxygen tensions.

It is noteworthy that the Earth is the only planet in the solar system on which molecular oxygen is present in large amounts. Since, at the present time, the primary source of atmospheric oxygen is plant photosynthesis, it is reasonable to conclude that no other planet in our solar system has large-scale plant photosynthesis accompanied by oxygen evolution. Mars, for example, has the starting points of the photosynthetic process—namely, carbon dioxide, water and light—but does not have any detectable molecular oxygen. If there is large-scale biological activity on Mars, then its ecology is constructed on a different model from that of life on Earth.

Substitutions for Carbon

It is sometimes suggested that silicon may replace carbon in extraterrestrial life forms. In silicon the valence electrons are bound to the nucleus much more loosely than in carbon because of electrostatic shielding by the K and L shell electrons and because of the greater distance of the valence electrons from the nucleus. As a result, silicon compounds participate in redistribution reactions that tend to maximize the randomness of silicon bonding. Therefore, the stable retention of genetic information over long periods of time in silicon compounds on hot planets is very improbable. In low-temperature environments, silicon may be a much more useful biological element. Since silicon compounds do not exhibit double bonds, their diversity is accordingly limited. For the same reason the strong absorption of near ultraviolet radiation, which may have played a key role in prebiological organic syntheses on Earth, is absent when silicon replaces carbon. Other aspects of the "fitness" of silicon are discussed in Chapter 12. The primary reason for considering silicon is that on the Earth's surface, its abundance is about a hundred times greater than the abundance of carbon. However, low-temperature planets, far from their central star, are also planets with low exospheric temperatures. The escape of gases from the tops of these atmospheres is inhibited, and therefore the abundance of carbon should be relatively much larger as, indeed, we find in the Jovian planets of our own solar system. Thus, the relative abundance of silicon with respect to carbon and the relative stability of silicon and carbon compounds place conflicting requirements on the environments in which silicon compounds could most profitably be used. However, it is still not entirely out of the question that silicon compounds may be intimately involved in extraterrestrial biological processes on low-temperature planets.

It is sometimes asked whether other planets may have living systems based on principles entirely different from those on Earth. This question is operationally undefined. If a system is completely different from anything with which we are familiar, we are in no position to comment on it. However, there is a perfectly general reason why some metabolic activity must be expected from an organism constructed even of the most exotic molecules. Whatever the basic molecular architecture of an organism, it is clearly important that the architecture be maintained. Two tendencies oppose this maintenance—random thermal degradation and the effects of the Heisenberg uncertainty principle, such as barrier tunneling. The former is greatly diminished in low-temperature environments; the latter is not. As a result, all living systems must have *repair* in some sense. Reproduction itself is a very basic kind of repair, a new organism appearing with none of the defects which the parent organism acquired during its lifetime.

The foregoing summary of required environmental properties may be useful, if only to indicate that many possibilities are still open; that terrestrial biochemistry may not be the only possible biochemistry or even the best possible biochemistry; and that in searching for extraterrestrial life an open mind is a prime asset.

PLANETARY AND SATELLITE ENVIRONMENTS

Let us now make a brief survey, to the best of present knowledge (early 1965), of the physical environments of the moons and planets in our solar system, and try to assess the *a priori* likelihood of indigenous life on them.

Mercury

A drawing in Mercator projection of the visually observed surface features on the bright side of Mercury is displayed in Figure 2.

The closest planet to the Sun, Mercury, is frequently dismissed from any biological considerations with references to the absence of atmosphere and surface liquids, extremely high temperatures on its illuminated hemisphere and extremely low temperatures on its unilluminated hemisphere. (This last circumstance was concluded from the fact that Mercury rotates synchronously, always keeping the same face to the Sun.) Mercury was sometimes called both the hottest and the coldest place in the solar system. Most of these older conclusions now appear to be false. A small atmosphere, with total pressure about 1 mm Hg, was detected polarimetrically by *Dollfus* [1957]. Recent spectroscopic observations by *Moroz* [1963] suggest that most of this atmosphere may be carbon dioxide, although this result awaits confirmation. Infrared measurements of the illuminated hemisphere of Mercury give temperatures characteristically about 600°K. Microwave observations of both the bright and the dark sides now lead to the rather remarkable conclusion that the unilluminated hemisphere of

Figure 2.
Map of the illuminated hemisphere of Mercury constructed by A. Dollfus. The differences between the bright and dark markings are entirely unknown, and no information at all is available on the topography of the dark side. (Courtesy of Dr. A. Dollfus, Meudon Observatory.)

Mercury has characteristic temperatures in the 250-300°K range [*Kellerman*, 1964]. On a synchronously rotating planet, such temperatures can be maintained by atmospheric convection from the bright to the dark sides. The low atmospheric pressure is very likely maintained by an equilibrium between outgassing from the Mercurian interior and escape from the Mercurian atmosphere. The possibility of temperatures approaching 300°K on the dark side of Mercury opens up serious biological possibilities on that planet for the first time. The temperatures and radiation fluxes in the illuminated hemisphere are probably too high, at least for familiar biochemistries; but the moderate temperatures and absence of sunlight from the dark side are not deleterious. The primary problem in attempting to assess the likelihood of biologically interesting phenomena on the dark side of Mercury concerns the availability and thermodynamic accessibility of an energy source. Such considerations are very new, and before very much study is made of them, the astronomical data should be confirmed. These do, however, appear definite enough to suggest that Mercury be included in any exobiological planetary inventory. [Since the foregoing remarks were written, radar observations of Mercury have shown it to be nonsynchronously rotating, in contradiction to earlier optical data. At depth ∼ 1 meter mean temperatures near 300°K are now expected.]

Venus

Observed through the telescope under ordinary seeing conditions, the planet Venus appears to be a featureless disk. Ultraviolet photography reveals the changing features shown in Figure 3. Such features almost

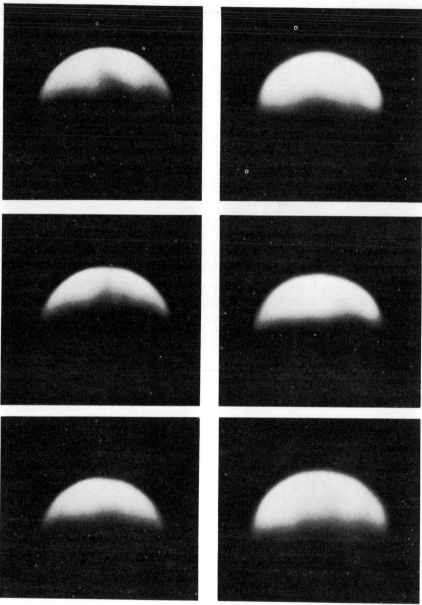

Figure 3. Six photographs of Venus in ultraviolet light, obtained with the 100-inch telescope at Mt. Wilson Observatory. The time-variable markings are attributed to changes in the upper clouds of Venus, and are probably uncorrelated with surface features. (Courtesy of Mt. Wilson and Palomar Observatories.)

certainly refer to the region above the Venus cloud layer and have no relation to the surface. Nevertheless, in the near infrared, radiation from considerable depths below the cloudtops of Venus can be detected spectroscopically. There is some promise of ultimate observation of surface features at wavelengths where the clouds are transparent.

The spectroscopic observations suggest that the atmosphere of Venus is composed of about 5 per cent carbon dioxide and about 95 per cent molecular nitrogen [*Spinrad*, 1962]. More recent estimates [*Chamberlain*, 1965] lower this CO_2 abundance. It should be emphasized, however, that the identification of nitrogen has not been performed directly. Indeed, it is deduced by default. Every other plausible and cosmically abundant absorber has been searched for unsuccessfully. Molecular nitrogen has its absorption features at wavelengths inaccessible from the surface of the Earth. After a long period of conflicting claims, it now appears that water vapor has been detected in the atmosphere of Venus, but in very small amounts [*Bottema, Plummer, and Strong*, 1964]. The detection of water vapor lends some credence to the possibility that the clouds of Venus are also made of water. The three major candidates for the cloud composition which have been proposed in recent years are water, hydrocarbons, and dust stirred up from the planetary surface. Despite some statements to the contrary appearing in semipopular literature, there is no direct evidence from the Mariner II mission, or from any other observational technique, for hydrocarbons on Venus, and the absence of simple hydrocarbons from the spectrum of Venus argues against their presence in the visible clouds.

A recent infrared spectrum of Venus taken from balloon altitudes [*Bottema, Plummer, Strong and Zander*, 1964] has given a continuous spectrum very similar to that of ice crystals, although all possible varieties of minerals are not thereby excluded. However, ice crystal clouds with a liquid water bottom are consistent with a wide variety of observations in the visible, infrared, and microwave regions of the spectrum, and also play a major role in some explanations of the high surface temperatures deduced on Venus from radio-astronomy [*Sagan and Pollack*, 1966]. But the evidence for water clouds on Venus, while suggestive, cannot yet be considered conclusive.

We now have further reliable information on the lower atmosphere and the surface of Venus through microwave observations. At microwave frequencies, we see a level in the Venus atmosphere or surface which corresponds to temperatures of 600°K or larger. Microwave brightness temperatures are greater for the bright side of Venus than for the dark side. Radar observations suggest that Venus is rotating very slowly, but in a retrograde sense, so it does not always keep the same face to the Sun. Instead, there may be about two sunrises and sunsets per year.

If we wish to retain consideration of the surface of Venus as a possible abode for life forms with familiar biochemistries, we must attribute the microwave emission to some level in the atmosphere. This is the point of the ionospheric model of the Venus microwave emission, in which the observed radiation arises from free-free emission of electrons in an ionosphere at a temperature of 600°K. This model requires electron densities of about 10^9 to 10^{10} cm^{-3}, 10^3 to 10^4 times larger than in the terrestrial ionosphere. There seems to be no way to produce such a dense ionosphere [*Walker and Sagan*, 1965]. In addition, the ionospheric model predicts that in the vicinity of 1 cm wavelength, Venus should appear brighter at the edge of the disk than at the center. Instead, Mariner II found that Venus appeared brighter at microwave frequencies at the center of the disk than at the edges. Consequently, we must abandon the ionospheric model and attribute the high microwave temperatures to the surface of the planet; this assumption explains many details of the microwave emission in a straightforward manner.

Figure 4 gives typical thermal maps of the bright and dark sides of Venus at a level some tens of centimeters subsurface. Surface temperatures will be somewhat higher. These maps are obtained from interpretations of passive microwave interferometric and active radar observations of Venus. They are not intended to be exact, but merely to illustrate typical ranges of temperature over the surface of Venus. The coldest places on the planet are above the normal boiling point of water; the warmest places approach 1000°K. The atmospheric pressure seems to be several tens of atmospheres. This is a large value, but not nearly enough to condense much water from the atmosphere over a substantial fraction of the disk. The total amount of water in the atmosphere of Venus does not appear to be much larger than in the atmosphere of the Earth. However, so far as we can now tell, there is no equivalent of the terrestrial oceans on Venus. Unless water is preferentially more bound in Cytherean rocks than in terrestrial rocks, there must have been a preferential depletion of water from Venus during the early history of the solar system. The phase variation of the microwave temperatures of Venus points to a sandy or powdery surface; a wide variety of geochemically abundant materials may be present, but hydrocarbons are unlikely [*Pollack and Sagan*, 1965].

The temperature of the Venus cloudtops is generally quoted at about 230°K, but it is not out of the question that cloud bottom temperatures approach 300°K. The atmospheric pressures at the cloudtops are probably between 0.1 atm and 1.0 atm, and especially if mineral material is being convected up from the surface and if the clouds are composed of water, we should not exclude the Venus clouds as a possible biological habitat. But excepting the possibility of an indigenous biological aerosol, perhaps

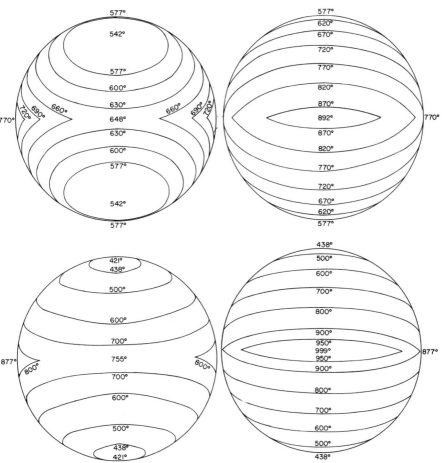

Figure 4.   Four theoretical maps of the temperature of Venus some tens of centimeters below its surface. Surface temperatures will be somewhat higher. The two maps on the left correspond to the unilluminated hemisphere of Venus; the two maps on the right, to the illuminated hemisphere. The lower pair corresponds to a much steeper equator-to-pole temperature gradient than the upper pair, but both sets of maps are in agreement with the observed microwave phase effect and interferometric data. (After J. B. Pollack and C. Sagan (1965) *Astrophys. J. 141*:1161.)

in the clouds, the chances of indigenous life on Venus based on familiar biochemistries appear to be small.

Satellites and Asteroids of the Solar System

There are some substantial similarities among the 31 satellites and thousands of asteroids in the solar system. All are comparatively small bodies, with little or no atmospheres, and probably small magnetic field strengths. All are therefore subject to the progressive ravages of the solar proton wind and short wavelength solar electromagnetic radiation. We will discuss later the evidence for material of biological interest in the meteorites, which are presumed to be asteroid fragments. For the moment, let us consider our own Moon as a possibly typical member of this class of objects. The Moon's surface temperatures characteristically range from 100°C to 100°K over the month-long lunar rotation period. It rotates synchronously with respect to the Earth, but non-synchronously with respect to the Sun. Its crater-pocked surface is generally interpreted in terms of bombardment in past epochs by meteors and asteroid-sized objects. It is generally agreed that the surface of the Moon is covered by a fine layer of pulverized material, arising both from accreted interplanetary debris and from powdered lunar surface material. The individual grains in the powder are vacuum-welded on the Moon, and provide a certain but undetermined bearing strength. One principal debate concerns the depth of this layer, estimates ranging from centimeters to tens of meters. The lunar surface has been photographed at comparatively close range by means of the Ranger spacecraft but differing conclusions have been reached concerning the significance of such photographs for studies of the lunar dust layer.

The probability of survival of either indigenous or exogenous life forms on the lunar surface when exposed to solar electromagnetic and corpuscular radiation is nil. However, for the lunar subsurface, the situation is not nearly so clear. The microwave brightness temperature of the Moon appears to increase towards longer wavelengths, while the radar-determined emissivity of the Moon seems to be independent of wavelength. But longer wavelengths come from greater depths below the lunar surface. According to the results of *Krotikov and Troitskii* [1964], the temperature gradient in the upper layer of the lunar surface is about 1.6°K per meter. Thus, at a depth of roughly fifty meters, we expect temperatures on the Moon near 300°K. At that depth the diurnal temperature fluctuations are damped, and temperature should remain quite constant over the lunar diurnal period. It has also been suggested [*Gold,* 1963] that the Moon today may have a layer of subsurface permafrost beneath which liquid water may be trapped. This layer would be at about the same depth as the layer of moderate temperatures. It is possible that processes in the early history of the Moon led to the formation of organic matter, just as in the early history of the Earth [*Sagan, 1961b*]. If such organic matter were also sequestered at such a depth, we see that the possibility of indigenous life in the Moon's subsurface is not out of the question.

In a remarkable spectrum obtained in 1958, *N. A. Kozyrev* [1962] detected the gas C_2 above the central peak of the lunar crater Alphonsus (Figure 5) at the same moment that the area apparently had a temporary reddish discoloration. Similar discolorations have been found subsequently near the crater Aristarchus and elsewhere. The most likely explanation for the Alphonsus spectrum is that solar radiation produced the radical C_2 by fragmenting other substances that were escaping from the lunar interior. Such larger molecules are most likely organic, and therefore Kozyrev's observations may be taken as evidence for lunar subsurface organic matter [*Sagan, 1961b*]. It has also been suggested that the parent molecule of the C_2 was acetylene, produced by the interaction of carbides and liquid water in the lunar subsurface [*Urey, 1961*]. In either case, these observations suggest the presence of liquid water or organic matter, or both, beneath the lunar surface.

In the absence of solar radiation tens of meters beneath the lunar surface, biological utilization of the free energy in sequestered organic matter would not permit very many generations of evolutionary advance. It is not impossible, however, that terrestrial microorganisms inadvertently carried by space vehicles to the lunar subsurface might there survive, or even replicate, thereby confusing subsequent searches for lunar organic matter or indigenous organisms. The possibility of extensive lunar bio-

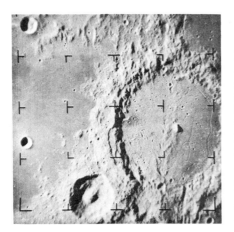

Figure 5.
Ranger IX photograph of the crater Alphonsus (the middle crater in the sequence of three). The gas emission from Alphonsus which has been observed has emanated from the central peak in the crater. This Ranger photograph is slightly superior to the best Earth-based photographs; other Ranger IX photographs of Alphonsus exist with vastly better resolution. (Courtesy of the National Aeronautics and Space Administration.)

logical contamination depends on the product of two improbable events: that a favorable subsurface habitat for terrestrial microorganisms exists and that terrestrial microorganisms will be introduced into this habitat [*Sagan*, 1961*b*]. The probability of contamination is therefore small, but it is not clearly negligible.

There is mineralogical evidence that the meteorite parent bodies passed through an epoch when extensive subsurface regions were at biologically moderate temperatures and possessed liquid water [*Anders*, 1963]. These conclusions apply to the asteroids and, probably, to several of the moons in the solar system. In Figures 6–9, we see preliminary visual maps of the four Galilean satellites of Jupiter. The satellite Io is now suspected to have an atmosphere [*Binder and Cruikshank*, 1964], as is the large satellite of Saturn, Titan [*Kuiper*, 1944], where methane has been spectroscopically identified. Very little is known about these bodies, but if we can conceive of life proceeding at low temperatures, they must be considered of potential biological interest.

The Jovian Planets

The planets Jupiter, Saturn, Uranus and Neptune present at first sight very hostile environments, primarily because of their low observed temperatures ($< 180°K$) and highly reducing atmospheres. However, the temperatures determined through astronomical bolometry refer to the top of the cloud layers on these planets. There is almost certainly a positive downward temperature gradient below the clouds, and therefore, some regions that are biologically interesting. Because of the extensive atmospheres of the Jovian planets, it seems likely that, at least for Jupiter and Saturn, these optimum temperatures occur in the atmosphere and not on the solid surface, if there is one. However, *Gallet* [1963] has recently shown, from an integration of the Jovian atmospheric structure using the wet adiabatic lapse rate and allowing for the fact that both ammonia and water will condense out below the visible clouds, that an extensive water condensation layer may exist at an atmospheric level where the temperatures are about $300°K$, and the atmospheric densities approach 0.1 gm cm^{-3}. In such an environment, the atmospheric density itself will be sufficient to permit extensive molecular interaction, one primary function which a solvent medium ordinarily provides. In addition, the water droplets of this lower cloud layer will provide solvent properties. Organic matter should be produced from the methane, ammonia, hydrogen and (very likely) water that constitute the Jovian atmosphere [*Sagan and Miller*, 1961], in a manner quite analogous to the processes which led to the synthesis of organic molecules in the early history of the Earth. It is

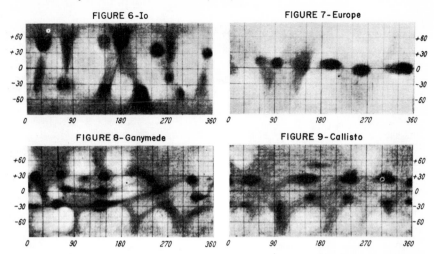

Figures 6–9. Maps of the Galilean satellites of Jupiter, constructed from visual observations by A. Dollfus. Of these four largest satellites of Jupiter, Io has distinctive reflecting properties, and there is a suspicion that it holds an atmosphere. The satellite labelled "Europe" (Figure 7) in the diagram is, in English, "Europa." (Courtesy of Dr. A. Dollfus, Meudon Observatory.)

even likely that the mass of organic matter on Jupiter exceeds the mass of the terrestrial biosphere. Whether organic matter plays any role in the vivid coloration of Jupiter's atmospheric belts and bands (Figure 10) is not now known.

In this and the preceding discussion, the word "organic" is used for compounds based on carbon, and does not necessarily imply biological origin. The possibility that life has come into being on Jupiter during the four or five billion year period in which it has retained a reducing atmosphere is difficult to assess. We do not know whether visible radiation penetrates down to the level of the presumed water cloud; nor can we predict the effect of the extensive Jovian internal energy sources on the energy available at the water cloud level. The opinion has been expressed that the relatively static environment of the Jovian atmosphere is unlikely to provide the selective stimulus for extensive evolutionary development. But this is not an entirely tenable argument. The atmosphere is in such a state of extensive turbulent motion that local environmental changes should be both frequent and stimulating. Such possibilities are, however, clearly very tentative, and here it is especially important to temper enthusiasm with caution, an admonition equally valid in many other phases of this subject.

Figure 10. Photograph of Jupiter, taken in blue light with the 200-inch telescope at Mt. Palomar. The Red Spot, which strongly absorbs in the blue, is particularly prominent in the upper left-hand corner of the photograph. The Jovian belts and bands parallel to the equator have distinctive colorations in naked eye observations. The flattening of Jupiter, noticeable in the Figure, is due to its rapid rotation (once every 9 hours, 55 minutes), and the fact that much of the planet is actually atmosphere. (Courtesy of Mt. Wilson and Palomar Observatories.)

Mars

The surface features of Mars have been mapped visually and photographically for many decades, and will be described below. Its physical environment, insofar as it is known, is summarized in Table 2. Mars has

TABLE 2. Summary of Data on the Physical Environment of Mars

Parameter	Method	Value	Reference	Remarks
Surface temperature	8-13μ infrared radiometry	Mean daytime $T_s \cong 240°K$ Warmest recorded $T_s \cong 300°K$ Equatorial diurnal $\Delta T_s \cong 90°K$ Middle latitude seasonal $\Delta T_s \cong 60°K$	Gifford [1956] Sinton and Strong [1960]	Temperatures are in good accord with theoretical values determined from the Martian albedo. In the nuclei of the dark areas, temperatures will be larger. Subsurface temperatures will have smaller diurnal and seasonal amplitudes.
Surface pressure	Polarization of reflected sunlight assuming pure Rayleigh scattering in atmosphere	$P_s = 85 \pm 50$ mb	Dollfus [1957; 1965]	The method gives an overestimate if large-particle scattering is not properly allowed for.
	Pressure broadening of near infrared CO_2 bands	$P_s = 25 \pm 15$ mb $P_s = 15 {\,}^{+15}_{-5}$ mb $P_s = 55 \pm 30$ mb	Kaplan, Münch, and Spinrad [1964] Moroz [1964] Hanst and Swan [1965]	To resolve these discrepancies, which are fairly minor astronomically, but important for engineers designing Mars entry vehicles, more laboratory CO_2 calibration and observatory Mars spectra are needed.
Atmospheric composition: CO_2	Infrared spectroscopy	$W_{CO_2} = 5500 \pm 200$ cm-atm $W_{CO_2} = 3000 \pm 1100$ cm-atm	Kaplan, Münch, and Spinrad [1964] Hanst and Swan [1965]	Composition is here given in absolute amount, rather than in percent by volume, because of the uncertainty in total pressure.
O_2	Infrared spectroscopy	$W_{O_2} < 70$ cm-atm	Kaplan, Münch, and Spinrad [1964]	Never detected in the Martian atmosphere. Expected steady-state O_2 content from CO_2 photodissociation alone is many orders of magnitude smaller.
NO_2	Infrared spectroscopy Infrared spectroscopy and photochemical equilibrium	$W_{NO_2} < 0.1$ cm-atm $W_{NO_2} < 10^{-3}$ cm-atm	Spinard [1963] Sagan, Hanst, and Young [1965]	

TABLE 2. (Cont'd.)

Parameter	Method	Value	Reference	Remarks
Atmospheric composition (cont'd)				
H_2O	Narrow band infrared radiometry	$W_{H_2O} \cong 2 \times 10^{-2}$ gm cm^{-2}	*Dollfus* [1964]	These values are also in agreement with theoretical values based on the identification of the polar caps as ice.
	Infrared spectroscopy	$W_{H_2O} = 1.4 \pm 0.7 \times 10^{-3}$ gm cm^{-2}	*Kaplan, Münch, and Spinrad* [1964]	
N_2	Arguments from cosmic abundances and terrestrial analogy	Bulk of the Martian atmosphere?	e.g., *de Vaucouleurs* [1954]	The identified gases account for only a small fraction of the total atmospheric pressure unless total pressure is <15 mb. N_2 has no absorption features in currently accessible wavelength intervals.
Surface composition:				
Polar caps	Infrared spectroscopy	H_2O ice	*Kuiper* [1952] *Moroz* [1964]	
	Polarization as a function of phase angle	H_2O hoarfrost	*Dollfus* [1957]	
Bright areas	Visible photometry and colorimetry	Limonite, $Fe_2O_3 \cdot nH_2O$	*Sharonov* [1961]	These investigations do not require the bright areas to be exclusively limonite dust. The question of the composition of the dark areas is much more debatable, and intimately tied to the question of life on Mars.
	Infrared photometry and spectroscopy	Finely pulverized ferric oxides, including limonite	*Sagan, Phaneuf, and Ihnat* [1965]	
	Polarization as a function of phase angle	Finely pulverized limonite	*Dollfus* [1957]	
Ultraviolet flux at surface, $\lambda \leq 3000$ Å	Flux at top of Martian atmosphere and anticipated atmospheric extinction	0 to 4000 ergs cm^{-2} sec^{-1}	*Packer, Scher, and Sagan* [1963]	The uncertainties here are very large, and depend on such questions as the atmospheric ozone content and the nature of the Martian blue haze.

TABLE 2 REFERENCES

Dollfus, A. (1957), Étude des planètes par la polarisation de leur lumière. *Ann. d'Astrophys.*, Suppl. 4.

Dollfus, A. (1964), Observations of water vapor on Mars and Venus, In: *The Origin and Evolution of Atmospheres and Oceans*, P. J. Brancazio and A. G. W. Cameron, eds., Wiley, New York, Chapter 12.

Dollfus, A. (1965), private communication.

Gifford, F. (1956), *Astrophys. J. 123*:154.

Hanst, P. L., and P. Swan (1965), *Icarus 4*:353.

Kaplan, L. D., G. Münch, and H. Spinrad (1964), An analysis of the spectrum of Mars. *Astrophys. J. 139*:1-15.

Kuiper, G. P. (1952), Planetary atmospheres and their origin. In: *The Atmospheres of the Earth and Planets*, G. P. Kuiper, ed. University of Chicago Press.

Moroz, V. I. (1964), The infrared spectrum of Mars (λ 1.1-4.1 μ). *Astronomicheskii Zhurnal* (USSR) *41*(2): 350-361.

Packer, E., S. Scher, and C. Sagan (1963), Biological contamination of Mars: II. Cold and aridity as constraints on the survival of terrestrial microorganisms in simulated Martian environments. *Icarus 2*:293.

Sagan, C., P. L. Hanst, and A. T. Young (1965), Nitrogen oxides on Mars. *Planet. Space Sci. 13*:73.

Sagan, C., J. P. Phaneuf, and M. Ihnat (1965), Diffuse reflection spectrophotometry and thermogravimetric analysis of simulated Martian surface materials, *Icarus 4*:43.

Sharonov, V. V. (1961), A lithological interpretation of the photometric and colorimetric studies of Mars. *Soviet Astron.-AJ 5*:199-202.

Sinton, W. M., and J. Strong (1960), Radiometric observations of Mars. *Astrophys. J. 131*:459.

Spinrad, H. (1963), The NO_2 content of the Martian atmosphere. *Publ. Astron. Soc. Pacific 75*:190.

de Vaucouleurs, G. (1954), *Physics of the Planet Mars*, Faber and Faber, London.

no detectable oxygen, small amounts of water vapor, a relatively high abundance of carbon dioxide and possibly a large surface flux of solar ultraviolet radiation. Mean daytime temperatures in middle southern latitudes on Mars during the southern summer may approach $+30\,°C$, temperatures optimal for most terrestrial organisms; but at the same locale, the temperatures before sunrise the following morning may be as low as $-40\,°C$; and the following winter, the *mean* daytime temperatures may be as low as $-40\,°C$. Diurnal temperature variations of $100\,°C$ are expected at many Martian latitudes. The seasonal temperature variation is much less marked at equatorial latitudes than it is towards the poles.

The reason that low temperatures are biologically deleterious is essentially twofold: (1) In some (mostly larger) organisms, the freezing process leads to ice crystallization within the organism and consequent disruption of cellular structure. This is not a factor in many microorganisms. (2) Freezing makes liquid water unavailable. This is the primary deleterious effect of low temperatures for microorganisms. The extent of damage depends upon a variety of factors, including the species of organism, the rate of freezing and thawing and the presence of eutectic substances which lower the freezing point.

It has long been known in the soil science and food technology literature that many varieties of microorganisms can survive freeze-thaw cycles comparable to those available on Mars. Recently, a series of experiments has been performed with the particular aim of assaying survival and growth of terrestrial microorganisms in simulated Martian environments. With very low water contents, characteristic of the Martian atmosphere and surface for most of the year, it has been found that in every sample of terrestrial soil tested, some microorganisms were present that could survive apparently indefinitely under simulated mean Martian conditions [*Packer, Scher and Sagan,* 1963]. In another set of experiments, where more plentiful supplies of water were assumed, the growth of many varieties of terrestrial microorganisms in such anomalous simulated Martian conditions could be demonstrated [*Young et al.,* 1964]. Increased availability of water occurs on Mars at the edge of the polar ice caps; through the seasonal transfers of water vapor from hemisphere to hemisphere, which accounts for the waxing and waning of the polar ice caps; and locally, perhaps because of geothermal penetration of an hypothesized Martian subsurface permafrost layer [*Lederberg and Sagan,* 1962].

The surface flux of solar ultraviolet light on Mars may be, in the absence of ozone or other atmospheric absorbers, as high as 10^4 ergs cm^{-2} sec^{-1}; with this flux, most exposed terrestrial organisms would receive mean lethal doses in a matter of hours. However, radiation protection mechanisms for indigenous organisms can be easily envisioned, particularly on a planet which has so plentiful a supply of ultraviolet-absorbing iron compounds as Mars appears to have.

Terrestrial microorganisms transported to Mars might there survive, and even grow. While underscoring the necessity for sterilization of Mars landing spacecraft, these results also suggest that biologically tractable mechanisms exist for dealing with the apparent inclemency of the average Martian environment. But growth of microorganisms under the probably arid average conditions of Mars has not been demonstrated, and certainly not in a time scale of weeks, the characteristic time interval for visual changes on Mars imputed to biological activity. Nothing is known directly about the water content of the Martian surface and subsurface, and this remains the principal environmental uncertainty in assessing the *a priori* possibility of life based on familiar biochemistries on Mars. The low nighttime temperatures would ordinarily pose serious hazards to large plants and animals, because of the problem of ice crystallization. However, a variety of physiological and ecological adaptations can be envisioned to deal with this circumstance, and it seems premature at the present time to exclude on environmental grounds the possibility of larger organisms on Mars.

There have been some reports of large quantities of nitrogen peroxide (the equilibrium mixture of nitrogen dioxide and its dimer, nitrogen tetroxide) on Mars [*Kiess, Karrer, and Kiess,* 1960]. We do not know whether detectable amounts of NO_2 are a pervasive or even an occasional feature of the Martian environment; but in any case, the steady-state abundance of NO_2 on Mars is 1 mm-atm. or less, an amount smaller than the NO_2 abundance above Los Angeles in the daytime [*Sagan, Hanst, and Young,* 1964]. While NO_2 is poisonous to many organisms, its abundance on Mars is far too small to pose any biological hazards.

DIRECT EVIDENCE FOR EXTRATERRESTRIAL ORGANIC MATTER

The only samples of extraterrestrial material accessible for laboratory analysis at the present time are the meteorites. Of these, about one per cent by number are carbonaceous chondrites. Approximately one per cent by mass of the carbonaceous chondrites are composed of organic matter. Thus, some 10^{-4} to 10^{-5} of meteoritic material is organic. This fraction is much larger than the corresponding fraction, $\sim 10^{-10}$, for the Earth—that is, the ratio of the mass of the biosphere to the mass of the Earth. The source of the long-chain aliphatic and polycyclic aromatic hydrocarbons and fatty acids of the carbonaceous chondrites is a subject of some dispute. The cracking pattern in mass spectrometric analyses resembles that of organic matter in terrestrial sediments and other sources of undisputed biological origin [*Meinschein, Nagy, and Hennessy*, 1963]; but the resemblance is at best rough, and in any case, it is not known what the structure of similar molecules produced under a variety of anticipated prebiological conditions might be [*Anders*, 1963].

Recently, saponified fractions of carbonaceous chondrites have been analyzed for optical activity [*Nagy et al.*, 1964]. Where all samples of terrestrial organic matter examined, prepared in a similar way, showed dextrorotary optical activity, the saponified carbonaceous chondrite fractions showed levorotary activity. This experimental finding has, however, been challenged [*Hayatsu*, 1964]; in any case, there are possibilities of contamination, as, for example, if a racemic mixture of carbonaceous organic matter were ingested by a terrestrial contaminant that metabolized only the dextrorotary fraction.

Some claims have been made for the extraction of viable microorganisms from carbonaceous chondrites, but these results are almost certainly spurious [*Sisler*, 1961, and ff. discussion]. Structured inclusions superficially resembling microorganisms have been found in carbonaceous chondrites [*Claus and Nagy*, 1961; *Claus, Nagy, and Europa*, 1963]; but some of these have been shown to result from terrestrial biological contamination —for example, by ragweed pollen [*Fitch and Anders*, 1963a, b]. It is not now known whether there is a remaining category of such highly structured and symmetrical forms in the 10μ size range, composed of organic material (or a likely fossil replacement), that can be shown *not* to be terrestrial contaminants. Nevertheless, large amounts of complex organic matter have been produced on the parent bodies of the carbonaceous chondrites—presumably, the asteroids, although *Urey* [1962] has suggested the Moon— and whether of biological or abiological origin, its existence is certainly relevant to the question of extraterrestrial life. The difficulties experienced to date in assessing putative biological activity in the parent bodies of the carbonaceous chondrites provide useful preparation for the problems and cautions involved in any future analysis of a returned lunar or Martian sample. Further discussion of this subject is given in Chapter 4.

Other evidence of extraterrestrial organic matter can be found in cometary and interstellar spectra, which show groups such as C_2, C_3, NH_2, CH, OH, etc. We have already referred to the appearance of the spectrum of C_2 in material outgassed from the lunar crater Alphonsus.

THE DETECTION OF LIFE ON EARTH

Of the other planets in our solar system, serious evidence for indigenous life exists only for Mars. That there should be any evidence at all is in itself remarkable, a fact that can perhaps best be appreciated by considering the circumstances reversed. Imagine that we are situated on Mars and provided with the same kinds of astronomical instruments that exist on Earth today. Is there life on Earth?

The largest engineering works would be invisible. In a preliminary survey of about 10^4 Tiros photographs of Earth, with much better resolving power than could be obtained with a 200-inch aperture from Mars, only one image showed any clear sign of the works of man [*Stroud, 1963*]. A more detailed discussion of problems in planetary biological reconnaissance is presented in Chapter 9. The diffuse emission from large cities with high surface brightness, such as Los Angeles, would be marginally detectable from Mars, but interpretation would not be easy. Emission lines of neon, argon, krypton and sodium might be discovered. The observations themselves would be difficult, because the night hemisphere of Earth could be observed at night on Mars only when the Earth lies low in the evening Martian sky. Seasonal color changes of crops and deciduous forests would be observed, for example, in the American midwest, or in the Ukraine, but vexing questions would arise on the reliability of Martian color vision, ocular physiology and the chromatic aberration of telescope objectives. Even if the color changes were accepted as real, a variety of interpretations could be proposed; some might be inorganic and still feasible. A search might be made for H-C absorption features in the 3.5μ region in sunlight reflected from the Earth. It is unlikely that these attempts would be successful, if laboratory spectra of terrestrial vegetation performed on our planet are any guide. Perhaps this failure would be attributed to the fact that the intensity distribution curves for reflected sunlight and for thermal emission from the Earth cross over in the 3.5μ region.

Until fairly recently, bright flashes of light would be discernible at times. They would last only several seconds and there would be some evidence of their recurrence only in a few restricted locales, such as Eniwetok and Novaya Zemlya. It is doubtful whether these would be considered evidence for life on Earth, much less intelligent life. If the hypothetical Martians had radio reception equipment and chose to scan Earth in narrow wave bands, they would certainly be rewarded, if that is the word, by television transmission from Earth. There would be an intensity maximum when the North American continent faced Mars and it would doubtless be possible to determine that this radio frequency emission was not entirely random noise. Of course, the hypothetical Martians would have to have developed radio technology; they also would have to think of selecting a narrow radio frequency bandpass in observing the Earth. The capability alone is not the only prerequisite. For example, there has been no program of narrow bandpass radio frequency observations of Mars made from this planet. Of course, we feel that the prospects for intelligent life on Mars are very small.

The preceding intellectual exercise suggests that there might be life forms on Mars—in fact, fairly complex organisms—that would be entirely undetected from Earth. But the advent of interplanetary spaceflight provides a reasonable expectation that such possibilities will at last be experimentally tested.

EVIDENCE FOR LIFE ON MARS

The Martian surface is, in general, divided into three kinds of regions: bright areas, which are probably deserts; dark areas; and the polar caps, which we know from polarimetric and spectrometric evidence to be made of ordinary ice hoarfrost. Two high quality photographs of Mars, taken with the superb seeing conditions of the Pic du Midi Observatory in France, are displayed in Figure 11. Figure 12 is the International Astronomical Union Mars cartography. The relative configurations of bright and dark areas displayed are those common to photographs of the last several decades. Visual observations show much greater detail, the dark areas breaking up into mottled fine structure. However, because of difficulties in the reproducibility of these details when observations of different observers are compared, the map has indicated only those features which have been, beyond doubt, present on Mars in recent years.

The general coloration of the Martian dark areas is a neutral gray; the bright areas, a kind of orange ochre, or buff. Primarily due to contrast with the orange deserts and to chromatic aberration in early refracting telescopes, it was formerly believed that the dark areas were predominantly green. This now appears to be a psychophysiological and optical distortion.

A second observation that once was thought to be evidence for life on Mars was of rectilinear features extending from the dark areas and crossing over enormous distances through the bright areas. These so-called "canals" were interpreted as massive engineering works of a race of intelligent Martians. While there is little doubt that rectilinear features can be seen on the planet, observations under the best seeing conditions show a resolution of the canals into disconnected fine detail, quite analogous to observations of the dark areas under the best seeing conditions [Antoniadi, 1929; Dollfus, 1961]. Nevertheless, there must be some explanation for the disconnected detail which the eye organizes into rectilinear features. It has recently been suggested [Gifford, 1964] that they

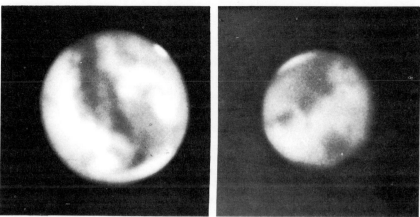

Figure 11. Typical high-quality photographs of Mars, taken at Pic du Midi Observatory, in the French Pyrenees. On the left is a photograph taken in 1941, near the maximum of the wave of darkening. Syrtis Major appears foreshortened at the bottom right of the photograph. Nepenthes-Thoth can be seen with a break in it, extending left from Syrtis Major. The appearance of Nepenthes-Thoth in this photograph may be compared with that of Figure 12, which is based upon later photographs. On the right is a photograph taken at the same observatory in 1954. The southern polar cap has a greater extent, and the contrast between bright and dark areas is generally less than in 1941. Sinus Meridiani is at left center, Solis Lacus at right center. (Courtesy of Meudon Documentation Center, International Astronomical Union.)

are sand dunes of considerable length, which may be expected under the Martian atmospheric pressure regimes and expected sizes of the particles in the Martian deserts.

The present evidence for life on Mars is based on three kinds of observations: visual, photographic and photometric; polarimetric; and infrared spectrometric. It has long been known that as the polar ice cap in a given hemisphere undergoes its seasonal regression, a wave of darkening courses across the dark regions of Mars, crossing the equator and traveling some twenty degrees of latitude into the opposite hemisphere. As the wave front progresses, the dark areas decrease in albedo, their boundaries with the adjoining deserts become more sharply defined, and occasionally, fairly delicate color changes can also be observed, individual regions of Mars undergoing their own characteristic seasonal color cycle.

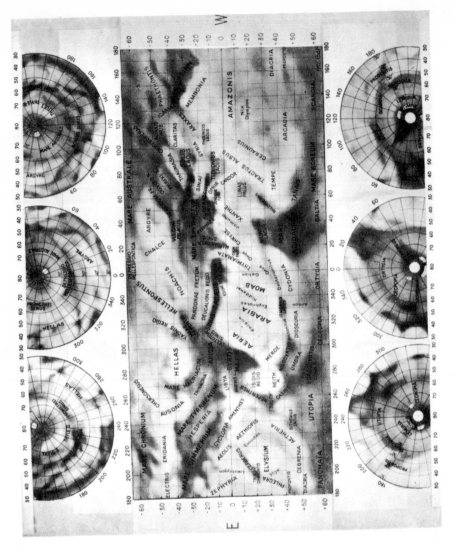

Figure 12.
The International Astronomical Union map of Mars. The bright areas are deserts; the polar caps are composed of ice. The dark areas are the sites of suspected biological activity. Secular changes in topography are observed, e.g., in Solis Lacus, at 90° longitude, —30° latitude. Evidence for organic matter and seasonal polarization changes exists, e.g., for Syrtis Major, at 290° longitude, +10° latitude.

At the same time, a dark collar, variously reported as black, brown or blue, is observed to follow the retreating edge of the polar cap on its journey toward the pole. There is no doubt about either darkening phenomenon; and the wave of darkening has been adequately registered photometrically [*Focas*, 1959]. Some dispute exists about the reality of the color changes. It is fairly certain that the color changes in the last few decades are not nearly so pronounced as the color changes recorded by earlier observers, who reported vivid blues, greens and a variety of other hues. Changes in contrast of dark neutrally colored surfaces adjacent to highly colored surfaces may appear to the eye as true color changes, when in fact there has been no change in the spectral distribution of the absorption by the dark area [*Schmidt*, 1959; *Hurvich and Hurvich*, 1964]. Thus, the seasonal color changes of the Martian dark areas may be entirely a psychophysiological phenomenon.

The biological interpretation of the wave of darkening is as follows: The Martian dark areas are covered with organisms—possibly, but not necessarily, plants—whose metabolism is very sensitive to the availability of water. During most of the year, they are in a dormant state. As the wave front of water from the vaporizing polar cap arrives, the local water abundance surpasses the critical value for metabolism, and a rapid growth and proliferation of the organisms occur. The changes in albedo and color of the dark areas are attributed to these metabolic activities. As the water vapor wave front passes, the local water abundance declines, and the organisms once again fall into a state of minimal metabolism.

In Figure 13 the progress of the Martian wave of darkening is plotted as a function of latitude and season of the year. The high-contrast, medium-contrast and low-contrast thirds (all compared with the invariant brightness of the deserts) are illustrated by the different degrees of irregular shading. The southern wave of darkening is the more pronounced, in that the contrast with the deserts reaches higher values than are observed in the northern wave. We see that the southern hemisphere wave of darkening begins at the end of southern hemisphere spring; and the northern hemisphere wave of darkening begins in the middle of northern hemisphere spring. Where there is no shading, the available data are sparse. The wave of darkening here plotted is taken from the photometric data of *Focas* [1959].

Superposed on this diagram are isotherms computed from the inclination of the axis of rotation of Mars to the ecliptic plane, and from the eccentricity of the Martian orbit. The temperatures have been calculated for an almost transparent atmosphere and for a perfectly insulating surface with a bolometric albedo of 10 per cent. Therefore, they refer approximately to the dark nuclei that are observed under highest resolution within

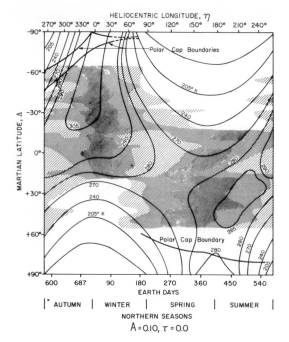

Figure 13.

Thermal regimes of the Martian wave of darkening. See text for details.

the dark areas. The temperatures indicated are mean temperatures from sunrise to sunset within the dark nuclei at the appropriate latitude and season. We observe that the wave of darkening generally follows the loci of maximum temperature. Similar conclusions follow for other choices of the bolometric albedo and the transparency of the Martian atmosphere. Thus, the wave of darkening proceeds from the receding edge of the polar cap through those areas of Mars which are at moderate temperatures. In the dark nuclei of the dark areas, these temperatures may be equable, even by terrestrial standards. Computations based upon this method, using the albedo of the dark or bright areas as a whole, give results consistent with those obtained observationally by infrared bolometry.

This correlation between the loci of the wave of darkening and the loci of highest temperature on the planet is consistent with the view that the wave of darkening is due to biological activity of organisms whose optimum temperatures are similar to the optimum temperatures of familiar ter-restrial organisms. But other, nonbiological alternatives have been sug-gested. *Arrhenius* [1918] postulated that the Martian dark areas are covered with deliquescent or hygroscopic salts, whose color and albedo vary with the relative humidity. It has not been possible to specify which salts change color and albedo at Martian humidity and temperature regimes, in a manner that might explain the visual observations; but neither has anyone suggested which Martian organisms might account for the observations. There is strong polarimetric evidence [*Dollfus,* 1963] that the dark areas are not covered with semi-transparent crystals, as the presence of large amounts of deliquescent salts would imply; but it is not known whether an amount of such salts too small to be detected polarimetrically could still be detected photometrically and colorimetrically. Occasionally, a dark area may appear rather suddenly in a region that was formerly primarily desert. A spectacular instance of this sort occurred several decades ago, in the Thoth-Nepenthes area (latitude $+20°$, longitude $260°$ on Figure 12.) Advocates of the biological explanation hold that such incursions represent ecological successions, possibly stimulated by some change in the physical environment—for example, fumarole eruptions.

Observations of the fractional polarization of sunlight reflected from the Martian dark areas yield a characteristic polarization curve when plotted as a function of phase angle (the angle Sun-Mars-Earth). This curve can then be compared with laboratory samples [*Dollfus,* 1957]. Such comparisons suggest that the Martian dark areas are covered with small, very opaque granules in the size range from 0.1 mm diameter down. The polarization curve for the bright areas shows similar features and must have a similar interpretation. Attempts to match the polarization curve for the bright areas have led to an apparently unique identification with a metallically absorbing iron oxide polyhydrate, the mineral limonite. The polarization curve for the dark areas is even more extreme, compared with the several hundreds of terrestrial samples that Dollfus has investigated. The nature of this "super-limonite" is a mystery, but apparently it must be attributed to an unusually dark substance, consistent with the observed very low albedo of the dark areas. The polarimetric identification of limonite provides, with no additional assumptions, a ready explanation of the albedo and reflectivity of the Martian bright areas, matching the observed reflection spectrum from the visible through the near infrared.

The polarization curve for the dark areas shows a seasonal displacement which the polarization curve for the bright areas does not [*Dollfus,* 1957]. The only successful laboratory reconstructions of this displacement require either a change in the size distribution of the opaque particles, or a change in their opacity. A biological interpretation of this phenomenon holds that the dark areas of Mars are covered by organisms in the 0.1 mm size range, which proliferate as the wave of darkening arrives. In a fairly brief period of time, the smaller, recently formed organisms must grow to "adult" size, so that the winter form of the polarization curve can be reestablished. The inorganic interpretation of the polarization phenomenon holds that a reproducible physical redistribution of sizes of inorganic grains occurs at the time of the wave of darkening. Perhaps the winds that may accompany the water vapor front redistribute the surface dust, which in the absence of winds has settled, with the larger particles deepest. It must also be asked why the bright areas of Mars, which are presumably nonliving, are covered by the same kind of granules that cover the dark areas. A uniformitarian explanation for the existence of small, opaque particles in both the bright and the dark areas is desirable.

There is, at the present time, no acceptable inorganic model to explain the wave of darkening and the polarization observations. However, such models should be pursued. A successful model should explain, in terms of allowable meteorological postulates and geochemically plausible materials, not only the obvious photometric and polarimetric data, but also a wide range of other phenomena. These include the reappearance of the dark areas after a dust storm, the absence of dark clouds obscuring the bright areas, the presence of finely pulverized material in the dark areas as well as the bright areas, and the differences in radar reflectivities between the bright and the dark areas. It may be that these phenomena are explicable in terms of systematic elevation differences between bright and dark areas, of seasonal variations in the prevailing wind patterns on Mars, and of the size distribution of finely pulverized materials; but no such detailed model has yet been formulated. For this reason it seems desirable also to pursue the hypothesis that the wave of darkening and the polarization phenomena are of biological origin.

In recent years, observations of the infrared spectra of the dark regions of Mars have been reported to show absorption features at about 3.45μ, 3.58μ, and 3.69μ [Sinton, 1957; 1959; 1961; Moroz, 1964]. Several attempts have been made to account for these absorptions in terms of the putative presence on Mars of organic or inorganic compounds known to show similar spectral features (e.g., compounds containing methyl or methylene groups, aldehydes, inorganic carbonates, deuterated water). Nevertheless, while suggestive, none of these hypotheses has been entirely satisfactory [Lederberg, 1959; Sinton, 1961; Colthup, 1961; 1965; Rea, 1962; Rea, Belsky and Calvin, 1963; Shirk, Hazeltine and Pimentel, 1965].

More recently, reexamination of the experimental evidence suggests that the two long-wavelength Sinton bands are due to deuterated water (HDO) in the atmosphere of the Earth [Rea, O'Leary and Sinton, 1965]. The remaining band's Martian origin remains unquestioned; it has been attributed both to organic molecules and to carbonates.

Problems of this sort emphasize the difficulties inherent in detailed astronomical studies of planetary surfaces by conventional means, no matter how painstaking. However, improvements in technique and the prospect of new methods of observation hold the promise of more exact formulation—and exclusion—of hypotheses in such cases.

The foregoing observations and their possible interpretations, both inorganic and biological, were discussed at some length in a Conference on Remote Investigations of Martian Biology, Cambridge, Mass., 1964 (Proceedings to be published). With the still limited information currently available, it was nevertheless possible to formulate several hypothetical Martian ecologies. A description and elaboration of one of them is given in Chapter 11 of the present volume. In this model organic matter on Mars is imagined to be metabolized respiratively, with limonite serving as electron acceptor. The pool of organic matter is maintained photosynthetically, by processes that do not involve the the release of molecular oxygen.

The result of such an exercise is, of course, not to demonstrate the existence of life on Mars, but merely to show that its existence does violence to none of the facts of familiar biochemistry. There are, in addition, possibilities of more exotic biochemistries (cf., Chapter 12).

Of all the possible extraterrestrial habitats within our solar system and beyond, Mars is clearly the most promising. But at the present time, we have no rigorous answers to these enigmatic questions. Rigor can be provided only through a comprehensive program of observation from the vicinity of the Earth, from the vicinity of Mars, and eventually from unmanned and manned vehicles on the surface of Mars. With such a program, we may be fortunate enough to witness in our lifetimes the solution, one way or another, of the tantalizing problem of life on Mars, with all the scientific and philosophical implications that such a solution would suggest.

REFERENCES

Abelson, P. H. (1961), paper presented at the Denver meeting of the American Association for the Advancement of Science.

Anders, E. (1963), *Ann. N. Y. Acad. Sci. 108*:514.

Antoniadi, E. M. (1929), *La Planète Mars 1659-1929,* Hermann, Paris.

Arrhenius, S. (1908), *Worlds in the Making,* Harper, New York.

Arrhenius, S. (1918), *The Destinies of the Stars,* Putnam, New York.

Beadle, G. W. (1960), *Accad. naz. Lincei, Roma 47*:301..

Binder, A. B., and D. P. Cruikshank (1964), *Icarus. 3*:299.

Bottema, M., W. Plummer, and J. Strong (1964), *Astrophys. J. 139*:1021.

Bottema, M., W. Plummer, J. Strong, and R. Zander (1964), *Astrophys. J. 140*:1640.

Chamberlain, J. W. (1965), *Astrophys. J. 141*:1184.

Claus, G., and B. Nagy (1961), *Nature 192*:594.

Claus, G., B. Nagy, and D. L. Europa (1963), *Ann. N. Y. Acad. Sci. 108*:580.

Colthup, N. B. (1961), *Science 132*:529.

Colthup, N. B. (1965), private communication.

Dollfus, A. (1957), *Ann. d'Astrophys. Suppl. 4.*

Dollfus, A. (1961), Chap. 15 of *Planets and Satellites,* G. P. Kuiper and B. M. Middlehurst, eds., Univ. of Chicago Press, Chicago.

Dollfus, A. (1963), private communication.

Drake, F. D. (1965), *The Radio Search for Intelligent Extraterrestrial Life,* Pergamon Press. To be published.

Fitch, F. W., and E. Anders (1963a), *Ann. N. Y. Acad. Sci. 108*:495.

Fitch, F. W., and E. Anders (1963b), *Science 140*:1097.

Focas, J. H. (1959), *Comptes Rendus Acad. Sci., Paris 248*:626.

Fox, S. W., ed. (1965), *The Origins of Prebiological Systems,* Academic Press, New York.

Fox, S. W., and S. Yuyama (1963), *Ann. N. Y. Acad. Sci. 108*:487.

Gallet, R. (1963), private communication.

Gates, D. M., and C. C. Shaw (1960), *J. Opt. Soc. Amer. 50*:876.

Gifford, F. A., Jr. (1964), *Icarus 3*:130.

Gold, T. (1963), private communication.

Hayatsu, R. (1964), *Rept. EFINS 64-67,* Univ. of Chicago.

Horowitz, N. H. (1945), *Proc. Natl. Acad. Sci. U. S. 31*:153.

Horowitz, N. H., and S. L. Miller (1962), *Fortschr. Chem. Org. Naturstoffe 20*:423.

Hurvich, L. M., and D. J. Hurvich (1964), *Proc. Internatl. Conf. on Remote Investigations of Martian Biology,* C. Sagan, ed. To be published.

Jastrow, R., and A. G. W. Cameron, eds. (1963), *Origin of the Solar System,* Academic Press, New York.

Jokipii, J. R. (1964), *Icarus 3*:248.

Kamp, P. van de (1963), *Astron. J. 68*:515.

Kellerman, K. I. (1964), paper presented at the General Assembly, International Astronomical Union, Hamburg.

Kiess, C. C., S. Karrer, and H. K. Kiess (1960), *Publ. Astron. Soc. Pacific 72*:256.

Kozyrev, N. A. (1962), *In: Physics and Astronomy of the Moon,* Z. Kopal, ed., Academic Press, New York, p. 361.

Krotikov, V. D., and V. S. Troitskii (1964), *In: Life Sciences and Space Research II,* M. Florkin and A. Dollfus, eds., North-Holland, Amsterdam; p. 145.

Kuiper, G. P. (1944), *Astrophys. J. 100*:378.

Kuiper, G. P. (1952), *Atomospheres of the Earth and Planets,* University of Chicago Press, Chicago.

Lederberg, J. (1959), private communication.

Lederberg, J., and C. Sagan (1962), *Proc. Natl. Acad. Sci., U. S. 48*:1473.

Meinschein, W. G., B. Nagy, and D. J. Hennessy (1963), *Ann. N. Y. Acad. Sci. 108*:553.

Moroz, V. I. (1963), *Astronomicheskii Tsirkular,* No. 270.

Moroz, V. I. (1964), *Soviet Astron. J. 8*:273.

Moroz, V. I. (1965), *Soviet Astron. J. 8*:566.

Nagy, B., M. T. J. Murphy, V. E. Modzeleski, G. Rouser, G. Claus, D. J. Hennessy, U. Colombo, and F. Gazzarrini (1964), *Nature 202*:228.

Oparin, A. I. (1957), *The Origin of Life on the Earth,* Academic Press, New York.
Packer, E., S. Scher, and C. Sagan (1963), *Icarus 2:*293.
Pollack, J. B., and C. Sagan (1965), *Icarus 4:*62.
Rea, D. G. (1962), *Space Science Rev. 1:*159.
Rea, D. G., T. Belsky, and M. Calvin (1963), *Science 141:*923.
Rea, D. G., B. T. O'Leary, and W. M. Sinton (1965), *Science 147:*1286.
Rich, A. (1962), *In: Horizons in Biochemistry,* M. Kasha and B. Pullman, eds., p. 103, Academic Press, New York.
Sagan, C. (1961*a*), *Radiation Research 15:*174.
Sagan, C. (1961*b*), *Organic Matter and the Moon,* Natl. Acad. Sci.-Natl. Res. Council Publ. 757.
Sagan, C. (1964), *In: Life Sciences and Space Research II,* M. Florkin and A. Dollfus, eds., North-Holland, Amsterdam; p. 35.
Sagan, C. (1966), Origins of the Atmospheres of the Earth and Planets, *Internat. Dictionary of Geophysics,* S. K. Runcorn, ed.; Section I, H. C. Urey, Section Ed. Pergamon Press, London.
Sagan, C., P. L. Hanst, and A. T. Young (1965), *Planet. Space Sci. 13:*73.
Sagan, C., and S. L. Miller (1960), *Astronom. J. 65:*499.
Sagan, C., and J. B. Pollack (1966). To be published.
Schmidt, I. (1959), *Proc. Lunar and Planetary Explor. Colloq. 1,* No. 6, p. 19.
Shirk, J. S., W. A. Haseltine, and G. C. Pimentel (1965), *Science 147:*48.
Sinton, W. M. (1957), *Astrophys. J. 126:*231.
Sinton, W. M. (1959), *Science 130:*1234.
Sinton, W. M. (1961), *Science 132:*529.
Sinton, W. M. (1965), private communication.
Sisler, F. D. (1961), *Proc. Lunar and Planetary Explor. Colloq. 2,* No. 4, p. 67.
Spinrad, H. (1962), *Publ. Astron. Soc. Pacific 74:*156.
Stent, G. (1962), private communication.
Urey, H. C. (1961), *Astrophys. J. 134:*268.
Urey, H. C. (1962), *Nature 193:*1119.
Walker, R. G., and C. Sagan (1965), *Icarus,* in press.
Young, R. S., P. H. Deal, J. Bell, and J. L. Allen (1964), *In: Life Sciences and Space Research II,* M. Florkin and A. Dollfus, eds., North-Holland, Amsterdam, p. 105.

CHAPTER 4

BIOLOGICAL MATERIALS
IN CARBONACEOUS CHONDRITES

HAROLD C. UREY and JAMES R. ARNOLD

INTRODUCTION

In order to discuss this subject it is necessary to review briefly what our concepts are in regard to the fundamental problem of what life is and the conditions under which it might have evolved.

It is possible that in the early history of the Earth, or other planets where life evolved, a situation existed in which chemical reactions proceeded in an ocean in the direction of producing compounds of lower free energy. These compounds of lower free energy may have been returned to the atmosphere where they were converted into compounds of higher energy, and these again reacted in the ocean as before. In a way, this is a metabolic system, but it is not what we call life. Life must be segregated from its surroundings so that we recognize part of the material as living and part of it as non-living. There must be a distinction between the two. On the other hand, without reproduction there cannot be life. This is because any finite body in natural surroundings will in the course of time be destroyed. Thus a reproductive process that permits individuals to die while others survive is a necessary part of the living process.

Looking beyond the limits of the Earth and the kind of life that we see here, many questions can be asked. Are the living things based on com-

114

pounds of the same chemical elements? We are inclined to answer this question in the affirmative. We do not believe that the chemistry of any other elements except that based on carbon (together with hydrogen, oxygen, nitrogen and, to limited extent, other elements), and on aqueous ionic solutions, would duplicate the complicated chemistry that we associate with living organisms. Hence we believe that life would involve roughly the same chemical systems. This chemistry could mean that substances playing the same roles as proteins, fatty acids and carbohydrates will be important constituents of living things. Of course these substances may not be the same as those in our terrestrial organisms because the chemistry of carbon has enormous possibilities that are not realized among all the living things of the Earth that exist now or have existed in the past. One might ask whether the reproductive process must involve such substances as ribonucleic acid or deoxyribonucleic acid, or whether some other compounds could serve as the carriers of the hereditary information. This again we cannot answer, but we expect such information-carriers to be characteristic of life.

The requirements for the evolution of life, in our opinion, include the existence of liquid water and a continuous supply of energy, and it appears to us necessary that the source of energy be the Sun and not radioactivity, because radioactivity has such a destructive effect upon large organic compounds. What we specify then is a planet sufficiently large to hold an atmosphere containing water, illuminated by a star, and maintained at such a temperature that waters will remain liquid on its surface. Considering the situation in the present solar system, this limits us pretty much to the region from Venus to Mars inclusive, and probably excludes Mercury and the asteroids. Though the past history of the solar system may have included times when higher temperatures or lower temperatures prevailed, we can only say the evolution of life in the asteroidal belt would require a considerably higher solar temperature.

We think we can safely exclude Venus, the Earth and Mars from consideration as sources of meteorites showing evidences of life. The Earth and Venus can be excluded because the energy required to remove objects from their surfaces is unreasonably large. Mars is not a possible source, because if life were to evolve on this planet, water must have been present at some time in the past; in the course of time it must have escaped into space; and in this case erosion of the surface of the planet should have occurred, sedimentary rocks should have been produced, and if the carbonaceous chondrites could have been removed from Mars, sedimentary rocks should also have been removed, and they should appear among our meteorites. No such meteorites have been observed. Also, the energy of removal of objects from Mars, though not so large as that from Earth, is still substantial. The carbonaceous chondrites must come from smaller bodies, that is, the asteroids or the Moon.

THE CARBONACEOUS CHONDRITES

In discussing the meteorites from the standpoint of the possibility of extra-terrestrial life, we can exclude the great majority of the metals, the stony irons and most of the stone meteorites. These objects are strictly inorganic in characteristics, consisting of minerals that have been heated to high temperature and apparently have been agglomerated in the almost complete absence of water and so remained from the time that they were formed until the present. Only the carbonaceous chondrites contain much water and give us the suggestion that at least some of them were probably immersed in water at some time in the past.

The carbonaceous chondrites consist of several rather distinct types as pointed out by *Wiik* [1956] who classified them as Types 1, 2, and 3. *Mason* [1962] has accepted the first two types, but the Type 3 he prefers to classify as a non-carbonaceous group. All contain some carbon, but the first types contain substantial amounts of water and little metal. It is particularly the first two types, and especially Type 1, that we are concerned with in this discussion. Table 1 gives the composition in atomic percentages of samples of Type 1 and Type 2 carbonaceous chondrites as analyzed by Wiik, as well as a high iron group ordinary chondrite, and Table 2 gives the percentages by weight of carbon, water and sulfur in these types. It will be seen that the carbonaceous chondrites have a composition with respect to the elements other than water, sulfur and carbon that is very similar to a high iron group chondrite. It is evident from this that most of the elements have not been sorted, as is the case on the surface of the Earth. There is no appreciable sorting by water or by melting processes. These objects are not similar to sedimentary rocks and they are not similar to igneous and metamorphic rocks such as basalts, granites, gneisses, etc. In fact, the carbonaceous chondrites have abundances of some of the rarer elements that resemble more what we expect from our studies of the fundamental solar abundances than is true for the ordinary chondrites and the achon-drites. In this respect they would appear to be a more primitive material than the other stone meteorites. There are discrepancies with respect to solar abundances, most noticably in the case of iron, for the carbonaceous chondrites contain about four or five times as much iron with respect to silicon as does the Sun.

It is important to recognize these facts in connection with biological material in meteorites because the internal evidence shows that if living

TABLE 1. Composition of Carbonaceous and High Iron Chondrites
Atomic Percentages, S, C, H_2O Eliminated

	Type I Orgueil	Type II Meghei	Average H.Chondrites
Fe (Metal)	0.00	0.00	16.18
Fe (Oxide-Sulfide)	27.34	26.18	10.05
Ni	1.37	1.41	1.57
CO	0.07	0.06	0.09
Si	31.12	31.85	33.12
Ti	0.09	0.09	0.09
Al	2.68	2.90	3.60
Mn	0.22	0.19	0.25
Mg	32.48	33.19	31.68
Ca	1.81	2.04	1.60
Na	1.97	1.40	1.56
K	0.12	0.07	0.19
P	0.33	0.29	0.19
Cr	0.40	0.33	0.33
Total	100.00	100.00	100.00

TABLE 2. Composition of Carbonaceous and High Iron Chondrites
Weight Percentages

	Type I Orgueil	Type II Meghei	Average H.Chondrites
S	5.50	3.66	1.57
H_2O	19.89	12.86	0.37
Carbonaceous	6.96	2.48	——

organisms are present in these objects, they must have been introduced into the objects without any processes of sedimentation or sorting by running water.

Included in the Type 1 carbonaceous chondrites are some minerals that seem to have crystallized from water. The silicate minerals are the hydrated clay types. The meteorites contain a substantial amount of magnesium sulfate, which is soluble in water, and carbonate minerals of calcium, magnesium and ferrous iron have been observed in Orgueil. Magnetite also is present, and this is the first oxidation product produced by water acting on iron. Ammonium salts were reported by early observers of these objects. This whole pattern indicates that these objects have been subjected to liquid water. This was particularly shown by the work of *DuFresne and Anders* [1962]. What appears to be true is that some material of approximately primitive composition was acted upon by liquid water and a mild oxidizing agent to produce a mixture of reduced and oxidized materials. DuFresne and Anders show that this mixture of minerals might well be an equilibrium one in spite of its odd composition. It seemed probable that these materials were produced on the surface of a planetary object, subjected to ultraviolet light of the Sun, which would have supplied the energy to produce hydrogen peroxide, and this in turn may have oxidized sulfides and carbon compounds to sulfates and carbonates. In the presence of a reducing atmosphere, we might expect ferrous iron to be present in the water.

Where might such a situation have occurred? *Urey* [1962] suggests that it was on the surface of a planetary object and that these minerals are the residue of a primitive ocean that existed only for a short time and under conditions which did not produce sedimentary rocks or sorting by running water. *Anders* [1963] suggests that this mixture was produced on the interior of an asteroidal object due to water rising from a heated interior and acting upon mineral material nearer the surface of the asteroid. The suggestion by Urey may not be inconsistent with the possibility of the development of life. Anders' suggestion seems to be clearly inconsistent with the possible development of life in such objects.

The analysis of these carbonaceous chondrites goes back over a century. In 1834, *Berzelius* investigated the Alais (Type 1) meteorite and he recorded that it contained "humus and traces of other organic compounds." *Wöhler and Hörnes* [1859] studied Kaba (Type 3) and found humic and bituminous matter in an alcohol extract. *Cloez* [1864] analyzed the organic matter in Orgueil and reported that some 6.41 per cent was similar to peat and lignite. *Berthelot* [1868] recorded hydrocarbons in Orgueil. *Mueller* [1953] examined Cold Bokkeveld, which is a Type 2, and secured carbonaceous matter having the following analysis: C, 19.84 per cent; N, 3.18 per cent; S, 7.18 per cent; H, 6.64 per cent; Cl, 4.81 per cent; ash, 18.33 per cent; and O, by difference, 40.02 per cent. He expressed the view that this consisted of salts of carboxylic acids. It is a very old suggestion that this material was produced by living organisms. None of the older researches proved this. It should be remembered that during the early 19th century it was accepted that complex carbon compounds could not be produced except by the aid of living organisms. During the last century we have found that many kinds of very complex compounds are made in our chemical laboratories and that similar processes can occur in nature.

The more recent work started in 1961 with a paper by *Nagy, Meinschein and Hennessy* [1961]. They had been working on organic geochemistry, especially that pertaining to the origin of petroleum. The analytical methods which they used were those standard for this sort of work. Molecules and their fragments were volatilized and subjected to a high energy electron beam. The ionized products were analyzed in a mass spectrometer. Many peaks are secured in procedures of this kind. The data secured is difficult to interpret but in the opinion of these authors the pattern of peaks was very similar to those which they had seen in connection with their petroleum investigations. They concluded that the material was of biogenic origin, just as they believe and others believe is true for all deposits of petroleum and most of the carbonaceous material on the surface of the Earth. For the reasons that have been outlined above, students of meteorites did not believe this could be true.

This observation was followed by work by *Claus and Nagy* [1961] and by *Nagy, Claus and Hennessy* [1962] in which they described microscopic particles from Orgueil and Ivuna, both Type 1 carbonaceous chondrites. They suggested that these were microfossils. This was followed by papers by other authors. *Staplin* [1962] and *Timofejew* [1963] also maintained that they had found biological materials. There did not seem to be much overlapping in the type of materials described by the different authors. Some of the objects described by Nagy and his colleagues are certainly contaminants as was shown by *Anders and Fitch* [1962], and indeed the more complicated ones appear certainly to be contaminations by present-day biological material, ragweed pollen particularly. There remains a considerable number of the less complicated types of objects that appear to be indigenous to these meteorites. These latter objects are mineralized with limonite but they also contain residues insoluble in hydrochloric acid and hydrofluoric acid [*Nagy et al.,* 1963]. The bodies which remain after such acid treatment have the shape of the mineralized body. They do not contain elements of high atomic weight as indicated by the electron microprobe analysis. That is, there appears to be organic matter left after demineralization.

These objects also give absorption spectra in the ultraviolet that are similar to absorption spectra of biological material. The spectra are of an indefinite type, as is characteristic of such spectra, and it is difficult to be sure whether the material is of biological origin or not. What seems very probable is that it is, nevertheless, carbonaceous matter of some complex kind similar in a general way to biological material. Some maintain that these objects are artifacts and they may be so. But, of course, it would be far more interesting if they were the residue of biological material, as the authors of these papers indicate.

In further work, *Nagy et al.* [1964] have reported the presence of levorotatory materials in extracts from the Orgueil stone. The chemical composition of this material as determined by thin-layer chromatography appears to be quite different from terrestrial biological material with which it was compared. Some probable contaminants such as ragweed pollen, dust from the museum in which the object was stored, washings from human hands, were all dextrorotatory, whereas the material from the Orgueil stone was found to be levorotatory. Of course it is possible that some biological contaminants consumed the dextrorotatory compounds leaving the levorotatory compounds behind. If so, they did not leave behind any residues that have been identified in other respects (see the discussion of porphyrins and amino acids below).

Recently, *Hayatsu* [1964*a*] studied extracts of Orgueil using material from the very center of a fairly large stone. He has been unable to find any evidence for optical activity. Hayatsu, however, did not use the exact chemical procedures used by the previous authors. Nagy has repeated part of Hayatsu's work exactly and has obtained quite different chemical results with respect to the separation of sulfur and has found materials that are levorotatory, as reported previously. If optical activity is indigenous to the object, it would be strong evidence for biological activity, but at the present time this cannot be regarded as certain because of Hayatsu's work and because of the possibility (as mentioned above) that biological organisms growing in the meteorite after it landed on Earth destroyed preferentially the one optical isomer and left the other. At present this problem is not conclusively settled.

Nagy and Bitz [1963] showed by the use of infrared absorption spectra and gas chromatography that fatty acids were present in extracts from the Orgueil meteorite, and Hayatsu reports that he has confirmed this observation. Recently, *Oró* [1965] has extracted hydrocarbons from the Orgueil meteorite, studied them with a mass spectrometer, and finds that *n*-alkane hydrocarbons running from C_{15} to C_{30} are present. In the material from this meteorite he finds that the odd carbon-chain hydrocarbons are somewhat more abundant than the even carbon-chain hydrocarbons.

Hodgson and Baker [1964], on the basis of spectroscopic analysis, chromatographic separation and the chemical properties, found pigments in the Orgueil meteorite that are indistinguishable from vanadyl porphyrin. They also found that chlorins, which are prominent in all recent biological deposits, were not present in their samples. Incidentally, two of these samples were identical with those in which Nagy and his colleagues found optical activity. It is their conclusion that the porphyrin is indigenous and that it is not of recent origin. The Soret band in the ultraviolet is similar to such bands found in ancient terrestrial sediments. The wavelength of the Soret band changed with the solvent in which it was dissolved in the same way as the vanadyl porphyrin band does. The material from the meteorite was extracted in the same chemical fraction as is the porphyrin from terrestrial materials. Moreover, one sample that had been used by Nagy for other purposes did not show the presence of such a vanadyl porphyrin band. Subsequent to this, Hodgson and Baker subjected a non-terrestrial sample containing vanadyl porphyrin to the same chemical procedures as used by Nagy and they found that the vanadyl porphyrin band disappeared. It should be noted that terrestrial material containing porphyrin in any form is always regarded as being of biologic origin.

Calvin [1961] reported the presence of cytosine-like substances in Murray, but *Oró* [1963] argued that this was a laboratory contaminant. Calvin maintains that this is incorrect and the matter has not been settled. *Hayatsu* [1964*b*] reported the finding of adenine and guanine in Orgueil and thought he found a uracil type of compound. These are the four bases of RNA and the Watson-Crick model requires that the base pairs are adenine-uracil and guanine-cytosine. The presence of these bases in terrestrial material would lead to a strong presumption that it had been produced by biological systems. Other nitrogen compounds were reported by Hayatsu and he argues that this is evidence for a non-biological origin, but it should be noted that in terrestrial material of biological origin many compounds are present that, so far as is known, have no biological significance. This is therefore not a proof of the material being of abiologic origin.

If the Orgueil meteorite had become contaminated, by bacteria or other biological organisms, during the time that it has been on the Earth, one would expect to find the remnants of amino acids. *Calvin* [1961] and *Briggs* [1961] failed to detect amino acids, and recently *Hamilton* [1964], using very careful techniques, has also been unable to find these. *Kaplan et al.*, [1963] and *Vallentine* [1965] reported the presence of amino acids in Orgueil, but Kaplan *et al.* concluded that they were due to contamination of their sample and reported that the material from which these were extracted developed more amino acids in time, indicating definite contamination. Amino acids might be preserved for long periods of time if suitably protected (*Abelson* [1956] found amino acids inside cretaceous fossil shells), but might very well not be preserved for the long time that would be indicated if they were indigenous to the meteorite. Their absence indicates that the samples of Calvin, Briggs, and Hamilton were not contaminated with present-day organisms, and hence that some samples, at least, are not so contaminated.

These various lines of evidence are not entirely satisfactory and are certainly not conclusive. Surely if such material were of terrestrial origin very little doubt would be expressed about its biological origin. But we believe that life evolved from inanimate matter on the Earth. The initial stages of the evolution of life may have occurred in other places. Either the materials reported to be in the carbonaceous chondrites are of biotic origin, or they are materials of abiotic origin that are very suggestive of compounds of biotic origin. It would appear that the compounds that have been reported would indicate that at least considerable progress toward the evolution of life had occurred. The simpler fossil-like objects that are present in these materials certainly look much like micro-fossils and some of them are securely embedded in the matrix of the meteorite. The difficulties in deciding whether material of this kind is of biotic or abiotic origin suggest strongly that similar difficulties may be expected to occur if material is returned to us from the Moon or from the asteroidal belt or from Mars. Evidence of optical activity would probably be most definitive, but it is again difficult to exclude completely the possibility of contaminants.

As indicated in the introduction to this discussion, it seems very difficult to believe that biological material could have evolved in the asteroidal belt and that we could have received samples of this material without at the same time receiving some meteorites that showed some sorting of minerals due to running water. In particular, it is difficult to understand how life could have evolved and been deposited in material that is so primitive as is suggested by the inorganic composition of the Type 1 and Type 2 carbonaceous chondrites. It is the contention of Urey that the whole situation is consistent only with the hypothesis that life evolved on one object and contaminated for a brief period of time a more primitive object, and he suggested that the Earth was the object on which life evolved, and that the Moon may have been the primitive object contaminated by material of this kind. Today, some three years later, he maintains the same position. If it can be shown that the meteorites do not come from the Moon, it is exceedingly difficult to understand all the circumstances that would be consistent with life appearing in the carbonaceous chondrites.

It should be noted that we do not know what the composition of the surface of the Moon is. Evidence secured so far is not conclusive in regard to the questions discussed here. Certain features of the Ranger VII photographs are not inconsistent with fragmented material filling the mare basin where the spacecraft landed. These pictures are not conclusive in a positive sense either. It seems likely that the chemical analyses planned for the Surveyor program may give indications of a positive character in regard to this question, but probably the Apollo project must be successfully carried out in order to get definite answers.

That the Moon may have been contaminated from the Earth is a possibility. Two proposals for the origin of the Moon are considered seriously today. The first proposal is that the Moon escaped from the Earth some time during its early history when metallic iron, originally assumed to be distributed throughout the Earth, sank catastrophically to form the core, thus increasing the angular velocity of rotation. Most students of the subject do not subscribe to this view as a reasonable possibility. But if it did occur, the Moon would surely be contaminated with primitive oceans of the Earth and with any biological material that was present at that time. On the other hand, if the Moon was captured by the Earth, then it is a reasonable proposal that many moons were about and possibly a three-body perturbation enabled the Earth to capture the Moon. But if objects of this kind were about, they would be captured by the Earth with very violent processes in which material from the Earth may have even been thrown to great distances and possibly completely away from the Earth-Moon system. In such processes some capture of material from the Moon might occur, and if only small amounts of biological material escaped high temperature and other destructive processes and were captured by the Moon, they would rapidly multiply in any temporary seas and again contaminate the Moon. It is possible, and many think certain, that the maria of the Moon have not been subjected to water in this way. If this can be proved, then of course the carbonaceous chondrites cannot come from the Moon. Questions of this kind can be answered only by the much more extensive studies of the Moon that are being planned by the National Aeronautics and Space Administration.

REFERENCES

Abelson, P. H. (1956) *Sci. Amer. 195,* 83.
Anders, E. (1963) *Origin of the Solar System,* Academic Press, New York.
Anders, E., and Fitch, F. W. (1962) *Science 138,* 1392.
Berthelot, M. (1868) *Compt. rend. 67,* 849.
Berzelius, J. J. (1834) *Ann. Phys. Chem. 33,* 113.
Briggs, M. H. (1961) *Nature 191,* 1137.
Calvin, M. (1961) *Chem. Eng. News 39,* 21, 96.
Cloez, S. (1864) *Compt. rend. 59,* 37.
DuFresne, E., and Anders, E. (1962) *Geochim. Cosmochim. Acta 26,* 1085.
Hamilton, P. B. (1964) Unpublished data.
Hayatsu, R. (1964*a*) Preprint.
Hayatsu, R. (1964*b*) *Science 146,* 1291.
Hodgson, G. W., and Baker, B. L. (1964) *Nature 202,* 125.
Kaplan, I. R., Degens, E. T., and Renter, J. H. (1963) *Geochim. Cosmochim. Acta 27,* 805.
Mason, B. (1962) *Meteorites,* John Wiley & Sons, New York.
Mueller, G. (1953) *Geochim. Cosmochim. Acta 4,* 1.
Nagy, B., Claus, G., and Hennessy, D. J. (1962) *Nature 193,* 1129.
Nagy, B., and Bitz, M. C. (1963) *Arch. Biochem. Biophys. 101,* 240.
Nagy, B., Fredriksson, K., Urey, H. C., Claus, G., Andersen, C. A., and Percy, J. (1963) *Nature 198,* 121.

Nagy, B., Meinschein, W. G., and Hennessy, D. J. (1961) *Ann. N. Y. Acad. Sci.* *93*, 25.

Nagy, B., Murphy, M. T. J., Modzeleski, V. E., Rouser, G., Claus, G., Hennessy, D. J., Colombo, U., and Gazzarrini, F. (1964) *Nature 202*, 228.

Oró, J. (1963) *Nature 197*, 756.

Oró, J. (1965) Private communication.

Staplin, F. L. (1962) *Micropaleontol. 8*, 343.

Timofejew, B. W. (1963) *Grana. Polynol. 4*, 92.

Urey, H. C. (1962) *Nature 193*, 1119.

Vallentine, J. R. (1965) In press.

Wiïk, H. B. (1956) *Geochim. Cosmochim. Acta 9*, 279.

Wöhler, M. F., and Hörnes, M. (1859) *Sitzber. Akad. Wiss. Wien, Math-Naturw. Kl. 34*, 7.

PART IV

RECOGNITION OF LIFE AND SOME
TERRESTRIAL PRECEDENTS

CHAPTER 5

SIGNS OF LIFE*
The Criterion System of Exobiology

JOSHUA LEDERBERG

INTRODUCTION

The imminence of interplanetary traffic calls for systematic criticism of the theoretical basis and operational methods of *exobiology*, the initial search for and continual investigation of the life it might encounter. Very little science is totally irrelevant to it, and the policy-maker must face a riot of potential approaches to spaceflight experiments. By every standard, this is an epochal enterprise: an event unique in the history of the solar system and of the human species, and the focus of an enormous dedication of cost and effort. It requires a new perspective in experimental policy. The broader interfaces of eso-(Earth's own) biology, by contrast, permit its fruitful growth within the context of methodologies and instruments that can lag behind broadly established needs and imaginative possibilities. A system for orderly appraisal of the problem would rationalize the partition of labor, our only means of managing a complex problem.

Mars is our prime target. Our premised information is only (1) terrestrial observation: esobiochemistry, (2) the implications of Mars being a "terrestrial planet", and (3) a very small body of definite observational data. The choice of our first experiments must take account of a wide range of theoretical possibilities not yet narrowed by the experimental process.

---

* *Nature 207*, 9-13, 1965 (reprinted by permission).

Over this broad reach, logical necessity rarely coincides with logical sufficiency. The most compelling inferences might stem from the least likely event. Our speculation will be narrowed and policy simplified by tangible information about any aspect of Mars, especially if it encompasses the variability of the planet's features in space and time.

EVOLUTIONARY STAGES AND THE DEFINITION OF "LIFE"

Fundamental to all biological theory, eso- or exo-, is the evolutionary principle. As is now commonplace, we recognize the following stages in the Earth's history:

Chemogeny (Organic Chemistry)

The production of complex organic compounds by a variety of non-replicative mechanisms—the primitive cosmic aggregation, photochemistry of insolated atmospheres, thermal and spontaneous reactions of inorganically catalyzed, previously formed reagents.

Biogeny (Biology)

The replication of a specifically ordered polymer, DNA being the terrestrial example, that specifies the sequence of its own replicas, and of the working materials, like RNA and proteins, from which cells and organisms are fashioned. Random experiments of error in replication, and natural selection of their developmental consequences, result in the panoply of terrestrial life.

Cognogeny (History)

The evolution of the mechanisms of perception, computation, symbolic expression and interpersonal communication, whereby tradition can accumulate, culture unfold.

Mars must be supposed to have had an initial history similar to Earth. To ask whether Mars has life is to ask how far its chemogeny has gone; how like and how unlike the Earth's; has its evolution passed through the biogenic (ordered macromolecular) stage? Then through the cognogenic?

In evaluating a complex set of possibilities it is helpful to find classifying parameters that can be scanned systematically, if sometimes only implicitly, to generate a probability space. In this case, the evolutionary principle furnishes the parameter: chemical complexity.

The initial planetogeny and the consequent differences in physical and chemical environment determine the possible points of departure of the evolutionary processes. On these grounds, Jupiter must have special interest for comparative cosmochemistry, but it is still much less accessible to close investigation, and we have even less of a basis to predicate a homologous chemogeny there than we do for Mars. Insofar as Mars does retain some environmental analogies to Earth we might at least predicate, for one branch of our analysis, that any Martian life is based on chemical linkages, predominantly —C—C—, —C—O—, and —O—P—, that are barely stable in aqueous medium. We leave to hypothesis the extent to which the construction from these and other radicals emulate terrestrial biochemistry at each level of complexity.

The cosmic abundance of these elements is relatively high and there is every reason to believe that Mars is at least as richly endowed with them as is the Earth. If the initial budget of carbon has not, like that of the Earth's crust, been completely requisitioned by life, then in what form will we find it?

Chemogeny generates a vast mixture of products through the level of random macromolecules. Mars must have nurtured such chemistry, whether or not it had progressed to biogeny. A negative assay for organic materials would preclude biology, but could we believe such a result? It would properly be blamed on deficiencies in the particular sample. The positive assay, if it told something of the concentration and composition of organic molecules, would add to our understanding of Mars' development, and would contribute to our judgment of the life-detection problem. But it would not answer it. On the other hand, once life has appeared on a planet, it would dominate its organic chemistry—most carbon compounds would be witnesses of biogenic (or cognogenic) specificity. The cataloguing of organic molecules is a description of the consequences of evolution and must make up a large part of our effort.

THE CHEMICAL SCAN

To promise in actuality a complete scan of hypotheses of molecular complexity would be pretentious and witless; that a computer can now be programmed to visualize all the possibilities, notwithstanding. However, the fantasy of such a scan is a constructive exercise in evaluation of evidence for life. For each chemical species the imagination of the specialist might be challenged to ask (a) is there any information concerning the existence of this item relevant to scientific inference in exobiology; (b) what are my prior expectations on the distribution of this species, with and without life; (c) what other data could contribute; (d) how would the observation be interpreted from a terrestrial foray; (e) what special methods are available or could be devised to detect the species?

We might nurture a hope of turning up a special treasure, a rare example of a molecule that would reveal something about the evolution of the planet, and help narrow our choices among the confusing array of possible targets. In practice this advantage does not materialize so easily, for the hope is false. Not that *no* chemical species is potentially informative; paradoxically, *every* one is.

Consider hydrogen. In terms of the simple Venn diagram, Figure 1, most expected observations would fall in the region (B·C), that is, would be consistent with biogeny but not imply it. However, the sensible absence of hydrogen from Mars' surface would fall in region (— B·C), that is, virtually preclude life. But if we could produce no plausible physical model for the disappearance of hydrogen, we would have to reconsider the region (I· — C), that is, ask whether the anomaly implies a biogenic or cognogenic sequestration of the element. On the other hand, certain microscopic distributions of hydrogen are hard to reconcile with any chemogenic model, and point to the region (B· — C), i.e., an inference in favor of biogeny. This verges on morphology, but can still be formulated as molecular statistics.

On another tack, suppose a specimen consisted of pure protium, ^{1}H, to the exclusion of deuterium, ^{2}H. The price of pure protium on the terrestrial market hints at the obstacles to a chemogenic model. Apart from cognogenic activity, if a biogenic system were exquisitely sensitive to deuterium-toxicity it might evolve a discrimination against it.

The arguments have been labored, but are quite typical of those that discovery of any other species would arouse.

ENTROPY OR UNLIKELIHOOD?

Given the evolutionary continuity of life and our understanding of the organism as a chemical machine, there can be no absolutely distinctive signature of life. Some conjunctions—like a planetary depot of protium— would be so unaccountable to our present model of chemical behavior that we would feel obligated to postulate the operation of a goal-directed system (biogeny or cognogeny) rather than accept the improbability of such a conjunction occurring by chance. This choice plainly depends on our freedom of choice of models. For example, our present knowledge of chemogeny permits a wide latitude of hypotheses as to the range of molecular species that atmospheric photochemistry might generate. Further developments in our knowledge of chemogeny or of the available chemical

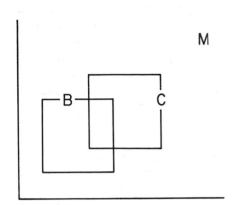

Figure 1.
Contingency Space. The universe of possible observations I includes the overlapping domains B and C, the predictions of biogeny and chemogeny respectively. The remainder is M, contradictions of these models, and possible consequences of cognogeny. Should this also be bounded?

and physical resources of Mars might confer useful constraints on the data that might now be "explained away" as chemogeny, and thus cannot yet make a crucial contribution to our search.

From terrestrial experience we judge that the occurrence of any of a number of compounds in high purity is a sign of life. Such deposits at a macroscopic level tend to signify cognogeny—a smelter, a chemical laboratory, a communications cable, rather than biogeny—organic structure usually being built of microscopically defined components. Negentropy is a necessary but not sufficient sign of life. However, it can help filter out the most promising situations. Then only the details of experience or confident use of available theory can decide whether the eddy has a chemical-kinetic explanation or a bio- or cognogenic one. Lacking our experience, a Martian visitor might credit diamantine carbon to some mysterious biogenic function, inhibited by Y chromosomes; if he were cleverer, to the General Electric Company. He would need very special knowledge of the Earth to predict that diamonds would be found in the ground (and even more to understand why men dig them up, only so that women will wear them).

Kinetic instability in the context of local chemical and physical conditions is another clue. For example, cover of photosensitive pigments (witness terrestrial chlorophyll) requires special attention to the magnitude of plausible synthetic processes, atmospheric-chemical versus biogenic, by which their steady-state concentration could be maintained. Analogous reasoning would apply to compounds that are thermolabile in relation to the ambient temperature, or chemically unstable species that should reach equilibrium with coexistent oxidants. Do we see a forest *fire?* Then we must think of the efficient system of photosynthesis that will restore the steady state vegetation. Top-heavy structures, that high altitude reconnaissance could perceive even without resolving single trees, houses or bipeds, likewise tell of kinematic instability, and in turn, some process to raise again what must some time fall. But geophysics competes with biophysics, and we must discriminate life from vulcanism and orogeny.

In sum, *unlikelihood* in terms of the chemogenic model gives weight to any finding as a datum for exobiology. It should be possible to express chemogenic likelihood quantitatively, and it is essential to do so if a datum is to be given a measured value in any decision-making program. The resolution of the measurement need not be very high to make it still very useful in comparing disparate approaches.

In more general terms, biota have a high density of internal *information:* the root of our conceptual distinction between matter and life is the rich story that life can tell about itself, a plot whose details we can hardly deduce from our simple knowledge of the initial conditions. But there must be a plot, that is, the information must have some interesting pattern, or we would not distinguish a cell from the dislocations in a snowflake.

OPTICAL ACTIVITY

Many molecular species can contribute in an important way to our appreciation of life. *A priori,* we have a very limited basis to predict which species will be most cogent. We should of course give high, but not exclusive, priority to terrestrial prototypes like amino acids and nucleotides. Fortunately, there is a generic classification of compounds that is relatively independent of detail of structure, yet should pervade a biogenic chemistry. This is optical activity.

The argument for the logical necessity of net optical activity has nothing to do with optical rotation. It depends on the crucial role of the informational macromolecule in a definition of life. When tetravalent carbon is incorporated into macromolecular structure, each carbon stands a reasonable risk of being an asymmetric center, of having a distinctive substituent on each of its four valences. Such an atom is subject to stereo-(optical) isomerism, and its orientation, D- or L-, must be specified if the macromolecule is to be fully ordered, or more concretely, if it is to have a well-defined three-dimensional shape. Conversely, biogenic macromolecules, having ordered asymmetric centers, have the necessary information to discriminate among the isomers of monomeric substrates. On Earth, where biogeny has dominated the statistics of organic molecules, we find that the ratio of D- to L-glucose residues is at least $10^{15}:1$.

Logical sufficiency can also be argued. Chemical enantiomorphs should be generated in equal proportions except under the influence of a catalytic system that is already asymmetrically organized. The global organization of a planet into one catalytic system of particular orientation is a catastrophe of a magnitude unique to biogeny. Spontaneous resolution might occur locally. Hence this criterion has its greatest weight when applied to a species that flows through the planetary circulation. A paragon would be labile molecules condensed from the atmosphere: optically active smog.

Within the biogenic system, both enantiomorphs of a metabolite might be generated, but this would be in precisely equal amounts with no greater likelihood than any two species designated at random. Chemogeny and sterically ordered biogeny thus give sharply contrasted expectations on these statistics; and biogenic chemistry can hardly avoid becoming sterically ordered.

These lines of inference do not account for such parochialisms as the undeviating series of L-isomers of amino acids in esobiologic proteins. For example, D-alanine would be at least as interesting as L-valine in expanding the homologs of glycine. But for that matter, why is α-amino butyric acid passed over? We may know better when the rules of polypeptide conformation are better known; more likely, from the details of evolution of amino acid anabolism and problems of discrimination among analogs. It is precisely at this level that the local biological theory fails, and thereby points to the crucial issues of a cosmic biology.

In view of the theoretical generality and historical tradition of the Pasteurian principle, it is paradoxical that the direct measurement of optical activity is weak by comparison to other instrumental approaches. However, the basic criterion is not optical rotation, but molecular statistics. Enantiomorphs can be assayed with optically active reagents to give resolvable diastereo-isomers, and exploit the most sensitive methods known to chemistry.

MACROMOLECULES

Informational macromolecules define the boundary of chemogeny and biogeny, of chemistry and life. Their description on another planet is the fundamental challenge of exobiology. Replication of macromolecules (genes) and the inevitability of random error (mutation) opens the door to natural selection and the evolution of more and more complex forms of life. A random polynucleotide is not life; routes to its photochemicosynthesis from simple gases and inorganic phosphate are in sight. Can we deduce the replication of a polynucleotide by any means short of the most recent achievements of direct observation and *in vitro* enzymology? Historically, we could deduce the informationality of macromolecules just from compositional data. When the same sequence occurs in many molecules—as in a sample of crystalline hemoglobin—we have to invoke an informational process to program and implement the synthesis of the protein. In fact, only recently and rarely could we gain complete specifications of an actual sequence. This is usually inferred from fragmentary analyses of a fraction found to be monodisperse on a few measures and then assumed to be sequentially homogeneous.

The sequence need not be the gene itself. Macromolecular sequencing is also manifest in gene products, RNA and proteins. It is important that the sequence imply ordering from a template that selects from an abundance of kinetically equivalent choices, not merely a pattern inherent in the chemistry of the monomer, as in crystallization.

Molecular esobiology faces the same methodological problems. This challenge gives us the groundwork for exobiology and assures that any instrumental advances will have redoubled utility. But it is a chastening note that biochemistry has barely reached the point of affirming that antibody gamma globulin has an informational sequence or is specified by a polynucleotide. That this abundant and medically important molecule can still be so controversial must evoke some humility in our postulations and experimental efforts concerning macromolecules on another planet.

NOTES ON HOW WE DETECT INFORMATIONAL MACROMOLECULES

Compositional Analysis

Does the sample contain macromolecules?
What is their composition?
Is there any evidence of informational ordering?

Esobiology is firmly founded on the isolation of macromolecular species and their purification before attempts at analysis. Some of the most successful methods are empirical recipes of extraction and precipitation.

More rational techniques include diffusional properties of large molecules, free diffusion, sedimentation, dialysis, molecular sieves and electrophoresis; in principle also, vapor phase diffusion (to remove monomers), molecular distillation, gas chromatography and mass spectrometry. Solution chromatographic methods may also rely on the coincidence of functional groups on one molecule, e.g., a polyelectrolyte.

Similar principles underlie non-separative methods of detection which have not been extensively developed to date. Rotational relaxation times can be measured by flow or electric birefringence, or the analogous polarization of fluorescence. Polyfunctionality is tested by intermolecular interactions of adsorbed dyes (e.g. optical shifts in acridine orange on DNA) or the monomeric units with one another in special cases (hypochromicity of DNA, diagnosable upon heat-denaturation). More direct chemical tests for polyfunctionality also suggest themselves.

The previous methods, insofar as they lack perfect generality, may give only a clue as to the *composition* of the macromolecule, as well as its molecular size. At the other extreme, we would seek the complete primary structure to emulate the recent *tours de force* of chemical technique. Reasonable inferences might be drawn from less complete evidence of structural individuality, hard to evaluate in advance: homogeneity in molecular weight or endgroup analysis, crystallinity, or sharp fractionation by any other procedure. A sharp x-ray diagram of a heteropolymer sample could imply its individuality long before it had yielded to full analysis.

Other partial measures of great utility include the scission of the polymer by specific reagents, especially enzymes, to give a pattern of characteristic fragments (the polypeptide "fingerprint").

The underlying generalization is "molecular speciation". Chemogenic synthesis of macromolecules should generate a continuum of nearly equiprobable forms. Biogeny chooses a few of these and generates a sharply discontinuous polydiscrete spectrum, i.e., it *speciates*. Speciation can be discerned by many measures, for example, the distribution of molecular weight. Thus a sample under analysis by a sophisticated instrument might reveal a sac of haem-polypeptide, containing about a billion atoms of iron. Virtually all of the iron-polypeptide consists of a single species, i.e., almost all of the molecules have 2936 carbon atoms, no more, no less. After removal of iron and porphyrin, equal numbers of subunits containing just C_{685} and C_{715} are assayed. It would be hard to escape an allusion to life after a single encounter with the red blood cell that has just been described.

FUNCTIONAL ANALYSIS

The adaptive values, the uses that biogeny has discovered for some species of macromolecules, reveal shortcuts to their singularity. These functions are all reducible to a structural specification: the stereo-specificity of the polymer in reacting with other molecules.

Function	Complex with	Example
Auto-replication	Incipient polymer (same species) and polymer-building monomer	DNA:DNA $+$ deoxynucleoside triphosphates
Hetero-replication	Incipient polymer (different species) and polymer-building monomer	DNA:RNA $+$ nucleoside triphosphates

Function	Complex with	Example
Morphogenesis Fibers, Membranes, Vesicles	Formed polymer, similar species	Collagen: collagen subunits
Enzyme	Substrate—catalytic effect Cofactors—to form holoenzyme Analogues—complexes inactive, *qua* enzyme	
Neutralizing	Any	Antibody: antigen, i.e. any chemical species foreign to the reacting organisms
Transport	Hormones, toxins, nutrients	Serum albumin: hormones, toxins Permeases: nutrients and metabolites for transport in and out of cells

In this list, the enzymatic functions are particularly promising in the light of their specificity and amplifying capability. Many enzymes have turnover numbers of 10^4 substrate molecules per second per enzyme molecule. If suitable precursors (nutrients) can be defined, integrated enzyme sequences of metabolic systems like respiration or photosynthesis, extend the versatility of this approach.

The simpler the level, the more likely are we to find a metabolic analog on Mars, for example, the assimilation of elementary nutrients, carbon, nitrogen, oxygen, sulfur, or phosphorus, into organic molecules. The next more complex molecules, water, carbon dioxide, oxygen and ammonia are the most pervasive metabolites of terrestrial life, and the choice among them for searching for evidence of their conversion into other compounds will depend mainly on instrumental considerations. In general, the more complex the metabolite being tested, the less our prior expectation that it was part of an extraterrestrial biogenic system. However, the complete system offers the largest amplification—a single bacterium could grow and multiply into tonnage masses in a few days, but might make the most exacting demands of the environment.

MORPHOLOGY

Biogeny rapidly elaborates higher forms of organization: cells, tissues, organisms, populations, which might be recognizable according to their own forms and to their rectifications of the environment. However, what systematic rules distinguish biological forms in general? Some forms are recognizable, e.g., a friend's face, and recognition then contains many bits of useful information. Compound vesicles, apparent cells, are most inescapable in morphogenesis; their absence would at least set an upper limit to the stage of biogeny. Their presence would be extremely provocative, but properly would raise many skepticisms of chemogenic artifact. Nevertheless, esobiology has so many roots in morphology that we could hardly ignore the insights that our historic practice of it would offer. Any recognizable forms would provoke tangible, and hence useful, working hypotheses of the Martian system.

Some aspects of morphology can be systematized. For an example which might illustrate speciation, ultrastructural spacings in the range of 20 to 500 Å could be detected by powerful optical (electron microscope, x-ray diffraction) as well as separative techniques. Approaches so cogent to esobial ultrastructure must play an important part in exobiology. Unfortunately, we have little empirical basis to prejudge the morphological detail that might be exhibited by an infra-biogenic planet, since so much of the chemical diversity of Earth has been preempted by life.

As is well known, fivefold symmetries are anathematic in crystallography. Hence, regular pentagonal and dodecahedral forms might occur as elementary units, e.g., cyclopentane or phosphorus pentachloride, but no simple law of crystal growth could account for their occurrence in diverse sizes. A glen of periwinkles has a deductively simple signature of life.

SIGNALS

So far we have tacitly assumed that whether or not Mars has achieved biogeny, it has not passed to cognogeny. Reaction to the once notorious Schiaparellian *canali* may account for a position that has no rigorous basis. True, we have had no scientifically admissable sign of intelligent activity on or communication from that planet. However, we can only fancy whether an exotic culture would have either the means or the motive to effect recognizable communication. We can generalize that the works of cognogeny would constitute the most startling unlikelihoods, exceptions to biogeny and chemogeny alike.

It is no trivial exercise to speculate how we could most compactly summarize our scientific culture. For example, a description of DNA and our amino acids could portray the convergence of physical and chemical ideas in biology, and some of the least predictable aspects of esobiogeny. If we could but do it, a detail of the inter-neuronal synapse and the cytoarchitecture of the cerebral cortex would go even farther. How much of our cognogeny would then be deducible from these facts and our awareness of them?

Purposeful emissions cost enough more than mere listening that we do not undertake them ourselves, but we have made casual efforts to hear them. Further, we might hope to eavesdrop on the internal communications of another planet, perhaps more likely far beyond the solar system. Among other difficulties, efficient information is, by definition, indistinguishable from noise to the unbriefed eavesdropper.

While a rigorous answer to any notions of Martian intelligence is hard, a realistic policy is not. Cognogeny would reveal itself in untold ways, and at least for Mars, we have no better recourse than to keep eyes, ears and noses alert for any signs of it, as we make progressively closer approaches to the planet.

INSTRUMENTATION

The rational classification of existing instruments, or those proposed for analytical purposes is a task as difficult as it is urgent. The real aim, a classification of *possible* instruments, requires a total knowledge of physics, and some system for classifying this information that will help us to understand the relationships among existing instruments and suggest new ones. A proposed scan parameter is the energy level of the transition by which the molecule is recognized. Further parameters include whether photons are introduced or emitted, whether chemical reagents are employed, including auto-reactions, whether the displacement or state of the analysand or of the probe is diagnostic, and for radiation probes, the role of power, polarization, phase, wavelength, or flux vector of the probe. The first step in a detailed rationalization is to determine whether any more dimensions are needed for our matrix of possible configurations.

Radiation probes are usually limited, either in selectivity (cf., absorptiometery), or sensitivity (cf., nuclear magnetic resource), but they have special value in conjunction with chemical reagents. Absorption (power loss) measurements have dominated instrumental analysis. Conventional optical methods rarely stabilize or measure input power to less than one part per thousand, with corresponding limitations on detectivity. For example, optical molar absorptivity rarely exceeds 10^5 so that 10^{-8} molar solutions (6×10^{12} molecules in a 1 cm^3 cell) would give the lowest useful signal under the most favorable conditions. By contrast, fluorimetric measurement (which can exploit shifts in wavelength, flux vector, polarization and phase) can easily measure 10^8 molecules and can be extended at least to 10^4. The delicacy of excitation methods (which could also include chemical, nucleonic and thermal excitation) stems from the measurement of a single signal merely against a detector noise background, as compared to the much larger power fluctuations of practical probes.

Optical activity is also usually measured as a power loss (attenuation of polarized light by a crossed analyzer): the molar rotations are relatively small, present detectivity being about 10^{15} molecules. If some method of transforming optical rotation to an excited signal were developed, it would enormously enhance the power of this technique.

The most sensitive approaches to analysis are two-stage mechanisms: the *selective displacement* of the analysand, then a *sensitive detection*. In principle, such methods might detect a single molecule, as in mass spectrometry: selective m/e displacement followed by the sensitive detection of an ion that can be accelerated to arbitrary energy. The potential information content of a mass spectrum is especially high since the theoretically measurable mass of a single molecule is defined to a resolution far better than 10^{-6}, and is independent of the variety of energetic states, which broaden other physical features. Existing instruments still lag behind theoretical limits of mass resolution, yet have already demonstrated their power in organic analysis. Further, the mass datum at high resolution for an intact molecular ion is deductively reducible to a molecular composition, unlike the inferential data given by most other spectroscopic techniques, and the statistics of the fragments also gives detailed insight into the complete structure of the molecule. From these considerations the combination of a mass spectrometer with a simple, rugged, separative device, like the gas chromatograph, promises to be the most powerful component of analytical systems for biochemistry. However, a science of metrology, the orderly study of methods of measurement, remains to be developed. We can have little confidence that the last word has been said on this issue.

SOME PRIVATE THOUGHTS ON EXOBIOLOGICAL STRATEGY

The multitude of possible means and detailed ends in exobiology leaves little hope that a brilliant flash will illuminate the whole picture as a happy substitute for the diverse paths of esobiology. Nor should there be any discouragement of the variety of talents and insights that would be needed, in any case, for the full development of the subject. The overriding problem in planning is, of course, how little we actually know about surface detail and atmospheric composition of Mars. We are also bedeviled by the uncertain hazards, but immense stakes, to either planet of an intemperate rupture of the interplanetary barrier. Earth-based telescopes can, to be sure, add significantly to our present appreciation of Mars, and hence of the hazards of landing. But the next significant step would be a Mars-orbiting observatory, keeping the planet under a constant synoptic scrutiny from a safe distance. close enough to measure significant surface detail, and large enough to maintain the most sophisticated instrumentation, telemetry to Earth, and perhaps even some Earth-based regulation of its surveillance schedule and precautions *against* accidental impact landing. Such an approach to Mars would also open the way to political agreements to unify terrestrial strategy and can allow constructive cooperations like the IGY of recent history. While it is essential to mount vigorous instrumental development efforts to assure that a landing can ever be achieved, the detailed specifications of experiments should take full advantage of the most current planetological information. This criterion lends further weight to the strategy of designing a general purpose laboratory for planetary investigation, in which many investigators can participate, and which has the flexibility to be readily reprogrammed in the light of new data. Even for such an orbital mission, and far more for any calculated landing, we would need considerable solidification of our art in sanitary engineering to insure the harmlessness of the probe. If only because the Earth's atmosphere is also contaminated, terminal decontamination implies some extraterrestrial operations on the spacecraft. Where these can best be done at different stages of the program must be studied as an engineering question. As one suggestion, however, a lunar base may ultimately find an important justification as a staging point, quarantine station and isolation laboratory for interplanetary traffic.

Several versions of this paper have been presented since October, 1961 to discussion groups advisory to the National Aeronautics and Space Administration, and I am indebted to a great many colleagues for their constructive criticism on many points.

CHAPTER 6

OPTICAL ASYMMETRY

LUBERT STRYER

What significance would we attribute to a finding of net optical activity on Mars? Suppose that several dozen samples taken from different parts of the planet were consistently to show a thousandfold preponderance of the right-handed form of a particular chemical species. A consideration of the possible sources of net optical asymmetry leads to the conclusion that such an observation would in itself be a strong criterion of life on Mars.

The invariant association of net optical activity and terrestrial life was first noted by Pasteur, "Artificial products have no molecular dissymmetry . . . I could not point out the existence of any more profound distinction between the products formed under the influence of life, and all others." [*Pasteur,* 1860]. A century of biochemistry has demonstrated that this distinction between L and D isomers is nearly always observed in biochemical processes. Sometimes, both enantiomers are utilized, but in that event they appear in different structures. The enzymes of bacteria contain only the L-amino acids, while both isomers are found in the cell walls. With glucose, only the D-form is found in nature. The molecular basis of this selectivity resides in the fact that the mirror image forms lose their equivalence upon interacting with a second optically active molecule; the resulting diastereoisomers in general have different properties. The relationship of optical activity to the origin of life has been discussed by numerous authors [*Wald,* 1957; *Fox et al.,* 1956; *Horowitz and Miller,* 1962; *Oparin,* 1957; *Ulbricht,* 1962; *Wheland,* 1953].

It is not merely our earth-bound experience that gives stress to optical activity as a criterion of life. We infer its significance from a more general consideration of the entropy of living systems. In a system in which left is equivalent to right, the existence of optical activity can be due only to fluctuations. We are, of course, interested in detecting the most extreme fluctuation from thermodynamic equilibrium, life itself. A search for optical activity is thus a direct attempt to establish the existence of one of the most general characteristics of life processes, their fluctuations, without any prior notion about the type of chemistry utilized by that particular form of life.

Can there be net optical activity without life? A thorough consideration of this question is indispensable in deciding the priority and emphasis to be given to optical activity in a search for extraterrestrial life. Three hypotheses for the acquisition of net dissymmetry have been cited in the literature. The first of these involves the use of circularly polarized light to effect a photochemical change [Kuhn and Braun 1929]. Net optical activity may arise through the preferential decomposition or synthesis of one of the enantiomers, as has been experimentally demonstrated. A second possibility is the dissymmetric action of an optically active catalyst, such as an L-crystal of quartz. For example, a racemic mixture of 2-butanol was selectively dehydrated at high temperature on a catalyst consisting of a metal deposited on a quartz crystal [Schwab et al., 1934]. A third mechanism, the spontaneous development of dissymmetry from optically inactive starting materials without the apparent participation of dissymmetric substances or forces has been reported. For instance, a solution of methylethylallylphenyl ammonium iodide in a test tube was found to have optically active crystals and an optically inactive mother liquor after the lapse of a few months [Havinga, 1954].

It must be stressed that each of these hypotheses can, at most, lead only to local dissymmetry, and not to the acquisition of net optical activity of the same handedness in many samples taken from sites geographically far apart. A fortuitous excess of left circularly polarized light may produce an excess of, say, the L-isomer. But it is equally likely that at some other site, an excess of right circularly polarized light shines, and in that environment the D-isomer will correspondingly predominate. The same considerations apply to optically active catalysts such as quartz. Here and there we may find an excess of one of the crystalline forms. But the preponderance is only local.

Moreover, these fluctuations will tend to disappear with the passage of time. Optical purity is bound to deteriorate, since the free energy of racemization is negative. Kuhn has derived an expression for the persistence time of optical purity that is produced by means of an optically active catalyst from inactive starting material [*Kuhn*, 1958]. Take a first-order reaction with a $\Delta F°$ of 3 kcal/mole, in which the synthesis occurs in 10 minutes, and where the products are 99.95 per cent L- and 0.05 per cent D-isomer. After 3 months, the concentration of the D-antipode will have increased to five percent. In time, the concentration of the D- will approach that of the L-antipode unless the reaction products are removed from the catalyst, either spatially or by subsequent chemical reactions. This is, of course, the manner in which a high degree of optical purity is assured in biological organisms. In the absence of life, such a unidirectional flow of optically active species is less likely. Thus the long-term persistence of optical activity generated via fluctuations is improbable in systems which are allowed to approach thermodynamic equilibrium. For this reason, greater significance should be attributed to a finding of net optical activity in atmospheric samples in contrast to samples derived from solid material that has had less opportunity to attain thermodynamic equilibrium.

In this discussion, the equivalence of left and right has been implicit. However, the non-conservation of parity vitiates this assumption, at least for weak interactions. Thus, when β-decay occurs, as in $^{60}Co \rightarrow ^{60}Ni + e^- + \nu$, the emerging electrons have excess left circular polarization [*Goldhaber et al.*, 1957]. This has raised the question whether there is a link between this dissymmetry of fundamental particles and the structural dissymmetry of molecules [*Ulbricht*, 1959]. Is it possible that optical activity arises through the action of the excess left circularly polarized electrons produced in all β-decays? The few experimental attempts to carry out asymmetric syntheses with circularly polarized electrons have yielded negative results [*Ulbricht*, 1959]. Unless it is shown that this intrinsic dissymmetry at the level of weak interactions can be imprinted on covalent chemistry, we are justified in retaining the notion that left and right are equivalent at our level of concern.

In summary, we conclude that net optical activity in the absence of life is highly improbable, and so a positive finding of net optical activity, defined previously, would be highly suggestive of the existence of life.

In contrast, a negative finding would be more difficult to interpret. It is conceivable that net optical activity might go undetected, due either to inadequacies of the sampling and fractionation procedures, or to limitations of instrumental sensitivity. These potential difficulties are not intrinsic to the use of optical activity as a criterion of the existence of life. Rather, they are imperfections that reflect the present state of experimental methods, and which can, and in fact must, be overcome in an appropriate development program for extraterrestrial explorations.

Let us assume that a finding of the absence of net optical activity can be taken with confidence at its full face value. The more subtle question then arises, namely, can there be life without optical activity? Our terrestrial experience strongly argues against this conjecture. Life as we know it rests on a high degree of steric selectivity. A biochemistry of racemic mixtures is entirely inconsistent with steric selectivity, since the distinction between an L- and a D-antipode in its interaction with an optically active molecule is so gross that it cannot be ignored. Alternatively, an absence of net optical activity might be due to a total lack of optical stereoisomerism, *per se,* rather than to the cancelling of optical activity by equal amounts of the antipodes. However, a biochemistry of this sort would, at best, be a primitive one. Obviously, a severe restriction would be placed on a carbon-based biochemistry that would be forced to exclude compounds with asymmetric centers or other sources of dissymmetry.

These considerations, which argue against the likelihood of life without optical activity, are suggestive but not compelling. We do not know enough about the evolution of terrestrial life to rule out the possibility that a primitive stage of racemic life once existed here. In fact, we are quite uncertain whether net optical activity preceded the onset of life on Earth, or closely paralleled its emergence, or was the consequence of natural selection by established, though primitive, organisms. In summary, we conclude that the absence of net optical activity virtually precludes the possibility of life possessing a degree of complexity akin to ours. The existence of primitive forms of life without optical activity is a matter of conjecture, but the possibility cannot be excluded on the basis of optical rotatory measurements.

At present, optical activity is a relatively insensitive measure of the predominance of one of the antipodes of a particular molecular species. Under the most favorable conditions, as little as 1 μg could be detected, as for example hexahelicene [*Moscowitz,* 1961] and d-urobilin [*Gray et al.,* 1959]. In general, the sensitivity is considerably less. Since the information gained from rotatory measurements can be highly significant, it is important that the method be developed as fully as possible. Two approaches should be pursued: (a) enhancing the physical sensitivity of the detecting apparatus; (b) enhancing the magnitude of the rotation itself through chemical means. We shall consider the second of these in the discussion which follows.

It is well known that the molar rotation of an optically active species can be increased through the formation of an appropriate derivative. Such a derivative may be either a covalent compound or a molecular complex [*Lowry,* 1935]. For example, the molar rotation of L-proline at 589 mμ is about —100°, while that of the dinitrophenyl derivative is nearly —2000°. A 20-fold enhancement of this kind is by no means unusual. However, at best, it will allow for the detection of not less than 1 μg of the optically active species.

If the sensitivity is to be enhanced by several orders of magnitude, then it is evident that the optically active molecule must act as a stereo-specific catalyst for a readily detectable process. For instance, the optically inactive dye pseudoisocyanine polymerizes under certain conditions to form high molecular weight helical micelles [*Rich and Kasha*, 1964]. Ordinarily, an equal number of right and left handed pseudoisocyanine helices are found. However, an optically active molecule may form a complex with pseudoisocyanine, and consequently one of the pseudoisocyanine helices may become favored. In fact, this has been observed in the case of the helical poly-L-glutamic acid:pseudoisocyanine complexes [*Stryer and Blout*, 1961]. A virtually catalytic amount of poly-L-glutamic acid leads to a gross excess of one of the screw-senses of the pseudoisocyanine helix, which has an exceptionally large optical rotatory power. In general, we can expect that a single optically active molecule will induce optical activity out of proportion to its molar concentration in a large number of molecules that were previously inactive or racemic.

Another chemical amplification of optical stereoisomerism is achieved when a supersaturated solution of a racemic mixture is seeded with a microcrystal of one of the antipodes. Preferential crystallization of that antipode has been shown to occur, thus leaving a solution that is optically active on account of the relative excess of the other antipode remaining in solution [*Harada and Fox*, 1962; *Greenstein*, 1954].

If an optically active compound can serve to initiate a covalent polymerization, an additional chemical amplification technique may prove feasible. The structure of the polymer may, in part, depend upon the stereochemistry of the initiator. For example, the conformation of poly-γ-benzyl-L-glutamate has been shown to be dependent to a certain extent upon whether the initiator is a short chain L- or D-glutamate peptide; for the L-initiator, a right handed α-helix is produced, while for the D-initiator, it is left handed [*Doty and Lundberg*, 1956]. In this particular case, the influence of the initiator persists over relatively few residues. In principle, however, the effect might extend over hundreds of residues if the free energies of the alternative structures that are produced by polymerization in the absence of an optically active influence do not differ too greatly.

Finally, we note that optical activity is merely one of a number of expressions of an excess of left or right handedness, which is the phenomenon of fundamental interest to us. Other physical manifestations of a preferred molecular screw-sense, such as circularly polarized scattering, fluorescence and dichroism, may prove to be more sensitive and should be explored.

REFERENCES

Doty, P. and Lundberg, R. D. (1956), Configurational and Stereochemical Effects in the Amine-initiated Polymerization of N-carboxyanhydrides. *J. Am. Chem. Soc. 78*, 4810.

Fox, S. W., Johnson, J. E., and Vegotsky, A. (1956), On Biochemical Origins and Optical Activity. *Science 124*, 923.

Goldhaber, M., Grodzins, L., and Sunyar, A. W. (1957), Evidence for Circular Polarization of Bremsstrahlung Produced by β-rays. *Phys. Rev. 106*, 826.

Gray, C. H., Jones, P. W., Klyne, W., and Nicholson, D. C. (1959), *Nature 184*, 41.

Greenstein, J. P. (1954), *Advances in Protein Chem. 9*, 129.

Harada, K. and Fox, S. W. (1962), A Total Resolution of Aspartic Acid Copper Complex by Inoculation. *Nature 194*, 768.

Havinga, E. (1954), Spontaneous Formation of Optically Active Substances. *Biochim. Biophys. Acta 13*, 171.

Horowitz, N. H. and Miller, S. L. (1962), Current Theories on the Origin of Life. *Fortschr. Chem. Org. Naturst. 20*, 423.

Kuhn, W. and Braun, E. (1929), Photochemische Erzeugung Optischaktiver Stoffe. *Naturwiss. 17*, 227.

Kuhn, W. (1958), Possible Relation Between Optical Activity and Aging. *Adv. Enzymol. 20*, 1.

Lowry, T. M. (1935), *Optical Rotatory Power*, Longmans, Green and Co., Ltd., London.

Moscowitz, A. (1961), Some Applications of the Kronig-Kramers Theorem to Optical Activity. *Tetrahedron 13*, 48.

Oparin, A. I. (1957), *The Origin of Life on the Earth*, pp. 189-196, 3rd Edition, Oliver and Boyd, London.

Pasteur, L. (1860), *Researches on Molecular Asymmetry*, 46 pp. Alembic Club reprint #14, E. and S. Livingstone, Edinburgh.

Rich, A. and Kasha, M. (1964), Personal communication.

Schwab, G. M., Rust, F., and Rudolph, L. (1934), *Kolloid-Z. 68*, 157.

Stryer, L. and Blout, E. R. (1961), Optical Rotatory Dispersion of Dyes Bound to Macromolecules. Cationic Dyes: Polyglutamic Acid Complexes. *J. Am. Chem. Soc. 83*, 1411.

Ulbricht, T. L. V. (1959), Asymmetry: The Non-Conservation of Parity and Optical Activity. *Quart. Revs. 13*, 48.

Ulbricht, T. L. V. (1962), The Optical Asymmetry of Metabolites. In: M. Florkin and H. S. Mason, eds., *Comparative Biochemistry, 4*, Part B, pp. 1-25. Academic Press, New York.

Wald, G. (1957), The Origin of Optical Activity. *Ann. N. Y. Acad. Sci. 69*, 352.

Wheland, G. W. (1953), *Advanced Organic Chemistry*, pp. 230-250, 2nd Edition, Wiley and Sons, New York.

CHAPTER 7

THE BIOCHEMISTRY OF TERRESTRIAL SOILS

A. D. McLaren

INTRODUCTION

In testing for life or for evidence for life processes in soil one can use either nutrient media in which organisms can grow or else choose reagents that will react specifically with products characteristically produced by living entities. The former presupposes either a universal medium or a medium in which some specific, universally-dispersed soil organism will proliferate. This type of test may fail in Martian soils if an unfamiliar biochemistry prevails. With the latter approach one must distinguish between compounds similar to those found in Miller-Urey experiments and those more characteristic of life such as enzymes and nucleic acids. These are usually monodisperse with regard to molecular weight and possess non-random structures. All of these exist in nearly undetectable amounts in Earth soils, since they are nutrients for at least some of the organisms present. On the other hand, a few of the soil organic constituents, the enzymes, may be revealed by their ability to "turn over" appreciable amounts of substrate. Here we make the assumption that although the nutritional requirements of organisms in strange soils may be unknown, the enzyme constituents released to the environment by decomposed organisms are universal in general properties and characteristic of life wherever it is found.

Obviously, life forms on Mars and elsewhere may differ too much from

147

those here to be detected within this framework. However, the following discussion may suggest something concrete and accessible in the way of "life testers."

GENERAL DESCRIPTION OF SOIL BIOCHEMISTRY

Earth soils are aggregates of minerals, water, humus and microorganisms. As a kind of graveyard of microorganisms, a soil may be expected to contain almost any naturally occurring organic compound [Waksman, 1938]. The relative abundance of these extracellular compounds is far from that found in living tissues, however. Additional substances, perhaps characteristic of soil per se, are also present in abundance.

From one point of view, the microbiologist is confronted with soil as a unique medium in which organisms live, not in pure culture but in highly complex populations comprising innumerable species; these exert a variety of associative and antagonistic effects [Waksman, 1945]. There seem to be countless numbers of different "species" of bacteria, yeasts, protozoa, fungi, as well as microfauna in soil. In assaying for unique biochemical activities, certain groups of these have been found to be geared to elemental cycles such as ammonification, nitrification and nitrogen fixation. From a somewhat different point of view, Quastel [1946] adopted another conceptual scheme, namely that the soil as a whole be considered as an organ, comparable in some respects to a liver or a gland, to which may be added various nutrients, pure or complex, such as degraded plant materials, together with rain and air, and in which enzymatic reactions can occur. The products of these reactions are important as steps in elemental cycles in the percolation (movement) of iron and aluminum, as humates, and in the formation of soil crumb structure. The notion here is that the soil biochemist is more concerned with the activity of microbes in soil than with precisely what they are with respect to size, shape or other characteristics that make up taxonomic schemes.

In the form of enrichment cultures these two approaches come together. If glycine is perfused repeatedly through a sample of native soil, together with the products of microbial activity, those organisms capable of metabolizing glycine, ammonia and nitrite will increase greatly in numbers, and isolates of these, for example Nitrosomonas sp. can be more easily prepared. In this example, certain cells of the soil-organ are encouraged to multiply and to "cooperate" in the conversion of glycine to nitrate, carbon dioxide and water as principal products. Together with these reactions, however, and in the presence of carbohydrate, other soil organisms can synthesize anionic, high polymeric substances, some of which are adsorbed on the clays. A kind of a steady state exists at any interval in time, depending on the rates of addition and loss of metabolites to and from the soil.

In the following is described some of what is known about biochemical reactions in soil and the nature of soil organic matter. It is not clear how well, or poorly, this information will be useful in anticipating the biological chemistry of Martian soils, if indeed, the surface of Mars has any areas comparable to Earth soils. It may, however, lead to some guesses as to what one should look for on Mars if life as we know it has some counterpart there.

ECOLOGICAL CONDITIONS IN SOIL

First of all, let us consider the environment in which the soil microorganisms dwell. It differs rather drastically from that of a culture flask or an agar slant. There is a point to point variation in concentration of all solutes, interspersed in a matrix of clays, sand and humus which characterizes a spectrum of microenvironments. Further, at the surfaces of these particles as well as at plant roots there is a variation in molecular environment characterized by gradation in pH and redox potential [*Thimann,* 1955; *Kubiena,* 1938].

Morphologists have dissected soil into three principal "horizons": A) the upper or alluvial layer that receives litter and from which material is, or has been, leached; B) the underlying illuvial layer that is, or has been, enriched; and C) the mineral, parent material underneath A and B horizons. These horizons may be well delineated in profile or the B horizon may arbitrarily grade into the other two. Pore space occupies 30 to 45 per cent of the soil and varies in water and air content. From A to C the total numbers of microbes per gram of soil decline and the ratio of aerobes to anaerobes declines. Soils with greater humus or clay content tend to hold more water, because of hydration and the presence of capillary pore space associated with small particle size, than do soils with the larger, silt particles. In "waterlogged" soils there are practically no air spaces, and in "air dry" soils, the pore liquid water has almost disappeared, leaving only water films about the particles.

Microorganisms cannot grow in the absence of water. The lower limit of relative humidity at which growth is possible depends upon the species. Their activities may depend on the thickness of the water film; for example, *Rahn* [1913] found the optimum film thickness to be 20 to 40 μ for *Bac. mycoides,* an aerobe. However, some bacteria can be stored under dry nitrogen, without growth. *Winogradsky* [1924] determined depths to which an aerobe, *Azotobacter,* and an anaerobe, *Clostridium* could grow in wet soils: at a moisture content of 23 percent the former were limited to the extreme surface and the latter were found throughout the soil.

Recently, from a study of widely different soils, it has been found that "changeover" from aerobic to anaerobic metabolism of organic materials takes place in widely different soils at an oxygen concentration less than about 3×10^{-6} M, a very low concentration indeed [*Greenwood, 1961*]. Decomposition below this concentration in soil leads to the accumulation of fatty acids. One implication is that water-saturated crumbs of a soil that are more than about 3 mm in radius have no oxygen at their centers, and since crumbs of this size are present in most soils it means that pockets with anaerobic conditions are ubiquitous, and this provides an explanation for the universality of strict anaerobes. Oxidative processes abound in relatively warm, dry soils. On the other hand, in relatively wet soils organic matter content increases with increasing rainfall [*Jenny et al., 1948*].

Waterlogged soils, high in organic matter, tend to become acidic due to fermentation, whereas well-aerated garden soils are near neutrality, i.e., the pH is of the order of 6 to 7.5 as measured with wet pastes and a glass electrode system. At higher pH, as in calcareous soils, growing plants may show Fe or Mn deficiencies because of the insolubility of the corresponding phosphates and carbonates. The addition of sulfur results in the lowering of pH and the liberation of these cations, as will be discussed below.

Upon examining the effective pH at the surface of soil colloids, however, a new concept emerges. Wherever charged surfaces exist in contact with water, the effective pH of the surface (pH_s) will be lower than the pH in bulk (pH_b). This difference has been expressed by Hartley and Roe as $pH_s = pH_b + \delta /60$ at 25° C where δ is the electrokinetic potential of the particle [*McLaren and Babcock, 1959*]. Thus, chymotrypsin acting on a protein adsorbed on kaolin has a different pH optimum for enzyme action than is found in solution with the same substrate. The optimum pH of succinate oxidation with cells of *E. coli* adsorbed on an anion exchange resin differs from that of free cells suspended in solution, and a study of the initial velocities of oxidation of this substrate with free and adsorbed cells at $pH_b = 7$ revealed that the velocity reached a maximum at a ten times higher concentration with adsorbed cells than with free cells [*Hattori and Furusako, 1959*]. These observations show that the heterogeneity of soil as an environment for microorganisms extends from the gross particle to the molecular level.

It is recognized that in a "living" soil the elements are continuously subjected to biochemical transformation and to biological, mechanical and hydrological translocations.

SOME METABOLIC PROCESSES IN SOIL

The oxidation of ammonia or sulfur in soil has been studied with a biochemical technique of broad application. A nutrient solution is continuously perfused through a column containing about 30 grams of soil in a water saturated, aerated condition [Lees and Quastel, 1946]. The technique is splendid for characterizing nitrification in soil nitrifying organisms until a "saturation" of numbers exists and that the conversion NH_4^+ → NO_2^{--} took place largely on particulate surfaces. In another study, sulfur was added to a sample of Fresno fine sandy loam (a black alkali soil initially of pH 10.2 and a salt concentration of less than 0.2%) in the proportion of 1 g to 30 g of soil [McLaren, 1963b]. The mixture was perfused with 200 ml water and the perfusate was analyzed for hydrogen ion and sulfate ions as a function of time. After a few days of perfusion, sulphate was found in the perfusate and the pH fell from the overall reaction $1\frac{1}{2}$ O_2 + S + H_2O → H_2SO_4. The addition of Thiobacillus thiooxidans to the soil did not greatly modify the rate of the reaction, showing that related organisms existed in the field soil initially. After 20 days of perfusion the soil was washed free of sulfate and perfused again; oxidation took place at the maximum rate. Clearly, at this stage the soil was enriched with respect to sulfur oxidizers.

Sulfide and ammonia are reduction products of decompositions of some common organic compounds; both may be oxidized by certain soil microbes and a few autotrophs can use these oxidations as sole sources of energy [Freney, 1958]. In a soil perfused under aerobic conditions, and containing an indigenous population, practically all sulfur in cystine becomes sulfate and the corresponding nitrogen becomes nitrate. The acidity of the soil increases and other organisms may be inhibited. A single sulfur compound, however, may yield different products on dissimilation by different microbes. From cystine, Achromobacter cystinovorum produces only elemental sulfur.

The following pathway must be considered as a logical overall process for the soil as an organ but is not meant to pertain to any particular organism: cysteine → cystine → cystine disulfoxide → cysteine sulfinic acid → cysteic acid → sulfate [Freney, 1961b].

It must be remembered that the amount of free cysteine normally in soil is minute and one of the great difficulties of interpreting such experiments is to decide if the reactions observed are typical of the microbial population under field conditions or only when the system is jammed with substrate. An abundance of cysteine changes the redox potential of soil and may lead in other ways to an enrichment of only a small proportion of the qualitative makeup of microbes present. Nevertheless, in some areas of the world, for example New England and Australia, most of the soil sulfur is locked up in some form of organic matter, and pasture lands in this region are, at present, mainly dependent for nutrition on a release of this sulfur by mineralization. From solubility studies the organic sulfur appears to be in the form of high molecular weight fulvic acid sulfates (see Humus, below). Here, an element has been taken out of circulation by the formation of macromolecules. A similar story pertains to nitrogen.

Perhaps it is needless to say that in the organ approach to soil we have no way of deciding which reactions may be attributed to a given species. Historically, isolates of single species have been studied, but in doing so, the possible interactions, mutual inhibitions and stimulations between species are missed. This difficulty is not unique to the concept of soil as a tissue, however. A good illustration involves manganese metabolism. Bromfield and Sherman found that manganese sulfate could be oxidized with the formation of a brown deposit of manganese dioxide on agar plates if particular pairs of species were growing as colonies near each other. Two such pairs had *Corynebacterium* in common; the other organism could be either a *Flavobacterium* or a *Chromobacterium*. Obviously, the existence of associative action between microbes makes it virtually impossible to count the number of Mn^{++} oxidizing organisms in soil [*Bromfield and Sherman, 1950*]. An ascomycete, *Cladosporium*, could oxidize this ion without association.

If manganese sulfate is perfused through a neutral or slightly alkaline soil it is found that after a few days all the Mn^{++} has disappeared from the perfusate. Above 0.02 M the rate of formation of manganese dioxide falls rapidly, indicating manganese toxicity. Metabolic poisons also, including azide and iodoacetate, bring about a marked inhibition of the oxidation. Detailed observations have been summarized as follows [*Quastel et al., 1948*]:

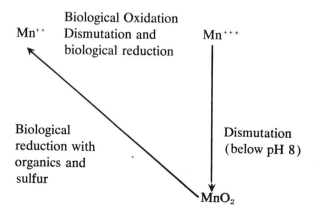

Reduction of manganese oxides in soils can be brought about with added glucose, thiols and polyphenols. These laboratory observations provide a useful explanation for the fact that applications of manganese sulfate to deficient field soils are often ineffective as MnO_2 represents an unavailable form of the element. An increase in concentration of available manganese can be brought about by the addition of reducing forms of organic matter, reduction of pH to shift the "cycle" toward Mn^{++}, inhibition of oxidation by specific poisons and stimulation of manganese reducing organisms. Here one can "overlap" the sulfur and manganese cycles to advantage: the addition of sulfur favors the reduced form of manganese by formation of sulfuric acid, with a reduction in pH, and by slow thiosulfate production. The addition of sulfur to a "manganese deficient" soil may exert a beneficial effect on the growth of plants [*McLaren*, 1962].

Generally, if appreciable amounts of an organic nutrient, such as glucose, are added to soil the results are profound and ramified. We mention phosphate accessibility as another example. Sperber has found that certain fungi, actinomycetes and bacteria can solubilize apatite $(Ca_3(PO_4)_2CaF_2)$ through production of lactic, glycollic, citric and succinic acids. Reports that soil microorganisms increase the availability of phosphates to plants are numerous [*Sperber,* 1958].

SOIL ORGANIC MATTER AND SOIL STRUCTURE

The addition of glucose to soil can have important physical consequences as well. Certain of the bacteria synthesize large amounts of polysaccharides as by-products or storage materials. Some of the added glucose goes into protein formation, thus removing soluble nitrogen from the soil solution (making nitrogen temporarily unavailable for plants). The polysaccharides, particularly those with carboxyl groups, become adsorbed to the soil colloids.

Organic matter in soil plays an essential part in securing the structure that is required for high fertility. From synthesis at the expense of substances of plant origin, and from autolysis of microorganisms, macromolecules are produced that have the capacity to bind to clay particles. This binding is presumably through bonds such as R—CO_2—Ca—clay, and may be represented $\widetilde{oo}$, where the lines indicate macromolecular chains and the circles depict negatively charged clay particles. Bacterial gums, alginic acid, pectic acid and a large class of synthetic compounds also have this capacity.

The net effects of adding such substances to soils high in clay and low in organic matter are improved aeration, tilth, water percolation rate, and sometimes crop yield, all resulting from the formation of a more stable crumb structure and an increase in resistance to compaction [*Quastel*, 1953].

ENZYME ACTION IN SOIL

We have reviewed some implications of soil biochemical activities in the fields of soil chemistry, physics and fertility. In these cases, the microbe has been an active contributor. Some investigators, however, have asked how much of the enzyme action in soil is due to this activity and how much is attributable to an accumulated "background noise" of enzyme activity in soil itself, that is, to enzymes adsorbed on clays or humus. One approach is to add toluene to soil to suppress microbial activity. Although toluene and even gasoline are substrates for some organisms, in short-duration experiments life activities may be considered suppressed. Similar results are obtained if soil is first sterilized with an electron beam [*McLaren et al.*, 1962]. With a Dublin clay loam, over half of the glycerolphosphatase activity was found after complete sterilization with a dose of 5 Mrep. It will be of significance to know if this residual enzyme activity is outside non-viable cells, and to what extent phosphatase in dead cells is capable of acting on substrate added to the sterile soil [*Skujins et al.*, 1962].

Haig [1955] has fractionated soils and found that most soil esterase activity is in the clay fraction. How the enzyme is held by the clay, how it is accumulated and how it can be isolated for study are intriguing questions.

An interesting and important problem of soil enzyme action requires a knowledge of the kinetics of enzyme action at solid-liquid interfaces. The phenomenon just described involves the action of an adsorbed enzyme on a soluble substrate. Conversely, microbes secrete soluble enzymes which act on insoluble substrates such as cellulosic debris, soil organic matter, chitin, etc. The kinetics of these reactions are not represented solely by equations of the Michaelis-Menten type for classical reactions in solution. Instead, the limiting rates of reaction involve diffusion of substrates to surfaces, adsorption of enzymes on particles and the local pH_s discussed above. Equations for these situations are now available for evaluation [*McLaren*, 1962]. The role of water and the minimum activities of water at which enzyme action can take place have yet to be evaluated.

SOIL DEVELOPMENT

Studies of the microbiology of soil development have only begun. Sand-dune communities were chosen by *Webley et al.* [1952] because the development of a soil microflora could be traced from the simple conditions of early colonization of bare sand through a series of communities of increasing botanical complexity accompanied by the formation of a soil.

Microbial counts were obtained from a transect across a dune at Newburgh (Aberdeenshire). In progressing from open sand past early fixed dunes to dune pastures and heath, the number of bacteria rise from a few thousand to millions per gram as soon as vegetation colonizes the sand. There is a fall in numbers of bacteria, but not of fungi, as heather, with an acid humus, enters as a dominant plant. In comparing rhizosphere soil with nearby soil there is a marked increase in microbes on passing from open sand to root surfaces of *Agropyron* and *Ammophilia*, with predominance of *Cornebacteria, Mycobacteria* and *Nocardia* among the "bacteria" throughout. Among the fungi, however, *Penicillum sp.* predominated in open sand and *Cephalosporium* near roots. Each plant species develops a unique rhizosphere flora which overlaps only in part those of other species. There can be little doubt that the activity of the microbes contributes to the development of the soil and the maturation of the habitat in a reciprocating way with higher plants growing from a sand and salt milieu.

Elucidation of the development of a soil profile, involving the leaching and translocation of aluminum, iron, humic acids and other chelating agents, etc., together with co-precipitation, will require experiments of long duration. The evidence is presumptive and *"ad hoc"* as in evolutionary theory generally, but no one seems seriously to question the overall picture.

SOME ORGANIC SUBSTANCES IN SOIL

Soil Enzymes

The bulk of organic substances in Earth soils undoubtedly arises from the decomposition of animal and vegetable residues by microorganisms. This does not imply liberation by autolysed cells, but rather cycling of the elements, first through the digestive and then the synthetic activities of soil flora and fauna. The microfauna are very important in the A horizon where leaf litter is degraded in the presence of abundant oxygen, particularly in acid, forest soils. Lower down in the soil, the flora tend to finish the catabolism begun by microfauna, and all recognizable vestiges of plant cytological structure vanish [*Kononova, 1961*]. These degradations release enzymes, the exoenzymes of digestion. On starvation, microflora and fauna may autolyse with release of intracellular enzymes. These details have not been worked out. In Table 1, *Briggs and Spedding* [1963] have listed some enzymes found in soil. We know nothing of the abundance of these en-

TABLE 1. Some Soil Enzymes

(From *Briggs and Spedding*, 1963)

Name of Enzyme	Reaction Catalyzed
1. Urease	Urea $\rightarrow$ ammonia + carbon dioxide
2. Amylases	Starches $\rightarrow$ sugars
3. Glycosidases	Glycosides $\rightarrow$ sugars + aglycones
4. Asparaginase	Asparagine $\rightarrow$ aspartate + ammonia
5. Aspartate-alanine transaminase	Aspartate + pyruvate $\rightleftharpoons$ alanine + oxalacetate
6. Catalase	$2H_2O_2 \rightarrow 2H_2O + O_2$
7. Invertase	Sucrose $\rightarrow$ glucose + fructose
8. Proteases	Proteins $\rightarrow$ peptides
9. Dehydrogenases	Reduced substrate $\rightarrow$ oxidized substrate
10. Glutamate-alanine transaminase	Glutamate + pyruvate $\rightleftharpoons$ alanine + α-ketoglutarate
11. Glycerophosphatase	Glycerol phosphate $\rightarrow$ glycerol + phosphate
12. Inulase	Inulin$\rightarrow$ fructose and fructose oligosaccharides
13. Leucine-alanine transaminase	Leucine + pyruvate $\rightleftharpoons$ alanine + α-ketoisovalerate
14. Nuclease	Purines, etc. $\rightarrow$ ammonia + keto-purines (etc.)
15. Peroxidase	Substrate + H_2O_2 $\rightarrow$ oxidised substrate + H_2O
16. Phosphatases	Organic phosphates $\rightarrow$ compound + orthophosphate
17. Polyphenol oxidase	Polyphenols + O_2 $\rightarrow$ quinones + H_2O
18. Tyrosinase	Tyrosine + O_2 $\rightarrow$ *o*-quinones + H_2O

zymes in soil and whether they may be found both in and outside soil microbes. Soil phosphatases are of several kinds, e.g., glycerol phosphatase and phytase. The latter is very important in the soil phosphorus cycle. About 60 per cent of soil phosphorus is typically organic but only a small fraction of this is of known structure, namely as in phytin.

Of all the soil organic substances, individual enzymes are most easily tested for. Although only small amounts are present, the turnover of substrate, particularly in the cases where the products are volatile or fluorescent, is easily measured quantitatively. In fact, B. Rotman has developed a test for one or more enzymes which is sensitive at the one-enzyme-molecule level. Clearly, there cannot be much free enzyme-protein in soil as proteins are nutrients for organisms, but enzymes may be chemically cross-linked with humus. It is known that such bound enzymes may still function [*McLaren*, 1963*a*].

It is also of interest that soil sterilized by ionizing radiation can still respire, but at a reduced rate, indicating the presence of some residual organized enzyme systems [*Peterson*, 1962].

Organic Nitrogen Compounds in Soil

Among the recognizable organic nitrogen compounds in soil are amino sugars, amino acids and nucleotides, Table 2.

Amino sugars such as glucosamine are derived from chitin. It is clear from the table that spectroscopic examination of soil for peptide bonds or amino acids, without suitable extraction from soil humus, is out of the question. Some infrared spectra of soil organic matter have been reported; the evidence for soil protein is almost nil [*Jenkinson and Tinsley*, 1960]. Further, the amino acids derived from soil organic matter following hydrolysis are not of protein origin. The liberated amino acids may have been in condensation products of phenols or quinones [*Kononova*, 1961]. Free amino acids may range from 2–4 mg per kg soil; in soil the polybasic amino acids are adsorbed to the clays; tryptophan is not [*Putnam and Schmidt*, 1959].

Organic Sulfur Compounds in Soil

At present we can conclude only that there are some organic sulfur compounds in soil; in fact, in some Australian soils most of the soil sulfur may be organic [*Freney*, 1961a]. Some of it is, of course, in amino acids (Table 2).

Organic Phosphorus Compounds in Soil

As already mentioned, most of the soil phosphorus is organic [*Bower*, 1949]. Very little nucleic acid exists in soil (1 ppm), perhaps no more than in the microbes themselves. In one such test the total organic phosphorus ranged from 300-500 ppm [*Adams et al.*, 1954]. Several forms of inositolhexaphosphate are found in soil [*Cosgrove*, 1962]; they occur from 100 to 300 ppm [*Anderson*, 1961].

Carbohydrates

Sugars added to soil are quickly metabolized and free sugars are absent in natural soil. On the other hand, polysaccharides of microbial origin are present in soil [*Whistler and Kirby*, 1956], to the extent of 0.1% [*Lynch et al.*, 1958]. These contain galactose, glucose, mannose, arabinose, etc.

Humus

The major portion of soil organic matter is called humus. It is insoluble in water, but about one third of this organic matter can be removed from

TABLE 2. Nitrogen Compounds in Soil

Substance Tested for	Conditions	N-Content of Soils Tested	Fraction of N as Substance Tested For	References
Amino sugars	After acid hydrolysis	0.17-2.8%	0.05-0.1	*Bremner and Shaw* [1954]
Amino acids	After acid hydrolysis	......	0.3–0.5	*Bremner* [1950]
Amino acids, free	NH$_4$OAc extraction	......	0.001-0.0001	*Paul and Schmidt* [1961]
Protein	Native soil	......	nil	*Van Driel* [1961]

soil by extraction with alkali. The extraction is improved by prior treatment of the soil with chelating agents, since humus seems to be held to clay by bonds involving di- and tri-valent metals. Alternately, treatment of soil with hydrofluoric acid removes sand and solubilizes clay minerals, thereby leaving the organic matter. Following neutralization of alkaline extracts, *humic acid* is precipitated and polymeric *fulvic acid* remains in solution. These composite acidic substances contain chemically bound nitrogen, phosphorus and sulfur. Of course, the solution phase also contains the nitrogen, sulfur and phosphorus micromolecular compounds described above, and polyuronic acids. Humus may be found in low amounts, about one per cent in desert soils and up to 80 per cent in so-called organic soils.

About one-half of the nitrogen in fulvic acid occurs as compounds that are deaminated on hydrolysis; about one-fourth appears as amino acid precursors and one-tenth as amino sugars [*Stevenson*, 1960].

Humic acid from one source has been found to contain about seven per cent methoxyl groups [*Johnson*, 1959], together with a number of other functional groups (Table 3). A summary of infrared absorbances of organic matter from A and B horizons is given in Table 4. [*Wright and Schnitzen*, 1959].

REMARKS CONCERNING TESTS FOR LIFE IN SOIL

This problem can be divided into two parts, namely the test for living creatures and testing for products of metabolism. The latter products must be distinguished from chemicals formed under the action of other natural agents, such as radiation. (For a review see *McLaren and Shugar* [1954].) The former products, as we have tabulated, include enzymes, polysaccharides, and certain aromatic substances of unknown structure that occur in a percentage that is perhaps higher in humus than in products formed by radiation.

Test methods for enzymes in soil are already under development, for example, phosphatase in the Multivator. We do not now know about the relative abundance of enzymes in soil and this should be actively explored. For example, urease is prevalent and urea labeled with radioactive carbon should provide a sensitive assay, comparable to that for phosphatase in the Multivator.

A difficulty with Gulliver, and the Wolf Trap, is that we do not know what universal substrate system can be supplied to the Martian "soil" and a test for autotrophs may require growth under light. On the other hand, all microbes contain some enzymes in common and a battery of enzyme

TABLE 3. Functional Groups Found in Humus

Group	Amount	Spectral Absorption	References
OH	2-3 meq per g	3.0μ	*Johnson* [1959], *Wright and Schnitzen* [1959]
CH_3	—	3.45	*Johnson* [1959]
Methoxyl	6.7%, 0.2-0.4 meq per g	6.3	*Wright and Schnitzen* [1959]
Carbonyl	4-6 meq per g	5.85, 6.22	*Johnson* [1959] *Wright and Schnitzen* [1959]
Carboxyl	2-9 meq per g	—	*Wright and Schnitzen* [1959]
Unknown	—	7.2	*Johnson* [1959]
Aromatic	27%	—	*Wright and Schnitzen* [1961]
Clay impurity	—	9.0	*Johnson* [1959]
Stable free radicals	10^{18} per g	(EPR)	*Steelink and Tollin* [1962]
Quinone	—	—	*Flaig* [1955]
Phenolic	3 meq per g	—	*Wright and Schnitzen* [1959]
(e.g., *epi*-catechin)			*Coulson et al.* [1960]
Unknown	—	(fluorescence)	*Waldron and Mortensen* [1961]

TABLE 4. Major Bands and Relative Absorbances in the Infrared of Extracted Organic Matter [*Wright and Schnitzen, 1959*]

Frequency (cm.$^{-1}$)	Relative Absorbance A horizon	B horizon	Interpretation
3,380	strong	strong	Hydrogen bonded—OH and bonded—NH groups
2,910	medium	shoulder	Aliphatic C—H stretching vibrations
2,840	medium	O	Aliphatic C—H stretching vibrations
2,600	shoulder	shoulder	Carboxyl C—H stretching vibrations
1,720	shoulder	strong	Carboxylic carbonyl
1,620	strong	strong	Joint interaction of hydroxyl and carboxyl with carbonyl [*McLaren, 1963b*], also possibly carboxylic groups associated with metals so as to give the carboxylate structure [*Hattori and Furusako, 1959*]
1,450	strong	O	CH_3 or CH_2, or both, in plane deformation vibrations
1,400	O	medium	Carboxylate
1,250	weak	O	Phenoxyl C—O
1,200	O	medium	Carboxyl
1,030	medium	O	Si—O of silica due to the presence of clay

assays may be more likely to succeed as a presumptive test for evidence of life.

When water is added to soil, after it has been air-dried, there is a burst of biological activity and a liberation of carbon dioxide [*Birch, 1958*]. This suggests another approach to the experimental recognition of life. One would expect that this metabolic activity would result in the liberation of heat and that the heat could be measured calorimetrically [*Glaser, 1964*]. (Cf., Chapter 20, Section 15.)

A microbiological fractionation of isotopes might also be useful in life detection; for example, fractionation of sulfur by *Desulfovibrio desulfuricans* is rather dramatic [*Kaplan and Rittenberg, 1964*].

Finally, since living things generally contain free radicals, and humus contains trapped free radicals, probably of the semiquinone and quinhydrone type, the finding of free radicals in Martian soil could be taken as presumptive evidence.

Offhand, both the calorimetric and free radical measurements appear to be potentially very important; they are non-specific in the sense that they do not depend on the presence of any particular form of life, nor on the provision of a medium suitable for its growth.

REFERENCES

Adams, A. P., W. V. Bartholomew, and F. E. Clark (1954), *Soil Sci. Soc. Am. Proc. 18*, 40.
Anderson, G. (1961), *J. Soil Sci. 12*, 276.
Birch, H. F. (1958), *Plant and Soil 10*, 9.
Bower, C. A. (1949), *Iowa Agr. Exp. Sta. Res. Bull.* 362.
Bremner, J. (1950), *Biochem. J. 47*, 538.
Brenner, J., and K. Shaw (1954), *J. Ag. Sci. 44*, 152.
Briggs, M. H., and D. J. Spedding (1963), *Science Progress 51*, 217.
Bromfield, S. M., and V. B. D. Sherman (1950), *Soil Sci. 69*, 337.
Cosgrove, D. J. (1962), *Nature 194*, 1265.
Coulson, C. B., et al., (1960), *J. Soil Sci. 11*, 30.
Flaig, W. (1955), *Proc. Natl. Acad. Sci.* (India), *24*, 271.
Freney, J. R. (1958), *Nature 182*, 1318.
Freney, J. R. (1961a), *Aust. J. Ag. Res. 12*, 424.
Freney, J. R. (1961b), *Thesis*, University of New England.
Glaser, D. (1964), Exobiology Study, Stanford.
Greenwood, D. J. (1961), *Plant and Soil 14*, 360.
Haig, A. D. (1955), *Thesis*, University of California, Davis.
Hattori, T., and C. Furusako (1959), *Nature 184*, 1566.
Jenkinson, D. S., and G. Tinsley (1960), Royal Soc., Dublin, *Sci. Proc. 1*, 141.
Jenny, H., F. Bingman, and B. Padilla-Saravia (1948), *Soil Sci. 66*, 173.
Johnson, H. H. (1959), *Soil Sci. Soc. Am. Proc. 23*, 293.
Kaplan, I. R., and S. C. Rittenberg (1964), *J. Gen. Microbiol. 34*, 195.
Kononova, M. M. (1961), *Soil Organic Matter*, Pergamon Press, New York.
Kubiena, W. L. (1938), *Micropedology*, Collegiate Press, Ames, Iowa.
Lees, H., and J. H. Quastel (1946), *Biochemistry 40*, 803.
Lynch, D. L., *et al.* (1958), *J. Sci. Food and Agr.*, 56.
McLaren, A. D., and K. Babcock (1959), *In:* T. Hayashi, ed., *Subcellular Particles*, Ronald Press, N. Y.
McLaren, A. D. (1962), *Archives Biochem. Biophys.* In press.
McLaren, A. D., R. A. Luse, and J. J. Skujins (1962), *Soil Sci. Soc. Am. Proc. 26*, 371.
McLaren, A. D. (1963a), In: *Recent Progress in Microbiology 8*, University of Toronto Press.
McLaren, A. D. (1963b), *Science 141*, 1141. The soil was first treated with 0.2% by weight of a polyelectrolyte in order to stabilize the crumb structure, air dried, crumbled and sieved in order to isolate the 2-5 mm fraction, and given a preliminary water wash. The washing treatment reduced the pH of the wet soil.
McLaren, A. D., and D. Shugar (1964), *Photochemistry of Proteins and Nucleic Acids*, Pergamon Press, New York.
Paul, E., and E. L. Schmidt (1961), *Soil Sci. Soc. Am. Proc. 25*, 359.
Peterson, G. H. (1962), *Soil Sci. 94*, 71.

Putnam, H. D., and E. L. Schmidt (1959), *Soil Sci. 87,* 22.

Quastel, J. H. (1946), *Soil Metabolism,* Royal Institute of Chemistry, London.

Quastel, J. H., E. J. Hewitt, and D. J. D. Nicholas (1948), *J. Agri. Sci. 38,* 315.

Quastel, J. H. (1953), *Nature 171,* 7.

Rahn, O. (1913), *Zentr. Bakt. II Abt. 38,* 484.

Skujins, J. J., L. Brael, and A. D. McLaren (1962), *Enzymologia 25,* 125.

Sperber, J. L. (1958), *Aust. J. Agric. Res. 9,* 782.

Steelink, C., and G. Tollin (1962), *Biochem. Biophys. Acta 59,* 25.

Stevenson, F. J. (1960), *Soil Sci. Soc. Am. Proc. 24,* 472.

Thimann, K. V. (1955), *The Life of Bacteria,* Macmillan Co., New York.

Van Driel, W. (1961), *Studies on the Conversion of Amino Acids in Soil.* North-Holland Pub. Co., Amsterdam.

Waksman, S. A. (1938), *Humus,* 2nd edition, Williams and Wilkins Co., Baltimore, Md.

Waksman, S. A. (1945), *Science 102,* 339.

Waldron, A. C., and J. L. Mortensen (1961), *Soil Sci. Soc. Am. Proc. 25,* 29.

Webley, D. M., D. J. Eastwood, and C. H. Giningham (1952), *J. Ecology 40,* 169.

Whistler, and K. W. Kirby (1956), *J. Am. Chem. Soc. 78,* 1755.

Winogradsky, S. (1924), *Compt. rend. Acad. Sci. 179,* 861.

Wright, J. R., and M. Schnitzen (1959), *Nature 184,* 1462.

Wright, J. R., and M. Schnitzen (1961), *Nature 190,* 703.

CHAPTER 8

PROPERTIES OF DESERT SOILS

R. E. CAMERON

Terrestrial soils have evolved in a dynamic situation under the influence of at least five major interacting factors. These factors include time (geological), topography, soil parent materials, climate (especially moisture and temperature combinations) and organisms (especially vegetation) [*Jenny*, 1941]. In regions of favorable climate, soil development is optimal with typical soil profiles and horizons. In desert areas, climate is especially arid and the dearth of organisms is noticeable. Organisms have little or no influence in the formation of true desert soils. Therefore, in very arid areas there is little, if any, classical soil development and no soil profiles of distinguishable horizons are present. Physical and chemical processes have been the primary agents in the development of desert soils, and in barren areas the biological system in soils is entirely restricted to desert microorganisms [*Cameron*, 1962; 1963; *Killian and Fehér*, 1939].

Virgin desert soils can be characterized on the basis of typical soil properties. These properties include or indicate limiting factors for life to a greater or lesser extent and determine the kinds of dependent and interacting biota in a particular soil ecosystem [*Cameron*, 1962; 1963]. For a given soil ecosystem the following properties can be considered: (a) moisture, bound and available, (b) surface and subsurface temperature, maximum, minimum and diurnal, (c) quantity and quality of solar radiation received and emitted at the soil surface, (d) gas exchange and gas compo-

164

sition, particularly the exchange and concentrations of carbon dioxide and oxygen, (e) essential elements, toxic elements, available forms and soluble salts, especially the biogenic salts of carbon, nitrogen, phosphorus, and sulfur, (f) organic matter, organic carbon and nitrogen and living organisms, (g) cation exchange capacity, (h) buffer capacity, (i) soil pH, (j) soil Eh, (k) porosity, (l) texture, (m) structure, (n) bulk density, (o) mineralogy, especially clay, (p) color. Most of these properties have been determined for typical soils of economic value in agricultural areas. It cannot be assumed that measurements on desert soils will yield the same information, or that measurements obtained for typical well-developed terrestrial soils should be relied upon for purposes of testing and evaluating extraterrestrial life detection systems.

Very little detailed information on the characteristics of desert soils is available, but some recent investigations provide information on the nature, abundance and distribution of microorganisms within a desert soil ecosystem and on the characteristics of their immediate environment.

Studies of several hundred North American desert soils have yielded results that may illuminate the problems of sampling and detection of life. Unless otherwise stated, the information presented here is based primarily on investigations of soils occurring in the Great Basin, Mohave and Colorado Deserts. Additional information is derived from soil investigations of volcanic deserts in the Kau Desert of Hawaii, the Valley of 10,000 Smokes Desert in Alaska and high altitude areas in the relatively arid White Mountains of California. Where no references are cited, unpublished data are quoted that contain details of methods and results of desert soil investigations [*Cameron et al.,* 1965].

Moisture in desert soils reaches very low levels, although desert soils are not always entirely dry. *In situ* moisture contents have ranged as low as 0.01 per cent for a dry sandy soil to more than 4.0 per cent for a dry clay (after drying to constant weight at 105°C). However, *in situ* soil humidity measurements, which showed diurnal variations, seldom ranged below 85 per cent R.H., even at the surface, despite air humidities below 15 per cent R.H. Desert soils seem to act as reservoirs for moisture and conserve moisture despite the arid atmosphere above the soil. Silt, clay and salt serve to hold moisture in desert soils rather than humus, which is low in amount. As determined in the laboratory, the amount of moisture held in some desert soils at 98 per cent R.H. (31 bar pressure) is shown in Figure 1. This water content, although high for some soils, is considered to be unavailable (bound) water for most plants. As indicated in Figure 1, one soil gained more than 65 per cent in water content over the air-dry state after exposure to 98 per cent R.H. in a closed environment. This increase in water content was due to the presence of deliquescent salts. The mini-

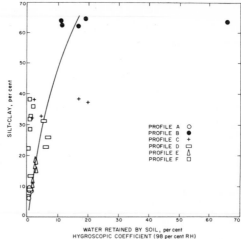

Figure 1.
Relationship of silt and clay content to soil moisture status at hygroscopic coefficient (98 per cent RH).

mum soil water suction required for activity of desert microorganisms in various soil ecosystems has not been determined.

Soil temperatures vary considerably depending on several factors, for example, amount of solar radiation received and emitted at the soil surface, soil color, mineralogy, moisture content, amount and distribution of plant cover, porosity, texture, structure, degree of slope and exposure. Light colored, barren desert soils generally show rapid and wide heat flux changes at the surface. Soil surface temperatures have been found to be 40 to 80°F (about 25 to 45°C) higher than the air temperature three feet above the soil surface, even at elevations of 12,000 to 14,000 feet. However, at a depth of three feet below the soil surface the temperature may be relatively constant for much more than a 24-hour period. Cold soils decrease microbial activity. Freeze-thaw cycles generally stimulate activity.

Gas exchange and variations in concentrations of gases in the soil atmosphere are especially important for soil microorganisms but have not yet been adequately investigated in desert soils. On the basis of carbon dioxide evolution in Sahara soils, *Killian and Fehér* [1939] found that the desert microflora are quite active. For typical soils, carbon dioxide concentrations can increase from 5 to more than 500 times that of the atmospheric concentration, depending on such factors as depth of soil, porosity, moisture content, solar radiation effects, time of day, season of the year and abundance and activity of microorganisms. Oxygen concentrations commonly decrease with soil depth. In soil investigations at high elevations, oxygen concentration was found to show diurnal variations, but sometimes it increased with depth as compared to the value at the surface.

Salt content is quite variable in desert soils, ranging from nil to total salt. These salts are commonly sodium, calcium, and magnesium carbonates, chlorides and sulfates. Nitrates, nitrites and phosphates may also be present. Typical electrical conductivity values for desert soils are plotted in Figure 2. Weight loss upon ignition of desert soils lacking in humus is greatly dependent upon the salt content as shown by a comparison of Figure 2 with Figure 3. In general, an increase in salt content decreases the abundance of common groups of desert soil microflora when the salt content approaches 5 per cent.

Organic matter content of desert soils is considerably below those of

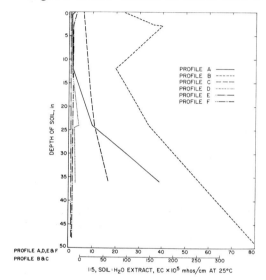

Figure 2.
Variation of soil electrical conductivity with soil depth.

Figure 3.
Variation of total loss on ignition at 700°C* with soil depth.

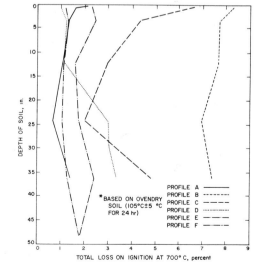

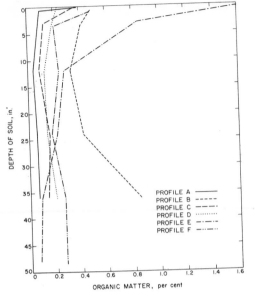

PROFILE A ——
PROFILE B —————
PROFILE C ——— ·
PROFILE D ··········
PROFILE E —··—··
PROFILE F —··—··

Figure 4.
Distribution of organic matter
with soil depth.

typical agricultural soils, approaching values of 1.0 to 0.05 per cent or less [*Cameron and Blank,* 1963; *Radwan,* 1956]. Reported values for soil organic matter, nitrogen and carbon are greatly dependent upon the method of analysis [*Cameron and Blank,* 1963]. Unless some surface litter is present, organic matter in desert soils may show little deviation with depth of soil, and sometimes increases with depth, as shown in Figure 4. Organic carbon and nitrogen values in desert soils frequently, but not always, have narrow ratios of less than 10:1, approaching 3:1 or 2:1 [*Killian and Fehér,* 1939; *Cameron and Blank,* 1963], values similar to those of protein or microbial cells. The greatest numbers of desert microorganisms are not always found in the greatest accumulations of organic matter.

The cation exchange capacity in desert soils is dependent on the same phenomena as typical well-developed soils. Factors influencing cation exchange include soil texture, the degree of aggregation of soil particles, the kinds and amounts of clays, salts and organic matter. The cation exchange capacity of desert soils low in clay and organic matter is also commonly low. Cation exchange capacity curves for desert soils are shown in Figure 5. With available moisture present, a high cation exchange capacity of balanced elements is favorable for microorganisms.

Buffer capacity, pH, Eh, salts and cation exchange capacity are related phenomena. Some desert soils have an appreciable buffer capacity and greatly resist a change in pH upon addition of acids or bases. Values for pH may or may not vary with depth of desert soils as shown in Figure 6.

Many, but not all, desert soils show a pH value above neutral, but this depends on a number of factors such as porosity, kinds and concentrations of exchangeable cations and the moisture content. Values of pH 8.5, or greater, almost invariably indicate an exchangeable sodium percentage of

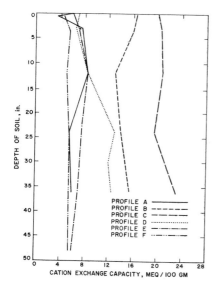

PROFILE A
PROFILE B
PROFILE C
PROFILE D
PROFILE E
PROFILE F

CATION EXCHANGE CAPACITY, MEQ / 100 GM

Figure 5.
Variation of cation exchange capacity with soil depth.

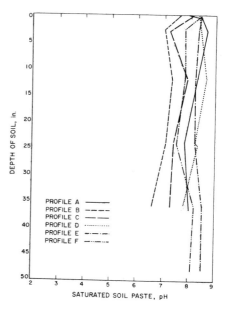

PROFILE A
PROFILE B
PROFILE C
PROFILE D
PROFILE E
PROFILE F

SATURATED SOIL PASTE, pH

Figure 6.
Variation of pH saturated soil paste with soil depth.

TABLE 1. Comparison of Numbers and Kinds of Microorganisms in Surface Soil Fractions Above and Below 2 mm Diameter

Soil No.	Soil Fraction	Aerobes; Bacteria + Actinomycetes $\times 10^3$/g Soil	Facultative Anaerobes Growth in Dilutions/g Soil 10^5	10^6	Anaerobes $\times 10^3$/g Soil	Fungi $\times 10^3$/g Soil	Algae: Growth in Dilutions/g Soil 10^2	10^3	10^4	10^5
43	<2 mm	1460	+	+	430	32	+	+	+	−
43	>2 mm	105	+	−	3.2	4.0	+	+	−	−
50a	<2 mm	361	+	+	6.6	4.4	+	+	+	+
50a	>2 mm	165	+	+	46	0.3	+	+	+	−

15 or more and the presence of alkaline earth carbonates [*Richards,* 1954], which is unfavorable for many microorganisms. Measurements of soil pH, whether in the field or laboratory, show dilution effects. Usually the more dilute the soil, the higher the pH value. This dilution effect helps to explain *in situ* soil pH values of 5 or less for relatively dry desert soils which, when wet, show a pH of 8 or more. However, at high elevations in the White Mountains, relatively moist soils showed pH values of 7 or greater compatible with the observed indigenous microflora, but when the soils were tested in the laboratory at saturation percentages, pH values were between 7 and 5. Values of pH 4 or less have been obtained on comparatively raw desert volcanic soils from Hawaii and Alaska. Eh values are much more erratic than pH values for desert soils, but commonly have high positive values and show dilution effects. Some of the principal components of desert soil redox systems are iron, manganese and clay, while minor components are humus and organic acids. Many desert soil microorganisms can evidently tolerate a wide pH and Eh range, while others require a more narrow, specific range.

Porosity, texture, structure, and bulk density are interdependent soil physical factors. For desert soils, porosity measurements have ranged between 30 to more than 65 per cent, with the lowest values for compact sands and highest values for aggregated clays and raw pumice soils. Bulk density figures have commonly ranged between 0.70 to 1.00 for raw pumice soils and clays to more than 1.65 for sands. As indicated previously, desert soils show little typical soil structure, although there are sometimes accumulations of salts and clay and distinctive hardpans due to evaporation and leaching, Figures 12 and 13. Desert soils tend to show single-grained structure, and aggregation of particles is generally poor. Particle size distribution for three different desert soil profiles is shown in Figures 7, 8 and 9. It is worth noting that for a completely unfractionated soil sample there is no evidence that the varieties or distribution of desert soil microflora depend on particle size distribution (cf., Table 1).

Mineralogy and soil color are closely related and greatly dependent upon such factors as climate, degree of weathering, nature of the soil parent materials, and oxidation and hydration state of soil particles. Desert soils show wide variations in mineralogy, although quartz and plagioclase are common minerals. The glassy phase of certain volcanic soils is apparently detrimental to general microbial development. Colors of desert soils range through gradations and shades of red, yellow, pale-brown or gray, again showing dependence upon climate, minerals present, moisture and the oxidation and hydration state of iron compounds. Red soils are more prevalent in hot deserts while gray soils are more evident in cold deserts.

The kinds of microorganisms, their abundance and distribution in desert soils are of special importance with regard to sampling and life detection.

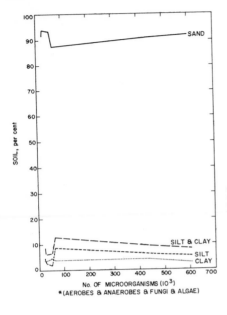

Figure 7.
Distribution of microorganisms* with particle size distribution for Profile "A".

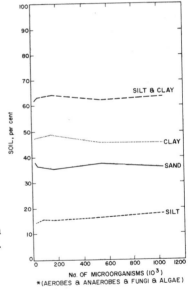

Figure 8.
Distribution of microorganisms* with particle size distribution for Profile "B".

Any of the above soil factors can determine how many microorganisms of what kinds exist within a given region of the soil ecosystem. Only a detailed examination of the soil and measurement of its various properties can show the relationship between the population of microorganisms and the characteristics of the soil environment.

In general, the soil environment is so complex, even for desert soils, that it is difficult to determine and correlate the effects of any specific property

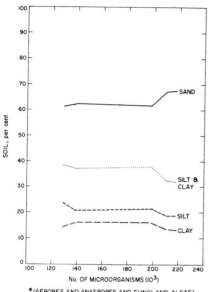

Figure 9.
Distribution of microorganisms* with particle size distribution for Profile "C".

*(AEROBES AND ANAEROBES AND FUNGI AND ALGAE)

of the soil environment on the microflora. However, information can be obtained as to the numbers of kinds of microorganisms that actually do exist in any sample of soil environment. Figures 10 and 11, for example, show the distribution of aerobes and anaerobes with depth of soil in two desert soil ecosystems. An examination of bacterial isolates from these and other desert soils has shown the predominance of soil diptheroids and filamentous motile spore-forming bacilli [*Bollen*]. Coccoid bacteria are seldom found in virgin desert soils.

It has been found that populations of different bacteria in desert soils are affected differently when the environmental conditions are varied. Desert soil bacteria develop at different rates when the available moisture and organic matter are increased or decreased, the concentrations and rates of gases change, and temperatures are varied. An immediate determination of the numbers of kinds of microorganisms at the sampling site does not usually duplicate results obtained at a later time in the laboratory. Tables 2, 3, and 4 indicate summaries of microflora for 34 processed air-dry desert soils from six sample sites. Distribution of desert soil microflora is not always directly correlated with organic matter content of soils as shown by a comparison of Figures 4, 10, and 11. Available moisture is evidently the most crucial factor in most desert soils for stimulating metabolism, repro- duction and growth of microorganisms. Desert soil algae, for example, have been observed to become active within 5 to 15 minutes after rain- storms or following the wetting of dry soil crusts in the laboratory. After wetting desert soil crusts that have been kept continuously desiccated for

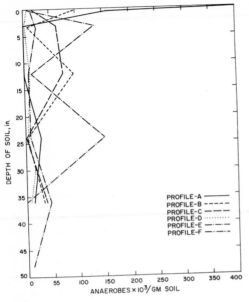

Figure 10.
Distribution of anaerobes with soil depth.

Figure 11.
Distribution of aerobes: Bacteria + actinomycetes with soil depth.

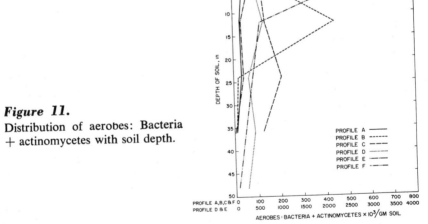

5 to 10 years, new abundant growth of oscillatorioid blue-green algae is macroscopically evident in less than 12 hours. This phenomenon may be analogous to color changes observed on the Martian surface following the recession and assumed melting of polar icecaps.

Of further interest for life detection experimentation is the variability of microorganisms in two adjacent desert soil ecosystems. Table 5 shows the distribution of soil microorganisms determined at a sample site in dune sand, Figure 14, adjacent to and overlapping a caliche soil, Figure 12. The facultative anaerobes (microaerophiles) are the most abundant group of bacteria present in both soil ecosystems. Wind-blown mixing of dune sand evidently gives a fairly even distribution of microorganisms with depth of soil, whereas more definite stratification is evident in the caliche soil. There is a definite change in physical and chemical properties of the caliche

Figure 12.
"Profile" of a desert soil, showing a compact, hard, structureless body beneath a sand dune, Yuma Desert, Calif.

Figure 13.
"Profile" of an ancient beach sand with a moist clay-pan layer, Colorado Desert, Thermal, Calif.

TABLE 2. Summary of Numbers and Distribution of Soil Microflora for Six Soil Profiles

Soil No.	Depth of Soil	Sum of Microflora $\times 10^3$/g Soil	Range (All populations), per g Soil	Average $\times 10^3$	Standard Deviation $\times 10^3$	Standard Error $\times 10^3$
1	Surface 1/16"	617	1.6×10^3 to 397×10^3	123	161	72
2	1/16" to 1"	453	1.0×10^3 to 272×10^3	90.6	121	54.3
6	Surface 1/2"	1038	95 to 840×10^3	208	357	160
4	Surface 1/8"	199	585 to 195×10^3	39.9	86.7	38.8
74	Surface 1/4"	1285	10^2 to 1275×10^3	257	569	254
75	Surface 1/4"	3929	10^3 to 3900×10^3	786	1741	779
3	Surface 1"	141	10^3 to 100×10^3	28.2	41	18.4
All Soils	Surface	—	—	219	690	117
51	1/16" to 6"	62.1	17 to 42×10^3	12.4	17.3	7.7
68	1/2" to 6"	170	340 to 140×10^3	34.0	59.4	26.6
62	1/8" to 6"	149	10^2 to 73×10^3	29.8	35.7	16.0
70	1/4" to 6"	394	240 to 388×10^3	78.7	173	77.3
76	1/4" to 6"	2855	10^3 to 2700×10^3	571	1191	533
4a	1" to 6"	224	10^3 to 10^5	44.8	47.3	21.1
All Soils	to 6"	—	—	128	491	89.8
65	1'	30.1	10 to 29×10^3	6.0	12.9	5.7
69	1'	549	10^3 to 443×10^3	110	190	85.1
66	1'	228	366 to 142×10^3	45.7	62.2	27.8
71	1'	187	10 to 165×10^3	37.4	71.5	32.0
77	1'	612	0 to 587×10^3	122	260	116
5	1'	245	0 to 135×10^3	49	63.8	28.5
All Soils	1'	—	—	61.7	134	24.4

53	2'	66.0	0 to 15.5 × 10³	13.2	17.7	7.9
63	2'	34.1	0 to 19 × 10³	6.8	7.9	3.6
64	2'	211	0 to 210 × 10³	42.3	93.8	42
72	2'	239	10 to 223 × 10³	47.9	98	43.8
73	2½'	65.4	0 to 36 × 10³	13	15	6.7
78	2'	608	0 to 440 × 10³	122	189	84.4
6a	2'	176	10 to 65 × 10³	35.2	45.1	20.2
All Soils	2'	—	—	40	89.6	15.1
54	3'	26.3	0 to 15.5 × 10³	5.3	7.1	3.2
61	3'	52.4	0 to 34 × 10³	10.5	13.9	6.2
67	3'	130	0 to 125 × 10³	26.0	55.4	24.8
60	3'	66	0 to 28.5 × 10³	13.2	10.8	4.8
79	3'	236	0 to 225 × 10³	47.1	99.5	44.5
7	3'	238	0 to 90 × 10³	47.6	47.4	21.2
All Soils	3'	—	—	24.9	49.5	9.0
81	4'	63.2	0 to 62 × 10³	126	27.6	12.3
8	4'	168	0 to 55 × 10³	33.6	43.3	19.4
All Soils	4'	—	—	23.1	25.9	1.1

TABLE 3. Summary of Distribution of Desert Soil Microflora with
Depth of Soil for Six Soil Profiles

Depth of Soil	Minimum	Maximum	Average	Standard Deviation	Standard Error
Aerobes $\times$ 10^3/g Soil					
0-1 in.	21	3900	945	1380	521
1-6 in.	42	2700	572	1050	429
1 ft.	29	587	250	215	87.9
2 ft.	19	440	147	155	58.5
3 ft.	8.3	225	79.5	86	35.1
4 ft.[a]	55	62	58.5	4.9	3.5
Anaerobes $\times$ 10^3/g Soil					
0-1 in.	1.9	397	98.4	145	54.7
1-6 in.	0.1	136	39.9	52.6	21.5
1 ft.	0.1	95	34.4	40.0	16.3
2 ft.	0.3	150	31.8	53.1	20.0
3 ft.	0.1	47	18.2	18.5	7.5
4 ft.	0.1	11.4	5.8	8.0	5.7
Facultative Anaerobes $\times$ 10^3/g Soil[b]					
0-1 in.	1	100	17.4	36.7	13.9
1-6 in.	1	100	23.5	37.6	15.4
1 ft.	1	100	23.5	37.6	15.4
2 ft.	1	100	20.3	35.4	13.4
3 ft.	1	100	22	38.4	15.7
4 ft.	1	100	50.5	70.0	49.5
Fungi per g Soil					
0-1 in.	95	19,750	3695	7,167	2709
1-6 in.	17	7,833	2852	3,558	1453
1 ft.	3	600	344	220	90
2 ft.	0	7,566	1229	279	1057
3 ft.	0	28,500	5052	11,494	4692
4 ft.	133	1,800	966	1,178	833
Algae $\times$ 10^3/g Soil[b]					
0-1 in.	0.1	100	30.4	47.6	18.0
1-6 in.	0.1	10	3.7	4.9	2.0
1 ft.	0	1	0.34	5.01	2.0
2 ft.	0	0.1	2.9	.005	.002
3 ft.	0	0	0	0	0
4 ft.	0	0	0	0	0

[a] Only two soils represented
[b] Growth at highest dilution

TABLE 4. Summary of Abundance of Desert Soil
Microflora for Six Soil Profiles[a]

Kinds of Microflora	Mean Minimum $\times 10^3$/g Soil	Mean Maximum $\times 10^3$/g Soil	Range	Average	Standard Deviation $\times 10^3$	Standard Error $\times 10^3$
Aerobes	29.0	1319	8.3×10^3 to 3900×10^3	798	136	136
Anaerobes	0.40	139	0.1×10^3 to 397.0×10^3	43.5	7.7	13.2
Facultative Anaerobes[b]	1	100	10^3 to 10^5	22.9	3.6	6.3
Fungi	0.41	11	0.0 to 28.5×10^3	2.5	6.0	1.0
Algae[b]	0.33	20.0	0.0 to 10^5	7.0	23.8	4.1
Coliforms	0	0	0	0	0	0
All populations (exclusive of Coliforms)	6.1	290	1.9×10^3 to 905.0×10^3	92.6	384.7	29.5

[a] For all soil levels, from surface to 3 or 4 feet.
[b] Growth at highest dilution.

TABLE 5. Comparison of Numbers and Kinds of Microorganisms from Two Different Soils at the Same Sample Site

Soil No.	Soil Depth	Aerobes: Bacteria + Actinomycetes $\times 10^3$/g Soil	Facultative Anaerobes: Growth in Dilutions/g Soil 10^5	10^6	Fungi per g Soil	Algae: Growth in Dilutions/g Soil 10	10^2	10^3	10^4
82[a]	Surf.1"	135	+++	++++	30	++	++	−	−
83	1"–6"	103	+++	++++	85	++	++	+	−
84	1'	131	+++	++++	155	−	−	−	−
85	2'	9.0	+++	++	0	−	−	−	−
86	3'	2.0	+	−	0	−	−	−	−
88[b]	Surf.1"	16.6	+	−	10	+	+	+	−
89	1"–6"	22.0	++	−	5	+	−	−	−
90	1'	21.3	++	+	10	+	−	−	−
91	2'	18.7	++	−	30	+	−	−	−
92	3'	14.7	+	+	0	+	−	−	−

[a] Caliche soil

[b] Dune sand

Figure 14.
Loose organic matter accumulation on the leeward side of a blowing sand dune, Yuma Desert, Calif.

soil below the one-foot level, with corresponding changes in the soil microflora.

The variability of microorganisms in a given surface area of a soil of similar properties at a single time of sampling is indicated in Table 6. These values are shown for 12 separate 10 gram samples of soil obtained within a plot 24 feet on each side. There is comparatively little variability, except in the case of the soil algae. Sampling from the same area over a period of several successive years and at different seasons has shown a number of changes in the relative abundance of the microflora, and certain species either disappear or become more numerous.

Specialized microorganisms are sometimes the most predominant microflora in some desert soils rather than common groups. The Valley of 10,000 Smokes Desert, for example, is an area in which there are comparatively few common soil microflora. Numbers of these common microorganisms in the surface one inch of soil are shown in Table 7. Sample site locations for three of these soils are indicated in the following photos: (a) soil 115, Figure 15, (b) soil 118, Figure 14, and (c) soil 119, Figure 16. Water was not a limiting factor in this case, although sulfur fumes and a unique mineralogy with unusual ratios or absence of certain elements were evident. Soil algae were usually the most abundant group of soil microflora present on barren "soil" within the valley, whereas microaerophilic bacteria were the most predominant group present in the periphery of the valley, near vegetation and in soil of greater development.

Microenvironments in soil ecosystems are extremely important: One microenvironment evident in some desert soils consists of accumulations of organic matter and populations of microorganisms in surface soil crusts, Figures 17, 18, and 19. These crusts contain greater accumulations of organic matter and greater numbers of heterogeneous populations of soil

TABLE 6. Variability of Microorganisms in Surface ½" of Soil in White Mountain Soil Plot

Soil Plot 9-2 Replicate No.	Aerobes: Bacteria and Actinomycetes × 10³/g Soil	Facultative Anaerobes: Growth in Dilutions/g 10⁶	10⁷	Anaerobes × 10³/g Soil	Fungi × 10²/g Soil	Algae Growth in Dilutions/g Soil 10³	10⁴	10⁵	10⁶
1	1150	+	−	670	34	+	+	+	−
2	1450	+	−	500	35	+	+	+	+
3	6900	+	−	370	40	+	+	−	−
4	1600	+	−	335	52	+	+	−	−
5	1080	+	−	68	49	+	−	−	−
6	730	+	+	600	29	+	−	−	−
7	1650	+	+	127	22	+	+	−	−
8	7500	+	+	37	26	+	+	−	−
9	1040	+	−	150	17	+	−	−	−
10	2200	+	+	58	27	+	+	+	−
11	4400	+	+	660	128	+	+	+	−
12	830	+	+	230	27	+	+	−	−
Av. of 12	2544	5.0 × 10⁶ (min)		292	40.5	112.8 × 10³ (min)			
Range:	730 → 7500	10⁶ → 10⁷		37 → 670	17 → 128	10³ → 10⁶			

TABLE 7. Microbiological Determinations for Valley of
10,000 Smokes Soils

	Microorganisms Per Gram of Soil				
Soil No.	Aerobes	Facultative Anaerobes	Anaerobes	Fungi	Algae
115	4700	1,000	12,500	1900	100,000
118	190	1,000	0	0	10,000
119	0	10	5	0	0
122	5200	10,000	15	15	100

Figure 15.
Close-up of wind-swept pebbly pumice pavement, Valley of 10,000 Smokes, Alaska.

Figure 16.
Close-up of loose mixture of unsorted, cohesionless, unstable pumice and ash on steep bank of eroded fumerole, Valley of 10,000 Smokes, Alaska.

Figure 17.
Loose gravelly surface (white granules) with irregular, stable, cohesive patches of algal-lichen soil crusts (dark areas), Colorado Desert, Thermal, Calif.

Figure 18.
Thin, fragile, dusty, eroded surface soil crusts between dead, wind-blasted vegetation and encroaching sand dune, Yuma Desert, Calif.

Figure 19.
Thin, coherent desert soil crusts over sand, Figure 13, contain accumulations of organic matter and microorganisms.

Figure 20.
Rocky desert pavement, Arizona
Upland Desert.

microorganisms than the surrounding soil. This accumulation is especially noticeable under the immediate surface of the crusts when it is separated from the underlying soil [*Fletcher and Martin,* 1948]. Moisture is also conserved in these crusts for a greater time period than in the surrounding area of surface soil, as shown in the moist dark areas of Figure 17. Translucent rocks, sometimes forming desert pavement, Figures 20 and 17, modify solar radiation and function as unique microenvironments in the desert. Portions of these stones extending beneath the soil surface to depths of one or two inches are covered by distinctive macroscopic adherent accumulations. This accumulation also serves as a moisture-conserving mechanism of organic matter and microorganisms [*Drouet,* 1959; *Vogel,* 1955]. Certain other microenvironments in desert soils can also easily enhance or limit the numbers of kinds of microorganisms distributed

Figure 21.
Hard, cohesive clay surface encrusted with evaporated salt, Mecca Hills, Colorado Desert, Calif.

Figure 22.
Hard, dense salt banks and flats
surrounded by rugged mountains,
Death Valley National Monument,
Calif.

in the soil ecosystem. Hard salt crusts occurring at the air-soil interface
can be detrimental, Figure 21. However, in some situations, Figure 22,
the opposite is true. In the latter case, a humid greenhouse effect has been
provided on a salt bank. Underneath the thin, upraised, translucent salt
crusts, soil algae were found to be macroscopically conspicuous.

REFERENCES

Bollen, W. B. Microorganism Study on Culture and Identification of Desert Soil
    Bacteria. *JPL Contract #950783,* Oregon State University.
Cameron, R. E. (1962), Soil Studies—Microflora of Desert Regions. *JPL Space
    Programs Summary No. 37-15,* pp. 12-20.
Cameron, R. E. (1963), The Role of Soil Science in Space Exploration. *Space
    Science Reviews 2*:297-312.
Cameron, R. E. and G. B. Blank (1963), Soil Organic Matter. *JPL Tech. Rep.
    No. 32-443.*
Cameron, R. E., F. A. Morelli, and G. B. Blank (1965), Desert Soil Charac-
    teristics. I. Preliminary Studies. In preparation.
Drouet, F. (1959), Distribution of Algae on the A. E. C. Nevada Test Site, 1958.
    In: *A Botanical Study of Nuclear Effects at the Nevada Test Site,* pp. 97-
    101. New Mexico Highlands Univ., Las Vegas, N. M.
Fletcher, J. E. and W. P. Martin (1948), Some Effects of Algae and Molds in
    the Rain Crusts of Desert Soils. *Ecology 29*:95-100.
Jenny, H. (1941), *Factors of Soil Formation.* McGraw-Hill Book Co., New
    York.
Killian, C. and D. Fehér (1939), Recherches sur la microbiologie des sols
    désertiques. *Encycl. Biol. 21*:1-127.
Radwan, M. K. (1956), A Field and Laboratory Study of the Soils of the
    Tahreer Province of Egypt. *Unpublished M. S. Thesis,* Univ. of Ariz.,
    Tucson.
Richards, L. A., ed. (1954), *Diagnosis and Improvement of Saline and Alkali
    Soils,* Govt. Printing Office, Washington, D. C.
Vogel, S. (1955), Niedere "Fensterpflanzen" in der südafrikanischen Wüste.
    Beiträge zur Biologie der Pflanzen 31:46-135.

CHAPTER 9

REMOTE DETECTION OF TERRESTRIAL LIFE*

CARL SAGAN, R. N. COLWELL, S. Q. DUNTLEY, V. R. ESHLEMAN,
D. M. GATES, AMRON KATZ, JOSHUA LEDERBERG, HAROLD MASURSKY,
D. G. REA, W. G. STROUD, VERNER SUOMI, and RALPH ZIRKIND

INTRODUCTION

Until very recently, observations of Mars and other planets of possible biological interest could be acquired only from the vicinity of the Earth. To acquire some degree of perspective on the problems of life detection over interplanetary distances, it is useful to consider the inverse problem— that of the detection of life on Earth from the distance of, for example, Mars (cf., Chapter 3). A related problem, somewhat less difficult, which we consider here, is the detection of life on Earth from Earth satellite altitudes. We are interested both in intelligent and in simpler forms of life.

In any reconnaissance of the Earth—for example, by photographic means—the reconnaissance expert has access to what is usually called "ground truth," that is, *in situ* information on the detailed structure of the terrain. In the case of observations of Mars, we lack ground truth. Indeed, Martian ground truth is the goal of reconnaissance of Mars. An open-air theatre, a housing development or an airport are readily identifiable in high-resolution photographs of the Earth. The discovery of similar well-ordered geometrical patterns on Mars would certainly be provocative, but by no means could we be sure of their identification. Yet the detection of highly ordered structures on the Martian surface would

* Report prepared by Dr. Sagan as chairman of a study group on this subject.

187

certainly pinpoint areas deserving closer study. In addition to geometrical patterns that may possibly indicate the presence of intelligent life, the spectral distribution of reflected and emitted radiation may be diagnostically significant for life detection; monochromatic radio signals being one obvious example. In addition, the characteristic infrared absorption features of organic matter are, at least in principle, detectable, and even with much poorer spectral resolution, the presence of terrestrial plants is indicated by their high infrared reflectivity. On the Earth, life is associated with regions of higher temperatures and greater moisture contents, and diagnostic features associated with hot, wet environments should have special weight. We now consider the various possible detection techniques in turn.

OPTICAL FREQUENCY RECONNAISSANCE

The possibility of optical detection of life on Earth clearly depends on the resolution of the optical system used. With a ground resolution of 10 km, cities, engineering works, cultivated crops—and essentially the entire range of phenomena that we might expect to indicate the presence of life on Earth—should be largely invisible, either because the intrinsic features are below the stated resolution limit or because their contrast with the surroundings is low. At a resolution of 1 km, the situation should improve somewhat. Cities located in high-contrast—for example, grassy—terrain should become barely visible, and many rectilinear features of high contrast with their surroundings should appear marginally. At a resolution of about 0.1 km, the range of detectable objects that indicate intelligent life on Earth should become very large. Roads, bridges and canals, which have high contrast with their surroundings, should be seen fairly easily, even if they are below the theoretical resolving power. Such rectilinear features should be at least several resolution elements long. According to S. Q. Duntley, the most readily detected rectilinear distribution of a given amount of high-contrast material corresponds to a length-to-width ratio of 6:1. There is no increase in detectability when this ratio exceeds 100:1. Reservoirs, some with the outlines of the capital letter "D," should be visible; wakes of ships often extend for many kilometers and would certainly be seen at 0.1 km resolution, and perhaps at the 1 km resolution level. Similarly, atmospheric condensation trails of jet aircraft should be detectable. Estuary and other pollution might be detectable as contrast changes. Shelter belts of trees, firebreaks and transmission lines through forests should begin to become discernible, as should tree plantations, contour farming and, particularly, fallow fields adjacent to growing ones, each with regular geometric shapes. Open pits, mine tailings and other industrial artifacts should become visible. It should be possible to follow pollution, condensation trails, and wakes to their sources.

When the resolution reaches 10 meters or slightly better, not only are all the foregoing features much more easily seen but also, the detailed contours of major avenues and the entire network of continental automobile highways and railroads should become clearly visible. In some cases, the contours in the terrain carved out for highways or railroads, rather than the structures themselves, will be visible. At this or slightly better resolution, there is a completely new range of detectable phenomena: shadows of living organisms observed at low solar elevation angles. Not only will the characteristic dendritic patterns of trees be visible, but the long shadows of such animals as cows and horses can also be detected when looking at the Earth in late afternoon. Even brief observations should show the articulation of limbs and motion of such animals.

These *a priori* expectations can be tested by an examination of high-altitude photographs of the Earth taken from aircraft and satellites. The Tiros and Nimbus meteorological satellites have yielded about 10^6 photographs of the Earth at 0.3-3.0 km resolution. These systems are intended primarily for study of terrestrial cloud systems, but the Earth is not perpetually cloudbound and so the photographs can also be examined for evidence of life on Earth. Through late 1964, eight Tiros satellites were launched. The characteristic scientific payload weighs about 300 pounds. The satellite is launched into an approximately circular orbit, with nominal altitudes of 400 statute miles. Tiros is equipped with a 500-line vidicon system and three lens subsystems with fields of view of 12°, 76° and 104°, respectively. Each of the Tiros vehicles has some combination of these three lens systems. At the nominal altitude, the 12° lens gives a resolution of about 0.3 km; the 76° lens, about 3.0 km.

The Nimbus meteorological satellite has a payload of about 1000 pounds and is launched into an orbit nominally ranging from 260 to 600 miles. Photographs from 300 miles altitude with a 32° field of view give a ground resolution of about 0.3 km.

The wide-angle lens of the Tiros vidicon system observes an area approximately 1000 km by 1000 km. The perpendicular field of view of the narrow-angle lens is approximately 100 km by 100 km. Tiros pictures have an information content of about 1.5×10^6 bits. The Nimbus vidicon system can accommodate 3.8×10^6 bits. For comparison, hand-held 35 mm cameras from manned orbiting missions yield pictures with about 10^9 bits information content. The spectral response of both Tiros and Nimbus optical systems lies in the 0.45- to 0.8-micron range.

It is generally well-known that both the United States and the Soviet

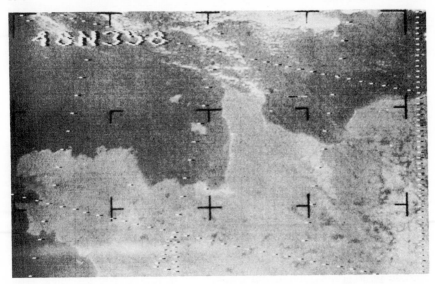

Figure 1.   Nimbus vidicon photograph of the northwestern coast of France. Courtesy of Goddard Space Flight Center, National Aeronautics and Space Administration.

Union maintain systems of military reconnaissance satellites for obtaining photographic information either by telemetry or direct recovery. It is easy to compute (cf., Chapter 15) that even with fairly modest apertures, 10-meter ground resolution should be possible from satellite altitudes, and resolutions approaching 1 meter should not be beyond the realm of possibility. Indeed, such resolutions would seem to be required if these satellite systems are to possess military utility. Such high-resolution photographs of the Earth are not available for reproduction here, but roughly comparable photographs can be obtained from airplane altitudes with aviation cameras.

Typical Nimbus photographs of the Earth in the 1 km resolution range are displayed in Figures 1 and 2. In Figure 1, we see the northwest coast of France and the English Channel. The black, right-angle markings are fiducial standards introduced into the camera system, and the sequenced white-and-black markings are latitude and longitude intervals. Clouds can be seen in the upper portion of the picture. The Cherbourg and Brest peninsulas and the region between the Seine and the Loire are heavily cultivated areas, but there is no apparent sign of such cultivation in this picture. In Figure 2, we see a montage of several photographs of North

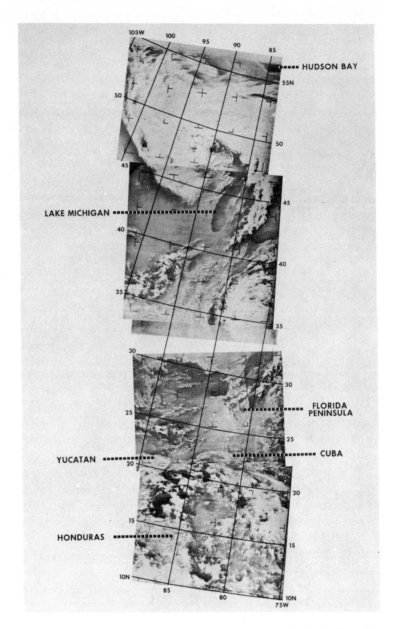

Figure 2.   Montage of Nimbus photographs of North America, taken on orbit 20, 29 August 1964, and orbit 35, 30 August 1964. Courtesy of Goddard Space Flight Center, National Aeronautics and Space Administration.

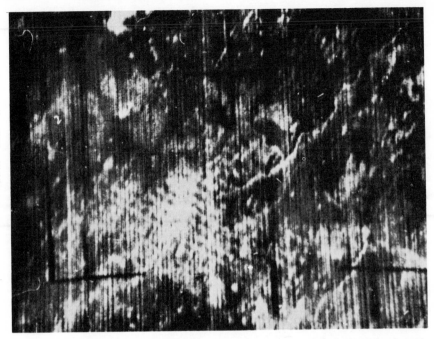

Figure 3. Tiros narrow-angle lens photograph of an area near Cochrane, Ontario, Canada. Courtesy of Goddard Space Flight Center, National Aeronautics and Space Administration.

America, from Hudson Bay to Nicaragua. These photographs were taken on 29 and 30 August, 1964, when much of the area was cloud-covered. The well-defined cloud pattern in the second frame is associated with the tropical storm Cleo. Note that while the area between Chicago and Milwaukee, on the shores of Lake Michigan, in the second frame, is almost cloud-free, there is no sign of life, intelligent or otherwise.

The vast majority of Nimbus and Tiros pictures are similarly lacking in signs of biological activity. Figure 3 is an exception. It shows an area near Cochrane, Canada, taken with the narrow-angle camera of the Tiros system. The ground resolution is about 0.4 km. The reader's attention is directed to the white orthogonal array in the lower central portion of the photograph. We are seeing forest clearings, logged through this region of Ontario in a rectangular pattern, so that the nearby trees left standing will reforest the logged area. The logged strips are about one mile wide; there are approximately two miles between the strips. After the clearing operation was completed, snow fell, producing the high-contrast effect visible in the photograph.

But suppose we had observed the same kind of pattern in a photograph of Mars. Would we immediately deduce this entire story about intelligent beings logging in a manner suitable for reforestation, deduce the existence of trees and the necessity for snow? It is much more likely that such details on Mars would be considered enigmatic, and judgment would be withheld until much finer resolution studies, preferably *in situ,* could be performed.

Kilston, Drummond, and Sagan [1965] have made a study of a set of enlargements of the best cloud-free Tiros and Nimbus photographs and have identified several more signs of life on Earth. Many highways in the United States were searched for unsuccessfully. Finally, Interstate Highway 40 was identified in Tennessee, because of its high contrast and because it was clearly distinguishable from the subsidiary rivers in the Mississippi system because it cut them at oblique angles. Actually, it is not the road that is seen, but the swath around the road, cut through the neighboring forests; the width of the swath is only some tens of meters, which is below the ground resolution of the Nimbus photograph in question. But rectilinear features can be detected, even when they are below the diffraction resolution limit, if they have high contrast, which in this case is provided by the surrounding forests. The road can be followed to Memphis, Tennessee, which is also discernible, although its relative contrast is low. Condensation trails of jet aircraft and wakes of ships can also be seen in some photographs of the Tiros and Nimbus series. The contrails are distinguishable because their shadows are visible. From the displacement between the contrail and its shadow, the altitude of the aircraft can be determined. The wakes of ships are immediately obvious because of their shape.

A further discussion of signs of life in Tiros and Nimbus Earth photography can be found, with relevant photographs and maps, in the reference cited above. The authors conclude that, even under the most optimistic assumptions, several thousand high-contrast photographs with resolution down to a few tenths of kilometers are necessary before one fairly good indication of life on Earth can be found—and that would be a rectilinear marking indicative of intelligent life. This number provides some measure of the difficulty of a photographic search for extraterrestrial life. For example, the Mariner 4 space vehicle of the United States was designed to take approximately 20 photographs of Mars with a ground resolution of a few kilometers—that is, about 100 times fewer photographs, each with 10 times poorer resolution, than would be required to detect life on Earth.

Searches for seasonal variations in surface albedo, due to the growth and harvesting of high-contrast crops (e.g., cotton) and the annual cycle

Figure 4. Aerial photograph of an area in the Sacramento-San Francisco Bay region of western United States. This photograph was prepared at the Smithsonian Astrophysical Observatory from a photo-mosaic compiled by the Aero Service Corporation, Philadelphia, Pennsylvania, and provided through the courtesy of Dr. Robert N. Colwell.

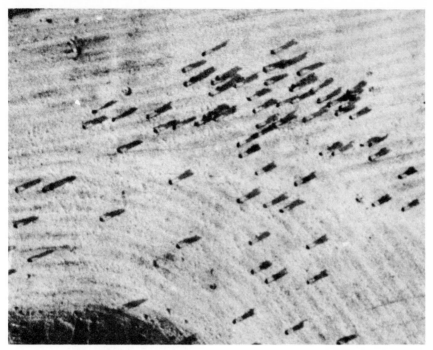

Figure 5. Aerial photograph of a California farm taken at a large solar zenith angle. Courtesy of Dr. Robert N. Colwell.

of deciduous forests, were unsuccessful [*Kilston, Drummond and Sagan,* 1965], although this is attributable in part to the transmission filters used in the Tiros and Nimbus systems (see below).

When the ground resolution is improved by about a factor 30 over the best Tiros and Nimbus photographs, results such as that of Figure 4 are obtained. This is an aerial photograph prepared from a photo mosaic of the Sacramento-San Francisco Bay area, prepared by Aero Service Corporation, Philadelphia, Pennsylvania, and provided through the courtesy of Robert N. Colwell. Highways, railroads, contour farming, an airport, housing developments, and city streets are all visible in the original, though some of this detail may have been lost in reproduction. Even if we had no previous experience with any of these artifacts of civilization, the regular geometrical arrangements of the structures on this photograph would be readily apparent. It is of interest to inquire how many random photographs of the Earth of this resolution and field of view would be required, before comparable geometrical detail would be obtained. This question has not been put to a rigorous test, but it would appear that a

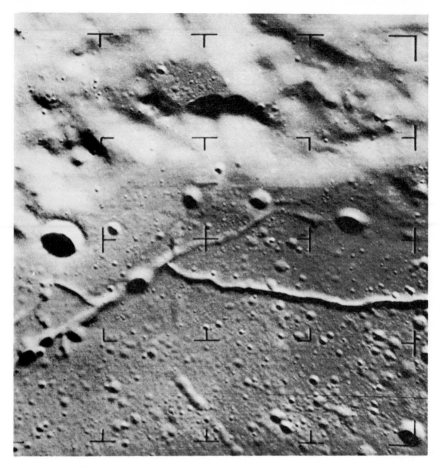

Figure 6. Ranger IX photograph of a rill system on the floor
of the crater Alphonsus. The photograph was taken
1 minute, 17 seconds before impact, at an altitude of
115 miles. Courtesy of Jet Propulsion Laboratory and
the National Aeronautics and Space Administration.

few hundred random photographs, perhaps only a few score, would be
adequate. Such a finding underscores the importance of providing photographs of the highest resolution of any extraterrestrial body that we suspect
to harbor living organisms.

When resolution is improved by another order of magnitude, it is possible to obtain photographs such as that in Figure 5, also provided through
the courtesy of Dr. Colwell. This photograph represents the direct detection of a living organism by observation from high altitude. From the

angle of the afternoon Sun and the length of the shadow, it is possible to deduce the size of the cow. While a very large number of photographs of the Earth with comparable resolution are required before quadrupeds can be detected by their shadows, a systematic program of observations near a planetary terminator can potentially provide unambiguous detection of large organisms and much information about them.

Several points emerge from this survey of remote photographic reconnaissance of the Earth. For reasons of efficiency, the constructions of intelligent beings (on planets large enough for Euclidean geometry to be a good approximation) should tend to be rectilinear. Networks and arrays of linear features (cf., Figure 4) should tend to indicate biological activity. However, some features of undoubted nonbiological origin are also linear. Approximately linear rills inside the crater Alphonsus are seen in Figure 6. Faults and other linear features of geological origin should be common features of any planetary or satellite surface. A narrow peninsula in northern Morocco, 25 km long and about 1 km wide, appears as a striking rectilinear feature in a Nimbus photograph of the Earth; however, it is not of biological origin [*Kilston, Drummond and Sagan,* 1965]. In the deserts of Africa and Asia Minor, there are systems of long, narrow, parallel and almost rectilinear seif sand dunes. These are characteristically several hundred kilometers long, several kilometers wide, and separated, one dune from another, by perhaps 10 km; a photograph of seif dunes in the western Sahara, taken from an unmanned Mercury capsule, and a discussion of the possibility that rectilinear markings reported on Mars are in fact seif chains, can be found in a paper by *Gifford* [1964]. Before rectilinear features found on other celestial objects can be imputed to biological activity, all reasonable nonbiological alternatives should have been eliminated; and even then, a fairly elaborate array of such features (again, cf., Figure 4) would be required.

High-resolution photography of the Moon, both ground-based and from spacecraft, indicates that the dominant processes of deposition and erosion are different from those on Earth. The resulting morphological character of the Moon is distinct and is best displayed in photographs within two degrees of the terminator. Minor differences in elevation are then brought out by the oblique lighting. The spatial patterns due to geological processes on the Moon and the Earth are, in almost all cases, clearly apparent and distinct from familiar patterns of biological origin. However, the interpretation of Martian photographs will depend on our ability to characterize the geological processes shaping the surface of that planet, and on the nature of the artifacts—if any—of Martian biological activity.

The prospect of detecting terrestrial plants and animals at low solar elevation angles and several meters resolution suggests a possible general-

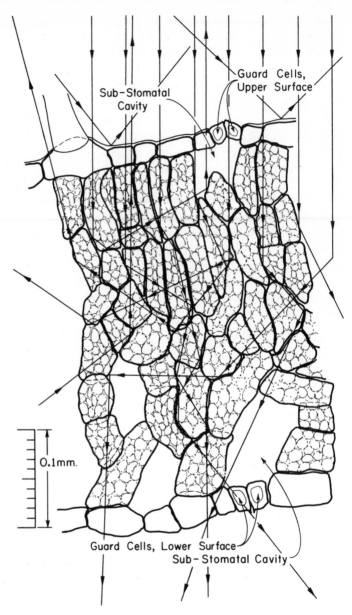

Figure 7.   Cross section of a *Mimulus cardinalis* leaf, showing possible paths of light rays which are critically reflected at cell walls within the leaf. Chloroplasts can be seen within the mesophyll cells. Courtesy of Dr. David M. Gates.

ization. Almost all naturally occurring structures of nonbiological origin are broader at their bases than at their tops. On planets subject to much aeolian or alluvial erosion, top-heavy structures are unstable over even relatively short geological timescales. Structures of biological origin, both plants (above ground) and animals, on the other hand, have a marked tendency to be as broad or broader at the top than at the bottom. Such structures throw long shadows that are easily distinguished from those of broad-based objects. Especially on a planet like Mars, where gravitational acceleration is lower, and, at least for short periods of time, more spindly structures might be stably maintained than on Earth, the search for top-heavy shadows might be a fruitful method for detection of indigenous life-forms of fairly large dimensions.

Both in the search for rectilinear and other regular geometrical patterns and in the search for top-heavy shadows, the highest possible resolution available for planetary reconnaissance should be used. In the search for long shadows, observations near the terminator are indicated.

NEAR INFRARED REFLECTIVITY

The extremely high reflectivity of common terrestrial foliage in the near infrared has long been known (see Figure 11b). To understand the origin of this effect, we refer to Figure 7, which displays the cross section of a *Mimulus cardinalis* leaf. The effects described for this leaf will apply in general to most terrestrial vegetation. A bifacial, mesomorphic leaf like that of *Mimulus cardinalis* has a waxy or fatty cuticle at the outermost layer which, except for the guard cells, is not green and contains no chloroplasts. Beneath the cuticle is the upper epidermis, which forms a transition region to the palisade mesophyll, or palisade parenchyma, the generally closely-clustered, chloroplast-containing systems in the upper half of the interior of the leaf. In the lower part of the mesophyll is the more disordered array called the spongy mesophyll, or spongy parenchyma. The lower surface of the leaf is terminated with a lower epidermal layer. The chloroplasts are generally most numerous in the palisade cells, where the bulk of the photosynthesis occurs.

Now, consider the progressive penetration of light of increasing wavelength into such a leaf. Ultraviolet light will be almost entirely absorbed in the cuticle and upper epidermis, and except in the near ultraviolet, such a leaf should appear black at ultraviolet frequencies. In the visible, the leaf appears green, because visible photons penetrate through the cuticle and upper epidermis into the palisade and spongy parenchymae. The chloroplasts in the mesophyll contain chlorophyll, which absorbs strongly in the

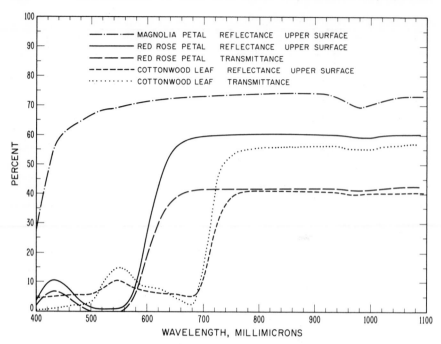

Figure 8.   Visible and near infrared reflectance and transmittance of petals and leaves. Courtesy of Dr. David M. Gates.

red and the blue. The green light is not absorbed, but why do we see it in reflection? Why do photons with frequencies in the green not continue through the leaf and penetrate out the other side? Inside the mesophyll cells are micelles and chloroplasts which are in the micron size range. Within the chloroplasts are the granae, with one dimension comparable to the wavelength of visible light. Fresnel reflection at air–cell interfaces, and multiple scattering by the granae gives an incident photon a significant probability of being reflected back. Because the absorption coefficient in the green is small, the average photon with wavelength in the green encounters many such interfaces in its random-walk through the leaf. Therefore, even if the probability of back-scattering is small per interface, the *cumulative* probability of back-scattering after penetration through many interfaces is large for green light. Photons in the red and blue do not exhibit this behavior, because the probability of absorption by the chloroplasts is so large. Some sample photon trajectories through the leaf structure can be seen in Figure 7.

As we go into the near infrared—say 0.7-1.2μ—the chlorophyll absorption coefficient declines sharply. Thus, incident photons of near infrared wavelengths are subject to the same fate as photons of green wavelength are. They random-walk through many interfaces in the leaf mesophyll until they are back-scattered. Many plants utilize either accessory photosynthetic pigments or large quantities of chloroplasts, and consequently, at least some absorption occurs in the green part of the spectrum where, after all, the Sun is radiating a significant fraction of its energy. Absorption in the near infrared is unlikely on physical grounds. In the ultraviolet and visible, electronic transitions can provide sizable absorption cross sections; in the middle infrared, the fundamentals due to vibrational transitions provide a large absorption cross sections. In the near infrared, absorption is provided only by intercombination and overtone bands of vibration fundamentals, and, more rarely, by electronic transitions of highly conjugated molecules. The strength of overtone and intercombination bands is many orders of magnitude below that of the fundamental. For this reason, the reflectivity of almost all plants in the near infrared is significantly higher than in the green (thereby explaining the appearance of the foliage in Figure 11b). As we go farther into the infrared, absorption by organic and other functional groups in the cuticle and outer epidermis of the leaf begin to become significant; and longward of about 6.2μ, where a strong water band exists, the infrared reflectivity of vegetation declines sharply with wavelength.

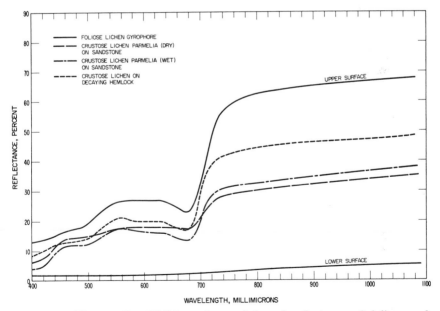

Figure 9. Visible and near infrared reflectance of foliose and crustose lichens. Courtesy of Dr. David M. Gates.

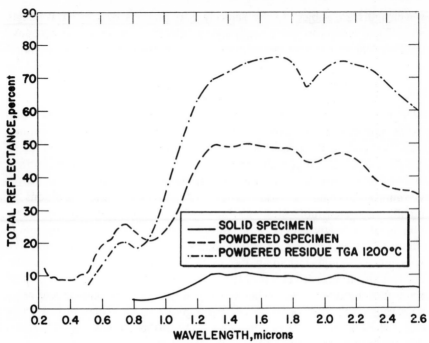

Figure 10. Near ultraviolet, visible, and near infrared total reflectances of limonite. The reflectivity of the solid specimen is shown by the unbroken line; the dashed lines show reflectivities of powdered specimens in the 0.1 mm size range; prepared in one case by grinding the solid sample, and in the other case by taking the powdered sample through thermogravimetric analysis to 1200°C. Reproduced from *Sagan, Phaneuf, and Ihnat* [1965].

The visible and near infrared reflectance and transmittance of some common petals and leaves are shown in Figure 8. The near infrared reflectivity of vegetation sometimes reaches 70%. In Figure 9 are shown similar curves for lichens. The near infrared reflectivity here is lower, not so much because of the small abundance of chlorophyll as because of the small opportunity for multiple scattering of infrared photons below the epidermis. Note, in the spectra of Figures 8 and 9, that the general reflectivity in the green ($\lambda \sim 0.55\mu$) of, for example, cottonwood leaves or lichens, while detectable, is not nearly so striking as the increase in reflectivity beyond 0.7μ. Other similar spectra can be found in *Gates et al.* [1965].

This general behavior, while characteristic of plants, is, unfortunately, not unique to them. In Figure 10, we see the visible and infrared reflectivity of three samples of the mineral limonite ($Fe_2O_3 \cdot nH_2O$), a solid specimen and two powdered specimens. We see that high reflectivity in the near infrared may also be characteristic of minerals. The reason is not hard to find. Because of the low absorption coefficients in the near infrared expected for fundamental physical reasons, a bulk sample of any powdered mineral whose particle size approximates a few microns should have a very large reflectivity in the near infrared. If it absorbs in the visible, as limonite does because of its iron moiety, its net spectrum will tend to resemble that of many terrestrial plants. Therefore, a finding of low reflectivity in the visible and high reflectivity in the near infrared is not a uniquely diagnostic test for vegetation on another planet.

The examples of Figures 9 and 10 are particularly relevant for Mars, which displays a near infrared spectrum rather similar to that of Figure 10. Figure 10 is, in fact, part of the body of evidence suggesting the presence of limonite on Mars [*Sagon, Phaneuf, and Ihnat,* 1965], although there is other, independent, evidence for its existence [*Dollfus,* 1957]. Because the reflectivity of Mars in the near infrared is not so striking as that of some green, broad-leaved plants, certain authors (e.g., *Kuiper* [1952]) have suggested that lichens, with their small near infrared reflectivity, may be better models for Martian organisms. It should be emphasized that the ecology of life on Mars may be extremely different from that of

Figure 11. Two aerial photographs of the safe region, *(left)* in visible panchromatic, *(right)* in the near infrared. Courtesy of Eastman Kodak Company.

life on Earth. The organisms may be very sparsely distributed and therefore make no perceptible contribution to the near infrared reflectivity; or they may utilize light in the near infrared for photosynthesis (as suggested by G. A. Tikhov) and therefore show a low infrared reflectivity.

A suitable study of terrestrial vegetation in the photographic infrared from satellite altitudes does not exist in the open literature. Such a study requires a comparison of photographs taken in regions longward of 0.8μ, where vegetation is highly reflective, with photographs taken in wavelengths shortward of 0.7μ, where the reflectivity of vegetation is very low. The peak sensitivity of the visible channel of the Tiros radiometer is about 0.7μ, but its sensitivity extends to 0.75μ, or even slightly longer wavelengths. As a result, the passband contains wavelength regions where vegetation has high reflectivity, as well as wavelength regions where vegetation has low reflectivity. Thus, in Tiros photographs, vegetation appears neither uniformly brighter nor uniformly darker than the surrounding terrain. Identifications of vegetation from satellite photography—for example, of a conifer forest in France [*Kilston, Drummond, and Sagan, 1965*]—are not clear-cut. The choice of filters in the Tiros and Nimbus satellites is, of course, not a defect in their design; they were intended for meteorological observations, not for vegetation surveys.

Figure 11 shows two photographs, one in the visible and one in the near infrared, of the same vegetated region, containing houses and a waterway. Since liquid water begins to absorb strongly in the near infrared, while vegetation begins to reflect strongly at the same wavelengths, we see that in comparing a photograph taken in the visible with one in the near infrared, the contrast between vegetation and liquid water is reversed. Similar high-resolution photographs, taken at two wavelength ranges from a Mars orbiter, might be a significant first step in the search for moist, vegetated regions on the planet, but no unique identifications of vegetation by this method are expected.

At longer wavelengths, beginning at about 1.2μ, the absorption by water and by organic functional groups in the upper layers of the leaf is manifested by depressions in the spectrum of light reflected from the leaf. Such absorptions at the methyl and methylene C—H stretching wavelengths near 3.5μ have been observed, for example, by *Sinton* [1959] and by *Rea, Belsky, and Calvin* [1963] in the reflection spectra of a variety of terrestrial plants. At longer wavelengths—for example, in the 4.0-6.5μ region —there are a large number of other organic functional groups of interest. However, especially for Mars, the intensity of reflected sunlight at these wavelengths is likely to be dominated by the thermal emission of the planet itself. Except for very thin covers of organic matter which have an optical depth in the infrared of unity or less, the organic functional groups ap-

Figure 12.
Infrared image of Italy, obtained with the Nimbus I radiometer between 3.4 and 4.2μ at night. Courtesy of Goddard Space Flight Center, National Aeronautics and Space Administration.

parently cannot be detected, either in absorption or in emission, over the background infrared thermal emission spectrum (cf., *Hovis* [1963]).

There exists no comprehensive catalogue of the reflectivities of terrains longward of about 0.8μ. The infrared specular reflection spectrum of many plants between 1.5 and 25μ has been reported by *Gates and Tantraporn* [1952]. Some preliminary measurements obtained from an Aerobee rocket at about 100 km altitude with a 10-channel infrared radiometer, reported by Ralph Zirkind, suggest that terrain observations at a variety of wavelengths in the near infrared may be of considerable interest. For example, with one-line scans from ocean to beach to forest terrain, the filter at 2.3μ with half-width 0.04μ shows approximately a factor of 4 increase in reflectivity over the forest; while at 3.9μ, with a half-width of 0.17μ, approximately a factor of 2 decline in reflectivity is observed. In order to exploit differential wavelength infrared imaging and scanning in applications to other planets, a program of laboratory and field measurements on the Earth is needed. Multicolor infrared imagery is feasible, but has never been used for observations of terrain.

INFRARED THERMAL MAPPING

Some Tiros and Nimbus satellites were equipped for infrared thermal mapping of the Earth. The Tiros infrared radiometers had a ground resolution of some 50 km, and with a thermistor bolometer as radiation detector, were capable of about 3°K temperature discrimination. Among the channels used were 5.8-6.8μ, 7.5-20.0μ, 8-12μ, and 14.5-15.5μ. Except

Figure 13. Two images of a populated region of the Earth, *(left)* an ordinary photograph obtained in visible light; *(right)* obtained at night by infrared imaging. Courtesy of Republic Aviation Corporation and Dr. Ralph Zirkind.

for the 8-12μ channel, these wavelength ranges are all in regions of substantial atmospheric absorption. Nimbus has a radiation-cooled lead selenide detector, maintained at temperatures above 200°K. With a channel between 3.4 and 4.2μ, it has a temperature sensitivity of 1°K and a ground resolution of some 3 km. An area 1000 miles by 1000 miles accommodates approximately 10^4 bits in the Nimbus radiometer. Especially with Nimbus, good nighttime images of the Earth have been obtained. For example, Figure 12 shows an infrared image of Italy, taken at night in emitted light. From detailed studies of single-line scans in such pictures, it is suggested that cities can sometimes be detected as hot spots. For example, Rome appears as an area some 5°K warmer than its environs. Figure 13, reproduced through the courtesy of the Republic Aviation Corporation and Dr. Ralph Zirkind, compares a daytime photograph of a populated region of the Earth, taken from aircraft altitudes, with a photograph taken in emitted light at night. The contrast seen in the left-hand photograph is due primarily to differences in thermal conductivity and specific heat capacity of neighboring materials; some retain the heat acquired from sunlight during the daytime much better than others.

Infrared thermal mapping is now in increasing use for geological surveys. For example, *Fischer et al.* [1964] describe aerial mapping with infrared imaging radiometers of Hawaiian volcanoes. These volcanoes have since been observed by Nimbus radiometry. Thus, infrared thermal mapping might be of considerable use in studying features of geological interest, as well as, perhaps, in acquiring clues for further biological investigations. We may note that the nighttime hemisphere of Mars has, because of phase angle limitations, never been observed from the Earth.

OBSERVATIONS AT MICROWAVE FREQUENCIES

Due to the activities of man during the last two or three decades, the brightness temperature of the Earth in the meter wavelength range has increased about a million times [*Shklovsky and Sagan, 1966*]. The Earth is now the second most powerful radio source in the solar system at these wavelengths, due to television broadcasting intended for local communication on the planet Earth. This fact could have been detected with quite modest equipment from the distance of Mars. It is, of course, by no means clear that an intelligent species developing on some other planet must necessarily undergo the same steps of technological evolution that result in very high brightness temperatures at meter wavelengths. But the example suggests that narrow-band radio observations may be the easiest method for detecting intelligent extraterrestrial life. While there has been no comprehensive program for observing Mars with narrow-band filters at any radio wavelengths, the few attempts that have been made have proved negative, and nothing approximating intelligible broadcasting has ever been reliably detected.

The existence of intelligent life on Earth could most easily be established from satellite altitudes with small radiotelescopes. Radar reflectivity and depolarization from satellite altitudes can give some information on surface and subsurface composition and structure. Progressive and synoptic observations of the same region as a function of phase angle and of angle to the local surface normal for a variety of wavelengths can give a vast quantity of information on subsurface thermal and electrical properties and the distribution of temperature, granularity, and composition with depth. Like observations on natural terrains at other frequencies, such passive and active microwave observations may be useful for excluding some materials, but they usually cannot provide a unique identification of materials. Occasionally, such techniques can be used to exclude the large-scale presence of organic materials; for an example of the application of such methods to Venus, see *Pollack and Sagan* [1965].

SUMMARY

At kilometer ground resolution, there is generally no sign of life on Earth. Both *a priori* considerations, based on terrestrial ground truth, and photographs taken by meteorological satellites and high altitude aircraft show that it is very difficult to detect life on Earth by photographic reconnaissance unless the ground resolution is about 0.1 km, or better. At this resolution, rectilinear features of intelligent origin become evident. Photographs of the Earth at 10 m resolution and at low solar elevation angles should permit the detection of the shadows of, e.g., stands of trees or herds of cattle. Perhaps a few thousand randomly distributed photographs of the Earth would be required for a significant detection of life on Earth at 0.1 km resolution; this number can probably be reduced by at least another order of magnitude for observations at 10 m resolution. High reflectivities in the near-infrared are indicative of the presence of vegetation, but not uniquely so. Many inorganic materials show similar behavior. Comparison of photographs of a body of water with vegetation along its banks, obtained in the visible, with similar photographs obtained in the infrared should show a significant reversal in relative contrasts. Infrared reflection spectra of vegetation, obtained from high altitudes, may show characteristic absorption features due to the presence of organic functional groups. Thermal mapping and other infrared techniques may be useful in specifying biologically promising locales which are warmer or wetter than their surroundings. Other than high resolution (~ 10 m) imaging of the surface, the most reliable technique for the detection of intelligent life on Earth from satellite altitudes appears to be observations of monochromatic emission in the radio-frequency range.

REFERENCES

Dollfus, A. (1957), *Ann. Astrophys.*, Suppl. 4.

Fischer, W. A., R. M. Moxham, F. Polcyn, and G. H. Landis (1964), *Science 146*:733.

Gates, D. M., H. J. Keegan, J. C. Schleter, and V. R. Weidner (1965), Spectral Properties of Plants. To be published.

Gates, D. M., and W. Tantraporn (1952), *Science 115*:613.

Gifford, F. A., Jr. (1964), *Icarus 3*:130.

Hovis, W. A. (1964), *Science 143*:587.

Kilston, S. D., R. R. Drummond, and C. Sagan (1965). To be published.

Kuiper, G. P. (1952), *In: Atmospheres of the Earth and Planets*, G. P. Kuiper, ed., University of Chicago Press, Chicago, Chapter 12.

Pollack, J. B., and C. Sagan (1965), *Icarus 4*:62.

Rea, D. G., T. Belsky, and M. Calvin (1963), *Science 141*:923.

Sagan, C., J. P. Phaneuf, and M. Ihnat (1965), *Icarus 4*:43.

Shklovsky, I. S., and C. Sagan (1966), *Intelligent Life in the Universe*, Holden-Day, San Francisco. In press.

Sinton, W. M. (1959), *Science 130*:1234.

PART V

SOME EXTRAPOLATIONS AND SPECULATIONS

CHAPTER 10

THE DEVELOPMENT OF RIGOROUS TESTS FOR EXTRATERRESTRIAL LIFE

SIDNEY W. FOX

Introduction.

The answer to the question of the existence of life on Mars will require adequate criteria and procedures for judging the evidence. Ideally, if several astronauts were to disembark upon the surface of Mars and be greeted by organisms that they could immediately recognize intuitively as living, the problem would be easily and cleanly solved.

The question to be put first, however, according to recommendations in this volume, will be one of judging the presence or absence of life by terrestrially monitored instruments and tests on Mars. Furthermore, evolutionary considerations support the belief that life, if any, on Mars might be microbial [Lipmann, 1964] and that microbial life, and the results of natural experiments which simulated but did not constitute life, would be extremely difficult or impossible to distinguish [Fox, 1964a]. Whereas advanced life could be recognized by laymen, a borderline type of life could be a cause of contention among experts.

The stage of general evolution on Mars might be

a) Prebiological, i.e., purely molecular,
b) Microbial,
c) Macroorganismic.

Until a few years ago, the general view stressed the possibility of a differentiation between various levels of complexity within the molecular stage of evolution, viz.,

a) small molecules, and
b) the complex macromolecules.

213

The difference between our understanding of small molecules such as amino acids, and macromolecules such as protein, is indeed immense. The thermal model has shown, however, that some of the same reactions that yield amino acids cause their immediate pyrocondensation [*Fox, Johnson, and Middlebrook*, 1955]. Operationally, therefore, reactions leading to the most complex compounds (and systems) are in some cases simple in a way that has often been precluded in theoretical considerations based on the involved mechanisms or the complicated relevant theories of the structures.

Related to the fact that the more advanced an organism the more surely it can be recognized as being alive, is the need for running more than one test on a common sample. The benefits should include economy in use of samples, and reinforcement of inferences from single bits of data.

Theoretical discussions of the validity of criteria of life serve as a background for the actual investigations. At this stage in the program of the biological exploration of Mars attention should, pragmatically, be on tests that can be performed by devices from which the results can be telemetered to Earth. Even more realistically, constraints based on the number of bits of information required, and the apportionment of total available bits among the various tests finally selected, are practical considerations in the solution of the problem as a whole.

In laboratory experiments performed in attempted imitation of molecular evolution in nature, many of the criteria that have been employed in identifying life have been satisfied [*Fox*, 1964a], whether these be micromolecular, macromolecular, or cellular. Since so many vital phenomena have recently been imitated under conditions that might occur on one or more planets, it seems imprudent to deny the possibility that other such phenomena might similarly emerge spontaneously. If one does not assume a discontinuity between prelife and life, mechanistic and evolutionary reasoning would also lead to the same conclusion.

Accepting the above emphasis, one is then led to the next question, namely, how may such criteria be ramified or otherwise improved to yield sufficiently rigorous answers that will not be distorted by the products of natural experiments? To use in advance a premise derived from extended study of the problem, we may seek especially those tests that will be positive only if Darwinian selection has occurred.

POTENTIALLY USEFUL CRITERIA OF LIFE

Criteria of life that may be useful will be listed in this section. Brief mention of the appearance of such phenomena in synthetic systems produced under geologically plausible conditions will be made, to provide an understanding of the need for rigorous tests. Ways in which some of these tests may be studied for further development will be discussed in a later section.

Biochemical Staples

The presence of key biochemical compounds has been considered as a test for life on Mars. Under geologically plausible conditions, however, carbohydrates such as deoxyribose [*Oró and Cox,* 1962], several amino acids [*Miller,* 1953], pyrimidines such as adenine [*Oró and Kimball,* 1961], uracil [*Fox and Harada,* 1961], guanine [*Ponnamperuma et al.,* 1964], almost all of the protein-bound amino acids [*Harada and Fox,* 1964], adenosine triphosphate [*Ponnamperuma,* 1964], and porphyrins [*Krasnovskii and Umrikhina,* 1964] have been produced in the laboratory.

Macromolecules

Poly-α-amino acids that are practically indistinguishable from terrestrial bioprotein have been produced from amino acids [*Fox and Harada,* 1958]. Polynucleotides of limited size have been produced from mononucleotides and ethyl metaphosphate (an unnatural reagent) [*Schramm,* 1964], and from polyphosphoric acid and cytidylic acid [*Schwartz and Fox,* 1964]. Further study seems more likely to yield larger synthetic macromolecules than to yield a surer criterion based on the polynucleotide structure. Coding ability has been claimed for the synthetic polynucleotide [*Schramm,* 1964]. Whereas the origin of the necessary mononucleotides has not been shown comprehensively, the fact that adenosine mono- and triphosphate AMP and ATP can be produced [*Ponnamperuma,* 1964] suggests the likelihood of similar possibilities for the monophosphates of guanine, cytosine and uracil.

Ordered Macromolecules

Although *Oparin* [1964] and others assume that a primitive protein would be "disorderly," thermal poly-α-amino acids, containing 18 or fewer types of amino acids, prove to be ordered as judged by comparison of total composition and terminal compositions [*Fox,* 1960].

Coding Relationship Between Macromolecules

As already stated, coding function has been claimed for synthetic polymers of mononucleotides (Matthei by Schramm in *Schramm* [1964]).

Also, an altered balance between total composition and N-terminal composition in thermal poly-α-amino acids when phosphoric acid is included in the reaction mixture has been shown [*Fox and Harada*, 1960*a*]. The phosphoric acid does not enter into the product. Accordingly, if one were to compare the results of terminal amino acid composition and total amino acid composition of poly-α-amino acids in samples from Mars and then find, by laboratory experiments, that the products did not have the same analytical values as those prepared simply by heating α-amino acids in the laboratory, he would not be able to conclude that this governance of order was due to terrestrial-type nucleic acids. Ordinary phosphoric acid or, conceptually, other materials might have been responsible for yielding a type of order that could not be attained by the amino acids themselves.

Catalytically Active Macromolecules

The ability of thermal proteinoids to catalyze hydrolysis of p-nitrophenyl acetate was reported in 1962 [*Fox, Harada, and Rohlfing*, 1962; *Noguchi and Saito*, 1962]. The capacity of such macromolecules for the breakdown of natural substrates such as glucose $\rightarrow$ glucuronic acid $\rightarrow$ carbon dioxide has recently been reported [*Fox and Krampitz*, 1964]. Unpublished experiments show also that many other natural substrates, such as urea, are broken down in aqueous solution by thermal proteinoids [*Krampitz, Harada, and Fox*, 1964].

Combinations of zinc and proteinoid split ATP, and this activity can be incorporated into microbially sized units [*Fox*, 1964*b*].

In this general context, one should bear in mind that *Siegel* [1957] showed that a mineral, chrysotile, catalyzes the decomposition of hydrogen peroxide and of glucose-1-phosphate.

Antigenicity

Antigenicity has not as yet been found in thermal proteinoids; this is probably the only significant, testable property found in proteins that is lacking in thermal proteinoids. However, a search for this property, which has been cooperative between two laboratories, was not carried out in a rigorous fashion, and deserves to be started again. Meanwhile, studies of Leuchs' poly-α-amino acids have demonstrated, in at least four laboratories, that chemically synthesized poly-α-amino acids can be antigenic [*Stahmann*, 1962; *Sela*, 1962; *Maurer*, 1962; *Gill and Doty*, 1962]. Accordingly, the finding of antigenicity in spontaneous Martian poly-α-amino acids would not be an indication of life.

The total number of tests that are positive for both proteins and thermal proteinoids is now between fifteen and twenty, the exact number depending upon how the criteria are classified [*Fox, 1963*]. The criterion which has not yet yielded the same result on both protein and proteinoid is that of antigenicity. Helicity, also, has not yet been demonstrated in thermal poly-α-amino acids although it has been found and studied extensively in Leuchs' poly-α-amino acids [*Blout, 1962*]. The test that might feasibly be used for helicity, however, is that of hypochromicity. This test is positive for many thermal poly-α-amino acids due to the somewhat unstable imide linkage [*Rohlfing, 1964*].

Structured Proteinaceous Microparticles

This heading connotes more than one criterion. The manner in which microparticles which appear as cocci has been demonstrated, under conditions that exist terrestrially, and which in earlier eons might have been even more common [*Fox and Yuyama, 1963a*]. As one example of the degree of control in the laboratory of the composition of formed units, microspheres have been produced under geologically plausible conditions [*Fox and Yuyama, 1963b*] in either the Gram-positive or the Gram-negative state, at will. *Stearn and Stearn* [1924] ascribed the Gram-staining of bacteria to their protein content. The simultaneous presence of protein-like quality and bacterial morphology is thus illustrated.

Configurational One-Sidedness or Net Optical Activity

A number of experimental demonstrations that lead to inferences about the origin of optical activity in the absence of cells has been reported in the literature [*Fox, Joseph, and Vegotsky, 1956; Wald, 1957; Northrop, 1957; Harada and Fox, 1962*]. Two examples are spontaneous resolution [*Fox, Johnson, and Vegotsky, 1956*] and the stereoselectivity favored in polymerization [*Wald, 1957*].

Morphological Variety

The forms that have been produced spontaneously from thermal poly-α-amino acids are several. Especially do microspherical units appear. These resemble cocci in size and shape (Figure 1) [*Fox and Yuyama, 1963a*]; they also resemble diplococci, tetracocci cilia, yeast-like buds, etc. (Figure 2).

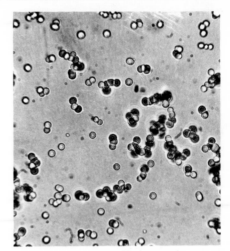

Figure 1.
Proteinoid microspheres with coc-coidal shape and range of diameter.

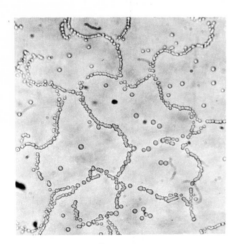

Figure 2.
Algae-like association of proteinoid microspheres.

Selective Membrane

The proteinoid microspheres clearly have a boundary, as demonstrated by electron microscopy (Figure 3) [*Fox and Fukushima,* 1964]. This boundary has been shown to have selective properties [*Fox and Yuyama,* 1964]. Unpublished data also support the conclusion that such spon-taneous membranes are selective in their action [*Fox and Fukushima,* 1963].

Organized Metabolic Pathways

In a quantitative sense, organized metabolic pathways are distinctive of terrestrial cells. The synthetic particles, however, have been reported to have at least one metabolic pathway of their own, i.e., glucose → glucuronic acid → carbon dioxide [*Fox and Krampitz,* 1964]. Other enzyme-like activities (unpublished) are being found in the polymers. These are weak, in comparison to contemporary enzymes, and possibly both the strength of individual activities and the ramified involvement of metabolic pathways in the contemporary cell can be used to distinguish life on Mars. However, evidence is at hand for some moderately strong catalytic activities in proteinoids; no statement can yet be made as to how diverse and ramified these may be. The practical question may prove to be one of how much extraterrestrial testing of this type is feasible in a single mission. Again, the allowable number of bits of information may impose severe limits.

Insofar as evidence of respiration in microbes is concerned, the proteinoid microspheres convert glucose to carbon dioxide, albeit at a low rate in the experiments performed to date [*Fox and Krampitz,* 1964].

Growth

Enlargement in size of the microspheres and of "buds" on microspheres [*Fox, Joseph, and McCauley,* 1964] is now documented on film, although not published. Time-lapse pictures of the growth of a "bud" on a microsphere have been published but not designated as such in the paper inasmuch as no confirming pictures were available at the time [*Fox and Yuyama,* 1964]. Such confirmation has since been obtained [*Fox, Joseph, and McCauley,* 1964].

Fission

The separation of microspheres into two "daughter" halves has been demonstrated [*Fox and Yuyama,* 1964]. Septate division is produced by the simple process of raising the pH of a suspension of proteinoid microspheres by 2-3 pH units. The fission occurs in typically 30-120 minutes.

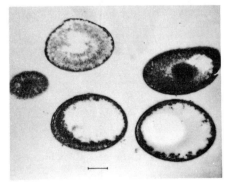

Figure 3.
Electron micrograph of section of osmium tetroxide-stained proteinoid microspheres. Marker—1 micron.

Although not published, complete separation of the halves into individual microspheres has been recorded on film.

Proliferation

In accord with the last sentence, the number of individual particles increases and proliferation is thereby signalled.

Osmotic Behavior

Microspheres shrink in response to hypertonic solutions, and swell in the presence of hypotonic solutions [*Fox, Harada, and Kendrick,* 1959]. This property is much less pronounced than in biological cells, but would be difficult to interpret in attempts to study osmosis in cells on Mars.

Active Transport

No study has been made of this property in the kind of synthetic system being discussed.

Excretion

No search has been made for this concomitant of life in the kind of synthetic system discussed here.

Bilamellarity of Membrane

Electron microscope studies have revealed that proteinoid microspheres have double layers (Figure 4) [*Fox and Fukushima,* 1964; *Fox,* 1964a],

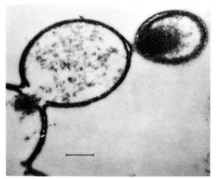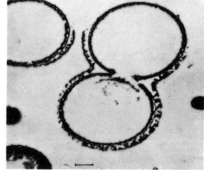

Figure 4.   Double layers in electron micrograph of section of proteinoid microspheres subjected to elevated pH.

and, in fact, that electron micrographs of sections of osmium tetroxide-stained microspheres are virtually indistinguishable from electron micrographs of sections of bacteria such as *Bacillus cereus* [*Murray,* 1960].

Energy Transfer

A rigorous demonstration of energy transfer in microspheres is not at hand. The incorporation of the ability to split ATP suggests, however, the possibility that this effect may be demonstrated.

Irritability

This property has not been demonstrated or found in truly synthetic systems of the kind here described.

Motility

Simulations of motility have been caught in unpublished cinematomicrographic sequences [*Fox and McCauley,* 1963]. This "motility" requires asymmetric particles containing zinc and ATP in the suspension. One sequence is very suggestive of a protozoan in the search for food, and simply "looks alive" to many biologists and nonbiologists.

Regeneration

This attribute has not been demonstrated, nor sought in the synthetic particles.

Mutability

The quality of mutability is likely to require an involved form of testing. Any judgment on the extent to which this criterion could be operationally valid would depend first upon the manner in which the criterion could be reduced to a feasible test. The question of simulability would then depend upon the nature of the test. This criterion is also closely related to the general process of Darwinian selection, mentioned earlier.

Death

A criterion that has, perhaps, received less attention in this context than it merits is that of death. In practice, this would require the cessation of one or more positive tests for life. In practice, death of a living particle might be induced by added poison. The quality of death is capable of being imitiated by the synthetic coccoidally shaped and sized particles.

For example, the simulation of motility can be arrested by exhaustion of ATP in the suspension or by poisoning with high concentrations of sodium chloride.

SUMMARY OF CRITERIA

While some of the attributes of living things have not yet been found in synthetic microparticles produced from thermal poly-α-amino acids, many have. Most of those listed have been incorporated by guided experiments or have been found unexpectedly, e.g., double layers in the boundary. Most of the criteria listed have been met by the synthetic experiments. Inasmuch as so many criteria have been fulfilled, denial of the possibility that others may be met is deemed imprudent. The same conclusion can be reached on the basis of theoretical materialistic reasoning.

The conditions employed in the laboratory are unprecedentedly simple and geologically plausible [*Fox, 1964a, b, c*]. Terrestrial geological plausibility is, however, not necessarily equivalent to "geophysical" plausibility for Mars. Answers to the many questions raised in this context require a closer study of Mars.

The comments on this point apply especially to the microbial type of life and its imitation by natural experiments. As the level of life becomes increasingly the product of Darwinian selection, the tests are more easily susceptible to heightened rigor.

The conclusions derivable from the synthetic model are consistent with a descriptive definition of life by *Calvin* [1962]:

✳ *What is a Living System?* ✳

In any discussion of such a broad all-encompassing subject as this, we are always faced with the problem of trying to define the material system to which we are willing to attribute the adjective 'living'. Personally, I feel that this has a certain degree of subjective arbitrariness about it, since there are those who would be willing to allow the use of this term for systems which would not be acceptable to others. This peculiar characteristic of the problem immediately allows us to recognize that the qualities, or properties, which we require of a material system are of the nature of a continuous aggregation in time along which no sharp line of demarcation need necessarily exist.

Similarly, *Professor John Keosian* [1964] has stated in his recent book, *The Origin of Life:*

> This apparent confusion reflects the necessity of recognizing the gradual transition of matter into higher and higher levels of organization embodying newer and more complicated properties. . . . What is important is not an exact definition of life at the borderline on which we can all agree, but rather the recognition of the existence of increasing levels of organization of matter and the understanding of the mechanisms which operate to bring these about.

THE PHYSICAL CONDITIONS ON THE EARTH AND ON MARS

Examination of terrestrial geology reveals that the physical conditions necessary for the thermal sequence of primordial gases $\rightarrow$ amino acids $\rightarrow$ preprotein $\rightarrow$ precells exist in moderate abundance now and were very likely far more abundant during the earlier history of the Earth. Assumptions of the opposite sort have been made, but the geological opportunity for parts of the thermal sequence is related to the fact that even now over 450 active volcanoes exist on the surface of the Earth; with each active volcano, regions of subvolcanic temperature through the optimum of about 150°C, and above, are associated. Such temperatures are found also in regions not having active volcanoes.

The widespread nature of such thermal conditions is documented by *Professor Fred M. Bullard* who states in his book, *Volcanoes* [1962]:

> The average person may think that lavas are something rather rare on the earth's surface. To dispel this idea, he needs only to consider, in addition to the lava flows from individual volcanoes, the great plateau basalts such as those which make up the Columbia River Plateau of the Pacific northwest of the United States. Here, covering most of Oregon and parts of Idaho and Washington with an area of 200,000 square miles, are basaltic lavas reaching a thickness of 3,000 feet and representing hundreds of flows superimposed one upon another. When one realizes also that this is but one of many such areas of the earth he obtains some appreciation of the tremendous quantity of lava on the earth's surface.

No more esoteric contribution than rain would be necessary for bringing about the step of self-organization of formed systems from polymers arising in thermal zones.

The likelihood of pertinent conditions on Mars is more difficult to assess for two reasons. One is our lack of knowledge of the Martian facts. (*Urey* [1961] has stated "Even on Mars it seems likely that there is less volcanic activity than on Earth.") The other is that the limits of conditions necessary for the individual reactions have not been established in the laboratory.

EXAMPLES OF POTENTIAL DEVELOPMENT OF RIGOR IN TESTS FOR EXTRATERRESTRIAL LIFE

The ways in which the various criteria for detecting life might be made more rigorous are numerous. The laboratory studies indicated as consequences of such considerations are even more numerous and ramified. A sampling of possibilities is presented in this final section.

Optical Activity

Improvement in the use of optical activity as a criterion of life can be visualized in several steps:

a) The optical activity might be shown to be associated with compounds of carbon.

b) The optical activity might be shown to be associated with individual members of a class of biochemical substance, e.g., amino acids or monosaccharides.

c) If b could be shown to be referable to a single configuration type, optical activity would be a far more convincing manifestation of life.

d) An L isomer of an animo acid is decomposed by a sample of the Martian crust whereas the D enantiomorph is not, or *vice versa.*

Such a result as b, c, or d might indicate Darwinian selection at the microbial level. Evidence of Darwinian selection would, of course, be an indication that life had progressed beyond the initial stage.

The fact that these refinements can be visualized may be taken as an argument that the unqualified observation of net optical activity is a highly inadequate criterion.

Catalytic Activity

This criterion has lost some prestige as a criterion of life. As one example of possible confusion, *Siegel* [1957] showed that the decomposition of glucose-1-phosphate or of hydrogen peroxide is accelerated by the mineral, chrysotile. Other comparable demonstrations have been made by others. The demonstration of a network of catalytic activities in formed units would carry more conviction. Highly specific proteolytic activity might be suggestive of enhanced activity attainable by Darwinian selection for the significant function of feeding.

Ordered Macromolecules

The evaluation of order requires careful definitions of "order," "random," etc. The statistician's definition of a random sample is one in which each element in the whole population is equally represented. One can extend this definition to the sequence in a population of protein molecules. In a random polyamino acid, each kind of amino acid would thus be represented in each position in the polypeptide chain in proportion to its percentage in the total composition. Any other distribution would then be nonrandom, or, to some degree, ordered.

Such evaluations permit operational investigation, e.g., one may compare C-terminal analyses or N-terminal analyses of amino acids with total composition. Such comparisons have been made in many analyses of thermal poly-α-amino acids. The examinations show considerable disparities between C-terminal and N-terminal analyses and total compositions. The distribution of amino acid residues, by type, in thermal poly-α-amino acids is accordingly nonrandom. This degree of ordering must be ascribed to the interacting amino acids. In other words, some information is inherent in the monomers.

A derivative question is whether the influence of nucleic acids or another coding system can be invoked as a criterion of life. Operationally, one might visualize the recognition of such an "outside" coding influence through a different balance of terminal and total compositions. The relevant experiment has, in a sense, been done. Amino acids have been thermally polymerized in the presence of phosphoric acid, which does not enter into the product [*Fox and Harada,* 1960b]. The balance of terminal and total compositions differs between the phosphoric acid product and the control without phosphoric acid. One could not use this criterion, then, to differentiate between terrestrial pre-protein on one hand, and protein made by a Martian microbe.

The development of a more rigorous criterion of cellularly determined or RNA determined order in polyamino acids may emerge from further studies of total composition and terminal composition in synthetic polymers and in proteins. An extensive laboratory and computer program could be constructed. The starting point for such studies might best be the kind of analysis that is most likely to be feasible in an extraterrestrial study. This is perhaps the comparison between total amino acid composition and terminal amino acid compositions. If such analyses of unfractionated protein of biological origin were shown to give a balance sheet not attained in synthetic poly-α-amino acids (many such data are already at hand [*Fox, Harada, Woods, and Windsor,* 1963]), a basis for a test would be at hand. If a sample of organic material on Mars were shown to have a polyamino composition falling into the terrestrial range of protein and outside the range of the synthetic poly-α-amino acids, the indication of life could be regarded as powerful. The possibility of such a distinctive range of analytical specifications has yet to be established, and would constitute much of the research.

Morphology

Many instances of simulation of microbial morphology at the associated cellular, cellular, optical micrographic, and electronmicrographic level in synthetic systems have been observed [*Fox and Yuyama,* 1963a; *Fox,* 1964a]. Morphologies involving limb systems, etc., would, however, seem to require Darwinian selection. These latter should probably be considered as rigorous criteria of life. Fuller understanding of what forms might be assumed by spontaneously synthetic systems, however, requires further research.

REFERENCES

Blout, E. R. (1962), The dependence of the conformation of polypeptides and proteins upon amino-acid composition. *In:* M. A. Stahmann (Ed.) *Polyamino Acids, Polypeptides, and Proteins,* University of Wisconsin, 275-279.

Bullard, F. M. (1962), *Volcanoes,* University of Texas Press, p. 55.

Calvin, M. (1962), Communication: From molecules to Mars. *Bull. Am. Inst. Biol. Sci. 12,* 29-44.

Fox, S. W. (1960), How did life begin? *Science 132,* 200-208.

Fox, S. W. (1963), Experiments suggesting origins of amino acids and proteins. *In:* J. Kastelic, H. H. Draper, and H. P. Broquist (Eds.) *Protein Nutrition and Metabolism,* University of Illinois College of Agriculture, 141-154.

Fox, S. W. (1964a), Experiments in molecular evolution and criteria of extraterrestrial life. *BioScience 14*(12),13-21.

Fox, S. W. (1964b), Simulated natural experiments in spontaneous organization of morphological units from proteinoid. *In:* S. W. Fox (Ed.) *The Origins of Prebiological Systems,* Academic Press, 361-382.

Fox, S. W. (1964c), Thermal polymerization of amino-acids and production of formed microparticles on lava. *Nature 201,* 336-337.

Fox, S. W. and T. Fukushima (1964), Electron micrographs of microspheres from thermal proteinoid. *In:* V. L. Kretovich, T. E. Pavlovskaya, and G. A.

Deborin (Eds.) *Problems of Evolutionary and Industrial Biochemistry,* "Nauka" Publishing House, 93-100.

Fox, S. W. and K. Harada (1958), Thermal copolymerization of amino acids to a product resembling protein. *Science 128,* 1214.

Fox, S. W. and K. Harada (1960*a*), Thermal copolymerization of amino acids in the presence of phosphoric acid. *Arch. Biochem. Biophys. 86,* 281-285.

Fox, S. W. and K. Harada (1960*b*), The thermal copolymerization of amino acids common to protein. *J. Am. Chem. Soc. 82,* 3745-3751.

Fox, S. W. and K. Harada (1961), Synthesis of uracil under conditions of a thermal model of prebiological chemistry. *Science 133,* 1923-1924.

Fox, S. W. and G. Krampitz (1964), The catalytic decomposition of glucose in aqueous solution by thermal proteinoids. *Nature 203,* 1362-1364.

Fox, S. W. and S. Yuyama (1963*a*), Abiotic production of primitive protein and formed microparticles. *Ann. N. Y. Acad. Sci. 108,* 487-494.

Fox, S. W. and S. Yuyama (1963*b*), Effects of the Gram stain on microspheres from thermal polyamino acids. *J. Bacteriol. 85,* 279-283.

Fox, S. W. and S. Yuyama (1964), Dynamic phenomena in microspheres from thermal proteinoid. *Comp. Biochem. Physiol. 11,* 317-321.

Fox, S. W., K. Harada, and J. Kendrick (1959), Synthesis of microscopic spheres in sea water. *International Oceanographic Congress* preprints, 80-81.

Fox, S. W., K. Harada, and D. L. Rohlfing(1962), The thermal copolymerization of α-amino acids. *In:* M. Stahmann (Ed.) *Polyamino Acids, Polypeptides, and Proteins,* University of Wisconsin Press, 47-54.

Fox, S. W., J. E. Johnson, and M. Middlebrook (1955), Pyrosynthesis of aspartic acid and alanine from citric acid cycle intermediates. *J. Am. Chem. Soc. 77,* 1048-1049.

Fox, S. W., J. E. Johnson, and A. Vegotsky (1956), On biochemical origins and optical activity. *Science 124,* 923-925.

Fox, S. W., K. Harada, K. Woods, and C. R. Windsor (1963), Amino acid compositions of proteinoids. *Arch. Biochem. Biophys. 102,* 439-445.

Gill, T. J., III and P. Doty (1962), The immunological and physio-chemical properties of a group of linear-chain synthetic polypeptides. *In:* M. A. Stahmann (Ed.) *Polyamino Acids, Polypeptides, and Proteins,* University of Wisconsin Press, 367-378.

Harada, K. and S. W. Fox (1962), A total resolution of aspartic acid copper complex by inoculation. *Nature 194,* 768.

Harada, K. and Fox, S. W. (1964), Thermal synthesis of natural amino-acids from a postulated primitive terrestrial atmosphere. *Nature 201,* 335-336.

Keosian, J. (1964), *The Origin of Life,* Reinhold Pub. Corp., p. 7.

Krampitz, G., K. Harada, and S. W. Fox (1964), Unpublished experiments.

Krasnovskii, A. A. and A. V. Umrikhina in comment by A. I. Oparin (1964). *In:* S. W. Fox (Ed.) *The Origins of Prebiological Systems,* Academic Press, 252-253.

Lipmann, F. (1964), Projecting backward from the present stage of evolution of biosynthesis. *In:* S. W. Fox (Ed.) *The Origins of Prebiological Systems.* Academic Press, 259-280.

Maurer, P. H. (1962), Immunological studies with synthetic polymers. *In:* M. A. Stahmann (Ed.) *Polyamino Acids, Polypeptides, and Proteins,* University of Wisconsin Press, 359-366.

Miller, S. L. (1953), A production of amino acids under possible primitive earth conditions. *Science 117*, 528-529.

Murray, R. G. E. (1960), The internal structure of the cell. *In:* I. C. Gunsalus and R. Y. Stanier (Eds.) *The Bacteria, 1*, Academic Press, p. 91.

Noguchi, J. and T. Saito (1962), Studies on the catalytic activity of synthetic polyamino acids having an imidazole group in the active site. *In:* M. A. Stahmann (Ed.) *Polyamino Acids, Polypeptides, and Proteins*, University of Wisconsin Press, 313-328.

Northrop, J. H. (1957), Optically active compounds from racemic mixtures by means of random distribution. *Proc. Nat'l. Acad. Sci. U. S. 43*, 304-305.

Oparin, A. I. (1964), *The Chemical Origin of Life*, Charles C Thomas, Springfield, Ill.

Oró, J. and A. C. Cox (1962), Non-enzymic synthesis of 2-deoxyribose. *Federation Proc. 21*, 80.

Oró, J. and A. P. Kimball (1961), Synthesis of purines under possible primitive Earth conditions. *Arch. Biochem. Biophys. 94*, 217-227.

Ponnamperuma, C. (1964), Abiological synthesis of some nucleic acid constituents. *In:* S. W. Fox (Ed.) *The Origins of Prebiological Systems*, Academic Press, 221-242.

Ponnamperuma, C., R. S. Young, E. P. Munox, and B. K. McCaw (1964), Guanine: Formation during the thermal polymerization of amino acids. *Science 143*, 1449-1450.

Rohlfing, D. L. (1964), Catalytic activity and heat inactivation of thermal poly-α-amino acids. Ph.D. dissertation, Florida State University.

Schramm, G. (1964), Synthesis of nucleosides and polynucleotides with metaphosphate esters. *In:* S. W. Fox (Ed.) *The Origins of Prebiological Systems*, Academic Press, 299-315; also, Schramm, G., H. Grotsch, and W. Pollmann (1962), Non-enzymatic synthesis of polysaccharides, nucleosides and nucleic acids and the origin of self-reproducing systems, *Angew. Chem. Intern. Ed. Engl. 1*, 1-7.

Schwartz, A. and S. W. Fox (1964), Thermal synthesis of internucleotide phosphodiester linkages. *Biochim. Biophys. Acta 87*, 694-696.

Sela, M. (1962), Some contributions of the study of synthetic polypeptides to the understanding of the chemical basis of antigenicity. *In:* M. A. Stahmann (Ed.) *Polyamino Acids, Polypeptides, and Proteins*, University of Wisconsin Press, 347-358.

Siegel, S. M. (1957), Catalytic and polymerization-directing properties of mineral surfaces. *Proc. Nat'l. Acad. Sci. U. S. 43*, 811-817.

Stahmann, M. A. (1962), Chemotherapeutic possibilities of polyamino acids. *In:* M. A. Stahmann (Ed.) *Polyamino Acids, Polypeptides, and Proteins*, University of Wisconsin Press, 329-340.

Stearn, E. W. and A. E. Stearn (1924), The chemical mechanism of bacterial behavior. I. Behavior toward dyes—factors controlling the Gram reaction. *J. Bacteriol. 9*, 463-477.

Urey, H. C. (1961), The planets. *In:* L. V. Berkner and H. Odishaw (Eds.) *Science in Space*, McGraw-Hill Book Co., p. 204.

Wald, G. (1957), The origin of optical activity. *Ann. N. Y. Acad. Sci. 69*, 352-368.

CHAPTER 11

A MODEL OF MARTIAN ECOLOGY*

WOLF VISHNIAC, K. C. ATWOOD, R. M. BOCK, HANS GAFFRON,
T. H. JUKES, A. D. MCLAREN, CARL SAGAN, and HYRON SPINRAD

INTRODUCTION

Although the environment on Mars differs drastically from that on Earth, the difference is not so great that the terrestrial biologist cannot envisage a group of organisms that would not only survive but flourish under Martian conditions. In attempting to describe the activities that a Martian organism must carry out in order to survive, it should be remembered that Mars, like Earth, cannot be populated by any single type of organism. Any model of a Martian ecology must describe a community of organisms, the members of which compensate for each other's activities. The sum of these activities constitutes a biological cycle of matter. Ever since the opposite net effects of photosynthesis and respiration have been known [*Ingenhousz, 1779*] it has been understood, at least in general terms, that a worldwide balance between these two processes must exist. The Earth is therefore a gigantic balanced vivarium in which the various populations live at steady state levels that are limited by the energy flux through the system and modified for any one organism by other members of the same food chain. "Food" is here used in the most general sense and comprises not only organic matter but also all other necessary chemical components of the environment, such

* Report prepared by Professor Vishniac as chairman of a study group on this subject.

229

as oxygen, nitrogen, carbon dioxide, mineral salts, etc. On Earth the amount of food materials that is recycled maintains a biomass that approaches, within an order of magnitude, the limit imposed by the energy flux from the Sun. This relationship is exemplified by the following figures. Of the 5 $\times$ 10^{24} joules per year that reach the upper atmosphere from the Sun about 2 $\times$ 10^{24} joules reach the surface of the Earth [*Rabinowitch, 1945*]. Allowing for infrared radiation, which is not used in photosynthesis (50 per cent), and absorption and reflection losses (20 per cent), about 6 $\times$ 10^{23} joules are available for photosynthesis in forests, on prairies and arable land, and in the ocean. Photosynthesis in the field is about 2 per cent efficient, so that 1.2 $\times$ 10^{22} joules can be converted per year. The conversion of one gram of carbon from carbon dioxide to the constituents of a living organism requires at least 5 $\times$ 10^{4} joules (cf., Table 1). The availability of 1.2 $\times$ 10^{22} joules per year therefore limits the annual productivity of Earth to 2.4 $\times$ 10^{11} tons of carbon, of which about 2 $\times$ 10^{11} tons can be fixed in the ocean.

The actual productivity of the oceans is estimated at 100 to 200 grams of carbon per year per square meter [*Harvey, 1957; Riley*]. The area of our oceans, excluding the Arctic Sea and some marginal waters is 3.5 $\times$ 10^{14} square meters. The annual fixation is therefore 3.5 to 7.0 $\times$ 10^{10} tons of carbon per year, or 18 to 35 per cent of the theoretical maximum. Considering the uncertainty of the figures, it appears that primary productivity on Earth, and hence biomass, come within a factor of ten of the level at which energy flux would be directly limiting. On Mars, the biomass may be limited by the available water and a different relationship is therefore imposed on the members of the ecological community.

CONDITIONS ON MARS

This discussion of Martian ecology is based on the following description of the planetary environment. Mars possesses an atmosphere with a surface pressure between 10 and 60 mb. This atmosphere consists of about 30 to 90 per cent carbon dioxide with the remainder most likely a mixture of nitrogen and argon. The atmosphere is transparent to visible light and admits a high level of ultraviolet radiation. There is no evidence for oxygen; the spectroscopic upper limit is 50 cm-atm, or about 0.025 mb. In the following discussion two alternative assumptions are made: 1) that there is no oxygen, and 2) there is oxygen present to the detectable limit, namely a partial pressure of 0.025 mb.

Surface temperatures reach 30° C but a diurnal variation of 100° must be expected in many latitudes. The atmosphere contains water vapor to the

TABLE 1. Energy Required for Phototrophic Growth

The energy for conversion of unit weight of carbon from carbon dioxide to the constituents of a living organism is based on the requirements of a photoautotroph and is calculated as follows:

State in Biosynthesis	On Basis of	Required per Gram Atom Carbon	
		Cofactors	Energy in Joules
$CO_2 \rightarrow$ carbohydrate	Calvin-Benson Pathway	3.0 ATP	1.2×10^5
		2.0 NADPH	3.6×10^5
carbohydrate $\rightarrow$ amino acids	Survey of known pathways	approximately 0.5 ATP	0.2×10^5
amino acids $\rightarrow$ living cell	Yield of 10 g dry weight of cell material per mole ATP [*Bauchop and Elsden*, 1960]	2.4 ATP	1.0×10^5
			6.0×10^5

The minimum requirement for phototrophic growth on CO_2 is, therefore, about 5×10^4 joules per gram of carbon.

extent of 2×10^{-3} gm cm^{-2}. Hoarfrost may form during the Martian night, and water is frozen out at the Martian poles. The waxing and waning of the polar caps with the seasons implies an atmospheric water transport. The light areas of Mars are thought to be covered with limonite of an average particle diameter of 100μ or less and the dark areas may contain related material [Dollfus, 1957].

To form a stable ecological system a community of living organisms must not only survive in this environment, but the activities of the organisms must tend to maintain this environment. The following outline of possible biological activities on Mars is an extrapolation based on the principles of terrestrial biochemistry.

PRIMARY PRODUCTIVITY

The external source to support a community of organisms is the radiant energy of the Sun. Two types of mechanisms may exist to convert the radiant energy into chemical energy. There may be a non-biological sequence of reactions, similar to those that occur in experiments that produce organic matter from primitive atmospheres (Miller [1957]; and cf., Chapter 2), or there may be a biological energy conversion, namely photosynthesis. The incidence of ultraviolet radiation may bring about a reaction between carbon dioxide, water, and other atmospheric constituents to form carbohydrates or related compounds. The laboratory simulation of this process has now been performed by Young, Ponnamperuma and McCaw [1965] and both five- and six-carbon sugars have been produced, among other compounds. The rates of synthesis, while low, are increased in the presence of limonite. These organic compounds may accumulate on or precipitate to the surface and serve as the primary source of organic material on which Martian organisms could grow.

The alternative would be the existence of photosynthetic organisms that assimilate carbon dioxide in the light. Since oxygen is either absent from the Martian atmosphere, or at best present in extremely low concentration, the Martian photosynthesis would resemble that of terrestrial bacteria, rather than plants. Green plants and algae on Earth use water as the ultimate electron donor in photosynthesis with the consequent liberation of oxygen—which, indeed, is thought to be the major source of oxygen in the terrestrial atmosphere. Photosynthetic bacteria use compounds other than water as their electron donors, such compounds including hydrogen, a variety of reduced sulfur compounds, and other substances.

In the absence of direct information, it is nevertheless possible to advance arguments for or against the production of organic compounds by non-biological photochemistry, based on a consideration of the selective advantage that such a process may or may not have for the remainder of the Martian population. Should organic matter be produced by non-biological photochemistry at a non-limiting rate, so that there is always an excess of organic matter available to heterotrophic organisms, then there might be no selective pressure favoring the evolution of photosynthetic organisms. On Earth, accumulations of non-living organic matter are consumed by organisms which develop as rapidly as organic matter is formed, but on Mars life is limited by water and therefore organic matter might conceivably accumulate in excess of the biomass. However, water is also one of the raw materials of non-biological photochemical synthesis and the rate of formation of organic matter by this mechanism must therefore be restricted, much as life itself might be restricted. Another disadvantage of non-biological photochemical synthesis might be that only a fraction of the organic matter so produced might be useful to Martian organisms. In other words, the efficiency of energy conversion in the food chain would be low. Under these circumstances, selective advantages might favor the formation of photosynthetic organisms that would be the primary producers of organic matter and the converters of radiant energy into chemical energy. However, the activity of such photosynthetic organisms may be supplemented by the occurrence of "extraorganismal photosynthesis," so that the primary food supply might be in part organic matter synthesized by photosynthetic organisms and in part "manna from heaven."

RESPIRATION

On Earth, photosynthetic processes are counterbalanced by respiratory activities in which oxygen is the terminal electron acceptor. Whether even a small part of the respiration of Martian organisms is linked to oxygen will depend on whether the Martian atmosphere contains any oxygen at all. Present observations place an upper limit of 0.025 mb on the partial pressure of oxygen in the Martian atmosphere. Although on Earth the partial pressure of oxygen is nearly four orders of magnitude greater, even such a small amount of oxygen as might exist on Mars could be of biological significance, as the following calculation will show. At 0.025 mb the concentration of oxygen is $2.5 \times 10^{-5}/22.4 = 1.13 \times 10^{-6}$ moles per liter of oxygen in the atmosphere. The solubility of oxygen in water at NTP is 4.89×10^{-2} ml per ml. The concentration of oxygen in water at $0°$ C would therefore be $1.13 \times 10^{-6} \times 4.89 \times 10^{-2} = 5.46 \times 10^{-8}$ moles per liter. This concentration is marginal for terminal oxidative processes of some terrestrial organisms. Thus a micrococcus species has been reported to respire at 1° C under 0.1 mb oxygen as rapidly as under 200 mb oxygen [*Warburg and Kubowitz*, 1929], and light emission by luminescent bacteria can be observed at concentrations considerably below 0.1 mb [*Hastings*, 1952]. A variety of intestinal parasites is reported to respire at extremely low partial pressures of oxygen [*Bueding*, 1963] and germination of certain plant seeds has been observed by *Siegel et al.* [1963] at about 1 mb oxygen. Thus if the Martian atmosphere should contain 0.025 mb oxygen, Martian microorganisms may carry out respiratory activities comparable in their net balance to those of terrestrial organisms.

In the absence of any direct evidence for oxygen, we must proceed on the assumption that Mars is anaerobic, but it is worthwhile to consider, in passing, the biological significance of aerobic respiration. In the oxidation of organic matter with oxygen as a terminal electron acceptor, a greater change in free energy takes place than in the use of any other commonly available electron acceptor. Although such thermodynamic considerations bear no necessary relationship to the biological efficiency with which such energy is utilized, it is clear that more energy is available in aerobic respiration and that some organisms, at least, will take advantage of this possibility. In a competition for organic substrates, aerobic respiration provides an organism with a selective advantage since it gains the same amount of energy at the expense of less organic matter. Experiments on the growth of microorganisms [*Bauchop and Elsden*, 1960] show that growth is directly related to the biologically significant energy that is made available in substrate dissimilation, provided that the raw materials for cell synthesis are present. There is then first of all the advantage in numbers or mass bestowed on those organisms that utilize oxygen. Secondly, the availability of more energy and the use of an electron acceptor that diffuses readily through the living tissue makes possible the evolution of larger multicellular structures than is possible in fermentative organisms. It can be stated as a generalization that all multicellular organisms that we know are aerobic. It is the use of oxygen that enables an organism to devote part of its energy to the maintenance of a constant temperature, that is, to the maintenance of a constant activity, largely independent of temperature fluctuations in the environment. This means that an organism so endowed can be active in an environment in which some of its competitors are dormant. Undoubtedly, all these faculties are the prerequisite for the development of intelligent life, so that the prerequisites for intelligence were developed when photosynthetic organisms first learned to utilize water as electron donor and thereby discharge oxygen into the atmosphere. Nevertheless, it is premature to exclude the existence of anaerobic metazoa on Mars.

In the absence of oxygen, Martian respiratory organisms must use other electron acceptors. Terrestrial examples of anaerobic respirations include the reduction of sulfate to sulfide, in which the sulfur atom accepts electrons in terminal respiration, the reduction of nitrate to nitrogen, and the reduction of carbon dioxide to methane. Thus a number of common pseudomonads and enteric bacteria will grow at the expense of the reaction:

$$5 \; CH_3COOH + NO_3^- \rightarrow 10 \; CO_2 + 4 \; N_2 + 6 \; H_2O + 8 \; OH^-.$$

Some of the acetic acid is assimilated to make bacterial matter, but the reaction above summarizes the energy metabolism. Sulfate reduction, which is largely carried out by *Desulfovibrio,* proceeds according to the reaction:

$$2 \; CH_3CHOHCOOH + SO_4^= \rightarrow 2 \; CH_3COOH + S^= + 2 \; CO_2 + 2 \; H_2O.$$

As a final example a reaction in which methane bacteria produce methane is:

$$2 \; CH_3CH_2OH + CO_2 \rightarrow 2 \; CH_3COOH + CH_4.$$

All three processes are thermodynamically spontaneous reactions and the change in free energy supports the growth of the microorganisms, although the change in energy is not so great as it would have been if oxygen had been the electron acceptor. Should reactions of this type occur on Mars, that is, should organic matter produced in photosynthesis be oxidized with electron transfer to nitrogen, sulfur, or carbon, there must be balancing reactions that reoxidize the nitrogen, sulfide, and methane. This recycling of the reduced electron acceptors may be carried out by photosynthetic organisms. Terrestrial photosynthetic microorganisms include the purple sulfur bacteria that reduce carbon dioxide in the light and derive the requisite electrons from sulfide or thiosulfate. Such a metabolism can be ecologically linked to that of the sulfate-reducing bacteria as is shown in Figure 1. On Earth, such oxidations can also take place at the expense of oxygen. Thus there are microorganisms that will oxidize sulfide or methane and ammonia to sulfate, carbon dioxide and nitrate. Light has the same significance for photosynthetic organisms that oxygen has for respiratory organisms; in photosynthesis light is used to create an electron donor and an electron acceptor, and thus an electron flow is initiated. The electron acceptor is capable of oxidizing compounds, the oxidation of which was at one time thought to proceed only with oxygen. It was found by *Scher* [1964] that non-sulfur purple bacteria could photosynthesize with aromatic compounds such as benzoic acid as an electron donor. The oxidation of methane has also been observed [*Vishniac,* 1963]; it leads to a photosynthesis that probably proceeds as follows:

$$CH_4 + CO_2 \rightarrow 2 \; (CH_2O).$$

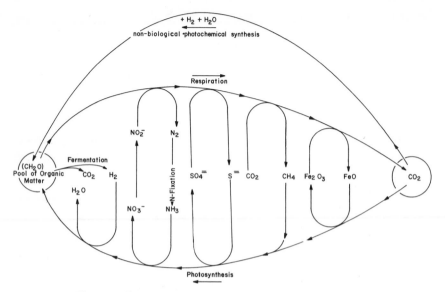

Figure 1.   Hypothetical cycles of matter on Mars.

ECOLOGICAL ROLE OF LIMONITE

The presence of limonite on the Martian surface is potentially of great ecological significance. Iron in its oxidized or reduced form may serve as an electron acceptor in respiration, or an electron donor in photosynthesis, while limonite, because of its water content, may serve also as a water reservoir on Mars. Limonite is a non-crystalline iron ore, containing chiefly goethite or lepidocrocite ($Fe_2O_3 \cdot H_2O$) and additional adsorbed water [*Deer et al,* 1963]. Its average composition is $(Fe_2O_3)_2 \cdot 3H_2O$, but only about ⅔ of the water is water of crystallization. The ferric iron of limonite may be thought to serve as a respiratory substrate for Martian organisms, a respiration in which iron serves as the terminal respiratory electron acceptor. This respiration can be described by

$$2n\ Fe_2O_3 + (CH_2O)_n \rightarrow 4n\ FeO + n\ CO_2 + n\ H_2O$$

In the reduction of limonite, that is ferric oxide, to ferrous oxide the bound water would be set free, in addition to whatever water is formed in the oxidation of organic substrates. Terrestrial organisms are known, at least in crude culture, that can live by the oxidation of organic substrates with ferric hydroxide as the terminal electron acceptor [*Vishniac,* 1965]. The reoxidation of the ferrous oxide to the ferric form can reasonably be expected to support a photosynthesis which would take the following form

$$\text{4}n \text{ FeO} + n \text{ CO}_2 + n \text{ H}_2\text{O} \xrightarrow{\text{light}} 2n \text{ Fe}_2\text{O}_3 + (\text{CH}_2\text{O})_n$$

There would therefore exist an ecological coupling between a respiration transferring electrons to ferric iron and a photosynthesis deriving electrons from ferrous iron. The limonite would at the same time serve as a water buffer, in the sense that its reduction to ferrous iron would give up water while the newly formed ferric oxide would gradually take up water to reform limonite. Martian organisms might therefore be thought of as swimming in an ocean of limonite. It is worth noting in this connection that the partial pressure of water in the Martian atmosphere corresponds approximately to that observed above limonite at typical Martian temperatures [*Adamcik,* 1963].

There is an additional consequence of such an iron cycle. Wherever living organisms are active on Mars there would be present simultaneously both oxidized and reduced iron compounds. In the presence of chelating compounds such a mixture is likely to produce intensely colored complexes of the type of which Prussian blue is an example. Should the dark areas on Mars be the result of biological activity their color (if real) may well find its explanation in the formation of such complexes.

ORGANIC MATTER ON MARS

We are at present in no position to estimate the Martian biomass, if there is any. Nevertheless it is instructive to carry out some speculative calculations that may lead to an estimate of the magnitude of the Martian biomass and a realization of the amounts that must be dealt with in any "life detection" experiment. As has been mentioned before, life on Earth is probably primarily limited by carbon dioxide and on Mars by water. A direct comparison between the terrestrial and a presumed Martian biomass is therefore not possible, unless we make certain assumptions regarding the water balance. On Earth the biomass is approximately 10 g per cm^2 or about ten times the amount of atmospheric water. On Mars a similar relation would give for 2×10^{-3} g water per cm^2 a biomass of 2×10^{-2} g living matter per cm^2. Whether this figure is regarded as high or low depends on what assumptions one wishes to make concerning underground water resources.

The amount of organic matter turned over by such a population can be calculated in terrestrial terms. For example, a cell of *Escherichia coli* weighs 10^{-12} g wet or 10^{-13} g dry. In order to synthesize that amount of material the cell requires 10^{-14} moles of ATP (based on *Bauchop and Elsden* [1960]), which are made in a glycolytic path from 5×10^{-15}

moles or 9×10^{-13} g of glucose. Adding to this amount the weight of material needed to synthesize a new cell mean that *E. coli* turns over 10^{-12} g of matter for every new cell. The total turnover of matter is therefore equal to the biomass per generation time. The generation time may be as short as twenty minutes, while the surface area of an *Escherichia coli* is about 10^{-7} cm². Thus a terrestrial turnover rate for a bacterium can be as great as 10^{-8} g cm⁻² sec⁻¹ under favorable laboratory conditions. However, for soil microorganisms, with starvation the rule and abundance the exception, average turnover rates are likely to be lower by about three orders of magnitude. For unit weight of microorganisms, these turnover rates are 0.8×10^{-3} g sec⁻¹ in the laboratory or 0.8×10^{-6} g sec⁻¹ in soil. Assuming the Martian biomass to be 2×10^{-2} g cm⁻², the rate of turnover of organic matter on Mars becomes 1.6×10^{-8} g cm⁻² sec⁻¹. Attempts to measure the activity of soil samples on Mars must therefore be prepared to measure rates of this order of magnitude.

An argument can be made for comparable rates of metabolism in Martian and terrestrial organisms if we assume a biological basis for the seasonal darkening of certain areas on Mars. The wave of darkening on Mars travels at 35 km per day, while spring in the U.S. Middle West advances 40 km per day.

STRUCTURE, MORPHOLOGY, AND GENERAL PHYSIOLOGY OF MARTIAN ORGANISMS

The structure of Martian organisms will be dictated by the need to withstand extremes in temperature and the need to exploit those conditions under which the fluid of the internal environment is liquid. Organisms must also compete for water and specialize in its conservation. In addition the high ultraviolet flux may require the evolution of shielding or other protective devices.

Organisms may maintain the liquid state of their body fluids by several techniques. Pigmented organisms absorb radiation and raise their temperature. The freezing point of their body fluids may also be depressed by the incorporation of solutes. Terrestrial halophilic microorganisms possess internal salt concentrations that approximate those of the external medium [*Larsen*, 1963]. Depending on the identity of the salts, the freezing point of an aqueous medium may be depressed to —50° C. Alternatively, organic solutes such as glycerol may not only depress the freezing point but also prevent the formation of crystalline ice that would otherwise disrupt the structures of the organism. Such a mechanism is known to contribute to the protection of insects that survive winters with extreme temperatures [Salt, 1959; 1961].

Because of the lower temperatures, Martian life may have evolved in a manner that makes far more diversified use of light reactions than do living things on Earth. Any chemical enzymatic reaction which because of low temperature would take a long time to proceed, could be speeded up when coupled to a light absorbing pigment fit to deliver the activation energies regardless of temperature. In other words, the Q_{10} of 2 that is typical for metabolic reactions on Earth may be lowered considerably by the right combination of light-dependent and light-independent reactions. While little is known of their action, catalysts that are active at low temperatures are known to exist. For example, isolated chloroplasts continue to deteriorate at $-20°$ C and the process responsible for this deterioration does not stop until the temperature has been lowered to $-40°$ C. Metabolism on Mars may therefore be more dependent on light than on temperature.

The necessity to conserve water is compatible with the maintenance of a temperature above that of the environment. Thus transpiration in photosynthetic organisms would be kept to a minimum. In the absence of transpiration photosynthetic organisms would not be cooled, but their temperature would be raised by the absorbed radiation. Without transpiration pull, water could rise only by osmotic and capillary mechanisms, but it is not clear to what extent this restriction limits the height of a plant.

Transpiration may be minimized by the absence of structures analogous to stomata and by the presence of a lipid cuticle. Similarly to known hydrophobic membranes, cuticle of this sort could allow the passage of carbon dioxide but be largely impermeable to water. In addition the cuticle might serve as a shield against ultraviolet radiation. Generally waxy or fatty structures would be more important on Mars than carbohydrate structures, if one can judge by terrestrial experience, in which carbohydrate storage is more frequently an aerobic process, while fats are stored in the absence of oxygen. Hence cellulose and lignin may be absent and plants either will be without rigid structural materials or will elaborate a silica skeleton. Fats are also a more efficient store of hydrogen than are carbohydrates.

For protection against ultraviolet radiation, Martian organisms may develop three kinds of defenses. Highly absorbent organic material may be incorporated in the cell wall or in a waxy cuticle, such as mentioned above. The radiation so absorbed would also serve to raise the temperature of the organism. An absorbent inorganic material such as the limonite of Martian soil, could be combined with the silica shell to make a rigid iron glass with strong ultraviolet absorbing properties. Finally, an organism might be shielded by fluorescent material and the emitted light could support photosynthesis.

The ecological niches that Martian organisms might occupy are summarized in Figure 1. The occurrence and significance of many of the individual reactions have been outlined above; only the nitrogen cycle requires additional discussion. The immediate source of biologically significant nitrogen is ammonia. This ammonia can be provided either as soluble ammonium compounds or it may arise by reduction of other nitrogen compounds. Many microorganisms are capable of reducing nitrate and nitrite to ammonia, and others are able to fix atmospheric nitrogen, which is reduced to ammonia. In the respiratory utilization of nitrate the end product is gaseous nitrogen, which then enters the nitrogen cycle by nitrogen fixation. The recycling of ammonia to nitrate is, in our experience, a strictly aerobic reaction, carried out by the autotrophic nitrifying bacteria that derive their energy by the oxidation of ammonia to oxides of nitrogen. Should the Martian atmosphere be entirely devoid of oxygen, the nitrogen metabolism of the Martian organisms may follow either of the two following patterns: 1) There may be no nitrogen cycle in the redox sense, but all biologically significant nitrogen shuttles back and forth between free ammonia or ammonium compounds and organic amines. 2) There may be an anaerobic oxidation of ammonia to nitrate, for which one likely candidate would be the utilization of ammonia as an electron donor in bacterial photosynthesis. An alternative would be an autotrophic organism using ammonia as the electron donor and ferric oxide as electron acceptor. No organisms of this type are as yet known on Earth.

CONCLUSIONS

Mars may be populated by a community of microorganisms and plants that utilize sunlight as the primary energy source and catalyze a cycle of matter on the surface of the planet. Microorganisms may vary from forms that live a few millimeters below the surface in a microclimate affording some protection from ultraviolet radiation and favoring retention of water and organic matter, to shielded organisms that expose themselves on the very surface of the soil. One attractive model for such shielded organisms are the *Testacidae,* the armoured sarcodina, such as *Arcella* or *Difflugia.* The shells of such organisms on Mars may be largely opaque to ultraviolet radiation and their amoeboid character could cause attachment to the substrate or to each other. Such attachment is suggested by the observation that Martian storms whirl up material from the bright areas and occasionally deposit it as a visible bright spot on a dark area, while aeolian transport of dark material has not been observed.

If the seasonal darkening of certain Martian regions is indicative of biological activity, one would ascribe a rate of metabolism to Martian organisms that is comparable to that of terrestrial organisms. This is judged from the darkening of the nuclei, which takes place in a matter of days, and from the rate of advance of the wave of darkening. These rates are compatible with a generation time measured in hours rather than in days or weeks. The largest organisms on Mars may be plants that do not transpire, and that lack rigid support unless they elaborate a silicious skeleton. It has been suggested that the disappearance of light areas that form in dark regions by the settling of dust after a "sandstorm," may be due to the soil particles sliding off the leaves or limbs of such plants. An alternative is that the soil microorganisms multiply and overgrow such soil deposits. Soil from light colored areas, carried by the wind into dark regions, may be a fertilizer and stimulate growth of organisms by supplying fresh limonite with additional water or trace nutrients.

For the Martian organisms, spring begins when the rise in average temperature makes water available for photosynthesis. If we assume that photosynthetic organisms are pigmented, while the heterotrophic organisms by and large are not, then the occurrence of photosynthesis and the absorption of light by multiplying photosynthetic organisms contributes to a further temperature rise in the microclimate. The heterotrophic part of the population follows suit and respires accumulated organic matter with the reduction of iron compounds. The formation of ferrous iron in the presence of ferric compounds and organic compounds, among which there may be chelating agents, will result in the formation of complexes that are strongly light-absorbing, and so the soil will darken. In the autumn, the falling temperature will inactivate heterotrophic organisms first, while the photosynthetic organisms, owing to their ability to warm themselves with absorbed light, remain active longer. Consequently iron compounds continue to be oxidized (see page *236*), ferrous compounds disappear, and the ground turns lighter. As winter descends, the ferric oxide slowly reacts with water and returns to limonite, thus storing water for the following spring.

CONSEQUENCES

This speculative outline of Martian ecology suggests those possibilities for which "life detection" experiments should be prepared. Instrument landings should take place in a dark area and sampling should take place during and after the wave of darkening has passed. If more than one landing is feasible then light and dark areas should be compared. Attempts to cultivate microorganisms should make use of sampling devices that are capable of gathering particles as large as 100μ in diameter and culture media should accommodate the major ecological niches, with allowance for halophilic organisms.

REFERENCES

Adamcik, J. (1963), *Planetary Space Sci., 11,* 355.

Bauchop, T., and Elsden, S. R. (1960), *J. Gen. Microbiol., 23,* 457.

Bueding, E. (1963). In: B. Wright, ed., *Control Mechanisms in Respiration and Fermentation,* Ronald, New York, pp. 167-177.

Deer, W. A., Howie, R. A., and Zussman, J. (1962), *Rock-Forming Minerals, 5,* Longmans, London, p. 124.

Dollfus, A. (1957), *Ann. Astrophys., Suppl. 4.*

Harvey, H. W. (1957), *Chemistry and Fertility of Sea Water,* Cambridge.

Hastings, J. W. (1952), *J. Cell. Comp. Physiol., 39,* 1.

Ingenhousz, J. (1779), *Experiments Upon Vegetables,* London.

Larsen, H. (1963), Halophilism. In: I. C. Gunsalus and R. Y. Stanier, eds. *The Bacteria, 4,* Academic Press, New York, p. 297.

Miller, S. L. (1957), *Biochim. Biophys. Acta, 23,* 480.

Rabinowitch, E. (1945), (Recalculated from) *Photosynthesis and Related Processes, 1,* Interscience, New York.

Riley, G., personal communication.

Salt, R. W. (1959), *Can. J. Zool., 37,* 59.

Salt, R. W. (1961), *Ann. Rev. Entomol., 6,* 55.

Scher, S. (1964), In: M. Florkin and A. Dollfus, eds., *Life Sciences and Space Research II,* North-Holland Publishing Co., Amsterdam.

Siegel, S. M., Rosen, L. A., and Giuarro, C. (1963), *Nature, 198,* 1288, and unpublished report: Qtly. Report No. 1, Sept. 30, 1963, submitted to NASA, Contract No. NASW-767.

Vishniac, W. (1963), Presented at Fourth International Space Science Symposium (COSPAR), Warsaw.

Vishniac, W. (1965), In: M. Florkin, ed., *Life Sciences and Space Research III,* North-Holland Publishing Co., Amsterdam.

Warburg, O., and Kubowitz, F. (1929), *Biochem. Z., 214,* 5.

Young, R. S., Ponnamperuma, C., and McCaw, B. K. (1965), to be published.

CHAPTER 12

EXOTIC BIOCHEMISTRY IN EXOBIOLOGY*

G. C. Pimentel, K. C. Atwood, Hans Gaffron, H. K. Hartline,
T. H. Jukes, E. C. Pollard, and Carl Sagan

Possibly the most interesting and important exobiological discovery that could be made would be a life-form based upon chemistry radically different from that on Earth. It would be as great an error to omit consideration of non-Earth-like biochemical possibilities as it would be to fail to look for DNA. Of course, possibilities must be assessed within the known chemical and physical principles and speculations must stay within bounds of reasonableness defined by the available knowledge about a given environment. Yet a significant argument can be made that a program of exploration for extraterrestrial life must include specific experiments directed toward what we shall call exotic biochemistry.

ARGUMENTS FOR EXOTIC BIOCHEMISTRY, OR, HAZARDS OF "DOWN-TO-EARTH" THINKING

If there is one principle upon which we might confidently build models of biogenic developments on other planets, it is that life-forms tend to evolve and persist that are amenable to their environment. Taken at face value, this principle makes it unlikely that any Martian biochemistry would be Earth-like. There are at least three highly probable features of

*Report prepared by Professor Pimentel as chairman of a study group on this subject.

the Martian environment that would imply that an Earth-like biogeny would have to evolve in opposition to its environment rather than in harmony with it.

1. In the Martian environment, free water is in extremely short supply; Earth organisms usually contain more than 75 per cent water (except in certain resting states, such as spores and seeds).

2. The Martian atmosphere apparently provides little protection from solar ultraviolet light in the 1700-3000 Å range. This spectral region is, in general, lethal to Earth organisms.

3. The average surface temperature on Mars probably ranges from 180°K to 300°K (-93°C to $+27$°C); thus chemical reactions that proceed with reasonable reaction rates in Earth organisms, namely, with a reaction half-time that is a small fraction of a diurnal period, would require many, possibly hundreds or thousands of diurnal periods in this low temperature regime.

With these forbidding challenges to its existence, will the Martian life hunt for a capillary (where there is water) under a rock (where there is shade) in a hot spot (it is hunting for our famous room temperature!) and then proceed to evolve into chlorella? Yes, that is a possibility. But there are also the reasonable possibilities that water will find quite a different role in the development of a Martian biota; that Martian evolution will take advantage of the greater range of photosynthetic reactions furnished by ultraviolet radiation; and that the Martian biochemistry will sort out and put to use reactions of much lower activation energy, so that a day's work can be done in a day. The importance of these considerations about the Martian environment is amplified manyfold when we remember that Mars is the solar planet that most closely resembles Earth, though the search for extraterrestrial life must include the other planets, as well as the more remote regions of the Universe. The chemical contrasts, for example, between Jupiter and Earth, are far more dramatic than those cited above.

With this background, perhaps we should look again at a few rather familiar reference points many of us use to justify "down-to-Earth" thinking about extraterrestrial life.

Elemental Abundance

One is led intuitively to expect a certain universality in biochemistry because of the evidence that there is a reasonably uniform cosmic abundance of the elements. However, what must matter is the elemental abundance *at the time* of biogeny. On Earth, life evolved in the presence of very large amounts of silicon, large amounts of aluminum and quite small concentrations of phosphorus. A comparison of the relative biochemical importance of these elements places the abundance argument in perspective. Geochemistry provides such significant fractionation and biogeny decides its elemental constituents with such selectivity that cosmic abundances furnish, at best, dubious guideposts.

Water, the Special Solvent

Because water plays such a key role in terrestrial biochemistry, it is not surprising that many persons have concluded that some of the distinctive properties of water are essential to the development of life. *Firsoff* [1963], for example, considers at length the possibilities of life developing in such solvents as NH_3, H_2S, SO_2, HCN, HF, F_2O, etc., each selected and evaluated by contrasting it to H_2O. A rather long list of properties of water is considered to identify its special value: its acid-base chemistry, high dielectric constant, long liquid range, high boiling point, large heat of fusion, large heat of vaporization, hydrogen bonding capabilities, large specific heat, ionizing solvent action, density inversion on freezing, high cosmic abundance (see, for example, *Henderson* [1958]). Only three or four of these properties need be considered to see that these properties are important, if at all, because of historical contingency only.

The fact that ice floats seems a great convenience to a fish that must spend the winter in a pond that freezes. On another planet, ponds may never freeze or, if they do, the biota may be well acclimated to hibernation, encased in solid, as are known life-forms on Earth.

The high dielectric properties of water account for its ability to dissolve salts to give electrolyte solutions. It is not at all clear, however, that electrolytic conduction plays an essential role in the development of life. While conduction and ion adsorption participate in the chemical processes that occur in cells, it does not seem that there are functions involved that cannot be otherwise discharged.

The acid-base properties of water are certainly important in the chemistry of aqueous solutions. There are, of course, many other solvents that possess analogous acid-base behavior. Ammonia is an obvious example of such a substance that might play a solvent role on Jupiter [*Franklin,* 1912; *Sisler,* 1961]. More important, however, is the question whether acid-base properties are indispensable to biochemical solvents. Hydrocarbon solvents, for example, are used in the laboratory in a multitude of organic synthetic reactions for which the chemist has at his disposal any solvent he wishes. Furthermore, the loss of solvent acid-base properties does not delete acid-base reactions (in the generalized definitions of acid and base) from the possible synthetic routes; it merely implies that the solvent itself is not a reactant or product.

The hydrogen bonding capabilities of water seem to be of crucial importance. They are not necessarily essential, however. It must be remembered that absence of water does not imply the loss of other hydrogen-bonding functional groups that could serve similar structural functions, as in terrestrial biochemistry. Secondly, the solvent action of water is augmented by its hydrogen bonding but this action is specifically effective for solutes that are themselves hydrophilic. In a non-aqueous biochemistry, hydrophobic substances might predominate, and in such a case the hydrogen bonding of water might be a liability rather than an asset.

The liquid range of water (100 C°) can be contrasted unfavorably to the rather short liquid ranges of other pure substances such as hydrogen sulfide, 21 C°, and methane, 22 C°. Such contrasts neglect, however, the possibility presented by solutions. For example, a hydrocarbon solution of isopentane in 3-methyl pentane boils above room temperature and it remains fluid at temperatures as low as 120°K (—153°C). On a hydrocarbon-rich planet, such as Jupiter, a variety of hydrocarbons would be expected, hence the boiling ranges of pure hydrocarbons are hardly relevant.

Careful reflection about each of the properties of water reveals that no matter how they are woven into the Earth-pattern of life, none of them seems to involve a functional uniqueness that would preclude life without that property (cf., *Blum* [1951]).

The Special Role of Carbon

The idea that some other element or combination of elements might replace carbon in biochemistry is usually assigned to science fiction, though the arguments are mostly quite contingent upon the assumption that every biogeny must parallel very closely our own. This point will be discussed at length later in this section but, for the moment, consider some specific arguments sometimes cited to eliminate silicon as a possible carbon substitute. First, it is sometimes noted that silicon is from a row of the periodic table in which double bonds are not important. Yet phosphorus, adjacent to silicon in the periodic table, has a busy role in our own biochemistry. It is sometimes remarked that the stability of the silicon-oxygen bond precludes the possibility that silicon-silicon bonds could be important. Putting aside the obvious thought that silicon-oxygen chains might themselves suffice as skeletal substitutes for hydrocarbon or amide chains, we must note that the prevalence of nitrogen in our biochemistry occurs in spite of the extreme stability of elemental nitrogen, N_2 (bond energy 225 kcal). We are reminded by this example that on Earth, nature has found innumerable ways to circumvent obstacles posed by thermodynamic instability.

EXOTIC BIOCHEMISTRIES: SOME SUGGESTIVE POSSIBILITIES

To explore the possibility that exobiology might furnish us some examples of unfamiliar biochemistry, we must make a preliminary examination of the biochemical functions that seem important to life. Only then can we support a contention that an exotic biochemistry is likely or unlikely. From a biological point of view, the most crucial manifestations of life seem to be the capability for information storage and for information transfer. The second of these implies replication and the two together imply mutability, and hence natural selection.

We might also find useful guidance in the chemical restraints that seem important:

1. A functioning biochemistry must include provision for energy storage and transfer through molecular rearrangements.

2. There must be reasonable synthetic routes toward biochemically important molecules, beginning with available starting materials.

3. There must be aperiodic, but informationally significant, molecular elements.

None of the constraints, nor their assembly, leads uniquely to terrestrial biochemistry. To illustrate this, consider the elements of an informationally significant polymer. First, there must be aperiodic but non-random functional appendages. Any polymeric skeleton that could be interrupted aperiodically will suffice. Symbolizing the functional appendages as R (which might be carbonaceous) some possibilities are illustrated below:

In the first example, information is contained in the chain lengths, and their order S_l, S_m, S_n, etc. In the second and subsequent examples, the information is contained in the nature of the functional groups, R_1, R_2, and R_3, and their order.

With this barest of introductions to the possibilities, we might consider the likelihood of chemical synthesis. The ease of rearrangement and re-assembly of sulfur chains is well known. Silicate structural elements are already prevalent in great variety around us. They could furnish skeletal stability in a biogeny that must adapt to higher ambient temperatures where hydrocarbons might be unstable. The conjugated carbon chain is included merely as a reminder that very many polymer possibilities are already known that could be utilized in a biogeny that evolved in an environment rich in hydrocarbons and deficient in water. It must be remembered that most hydrocarbons are not soluble in water and that most organic laboratory syntheses are carried out in non-aqueous media.

The conjugated carbon chain shown has another aspect of some importance. This is a chain type in which stereospecific control is now possible on a commercial basis. The laboratory development, within the last ten years, of stereospecific polymerization catalysts demonstrates that stereospecificity should not be considered to be uniquely connected with the examples we find in terrestrial biochemistry.

Finally, there are listed two chain types that will have quite low stability relative to amide chains. This would be the type of chain we might expect and look for in an environment in which an organism must carry out its metabolic processes on a diurnal time scale comparable to that of Earth, but at a temperature 50° lower (*viz.*, like Mars?).

In view of the unfamiliarity of the nitrogen chain shown in the last example, it warrants more discussion. Many nitrogen-rich compounds are well-known and well-characterized; they are not, however, widely known. It may surprise many readers, for example, to learn that the compound glyoxal *bis*-guanyl hydrazone, with a skeletal chain consisting of four carbon and six nitrogen atoms, is available commercially at a price below $2.00 per gram. The atomic ratio, N/C, in this compound is 2.

$$HN=C-NH-N=CH-CH=N-NH-C=NH$$

$$\overset{|}{NH_2} \qquad\qquad\qquad \overset{|}{NH_2}$$

glyoxal *bis*-guanyl hydrazone

As a second example, the compound diimine, N_2H_2, has just been prepared and spectroscopically identified by *Rosengren and Pimentel* [1964] through low temperature techniques. The indications are that this compound, which is the nitrogen counterpart of ethylene,

$$\overset{H}{\underset{H}{\diagdown}}N=N\overset{\diagup H}{}$$

diimine

has a well moderated and rich chemistry at temperatures well below room temperature, though the compound is extremely reactive under our ambient conditions. The likelihood that nitrogen-rich polymers could have biological importance on a low temperature planet cannot really be assessed (and it cannot be rejected) until we have much more laboratory knowledge of their properties. In any event, reactivity and instability can be used as a basis for rejection of a structural possibility only if due attention is paid also to the ambient temperature on the planet of interest.

Of the environmental factors, temperature has dramatic importance through its control of reaction rates. In evaluating this factor, it must be remembered that enzymatic reactions, like all chemical reactions, are characterized by activation energies that control their reaction rates. A metabolic reaction with a half-time of one minute at 27°C (300°K) might have an activation energy of 20 kcal. The same reaction would have a half-time of 25 hours at —27°C (246°K), possibly destroying its usefulness if the diurnal period is comparable to ours. On the other hand, consider a polymer that decomposes with a half-time of seven days at 27°C and a presumed activation energy of 25 kcal. This reaction would have a half-time of 175 years at $-27°C$. This change shows that a polymer that cannot even be stored at room temperature could be quite stable enough for biological utilization in a Martian climate. As a specific example, the Si-Si bond energy in Si_2H_6 is about 50 kcal/mole, in contrast to the 83 kcal/mole bond energy of the C-C bond in C_2H_6. This difference guarantees that silane chains would be unsuited to an Earth-like climate. On the other hand, the reaction rate considerations just given indicate that a low temperature environment might be quite favorable for biological utilization of such chemical linkages.

IMPLICATIONS IN THE EXOBIOLOGICAL PROGRAM

The possibility of exotic biochemistry is important insofar as it may affect experimental investigations and the interpretation of results. Thus the search for evidence of a biota leads to a search for characteristic forms. The significance of considering the exotic aspect of biochemistry, in this context, is that it may imply a revision in the manner in which the morphological investigation is conducted. A morphologically characteristic structure that is stable at an ambient temperature of $-27°C$ might be destroyed merely by warming it to $+27°C$ for the purpose of the experiment.

More generally, the considerations raised in this section lead to the assignment of high priority to experiments that disturb the sample as little as possible and that test the response of the sample to change of environmental conditions (e.g., the diurnal cycle, water vapor, pressure, temperature, organic solvents).

Finally, the possibilities of exotic biochemistries lead to the design of experiments that are less presumptive and more fundamental in intent (e.g., elemental and functional group analyses, passive calorimetry). Some of the most sensitive specific tests one might make for Earth-like biochemistry (e.g., a response to a particular enzyme) are of the least value for non-Earth-like biochemistries. The very specificity that makes the experiment significant if the test is positive, reduces its informational content almost to zero if the test is negative.

CONCLUSION

No matter how exciting the prospects of discovering an exotic biochemistry, the search for life on Mars will, no doubt, begin with an emphasis on the search for evidence of terrestrial biochemistry. Even so, the present discussion suggests two guiding principles that should be rigidly followed in this quest. First, the conclusion that life does not exist in a given environment cannot be established by experiments directed solely toward the biochemistry we know on Earth. Second, every set of exobiological experiments should yield some definite results that will serve to improve the next set of experiments, even if all direct tests for evidence of life are negative. This second guide, wisely applied, would slowly and surely lead us to the discovery of quite unexpected biological phenomena, if any exist.

REFERENCES

Blum, H. F. (1951), *Time's Arrow and Evolution,* Princeton Univ. Press.
Firsoff, V. A. (1963), *Life Beyond the Earth,* Basic Books, Inc., N. Y., p. 108-46.
Franklin, E. C. (1912), The Ammonia System of Acids, Bases, and Salts. *Am. Chem. J., 47,* 285.
Henderson, L. J. (1958), *The Fitness of the Environment,* Beacon Press, Boston.
Rosengren, K., and Pimentel, G. C. (1964), Unpublished.
Sisler, H. H. (1961), *Chemistry in Non-Aqueous Solvents,* Reinhold Publ. Corp., N. Y.

CHAPTER 13

HIGHER ORGANISMS ON MARS

CARL SAGAN

Introduction

In the present volume, we are concerned, for the most part, with the possibility that simple living things, chiefly microorganisms, may be found on Mars. Such an approach is certainly justified by terrestrial experience, where microorganisms are ubiquitous over the Earth's surface, and have been throughout geological time. Yet a mission to investigate life on Earth would certainly overlook some items of interest if attention were restricted to microorganisms.

The astronomical evidence suggests, but by no means proves, the existence of organisms in the 10^{-2} cm size range; and much larger plants seem ecologically possible (cf., Chapter 11). Where there are plants, there may be animals; but in the absence of oxygen, their metabolic efficiency might be less than that of terrestrial animals. There is an obvious selective advantage to intelligence, and it would be surprising if Martian animals, if any, lacked at least rudimentary intelligence. Here, we are already on very hypothetical ground. But because it is a topic of great scientific and popular interest, let us proceed even further. Is it possible that there is an indigenous civilization on Mars?

Statistically, the likelihood seems very small. The lifetimes of both Earth and Mars are about 5 billion years. If the putative Martians are behind us, it is most likely that they are far behind us, and have not yet achieved a technical civilization. If they are even slightly more advanced than we, their presence should be discernible. The telescope reveals no obvious signs of a reworking of the Martian environment by intelligent beings; although in the inverse situation, the detection of life on Earth with an optical telescope on Mars would be marginal (Chapter 9). The canals of Mars are probably psychophysiological in origin [*Antoniadi*, 1929; *Dollfus*, 1961]. A radio observatory of contemporary terrestrial manufacture on Mars could detect local television broadcasting on Earth. No formal searches have been made from Earth with narrow-bandpass receivers for comparable transmissions on Mars. The radio observations that have been performed are very broad-banded; their function was microwave radiometry, not the detection of intelligent signals. Finally, again extrapolating from terrestrial technology, an advanced Martian civilization might be expected, by this time, to have arrived on Earth. There is no evidence for such visits.

The arguments from terrestrial analogy have, of course, limited validity, because we do not yet know even one other example of biological evolution. Conceivably, an advanced civilization might develop, but it might not manifest any of the signs of life just mentioned. But if we uncritically apply terrestrial analogy, we find that if the Martians were 5000 years behind us, they would not yet have a civilization; if they were 50 years ahead of us, we should, by now, have deduced their existence. Then the probability of any civilization existing on Mars is $5 \times 10^3/5 \times 10^9 = 10^{-6}$; of a technical civilization more advanced than we, $50/(5 \times 10^9) = 10^{-8}$. These probabilities are very low.

The only serious extant argument supporting intelligent life on Mars was proposed by the Soviet astrophysicist I. S. Shklovsky, and concerns the Martian satellites, Phobos and Deimos [*Shklovsky*, 1963; *Shklovsky and Sagan*, 1966]. Observations of the motions of Phobos and Deimos between 1877, the date of their discovery, and 1941 were reduced by B. P. Sharpless in 1945. Sharpless found a secular acceleration for Phobos, the inner satellite, but not for Deimos. If Phobos is an ordinary kind of satellite, its secular acceleration cannot be explained by atmospheric drag; the Martian exosphere is too diffuse by several orders of magnitude. Shklovsky has investigated a large number of other conceivable causes of the observed secular acceleration, including tidal friction, magnetic braking, radiation pressure, and classical celestial mechanical perturbations; he finds that all are inadequate. He then returns to the possibility of atmospheric drag, and points out that if Phobos has a mean density of 10^{-3} gm cm^{-3} or less, the secular acceleration can be explained by drag on the basis of the probable density of the Martian exosphere. But a solid object of such density is unstable to tidal perturbations, and would long ago have been destroyed. Shklovsky therefore concludes that Phobos must be hollow. Its characteristic diameter would then be 16 km; its characteristic shell thickness, 30 cm; and its characteristic mass, 10^9 tons. Such an object, Shklovsky says, can only be an artificial satellite of immense proportions, launched by a Martian civilization vastly in advance of our own. Since, aside from Phobos and Deimos, there are no present signs of such a civilization, Shklovsky concludes that it is extinct, possibly for several hundreds of millions of years. He goes on to speculate that the function of the satellite may be the communication of the learning accumulated by the Martian civilization, in later epochs when its builders are extinct.

The argument for the artificiality of Phobos has not been convincingly criticized on substantive grounds. The only area of controversy concerns the observations themselves. G. A. Wilkins, of the Royal Observatory, Herstmonceux Castle, investigated the problem at the U. S. Naval Observatory, several years ago. His conclusions after that work [Wilkins, 1963] are as follows:

"So far I have re-reduced practically all of the observations of the satellites of Mars that were made from their discovery up to 1941— i.e., for the period covered by Sharpless' note. . . . The values found for the secular variations of the mean motions were insignificant, but I have not yet fully confirmed this result nor taken into account even those later observations that have been made available to me.

"There is no doubt that visual observations of the positions of these satellites with respect to the centre of the disk of the planet are difficult to make, but I do not have sufficient evidence to be able to state that Sharpless' determination was based on inadequate observations or that the method of treatment was not suitable. I consider that the question of the existence of the secular accelerations should be regarded as an open one until a new and more complete analysis of the observations is made; I do not consider that the evidence is sufficiently strong to justify any attempt to look for artificial causes."

Subsequently, Wilkins [1965] has reanalyzed the data, and finds two solutions that fit the observations. One solution shows no secular acceleration, but the other solution exhibits a large secular acceleration, and both, solutions have approximately equal weight. The observational reality of a secular acceleration, and the validity of Shklovsky's deductions, therefore remain in doubt.

A further reduction of observations of Phobos and Deimos, made since 1941, and the acquisition of additional high-precision data on the motion of these satellites, would seem to be of considerable interest.

REFERENCES

Antoniadi, E. M. (1929), *La Planète Mars,* Hermann, Paris.
Dollfus, A. (1961), *In: Planets and Satellites,* G. P. Kuiper and B. M. Middlehurst, eds., Univ. of Chicago Press, Chicago, Chapter 15.
Sharpless, B. P. (1945), *Astron. J. 51*:185.
Shklovsky, I. S. (1963), *Vselennaia, Zhizn, Razum,* Moscow.
Shklovsky, I. S., and C. Sagan (1966), *Intelligent Life in the Universe,* Holden-Day, San Francisco.
Wilkins, G. A. (1963), private communication.
Wilkins, G. A. (1965), *Proc. Intn'l. Astron. Un. Symp. No. 25,* Thessaloniki. In press.

PART VI

APPROACHES TO THE EXPLORATION OF MARS AND REMOTE OBSERVATIONS

CHAPTER 14

SOME TERRESTRIAL PROGRAMS

S. L. MILLER, G. C. PIMENTEL, and CARL SAGAN

INTRODUCTION

The exploration of Mars by means of spacecraft launched from the Earth is, at best, a very difficult undertaking. Opportunities are relatively infrequent and the experimental difficulties are formidable. When, as in the present case, plans for the investigations must take into account the possibility of encountering biological phenomena, these difficulties are further accentuated, for the recognition of life cannot yet be reduced to a simple and economical experimental procedure.

In these circumstances, it is only prudent to seek assistance from investigations in the laboratory and from observations from the Earth and its vicinity. Preparations of this sort include laboratory work on the chemistry of biopoiesis, collection and analysis of meteorites, studies of biological tolerance of, and adaptation to, the simulated planetary environment, and the development of experimental methods for the characterization of life and of its environment.

While astronomical studies of Mars are often limited by the Earth's atmosphere, many further contributions are to be expected from the application of modern techniques and instruments.

All of these studies merit encouragement, for not only will they facilitate the definition and planning of the planetary missions to come but they will also help in the interpretation of the results.

The sections that follow contain some additional suggestions for Earth-based work. They are not intended to be exhaustive, but rather to indicate the range of topics of interest. Discussions of the very important problems of developing methods and apparatus for later use on the surface of Mars are to be found in Part VII.

RESEARCH IN PREBIOLOGICAL CHEMISTRY

S. L. MILLER

Several discussions in this volume indicate the importance of understanding the processes leading up to the beginning of life on the Earth. This is important from the standpoint of the search for life on Mars because it will give significant boundary conditions for the design of life-detection experiments. At the same time one of the principle reasons for searching for life on Mars is to provide guidance and clues in studying how the process took place on the Earth. Thus each of these two areas of science—the search for life on Mars and the origin of life—benefits from progress in the other. The full meaning of a discovery of life on Mars and an investigation of its properties will not be elucidated until we have a greater understanding than we presently have of the origin of life.

It follows that the study of chemical evolution is an integral part of the program of Martian exploration. However, this does not mean that the chemical evolution program should be a large one. This is not an area of science where a "crash program" or massive infusion of money will yield commensurate progress. Progress in the past has been almost entirely the result of a good idea combined with a simple experiment. Only modest amounts of money have been used by modern scientific standards.

Care should be taken to ensure that the experiments are reasonable models of prebiological conditions. Considerable latitude can be envisioned in these conditions, and there will be legitimate differences of opinion, but it is clear that there are limits. For example, 100 per cent H_2SO_4 can by no stretch of the imagination be considered a suitable solvent for a prebiological experiment.

At the present stage of development of this field, it seems clear that theoretical discussions are not likely to result in progress comparable to that to be expected from a good experiment.

Chapter 2 of this volume discusses those specific problems in which no progress has been made as well as the areas where limited progress has been achieved but on which further experiments are needed. These areas and problems will not be repeated here, since the synthesis of all compounds of biological interest, from amino acids to polynucleotides, needs further investigation. In most areas it is not sufficient to report that a compound can be synthesized under one set of conditions. A study of the yield as a function of the concentration of reactants, temperature, pH, light intensity, etc., should be included. The mechanism of synthesis should also be studied.

It would also be helpful to have much greater knowledge of the stabilities of organic compounds, both in aqueous solution and in the dry state. Some work in this area has been done by Abelson and Vallentyne with amino acids, but more extensive data are needed for amino acids, and data should be obtained for the other organic compounds of biological interest.

It might be desirable to support a search for evidence of life in the early Precambrian. This does not mean that Precambrian geology in general should be supported. The earliest evidence of life is 2.7 billion years ago, and there is considerable evidence of life of 1.5 billion years. The need is to fill in the 1.5 to 2.7 billion year gap, and most important is to find evidence of life more than 2.7 billion years old.

POSSIBLE RESEARCH EXPLORATION OF EXOTIC BIOCHEMISTRY

GEORGE C. PIMENTEL

The optimum content of a laboratory program in support of a search for exotic biochemistries is decidedly more difficult to determine than if the search were for terrestrial biochemistries. An approach that readily comes to mind is the study of the effects of simulated planetary environments on terrestrial organisms. Yet this approach is, at best, peripheral to the problem. To be sure, the adaptability (or lack thereof) of terrestrial microorganisms to a given non-Earth-like environment *might* give suggestive leads to the possible line of evolution for life that might originate on that planet. More likely, the experiment would define only adaptability limits and "built-in" environmental preferences of an Earth-evolved organism; thus a terrestrial cell might adapt to a hydrocarbon sea by surrounding itself with a suitable membrane to protect its aqueous cellular chemistry. An organism that evolved in the hydrocarbon sea would be encouraged by its environment to utilize a non-aqueous medium in its cells.

We seem to be left with limitless possibilities, in the building of exotic chemical systems that might support life but without knowledge of the appropriate chemical constraints. The situation is not hopeless, however. What is needed are studies that strive to transfer into other chemical systems the properties and processes that characterize living systems here on Earth. Such transfer will serve to generalize our concept of a living system and, perhaps it will aid us in distinguishing possible exotic biochemistries from improbable ones.

To be specific, but not comprehensive, there would be value in the examination of chemical systems that retain similarity to our biochemistry *while pointedly abandoning certain essential characteristics*. The following specific proposals may furnish illustrative and suggestive examples that might serve as guides in evaluating and encouraging this type of research.

a) Investigation of processes analogous to photosynthesis but based upon ultraviolet light.

b) Formation of protein-like structures from α-amino acids that have high solubility in hydrocarbon solvents.

c) Synthesis of a high-temperature analogue of the protein structure in which the strong skeletal bonds (the amide linkages) are replaced by still stronger bonds (e.g., — Si — O — Si — bonds) and the weak bonds that fix molecular conformation (the hydrogen bonds) are replaced by C-C bonds.

d) Synthesis of a low-temperature protein analogue in which more labile bonds (e.g., — N — N — N) replace the skeletal bonds and the weak bonds are replaced by still weaker interactions (e.g., charge-transfer complexes).

e) Study of stereospecific polymerization.

f) Study of chemical information storage in non-proteinoid polymers.

On a more fundamental level, there would be benefit in any study of the chemistry of a planetary atmosphere and its surface in advance of direct exploration. Any study that forecasts the chemical environment to be found will suggest the chemical constraints that do exist for life on that planet. Again, illustrative examples are probably useful but to serve as comparisons, not as boundaries.

a) Prediction of gravitational fractionation of planetary atmospheres.

b) Laboratory investigation of chemical processes initiated in model planetary atmospheres by vacuum ultraviolet light.

c) Investigation of the planetary atmospheric composition by spectroscopic studies from afar (e.g., from earth-orbiting platforms).

d) Investigation of the planetary surface temperature and its variability from afar (e.g., again from earth-orbiting platforms).

ASTRONOMICAL STUDIES: USE OF TERRESTRIAL, BALLOON, ROCKET-BORNE, AND ORBITING OBSERVATORIES

CARL SAGAN

The utility of observations of Mars from the vicinity of the Earth, compared with observations from the vicinity of Mars is discussed in Chapter 15. The specific programs recommended there include further ground-based observations in the middle infrared (cf., Chapter 3); ground-based searches in the photographic infrared for molecular oxygen; ground-based microwave interferometric observations of Martian surface roughness and possible seasonal variations in Martian surface roughness; balloon-borne photographic and infrared spectrometric reconnaissance of Mars; and high-resolution ultraviolet spectroscopy of Mars from orbiting astronomical observatories. These programs are particularly well suited to their respective platforms, and would permit the allocation of scientific payload in space vehicles bound for Mars to experiments that could not be performed so well in any other way. In addition to the foregoing, there are programs of infrared spectroscopy devoted to a better determination of Martian surface pressures; infrared bolometric surveys in the $8\text{-}13\mu$ and 20μ windows; and long-term synoptic visual and photographic observations of Mars that are being pursued at the present time, and which are potentially very rich sources of information about Mars.

CHAPTER 15

POTENTIAL YIELDS OF BIOLOGICAL RELEVANCE FROM REMOTE INVESTIGATIONS OF MARS

CARL SAGAN

INTRODUCTION

Short of actually landing instruments on Mars, several other instrumental platforms are available for remote investigations of that planet. The bulk of our information about Mars has been obtained by astronomical observations from the surface of the Earth. Balloon astronomy is just beginning to be exploited. Orbiting Astronomical Observatories are scheduled to be launched beginning 1966 or 1967. Launchings of Mars fly-bys have been attempted, with partial success. The capability for launching a spacecraft that can be placed into orbit about Mars may be at hand within a few years. It is clear that each of these platforms cannot be given equal support, nor should they be. For a given purpose, there is usually one optimal platform.

While it is not impossible, there seems little prospect of directly and unambiguously detecting and characterizing life on Mars by any means short of landing ·on the planet. But remote observations are capable of determining physical parameters of the Martian environment that are constraints on any indigenous Martian ecology; testing biological hypotheses put forth to explain Martian phenomena; providing significant information for the selection of sites for landing missions; and detecting topographical or chemical artifacts or products of indigenous biological activity.

All conceivable methods of investigation involve the use of electromagnetic radiation and, excepting the use of microwave and, possibly, optical radar, all observations are passive. It is not yet possible to do anything to Mars; we must wait for Mars to do something by itself, and then observe it *in flagrante delicto.* At a given electromagnetic frequency, and from a given resolution element on the Martian surface, the acquired information may be radiometric or polarimetric—we ask how much radiation there is, and how it is polarized. If we scan in frequency, our observations become spectrometric; if we scan in angle, the measurements become cartographic. For a brief discussion of some of these techniques, the reader is referred to Chapter 1 of *The Atmospheres of Mars and Venus* (NAS-NRC Pub. 944, 1961), or to any standard astronomy text.

Generally speaking, the most useful techniques of the present and the immediate future seem to be these: ultraviolet spectroscopy and polarimetry; optical cartography, spectroscopy and polarimetry; near infrared spectroscopy and cartography; far infrared cartography and radiometry; and micowave cartography, polarimetry and spectroscopy.

For fundamental reasons, some of these techniques are better applied from certain platforms than from others. Thus, ground-based ultraviolet studies shortward of 3300 Å are essentially impossible, because of absorption in the terrestrial ozonosphere. Balloons generally rise to no more than 120,000 feet, which is well below the top of the ozonosphere; therefore, balloon platforms have limited usefulness for ultraviolet work. The simplest platform for ultraviolet studies of Mars is, then, an Earth satellite.

Because of turbulence in the Earth's atmosphere, astronomical "seeing" limits the angular resolution possible in optical photography, even from small ground-based telescopes. Since the turbulent elements are primarily in the lower terrestrial troposphere, observations from balloon altitudes can avoid essentially all of the seeing difficulties.

Infrared observations at almost all wavelengths, from the surface of the Earth, must customarily allow for absorption by substances in the terrestrial atmosphere, primarily carbon dioxide and water; but at some wavelengths such other substances as methane and ozone may also become troublesome. Where electronic transitions, or the rotational components of a vibration-rotation band, can be resolved, the Doppler effect is generally used to separate telluric from planetary absorption features. Absorption by substances uniformly mixed in the atmosphere cannot usually be avoided at balloon altitudes, but absorption by water, which, because of its condensation properties, is restricted to the terrestrial troposphere, can be avoided by using stratospheric balloons. Thus, except for wavelengths where carbon dioxide absorbs—in the near infrared, at 2.7μ, 4.3μ, the 10μ region, and the 15μ region—the atmosphere is essentially clear, for most spectroscopic infrared purposes, at stratospheric altitudes. In particular, infrared planetary spectroscopy beyond 20μ is now becoming possible, although it should be mentioned that there are no critical observations of Mars that suggest themselves in this wavelength region.

The terrestrial atmosphere is generally transparent at centimeter and longer wavelengths, but some absorption by water and other substances in the millimeter range provides a case for microwave observations from Earth satellites. Because of the great weights involved, there has been no development of equipment for astronomical observations at microwave frequencies with balloons.

Balloons and fly-bys have an inherent disadvantage that ground-based observatories, Earth satellites, and Mars orbiters do not. Much of the evidence relevant to the possibility of life on Mars has to do with seasonal or secular changes on that planet. However, the useful observational lifetimes of individual balloon flights (about 12 hours) or fly-bys (several hours) are so small that observations of these changes from such platforms become impossible. Several such vehicles could be flown, but intercalibration and other problems make this a less promising method. But the useful lifetime of ground-based instruments, Earth satellites and, probably, planetary orbiters, is large enough to allow significant seasonal and synoptic observations to be performed.

Ground-based observations have a number of great advantages which, while obvious, are difficult to belabor. Ground-based astronomical observatories can be operated and maintained by men who have the capability of changing the mode of operation and goal of an experiment at short notice if the observations seem to warrant it. The limitations in payload are generally not restrictive, so that much larger apertures and much more sophisticated ancillary apparatus and cryogenic systems are possible than with other platforms. Also, ground-based observations are by far the cheapest.

Some of the most promising potential sources of information about Mars, such as infrared and microwave spectroscopy, are energy-limited. Thus, experimenters use the radiation incident from the planet as a whole, since any attempt at topographical resolution (which is at least possible at infrared wavelengths) engenders a serious loss in signal-to-noise ratio. But if a given instrument were capable of flying close to the planet Mars, then its topographical resolution could be greatly improved, without any corresponding energy loss. In many cases, the disadvantages inherent in fly-bys and orbiters, such as low scientific payload and low data transmission capability, are more than offset by the high topographical resolution that these platforms make possible.

In the case of optical cartography, the advantage of fly-bys and orbiters is due to the fact that with a modest aperture, linear surface resolutions can be obtained that are impossible to obtain from greater distances because of the diffraction limitation on optical resolution. This point is illustrated in Tables 1 and 2. Table 1 shows the topographical resolution on the surface of Mars that can be obtained photographically with large telescopes from the surface of the Earth during the 1965-1971 oppositions; these resolutions range from 700 to 400 km, improving with time, as the favorable opposition of 1971 is approached.

During the same opposition, a smaller 36-inch telescope above the terrestrial atmosphere can obtain resolutions that are more than an order of magnitude superior, because it is not beset by seeing problems and can work at the limit of its diffraction disk. There are plans to perform video reconnaissance of Mars with a 36-inch telescope carried by balloon above the turbulence in the Earth's atmosphere. This system, directed by Professor Martin Schwarzschild of Princeton University, is called Stratoscope II. The photographic resolution that Stratoscope II should be able to obtain routinely is comparable or superior to the best recorded visual (human eye) observations made with telescopes of larger aperture from those terrestrial observatories with the best seeing conditions—for example, Pic du Midi, in the Pyrenees. With a given optical system, visual resolution is generally superior to photographic resolution because the human observer is able to reject the moments of bad seeing and remember the few moments of superb seeing. However, it is clearly preferable, in order to eliminate the personal equation and to permit recording and comparison of results, to perform photographic observations. Some further light can be shed on reports of rectilinear fine markings on the surface of Mars by such balloon observations, although the best visual observations suggest that the rectilinear features are spurious.

Table 2 shows linear resolutions on the surface of Mars that can be obtained by telescopes of various apertures carried on fly-by vehicles or orbiters. It is assumed here, as in the discussion of balloon observations above, that the stability of the platforms is consistent with the diffraction-limited resolution of their telescopes. At 20,000 km from the center of Mars, the planet would subtend an angle of 21° in the sky, and small telescopes would be capable of resolutions of several tens of meters. Much closer to Mars, at a distance of 5,000 km from its center (and about 1620 km from the surface), the planet subtends an angle of 85°, and resolutions down to some meters are possible with the apertures indicated. Such resolutions are very impressive, and vastly superior to any obtainable from the vicinity of the Earth.

To detect life on Earth unambiguously with an optical resolution of a few tens of meters, at a random location, is far from a trivial problem. If by chance an appropriate location—e.g., a city, or cultivated farmland —were selected, the presence of life would be immediately obvious (see Chapter 9). But to insure a reasonable expectation of detecting life, a

TABLE 1. Topographical Resolution of Mars from the Vicinity of the Earth

Date of Opposition	Distance in 10^6 km	Apparent Stellar Magnitude	Photographic Topographic Resolution from Earth's Surface	Photographic Topographic Resolution by Diffraction-Limited 36-inch Telescope above Atmosphere
9 March, 1965	98	—1.0	700 km	58 km
15 April, 1967	90	—1.3	640	53
31 May, 1969	72	—2.0	500	42
30 August, 1971	56	—2.6	400	33

TABLE 2. Topographical Resolution of Mars from the Vicinity of Mars

Experiment and Wavelength	Telescope Aperture	Distance from the Martian Surface:			
		500 km	1000 km	3000 km	10,000 km
Visible cartography 5000 Å	12″	1.00 meters	2.00 meters	6.0 meters	20.0 meters
	24″	0.50	1.00	3.0	10.0
	36″	0.33	0.67	2.0	6.7
Infrared radiometry 3.5μ	12″	7.00 meters	14.0 meters	42 meters	140 meters
	24″	3.50	7.0	21	70
	36″	2.30	4.7	14	47
Infrared radiometry 10μ	12″	20.0 meters	40 meters	120 meters	400 meters
	24″	10.0	20	40	200
	36″	6.7	13	27	13C
Microwave radiometry 3.5 cm	3 meters	7.10 km	14.2 km	42.6 km	142 km
	10 meters	2.10	4.3	12.9	43
	30 meters	0.71	1.4	4.2	14

systematic survey of the Earth would be required. The same is true of Mars. However, here we encounter problems of data transmission rate. Table 3, taken from *The Atmospheres of Mars and Venus* (*op. cit.*), indicates the characteristic number of bits required for a range of pictures with various degrees of fineness of detail. Currently tractable bit transmission rates from the vicinity of Mars seem to be between 20 and 300 bits per second. We see that 20 bits per second implies the capability of transmitting one ordinary television picture of Mars per day; 300 bits per second implies perhaps 15 such pictures. The question of improvement of the data transmission capability is discussed in the section on Mars biological orbiters below.

Infrared resolutions that can be obtained with telescopes of 12" to 36" aperture, and microwave resolutions that can be obtained with antennae of aperture between 3 and 30 meters are also shown in Table 2 for a variety of presumed periapsis distances from Mars. The resolutions are four to five orders of magnitude better than the corresponding resolutions obtainable from the vicinity of the Earth.

A REPORT ON SCIENTIFIC STUDIES WITH MARTIAN ORBITERS

With this as background, we now proceed to a discussion of the scientific investigations of biological relevance that might be performed with projected Martian orbiters in the period 1969-1971. This study, reported below, was made for the Bioscience Programs Division, National Aeronautics and Space Administration by a Working Group on Mars Orbiters. The participants were: Carl Sagan (chairman), Frank D. Drake (Cornell University), Richard M. Goody (Harvard University), Donald P. Hearth (NASA), John Martin (Jet Propulsion Laboratory), William M. Sinton (Lowell Observatory), W. G. Stroud (Goddard Space Flight Center, NASA), and Andrew T. Young (Harvard College Observatory).

The direct detection of life on Mars from an orbiter vehicle is considered unlikely, but there are promising possibilities for determining physical parameters of biological relevance as boundary conditions on the ecology of Martian organisms, and for detecting surface phenomena that may be due to the activities of Martian organisms. The 1969-1971 time period is especially favorable, both because of the moderate energy requirements of the trajectories, and because the southern hemisphere wave of darkening will reach its maximum extent within a few months of projected spacecraft arrival times.

For experiments of biological significance, the principal advantages of a

TABLE 3. Number of Bits Required to Send One Picture of
Given Quality From Mars to Earth

Kind of Picture	Resolution (and picture size)	Number of Picture Elements	Number of Bits with 16 Shades of Grey
Ordinary Television	600 lines	3.6×10^5	1.4×10^6
Aerial photo (ordinary film)	20 lines/mm (10×10 cm)	4×10^6	1.6×10^7
Aerial photo (highest quality)	100 lines/mm (10×10 cm)	10^8	4×10^8
Picture of Mars from a balloon-borne 36-inch telescope	0.1" of arc, or 30-40 km on Mars at opposition (see Table 1)*	4×10^4	1.6×10^5

*Assume a square picture just containing the disk of Mars at opposition, and a film grain that takes full advantage of the optical resolution.

Mars orbiter are the prospects of (1) obtaining high topographical resolution; (2) observing at phase angles greater than 43° (and thus, the night hemisphere of Mars); and (3) detecting seasonal changes on Mars.

Because of the importance of the seasonal changes, a long scientific lifetime of the orbiter is highly desirable, a three-month lifetime being perhaps the minimum acceptable value, and a four- to six-month lifetime being preferable (these are terrestrial months). In order to investigate the wave of darkening in its photometric, polarimetric, and possibly spectrometric aspects, it is important that the spacecraft be in orbit and functioning when Mars is at about 10° heliocentric longitude; and that it be functioning for at least 90 days prior to, or at least 90 days subsequent to this time. A more nearly ideal orbiter is one that functions for a six-month period, centered on heliocentric longitude 10°.

It is recognized that there is a trade-off among the lifetime of the orbiter, the weight available for scientific experiments, and the data rate for communication back to Earth. If any of these three parameters can be improved by the development of Earth-based facilities, this improvement should be strongly encouraged. It appears that for a cost small compared with that required for even a modest exploitation of the 1969-1971 opportunity, very great improvements in ground-based communication facilities can be made. As a rough example, for about $40 million, a phased array of twenty 85-foot radio antennas or three 210-foot antennas can be constructed, which give approximately a twentyfold improvement in the data rate obtainable from any given spacecraft. With such a facility, a data rate of 30 bits per second received from the vicinity of Mars with equipment now planned can be increased to 600 bits per second. The construction of even one such facility would permit a major improvement in our ability to obtain information from Mars. If any serious thought is to be given to high-resolution television pictures with reasonable surface coverage from the vicinity of Mars in the 1969-1971 time period, such improvement of ground-based communication facilities is mandatory.

It is also recognized that the higher energy required for a circular orbit implies a smaller scientific payload. Since the payload losses involved seem to be more serious than the diminished topographical resolution that an elliptical orbit implies, elliptical orbits are considered acceptable. A polar orbit, especially with a significant precession of the line of apsides during the orbiter's scientific lifetime, is scientifically much more desirable than an equatorial orbit because, among other reasons, of the great biological interest in the receding boundaries of the Martian polar caps.

It is recommended that instruments intended for Martian orbiters be designed, ground-tested, and then test-flown in the vicinity of the Earth well before the projected launch date. In many cases, significant scientific information about the Earth can also be obtained from such flight tests.

In the following discussion of possible instrumental techniques for 1969 and 1971 Mars orbiters, it will be assumed that the available scientific payload is in the range 50 to 200 pounds, and that the data rate lies in the range 30 to 200 bits per second. The minimum scientific lifetime acceptable is about three months, and the smaller the periapsis consistent with planetary quarantine requirements, the better. A highly elliptical orbit with a periapsis of 1000 km is useful from many points of view. It may be desirable to shut down some experiments when the orbiter is far from periapsis, if this can extend the useful life of the orbiter.

Ultraviolet Spectroscopy and Photometry

The primary scientific goals of this technique are: (a) determination of the ultraviolet flux at the Martian surface, (b) search for the biologically significant gases O_2 and O_3, (c) search for and topographical characterization of acetaldehyde (CH_3CHO), a gas suspected from infrared studies, and possibly relevant to Martian biological activities.

It is our opinion that such experiments of *biological* interest can be performed almost as well, and much sooner, by rockets and by Orbiting Astronomical Observatories; or by other techniques at different wavelengths. In particular, a search for acetaldehyde can be performed with higher reliability in the infrared, if high spectroscopic resolution or an appropriate selective-absorption gas cell filter is used. The search for oxygen and ozone can be made in the infrared and ultraviolet from the vicinity of the Earth. A computation of the ultraviolet flux at the surface of Mars requires spectral measurements of moderately high topographical resolution, but only relatively poor spectroscopic resolution. It is recommended that a vigorous program of ultraviolet spectroscopy of Mars from the vicinity of the Earth be performed, so that these important parameters can be determined without burdening the scientific payload of Mars orbiters late in the decade. Spectrometers can be launched from stabilized platforms by modest rockets such as the Aerobee. Orbiting Astronomical Observatories appear to have quite adequate capabilities for the above ultraviolet observations of the planet Mars. This is particularly true for the Goddard scanning spectrometer planned for OAO-2. It is recommended that a firm commitment for the few hours' required observing time be obtained at an early date. There should be no difficulty in finding qualified scientists to interpret the data.

Television

Potential experiments of biological relevance include (a) a detailed characterization of the nuclei and other fine structure details in the Martian dark areas, and (b) a detailed mapping of the seasonal progress of the wave of darkening.

Experience with photographs obtained in the Tiros series ($\sim 10^6$ bits per picture) and from the Mercury capsules ($\sim 10^9$ bits per picture) indicates that the reliable determination of life on Earth from orbital altitudes is a difficult undertaking. In order to have a high probability of detecting life on Mars by television pictures, a minimum resolution of 1 meter seems indicated. Such resolutions may be barely practical for an orbiter in the 1969 and 1971 missions. Whether more tractable resolutions in the 10-meter range are biologically significant is an undecided question. The potential gains may conceivably be very high; on the other hand, the cost in terms of data transmission rate is also very high. It is a question of assessment of *a priori* probabilities, and, as anticipated, the group was divided on this issue.

Television is not required in order to provide a firm topographical localization for other kinds of observations—for example, infrared spectroscopy. The expected topographical resolution of infrared spectrometric observations is comparable to the visible topographical resolution of existing maps of Mars. Correlation of dark areas with identifiable topographic features—for example, large impact craters—might be significant in attempting to interpret the dark areas and their seasonal changes. If the factor of 20 improvement in data transmission rate by construction of large ground-based communication facilities is obtained, then $\smile 2000$ bits per second becomes feasible from the vicinity of Mars. This is roughly 1.7×10^8 bits per day, and implies that $\smile 100$ Tiros-quality photographs of Mars could, under these circumstances, be transmitted to Earth per day.

A more modest television experiment, which is capable of determining with fairly high resolution secular and seasonal changes in the fine structure of the Martian dark areas, is a 1- or 2-line scan of the planetary surface. A statistical analysis of the intensity correlation of several scans of the same region, but spaced in time, will give some indication of the seasonal and secular variations of the surface features in two dimensions. Such a device, put into orbit for several months, can give information on the variations of fine structure of the Martian dark areas at a minimal cost in weight and data transmission.

The group felt that because most of the reported color changes on Mars appear to be psychophysiological in origin, and because of the intrinsic ambiguity in interpreting any authentic detection of color changes on Mars, color determinations should be given low priority, especially in view of the high data transmission cost that multicolor photography entails.

Optical Polarimetry

Polarimetric observations have the capability (a) of suggesting the composition of the Martian bright areas, and the distribution of this composition; and (b) of suggesting the composition, albedo, and granularity of the Martian dark areas. This last may be directly related to the presence of organisms on Mars. Polarimetry at visible and at microwave frequencies appears to be the only practicable method of detecting remotely the effects of individual small organisms on Mars directly, although even here, the hypothetical organisms can only be detected *en masse*.

Because of the necessity of positioning interference fringes over the disk of Mars, ordinarily only very poor topographical resolution can be obtained from Earth-based visual polarimetry, and astronomical "seeing" limits the resolution of photographic or photoelectric polarimetry. The improvement of resolution obtainable from an orbiter is more than an order of magnitude. In addition, orbiter polarimetry permits observations beyond phase angle 43°, angles which are inaccessible from the Earth. Extension of the fractional polarization-phase angle curve beyond 43° may provide a discriminant among competing candidates for Martian surface composition. Dollfus has suggested that if a complete extension of the polarization curve to 180° is for some reason impossible, observations at 90° should be a significant composition discriminant.

A modest improvement in existing polarimeters would permit measurement not merely of intensity and linear polarization, but instead, of all four Stokes parameters. The usefulness of such a Stokes meter could be substantially increased if it were to observe at three wavelengths—for example, in the far red or near infrared, where the contrast between the bright and dark areas is high and the effective scattering in the atmosphere is negligible; in the blue, where the Martian blue haze will dominate; and in the yellow.

A polarimeter or Stokes meter is an especially attractive instrument for a Mars orbiter because: it is light-weight; conservative in data rate transmission; performs measurements which can, uniquely, be performed only in the vicinity of Mars and only from an orbiter; performs measurements on the physical environment; and is capable of detecting very small hypothetical organisms themselves. A determination of particular areas on Mars that undergo especially striking seasonal polarization changes might be important in site selection for eventual landing missions.

Infrared Radiometry

An infrared radiometry observing in the 8-13μ region is capable of determining surface temperatures. Longer wavelengths (around 20μ) are better for seeking local temperature anomalies on the night side of Mars. At present, nighttime temperatures can be inferred only from temperature-time curves for the illuminated hemisphere of Mars. The nighttime temperatures provide a boundary condition on Martian organisms, since they are related to the condensation and concentration of water at the surface of the planet. An infrared bolometer in the 8-13μ or 20μ region also has the capability of detecting hot spots on Mars, if they occupy a sizable fraction of the field of view. Hot spots are significant as sites of geothermal activity and possible penetration of the hypothesized Martian permafrost layer. Such locales are presumptive loci of indigenous biological activity, and are therefore relevant to site selection for eventual landing missions. These scientific returns are, however, certainly not significant enough to justify an orbiter for radiometry alone. But because of its light weight and parsimonious data transmission requirement, such a device should nevertheless be considered, especially if the orbiter payload is small.

It is also possible, by observations of the same area of the planet at different local times of day, that detailed information of high topographical resolution can be obtained on the thermal properties of the Martian surface. Similar information can also be obtained by microwave observations.

Infrared Spectroscopy

Infrared spectroscopy is potentially an extremely useful technique for biologically significant observations from a Mars orbiter. The following observations can, in principle, be obtained:

(a) An improvement of at least an order of magnitude in our knowledge of the topographical distribution of the Sinton bands, if they are a *bona fide* Martian feature.

(b) Determination of possible seasonal or secular variation in the intensity or wavelength distribution of such bands, again with high topographical resolution. Seasonal variations in the intensity of the Sinton bands *correlated* with the wave of darkening would provide much stronger evidence for life on Mars than we have at the present time.

(c) Determination of other organic bands in the same (3.4-3.7μ) wavelength region. Earth-based observations of the Sinton bands, because of their low topographical resolution, are actually an integration of contributions from a large area of the Martian disk. Therefore, relatively underabundant organic molecules will have their spectral features diluted. High topographical resolution may permit such underabundant molecular species to be observed.

(d) Observations with high topographical resolution—for example, at 2.7μ or at 6.2μ—of the distribution of atmospheric water vapor over the disk of Mars. One of the most attractive explanations of the wave of darkening is as the response of Martian organisms to a discontinuous increase in the availability of moisture in the Martian atmosphere. While there are plausible arguments for this, it is, at the present time, not known whether the wave of darkening *in detail* follows the front of the wave of water vapor suspected to be traveling from the vaporizing to the re-forming polar ice cap.

(e) A search for organic functional groups other than methyls, methylenes, or aldehydes, by observing in the 4-6μ region at the dawn limb of the planet. Here, the temperatures are still so low that reflection dominates emission, and surface organic functional groups such as NH_2 and $C = O$ can be detected, if their abundance is comparable to that of CH. It will be important to determine the detailed topographical distribution and possible seasonal variations of these bands, to determine, for example, whether the organic matter on Mars is uniformly distributed over the disk, or whether some functional groups become more abundant at certain times and places.

(f) A search for other atmospheric gases of biological significance. Methane and carbon monoxide are photodecomposition products of acetaldehyde. Methane and nitrous oxide are metabolic products of terrestrial microorganisms, and their identification, localization, and seasonal variation may be relevant to Martian biological activities.

It is clear from the preceding characterization that infrared spectroscopy holds great potential for orbiter observations of Mars. Several types of "spectrometers" are conceivable. These include interferometers, multiplexing with multiple filter and multiple detector arrays, wedges, and conventional grating and prism spectrometers. A generally ideal wavelength range is 1.0 to 7.0μ. A more narrowly circumscribed but still useful range is 2.4 to 3.8μ. The spectroscopic resolution required is about 0.04 or 0.05μ at 3.5μ, and may deteriorate to about 0.1μ at 5μ. If a characteristic orbital velocity is 2 km per second, and spectra of areas 100 km on a side are desired, scan times <50 seconds are acceptable. Since the abundances of rare substances are being sought, the device should be capable of detecting one per cent depressions in the continuum. Since seasonal variations of absorption features are being sought, reliable calibration over a three- to six-month operating lifetime must be obtained. It is possible that the desert areas, whose spectral characteristics are expected to change little during the Martian wave of darkening, may provide one natural calibration source. For a reliable identification of such gases as acetaldehyde and water vapor, it is recommended that selective-absorption gas cell filter calibrations be considered, first from Earth-based experiments, and then possibly from Mars orbiters.

It is important that investigations be performed on the long-term reliability of detectors and other spectrometer components in simulated Mars trajectories and Mars orbits. It also must be determined whether high signal-to-noise ratios can be obtained by radiation cooling in Mars orbit. An investigation of the comparative merits of various dispersing systems is necessary. Because of the considerable importance of such a system, and because of its attendant complexity, the development of significant redundancy and "fail-safe" capability is recommended.

Searches for molecular oxygen on Mars can be made by observations of such forbidden transitions as those at 0.75 and 1.28μ. Since the lines are weak, the observed radiation will arise close to the surface of the planet, permitting a determination of total oxygen abundance not conveniently obtained at ultraviolet frequencies. Such observations of Mars can also usefully be performed from the vicinity of the Earth.

Active and Passive Microwave Radiometry and Polarimetry

Passive observations at several microwave wavelengths are capable of determining with high topographical resolution (a) the brightness temperature at several different levels beneath the Martian surface. By determining the variation in intensity of the two plane-polarized components as a function of angle of incidence at a fixed wavelength, the emissivity can be determined, thereby giving (b) the true thermometric temperatures at these depths. The polarization also gives some index of (c) the surface roughness and its seasonal variation, and, through the dielectric constant, (d) the surface composition. Seasonal variations in surface roughness may be evidence of biological activity.

Because of the inclemency of the Martian surface environment, a detailed characterization of the immediate Martian subsurface environment down to a depth of about one meter is of biological relevance. Measurements of the temperature on the dark side would permit a direct determination of that parameter for the first time, and in addition, such a survey may uncover hot spots of possible biological significance. The topographical resolution obtainable from the orbiter greatly exceeds that which can be obtained from the Earth.

Active radar observations might be thought useful in searching for the suspected subsurface permafrost layer; however, since the dielectric constant of ice is comparable to that of most common rocks, radar does not appear to be a promising technique for the detection of Martian permafrost. Radar altimetry could be useful in characterizing the topography of the Martian surface.

The potential returns from active radar seem to be so small, considering the very large power and weight requirements, that we do not recommend that radar be flown on early Mars orbiter missions.* On the other hand, the wide range of possible information obtainable from a passive microwave device makes it a promising instrument. A relatively large antenna is necessary, of aperture about 10 feet, but its weight can be small. The

---

* Prof. V. R. Eshleman has suggested, in the following remarks, that *bistatic* radar may be a much more useful instrument for planetary exploration:

". . . However, even more meaningful radar studies of the surface could be done with less weight than a microwave radiometer, or by use of such a radiometer, by using transmissions from the Earth. That is, even if the weight, power, and space were available for an on-board radar system, I believe that it should still receive very low priority as compared with the bistatic radar mode involving Earth-based transmissions and reception in the orbiter.

"The separation of transmitter and receiver in the bistatic mode of operation offers inherent advantages for studies which could be done neither from the ground alone nor from an orbiter alone. These include measurements of the scattering in various directions for various angles of incidence (including polarization effects), self-calibration of reflection coefficients and dispersive and Doppler frequency shifts made possible by the comparison of the direct ray from the Earth and the energy reflected from the planet, and occultation measurements of the atmosphere and ionosphere of the planet.

"Bistatic radar at several wavelengths would complement and extend the measurements outlined for passive microwave radiometry and polarimetry. Reflectivity as a function of depth, dielectric constant (a Brewster angle measurement would be particularly sensitive), loss-tangent, and large-scale (Fresnel-zone-size) and small-scale (wavelength-size) surface irregularities could be studied from measures of signal strength, frequency and time-delay spectra, and polarization. Phase path, group path, and amplitude measurements during probe occultation would provide a refractivity profile for the atmosphere and ionosphere, and this would give important information related to pressure, temperature, composition, and ionization reactions.

"It appears possible that much of the radiometry system itself could be used, on a time sharing basis, for the bistatic radar receivers, and in fact, the ground-based facilities discussed above for the increase in communication capacity might also be used as the ground terminal for the bistatic radar system. Basic differences for active and passive operation of the orbiter receivers include: (a) narrower bandwidth for active work; (b) desirability of using both pulses and CW for active work; (c) possible desirability of including lower frequencies in the active work; and (d) possibility in the active mode of using delay and frequency spectrum instead of antenna directivity for topographic resolution."

microwave equipment itself can be comparable to that used in the Mariner II mission. It should be reemphasized that since passive polarization measurements can determine some index of surface roughness, seasonal variations in surface roughness should also be detectable. Such observations can conceivably be related directly to Martian biological activity in the centimeter size range.

Conclusions

Significant experiments relevant to biology can be performed from a Mars orbiter in the 1969 and 1971 opportunities. These experiments, for various reasons, cannot be performed from the vicinity of the Earth, or from Mars fly-bys. An orbiter has an intrinsic capability for high topographical resolution over a significant fraction of the planetary surface; for observations of seasonal changes; and for measurements at large phase angles. Below are four suggested experimental packages agreed upon by the participants, in order of increasing weight, data rate requirements, and complexity. We believe that Payload 1 represents a significant set of orbiter experiments for a scientific package in the 20-pound range. Payload 4, which appears to be feasible in 1969 and 1971 only if ground-based communication facilities are improved, provides a wide variety of significant experiments, and still weighs in the 200-pound range.

Payload 1: Optical polarimeter
1- or 2-line optical scanner
Infrared radiometer

Payload 2: Optical polarimeter
1- or 2-line optical scanner
Infrared radiometer
Infrared spectrometer

Payload 3: Optical polarimeter
1- or 2-line optical scanner
Infrared spectrometer
Microwave radiometer for passive observations and for bistatic radar

Payload 4: Optical polarimeter
Infrared spectrometer
Microwave radiometer for passive observations and for bistatic radar
10^6 bit-per-picture television

In order to take advantage of the scientific opportunities for 1969-1971 Mars orbiters, it is recommended that immediate instrument development and early near-Earth test flights with these devices be performed. In addition, the following undertakings are strongly recommended:

(1) development of large, ground-based, phased-array deep space communication facilities to improve substantially data transmission rates from the vicinity of Mars;

(2) performance of high-angular-resolution ultraviolet spectroscopy of Mars from the vicinity of the Earth, particularly from rockets with stabilized platforms and from the Orbiting Astronomical Observatories;

(3) observations of Mars with gas cell filter calibration to check the identification of the 3.69μ feature;

(4) a search in the near infrared for molecular oxygen on Mars.

ADDITIONAL REMARKS

Thus, as we see from the report presented here in the preceding pages, the Earth satellite experimental procedure that the Mars Orbiter Working Group found of greatest importance is ultraviolet spectroscopy of Mars; such an experiment is well within the capabilities of equipment designed for the Orbiting Astronomical Observatories, which have primary scientific missions in stellar and galactic astronomy.

In addition to the near infrared investigations of molecular oxygen and the 3.69μ feature that were recommended, several other promising ground-based observational programs can be suggested. By observing intrinsically weak spectral lines of water vapor (so band saturation is avoided), it seems possible that changes in the precipitable water content of the Martian atmosphere of 50 per cent or more can be detected over the disk of Mars with large ground-based telescopes. In such searches for water vapor, topographical resolutions of some 20 per cent of the planet are possible.

A significant improvement in signal-to-noise ratio and topographical resolution of the Sinton bands in the 3.5μ region can be obtained if a Michelson interferometric spectrometer and a liquid-helium-cooled detector (for example, mercury- or gold-doped germanium semiconductive detectors, or germanium bolometers) were used with the largest-aperture telescopes available. Of these three improvements in technique—large apertures, superior spectrometers, and sensitive detectors—no two in combination (much less, all three together) have been used in investigations of the Sinton bands. Using 82-inch apertures and smaller, cooled lead sulfide detectors, and traditional spectrometers, Kuiper has recently obtained spectra of Mars in the region short of 2μ that are an order of magnitude better than previous work. Substantial improvement in ground-based spectroscopic techniques seems feasible, if properly encouraged. Infrared observations in the 0.7–2.2μ region are also greatly needed, to provide a firm determination of the carbon dioxide partial pressure and the total surface pressure on Mars.

Ground-based observation of possible organic groups in the $\lambda > 4\mu$ region does not seem very promising, because at these wavelengths, Mars is observed primarily in emission. In order to observe these wavelengths in reflected sunlight, observations must be made close to the morning limb, and this requires high topographical resolution, which is not available from the ground.

Since one of the most exciting of possible remote observations of Mars relevant to biology would be a seasonal variation in the intensity and wavelength distribution of the Sinton bands, if indigenous to Mars, a 3.3–3.8μ synoptic patrol of Mars is desirable. Since, however, the angular diameter of Mars is very small at phase angles far from opposition, such a patrol requires an optimum combination of aperture, spectrometer and detector. There seems little prospect of obtaining large amounts of major observatory time for this project, because the majority of astronomers are occupied with other endeavors. The desirability of related observations, however, may provide some impetus for the construction of a moderately large planetary observatory.

Ground-based radar observations of Mars have already provided a crude map of the Martian surface, and have indicated the presence of reflectivity anomalies. Future higher-resolution studies promise significant new knowledge. It is not impossible that indigenous biological activity can change the surface texture of Mars. It is possible to detect not only the conformation of surface texture, but also changes in this conformation, by microwave interferometric observations from the Earth. Conceivably, it may be possible to detect growth of Martian plants by ground-based radio astronomy, as Frank Drake has suggested.

Thus a number of experiments naturally suggest themselves for each observational platform: observations in the infrared and microwave domains from the ground, infrared spectroscopic and optical photographic observations from balloons, ultraviolet spectrometric observations from Earth satellites, and a wide range of observations from fly-bys, and especially, orbiters, as discussed in the above report.

CHAPTER 16

LAUNCH OPPORTUNITIES
AND SEASONAL ACTIVITY ON MARS

CARL SAGAN and J. W. HAUGHEY

The orbits of Earth and Mars are, within $1°51'$, coplanar. The sidereal period of revolution of the Earth is 365.257 days; that of Mars, 686.980 days. Thus, the synodic period, the time for a given configuration Sun-Earth-Mars to be repeated, is 779.94 days, or approximately 26 months. This is also the period between successive oppositions of Mars, that is, successive configurations in which the Sun, the Earth and Mars are in a straight line, with Earth in the middle. The time of closest approach of Mars to Earth during a synodic period occurs within a few days of opposition. For this reason, most astronomical observations of Mars are made near opposition. Not all oppositions are, however, equally favorable, because the orbit of Mars is highly eccentric ($e = 0.0933$). Figure 1 illustrates the relative orbits of Mars and Earth. The eccentricity of the Martian orbit is discernible. The figure shows the dates of all oppositions between 1960 and 1975; and, for each opposition, the distance to Mars in miles and the diameter of Mars in seconds of arc. The ensemble of relative planetary configurations at opposition in Figure 1 constitute a Metonic cycle, a period of 15 or 17 years during which the configurations repeat themselves. The oppositions of closest approach are called "favorable" oppositions; in the present Metonic cycle, they occur in 1969 and 1971. Such favorable oppositions will not recur until 1984.

For a given vehicle system, a spacecraft launched to Mars at certain

283

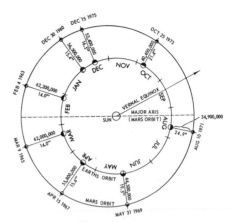

Figure 1.
Diagram of the orbits of Mars and
Earth.

times during the synodic period requires much less energy than a launch
at other times. The time of launch is a function of the desired payload,
the desired flight time, and the three-dimensional configuration of Mars
and Earth. In a given synodic period there is one time interval during
which the energy required for a given planetary mission is minimized.
This is called a launch window, or a planetary opportunity. Roughly
speaking, Martian opportunities occur about three months before Martian
oppositions. Since characteristic flight times are about 200 days, spacecraft launched to Mars during the launch window leave the Earth before,
and arrive at Mars after, opposition.

An "opportunity" is defined by the existence of a launch vehicle with
adequate thrust to place a spacecraft on a Martian transfer trajectory
during the time interval of interest. The mission may be a fly-by, an
orbiter, or a lander. In a fly-by, the spacecraft spends a brief period of
time (of the order of a few hours) within close range of the planet. An
orbiter may spend a much greater period of time at close range, depending
upon the eccentricity of the orbit and the useful lifetime of the orbiter.
A lander is a spacecraft that is designed to be deposited on the planetary
surface (preferably at a selected site), and in most cases, is designed to
give useful information about conditions at and near the surface for some
period of time after landing. The simplest planetary mission is a fly-by.
A planetary fly-by trajectory comprises, essentially, two segments: powered
flight and ballistic flight. During powered flight, the necessary velocity
vector is imparted to the vehicle. The powered flight trajectory desired
is a function of the characteristics of the launch vehicle, the engineering
constraints (payload, guidance, tracking, and telemetry), and the geometric constraints (launch site location, launch azimuth, and the relative
configuration of the Earth and Mars). In the powered flight segment,

either the direct ascent or the parking orbit mode may be adopted. In the direct ascent mode, the launch vehicle fires in one time interval only; at the end of the powered phase, the spacecraft must have the required velocity. In the parking mode, the spacecraft is first established in an approximately circular parking orbit about the Earth. After this has been done, one of the booster stages must be fired in order to leave the parking orbit for the planet. In general, the parking orbit mode is more efficient than the direct ascent mode, and allows a larger payload to be carried.

The planetary transfer trajectories, after either direct ascent or parking modes, can be divided into two categories, Type I and Type II. If the path of a spacecraft traverses less than 180° of heliocentric longitude, it is said to be on a Type I trajectory. Should the range of heliocentric longitude traversed by a spacecraft lie between 180° and 360°, it is on a Type II trajectory. Spacecraft in Type I trajectories generally require more energy, but take less time to reach their destinations than do spacecraft on Type II trajectories. Thus, it is possible for a spacecraft launched on a Type II trajectory to arrive at Mars after a spacecraft launched later, but on a Type I trajectory. Use of Type I and Type II trajectories is determined in part by the non-coplanarity of the orbits of Earth and Mars, and by the fact that it is difficult to launch two space vehicles from the same launch pad in a short period of time. In Figure 2, the required launch or injection energy per unit mass of spacecraft, C_3, is shown for the 30-day launch windows in each opportunity between 1969 and 1979. The larger the value of C_3, the smaller the payload, and the shorter the launch period during which a given launch vehicle may be used effectively. We note that by far the most favorable opportunities in the next

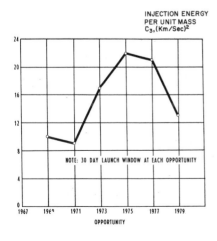

Figure 2.
Injection energy C_3 required to transfer unit mass from Earth to Mars at six opportunities between 1969 and 1979. The parameter C_3 is, by convention, twice the kinetic energy per unit mass.

INJECTION ENERGY
PER UNIT MASS
C_3,(Km/Sec)^2

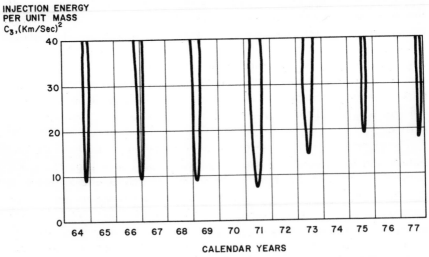

CALENDAR YEARS

Figure 3.   Variation of injection energy C_3 with time of launch, for transfer of unit mass from Earth to Mars. The parameter C_3 is, by convention, twice the kinetic energy per unit mass.

decade and a half occur in 1969 and 1971. The injection energy per unit mass required in the middle 1970's is approximately twice that required in 1969 and 1971. Not until 1984 will a launch opportunity as favorable as those of 1969 and 1971 recur.

There are also two restrictions on utilization of planetary opportunities that are functions of the launch azimuth. They arise from limitations due to the declination of the outbound velocity vector, and due to range safety considerations. In general, if the declination of the outbound velocity vector is greater than the launch site latitude, a range of launch azimuths, symmetrical about due East, are excluded for a given launch site. If the outbound velocity vector declination is less than or equal to the launch site latitude, it is then possible to launch at all azimuths within the range safety limits. The range safety requirement restricts the use of launch azimuths that would cause overflight of populated areas, and unnecessarily jeopardize the lives and property of the inhabitants. A synopsis of the energies, C_3, launch azimuths, and flight times for Martian opportunities within 30-day launch periods between 1969 and 1977 is shown in Table 1.

From Figure 3, it is clear that great gains in cost, fuel, and mission reliability can be achieved by synchronizing the launch schedule with the firing windows. A given spacecraft, launched along a minimum-energy

TABLE 1. Launch Conditions for Mars

Year	Launch Period	Launch Azimuth	Approx. C_3 $(km/sec)^2$	Flight Time (Days)
1969	Mar. 11-Apr. 10	48-58	10-16	194-219
1971	May 8-June 7	75-90 90-105	8-10	194-219
1973	July 19-Aug. 18	70-82 98-110	15-19	196-203
[a]1975	Sept. 1-Sept. 29	45-60	19-22	190-208
[b]1977	Oct. 5-Nov. 4	45-63	17-22	205-250

[a]Minimum injection C_3 excluded from Sept. 1-Sept. 11 due to launch azimuth restriction.
[b]Minimum injection C_3 excluded from Oct. 5-Oct. 15 due to launch azimuth restriction.

trajectory, will, of course, arrive at Mars at a known time during the Martian year. The astronomical observations suggest that not all arrival times are of equal interest. Much of the visual and polarimetric evidence that is suggestive of life on Mars has a seasonal character. Markedly periodic is the wave of darkening, a progressive albedo decline of the Martian dark areas (but not the bright areas) starting in local springtime from the edge of the vaporizing polar ice cap, and moving towards and across the equator.

The wave of darkening has been observed photometrically by *Focas* [1959], and his measurements are shown in Figure 4. Here, we have plotted Martian latitude against heliocentric longitude. Following the astronomical convention, south is at the top. The heliocentric longitude is shown related to the Martian season and the day of the Martian year. Differences in the nature of the darkening between adjacent dark areas at the same latitude have been suppressed. The shading shows the high-contrast third, the medium-contrast third, and the low-contrast third of the wave of darkening. The contrasts are with respect to the neighboring bright areas, deserts of seasonally constant albedo. If, as has been re-peatedly suggested, the Martian wave of darkening is related to the spring-time metabolic activities of Martian organisms, then a spacecraft intended for biological exploration of Mars should be operative during the high-contrast third of the darkening wave, whether the vehicle is an orbiter or a lander. The southern wave of darkening is much more striking than the northern; therefore, particular concentration on the southern wave is desirable. The latitudes of particular interest on visual, photometric, polarimetric, and spectrometric grounds are within 30° of the equator and at the edge of the receding polar ice cap.

In a study of the Voyager concept of Mars landing missions, *Swan and Sagan* [1965] have computed the arrival window of Mars-bound space-craft launched along approximately minimum-energy trajectories. Each space vehicle was intended to land two 1700-pound packages on the Martian surface. The accessible latitude ranges shown depend upon the design specifications of the system, its experimental objectives, and the use of the Saturn IB booster. But the position and width of the arrival windows apply approximately to minimum-energy trajectories for any space vehicle system. There are no restrictions in longitude. The dashed arrows are 180 days in length, and represent hypothetical lander life-times.

Arrival windows were computed for the entire Metonic cycle from 1969 to 1982. We see that only in 1969 will a minimum-energy trajec-tory lead to arrival at an appropriate time for investigation of the southern hemisphere darkening wave. The 1973 opportunity is favorable for

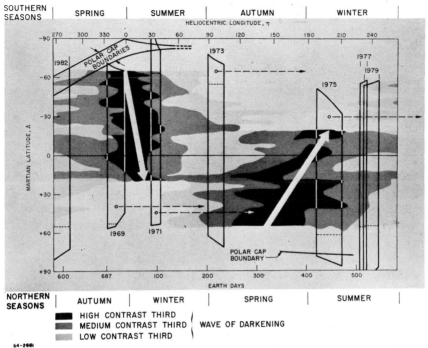

Figure 4. Martian wave of darkening and Voyager lander footprints. See text for details.

observation of the northern wave of darkening; the 1971 and 1975 mini-mum-energy arrival windows may permit some observation of the high-contrast third of the wave of darkening in the southern and the northern hemispheres, respectively; but they are not advantageously placed. The 1977, 1979, and 1982 opportunities are, from this point of view, particu-larly unfavorable.

However, payload can always be exchanged for a high-energy Earth-to-Mars transfer orbit. With the Saturn IB, for example, the time of the 1971 arrival window can be changed until it overlaps that of the 1969 minimum-energy window, if we are willing to forego one of the two pro-posed 1700-pound landers. For the 1973 and later opportunities, how-ever, large reductions in payload must be made if the arrival windows are to be timed to allow observation to begin just before the southern or the northern waves of darkening, even if the Saturn IB booster is used. This argues for utilization of the 1969 and 1971 opportunities for biological exploration of Mars.

However, if the Saturn V were available for Mars missions by the

TABLE 2. Saturn V Capabilities for Martian Missions

Launch	Wave of Darkening	C_3 (km/sec)^2	Flight Time (Days)	Injection Velocity (ft/sec × 10^{-4})	Saturn V Injected Payload (lbs × 10^{-3})	Landed Scientific Payload (lbs × 10^{-3})	Remarks
1973	North Hem.	75	100	4.7	20	5	Relatively high Mars arrival velocity
1973	South Hem.	35	250	4.2	43	8	
		20	300	3.9	58	10	
1975	North Hem.	150	400-450	5.5	Impossible for Saturn V	—	Even if possible (with nuclear upper stage, for example) would entail very high arrival velocity
1975	South Hem.	25	210	4.0	53	9	
1977	North Hem.	Similar to 1975 Northern Hemisphere					
1977	South Hem.	Similar to 1975 Southern Hemisphere					

middle 1970's, it appears that a significant application of the extra launch capability could be made; high-energy transfer orbits could be selected, and arrival windows opportunely timed for investigations of the wave of darkening. A preliminary analysis of the Saturn V's capabilities has been made by Dr. Paul R. Swan, of the AVCO Corporation, as a courtesy to this study. His computations disregarded launch azimuth restrictions. Swan finds that generally, 120-day to 150-day maneuverability in heliocentric longitude could be achieved by use of the Saturn V. This means, roughly, that 3000 pounds of payload could be placed on Mars in the 1973 through 1982 opportunities. Launches in 1975, 1977, and 1979 would result in arrival just before or in the midst of the high-contrast third of the northern wave of darkening; the 1982 launch, just before the high-contrast third of the southern wave of darkening and the 1973 launch would allow observation of either wave of darkening.

A further study of the Saturn V's capabilities has been made by Dr. F. G. Beuf, of the General Electric Company, as a courtesy to the study. The General Electric study involves a different spacecraft and is more detailed than the AVCO Saturn V study. The overall conclusions are generally in agreement, except in the case of the 1975 opportunity. The General Electric results are contained in Table 2. We see that quite sizable payloads could be landed in the midst of the wave of darkening throughout the 1970's, if a Saturn V booster is used.

It is possible that more favorable arrival dates may be obtained by use of a different kind of transfer trajectory in which the spacecraft is launched first towards Venus, where it makes a close fly-by with a hairpin trajectory [*Seiff*, 1964]. This imparts momentum to the spacecraft in a way that could not be achieved with the vehicle's own fuel supply. The concept is the same as the "gravitational machine" of *Dyson* [1963]. The synodic period of Venus is 584 days. Therefore, if such Venus fly-by trajectories can be exploited, a much larger range of launch opportunities and arrival windows becomes available. The practicality of such a trajectory, with its high accelerations, long transit times, and range of distances from the Sun, remains to be explored.

REFERENCES

Dyson, F. J. (1963), *In: Interstellar Communication*, A. G. W. Cameron, ed., Benjamin, New York.
Focas, J. H. (1959), *Compt. Rend. 248*:924.
Seiff, A. (1964), private communication.
Swan, P. R., and C. Sagan (1965), *J. Spacecraft and Rockets 2*:18.

CHAPTER 17

SPACE VEHICLES FOR PLANETARY MISSIONS

Elliott C. Levinthal

INTRODUCTION AND SOME DEFINITIONS

The *launch vehicles* contain the booster engine or engines arranged in one or more stages. These provide the thrust necessary to launch the *spacecraft* containing the payload on the desired trajectory. The launch vehicles associated with the possible unmanned planetary missions of immediate interest all use chemical propellants, as distinct from nuclear propellants, and are known as *Earth launch vehicles*. *Orbit launch vehicles* are assembled in Earth orbit from payloads placed there by Earth launch vehicles. If several vehicles are required to place this payload in orbit, the procedure would be known as a *multi-Earth launch*. This practice is encountered in studies of manned interplanetary missions where, because of the limitations in thrust, the vehicles are launched from an initial orbit about the Earth.

For a given vehicle system, a spacecraft launched to Mars at certain times during the synodic period requires much less energy than it would at other times. The selection of a time for launch is affected by the desired payload, the desired flight time, the three-dimensional configuration of Mars, Earth and the Sun, the particular trajectory desired, including considerations of arrival time during the synodic period, approach velocity of the vehicle relative to the planet, the type of mission to be accomplished on arrival, and the energy that can be provided by the launch vehicle. In a given synodic period there is a particular interval of time during which the energy required for a given planetary mission is minimized. This is called a *launch window* or a planetary opportunity.

The mechanics of interplanetary flight is a complex subject. To study the feasibility of a particular mission, however, one can often make use of simplifying assumptions. The problem can be reduced to a two-body problem to the extent that the trajectory can be considered to traverse different regions of space, starting from the departure *planetocentric space,* crossing *interplanetary* or *heliocentric* space and arriving at the target *planetocentric space.* Each of these regions can be described in terms of a central force field, in which the vehicle's motion is essentially that of a comet with constant orbital elements. The *transfer orbit* is that orbit connecting the departure planet and target planet. To the extent to which orbits are Keplerian (i.e., non-powered) and lie in heliocentric space, their orbital elements are invariant. However, as they enter different regions of space, they are perturbed and elements change. Rocket thrust, either impulsive or continuous, can be used to effect an *orbit change.*

If transfer orbits are tangential to their departure and target orbits, they require very low and, in most cases, the minimum transfer energy. These orbits generally require a comparatively long transfer time and are known as *Hohmann transfer orbits.* For such an orbit, the Martian opportunities occur about three months before Martian opposition. Since characteristic flight times are about 200 days, spacecraft launched to Mars during the launch window leave Earth before, and arrive at Mars after, opposition. At such a time in the synodic period, the Earth to Mars distance is increasing, and this is especially significant in connection with the transmission of data back to the Earth. *Fast transfer ellipses* are transfer orbits that intersect one terminal orbit or both. They provide the means for reducing the Earth to Mars distance at encounter. A fast transfer orbit might reduce this distance by a half, thus providing four times the data transmission for the same transmitter and receiver. The process of transfer from a helicentric orbit to a planetocentric orbit is known as *capture.* The reverse process is known as *escape.*

For circumplanetary probes that are captured by the central force field of the target planets, fast orbits are particularly expensive in energy. This is because the relative velocity between the spacecraft and the planet at encounter is large. While this is important, no matter what the type of mission may be, it is more important for orbiter missions, for the relative velocity between the spacecraft and the planet has a direct bearing upon the amount of retro-propulsion that must be carried in order to put the spacecraft into orbit about the planet. Changes in the three-dimensional configuration of Mars and Earth during the Metonic cycle, can cause the weight of the retro-propulsion system for otherwise similar missions to vary by a factor of three. The approach velocity is also important for landing missions because this changes the velocity at which the capsule would enter the Martian atmosphere and, hence, the amount of heat-shielding material with which it must be equipped.

Trajectories are often classified by the angle traversed with respect to the Sun, from Earth launch to Mars encounter. Those sweeping out less than 180° are known as *Type 1 trajectories,* and those between 180° and 360° are known as *Type 2 trajectories.* Figures 1 through 4 show typical trajectories from Earth to Mars for the opportunities in 1969, 1971, 1973 and 1975.

Launching requirements for planetary missions are often described in terms of the over-all minimum velocity required for surface launching to accomplish the particular mission. This defines an *ideal velocity* that will give the correct potential and kinetic energy with respect to the Earth's surface for the desired transfer orbit. For example, the circular velocity in a 300 nautical-mile-high Earth orbit is 24,900 feet per second, and the corresponding ideal velocity is 27,000 feet per second. The difference of 2100 feet per second is accounted for as potential energy.

To achieve a trajectory that would yield hyperbolic passage to Mars, additional energy is required. This is often expressed in terms of a velocity known as the *hyperbolic excess velocity* or *injection velocity.* It is the velocity of the vehicle with respect to the Earth when the vehicle-Earth distance is large. Thus, the ideal velocity for a Mars mission is obtained by adding the ideal velocity, corresponding to the initial 300-mile Earth orbit (27,000 feet per second), and the hyperbolic excess velocity of approximately 11,600 feet per second, giving a total of 38,600 feet per

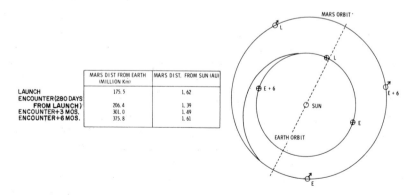

	MARS DIST. FROM EARTH (MILLION Km)	MARS DIST. FROM SUN (AU)
LAUNCH	175.5	1.62
ENCOUNTER (280 DAYS FROM LAUNCH)	206.4	1.39
ENCOUNTER+3 MOS.	301.0	1.49
ENCOUNTER+6 MOS.	375.8	1.61

Figure 1.   Earth to Mars, February 24, 1969

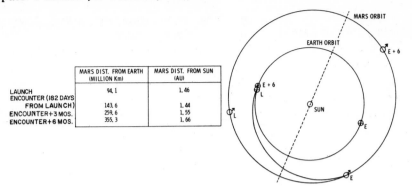

	MARS DIST. FROM EARTH (MILLION Km)	MARS DIST. FROM SUN (AU)
LAUNCH		
ENCOUNTER (182 DAYS FROM LAUNCH)	94.1	1.46
	143.6	1.44
ENCOUNTER+3 MOS.	259.6	1.55
ENCOUNTER+6 MOS.	355.3	1.66

Figure 2. Earth to Mars, June 3, 1971

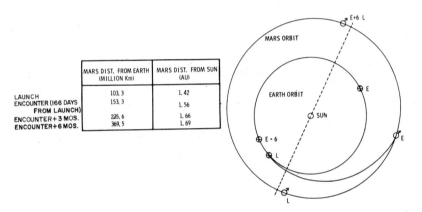

	MARS DIST. FROM EARTH (MILLION Km)	MARS DIST. FROM SUN (AU)
LAUNCH	103.3	1.42
ENCOUNTER (166 DAYS FROM LAUNCH)	153.3	1.56
ENCOUNTER+3 MOS.	235.6	1.66
ENCOUNTER+6 MOS.	369.5	1.69

Figure 3. Earth to Mars, August 7, 1973

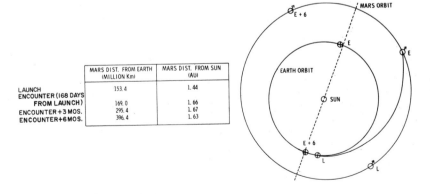

	MARS DIST. FROM EARTH (MILLION Km)	MARS DIST. FROM SUN (AU)
LAUNCH	153.4	1.44
ENCOUNTER (168 DAYS FROM LAUNCH)	169.0	1.66
ENCOUNTER+3 MOS.	295.4	1.67
ENCOUNTER+6 MOS.	396.4	1.63

Figure 4. Earth to Mars, September 17, 1975

second. In Figure 5, the launching requirements for several different planetary missions are shown in terms of ideal velocity.

The evidence of extremely low Martian atmospheric densities has imposed additional constraints on missions that involve landing. Assuming ballistic entry and parachutes for descent, the low densities have a direct effect on mission capability. Figure 6 shows the percentage of entered weight remaining at impact as a function of the Martian surface pressure. Curves for different impact velocities are shown. These curves are meant simply to show typical examples of trends. They indicate a significant reduction in the weight available for instruments, power and communications as the Martian atmospheric pressure is reduced. In designing a spacecraft one must take into account the uncertainties in our knowledge of the atmospheric density. Assuming that the uncertainty is 10-40 millibars, the capsule must be designed to cover this total range. If the surface pressure is 10 millibars, a large penalty in capability is not paid in designing for 10-40 millibars. If the surface pressure is much above 10 millibars, a large penalty *is* paid in designing for pressures as low as 10 millibars. Another effect of the low surface pressure is on the physical size of the entry capsule. Figure 7 shows the diameter of the capsule as a function of its weight at entry into the Martian atmosphere. Four curves are shown for different surface pressures. The physical size of the capsule is very large for the 11 millibar atmosphere. This has a direct effect on the selection of the launch vehicle because some rockets have small shrouds, whereas

Figure 5.
Velocities required for planetary missions and corresponding durations of flight. (Courtesy of the National Aeronautics and Space Administration)

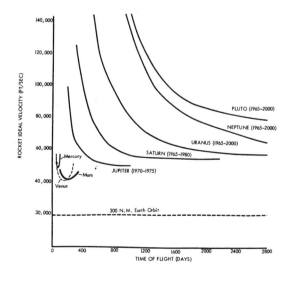

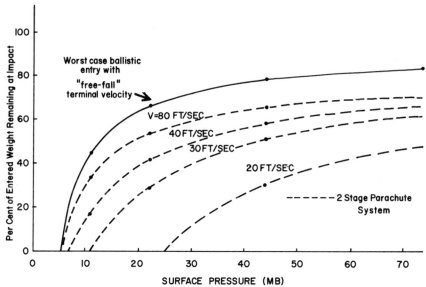

Figure 6. Effect of surface atmospheric pressure on the fraction of the weight of a Martian lander that could be allocated to instruments, power, communications, etc. Atmospheric retardation is assumed and the terminal velocities indicated. (Courtesy of the National Aeronautics and Space Administration)

others allow larger diameter spacecraft to be carried. In some cases, it may be necessary to provide the capsule with extensible flaps in order to achieve the effective diameter required by the conditions of atmospheric entry.

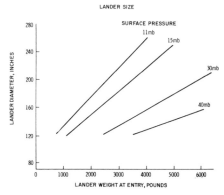

Figure 7.

Effect of Martian atmospheric pressure on size and weight of a lander. (Courtesy of the National Aeronautics and Space Administration)

LAUNCH VEHICLES

Several potentially suitable launch vehicles are available or under development; they are shown in Figure 8. The Atlas-Agena has a Mars or Venus capability of about 500-600 lbs. It was used for the Mariner flight to Venus in 1962 and for the 1964 Mars flight (Mariner IV). The approximate cost of this rocket system, including launching costs, is $8 million. (The costs given here are approximate and do not include development costs or the costs of the spacecraft.) The Atlas-Centaur is under development and is scheduled to be available by 1966; it will have a 1200-1500 lb planetary transfer capability and will cost about $11 million per launch. The next largest launch vehicle with potentialities in the planetary program

Figure 8.   United States launch vehicles capable of planetary missions. (Courtesy of the National Aeronautics and Space Administration)

is the Titan IIIC; it is being developed under contract from the United States Air Force. It could be available for planetary exploration in 1966 at a unit cost for launch of between $12-20 million, depending upon the level of production. The Titan IIIC would be able to inject approximately 3000 lbs on a Mars transfer trajectory. The largest launch vehicle now under development with planetary transfer capability is the Saturn V. It is being developed under the direction of the Marshall Space Flight Center and would be able to inject spacecraft weighing up to 60,000 lbs into a transfer trajectory to Mars. The availability of the Saturn V for planetary exploration would depend on the progress of the manned lunar landing program, for which it was designed. It could, perhaps, be available for planetary exploration in 1969. The cost per launch is estimated at approximately $100 million.

In addition to these rocket systems, other configurations are being studied. For example, if fluorine were added to the liquid oxygen used in the Atlas-Centaur, it would increase its payload capacity to 2000 lbs and slightly increase the launch cost. A Titan II with a Centaur upper stage would be able to transport about 2500 lb to Mars at a cost of $11 million per launch. Extensive studies have been made of the capabilities that would result from the addition of a third stage such as the Centaur, to the Saturn IB. It is proposed to use a rocket system of this kind in the Voyager program; it would be able to transport 6000 to 7000 lb to Mars at an estimated launch cost of $25 million. The costs for developing the three-stage Saturn IB have been estimated at between $100-300 million.

All planetary missions require the use of a rocket system capable of an ideal velocity greater than about 40,000 feet per second; the launch vehicles mentioned above that meet this requirement are listed in Table 1.

UNMANNED MARS MISSIONS

Even with all the limitations that have been described, the number of different missions that could be flown is very large. This is particularly true when one is considering the launch vehicles with the larger payload capabilities. While generalizations about their characteristics are possible, they must be applied with great caution. Determination of the feasibility of any particular mission requires detailed study. For example, more than 1000 man-months was expended on a study of a few of the very many possible Saturn IB planetary missions. In these studies the scientific payload varied from 8-12% of the capsule weight; while this ratio is fairly common, it may not apply in all such cases. For orbiter missions, approximately half of the weight injected on a transfer trajectory to the planet

TABLE 1. Launch Vehicle Summary Data for Planetary Missions

LAUNCH VEHICLE	APPROXIMATE COST (INCL. LAUNCH COSTS) In Millions of $	TOTAL PAYLOAD CAPABILITY (Pounds)	REMARKS
Atlas-Agena	8	500-600	Operational
Atlas-Centaur	11	1200-2000	Development (Available 1966)
Titan IIIC	20	3000-4000	Development (Available 1966)
Saturn V	100	40,000-60,000	Development (Available 1969)
Saturn IB (3-Stage)	25	6000-8000	Under Study
Titan II Centaur	11	2500	Under Study

must be reserved for the propulsion required to place the payload in orbit. Thus, the effective payload for orbiters is about one-half of fly-bys on otherwise similar missions. About one-half the payload may be landed if it is first put into orbit, rather than landed directly from a ballistic trajectory.

The nature of the search for extraterrestrial life is such that it is not possible to estimate quantitatively the potential yield from any particular mission. One can only approach this problem by considering individual experiments, such as the potential spectral and spatial resolution for a given orbiting infrared spectrometer and, with this information, attempt to assign a value to the inferences that might be drawn from the results. A highly oversimplified criterion of the yield of a mission is the number of bits of information that the scientific payload can transmit back to Earth. The significance of this criterion is again dependent upon the objective of the mission. For example, the payload that a Saturn V could put into orbit about Mars could, for lifetimes in orbit greater than a certain value, transmit more data for the duration of its mission than could the maximum payload of the same launch vehicle if put into a fly-by trajectory past the planet. It might turn out, however, that because of its larger payload, the fly-by mission might take a few pictures of a limited area of the planet's surface at a higher resolution than would be achieved by the orbiter. This is not to suggest that a fly-by is a better mission for video reconnaissance than an orbiter, but simply to emphasize the care that is required when using a single criterion for the yield of a mission. Prof. Bruce Murray of the California Institute of Technology has suggested a trajectory that is intermediate between that of an orbiter and a fly-by: some energy is used at encounter to change the fly-by hyperbolic trajectory to another hyperbola that brings the spacecraft back towards the Earth. This might be called a bi-hyperbolic trajectory. It has some interesting properties with respect to reconnaissance data. For a given risk of collision, the fly-by can approach closer to the surface. This gives a linear gain in resolution for the same payload. The time in orbit, which has a linear relationship to total bits transmitted, must be compared to the inverse R^2 dependence of transmitted bandwidth or the bit-rate for a given transmitter power, R being the Earth-to-spacecraft distance during transmission of data. Thus the situation can be reversed and the non-orbiting mission could give more total bits and higher resolution (closer approach). It should be pointed out, however, that the duration of the mission becomes large if much advantage is to be taken of the procedure outlined above. Some of the missions that have been planned or studied for each of the possible launch vehicles are reviewed below.

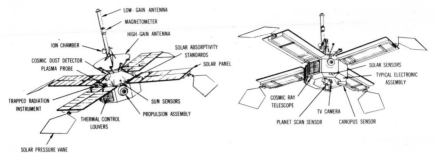

Figure 9. The Mariner IV spacecraft, shown here in diagram, was launched with an Atlas Agena rocket on November 28, 1964, and completed a successful flight to within 6,000 miles of Mars in July 1965. With solar panels extended, the spacecraft spans about 22½ ft; its gross weight is 575 lb, including about 60 lb of instruments, as follows: television camera, plasma probe, ionization chamber, trapped radiation detector, cosmic-ray telescope, vector magnetometer, and cosmic dust detector. (Courtesy of the Jet Propulsion Laboratory and the National Aeronautics and Space Administration.)

Fly-By Missions

All the launch vehicles mentioned above have the capability of carrying out fly-by missions. The 1964 Mars Mariner was such a mission utilizing the Atlas-Agena. The payload included a television system designed to obtain about twenty pictures of the Martian surface with 5 km resolution, together with instruments for observing micrometeoroids, charged particle fluxes and the magnetic field. The characteristics of this spacecraft are illustrated in Figure 9. This represents the minimum mission studied and essentially exhausts the capability of the Atlas-Agena.

Fly-by missions have generally been considered worthwhile only in connection with launch vehicles of moderate capability. Larger rockets may find some application in this fashion if the suggestion of Murray is followed (see above). A spacecraft contemplated for the Saturn IB, with Centaur upper stage, comprises a 2000 lb "bus" that could serve either as a fly-by or, with the addition of a retro-rocket, as an orbiter. This bus could carry 200 to 300 lb of scientific instruments with 600 watts of power, a 10 foot diameter microwave antenna and could transmit at a 2000 bits per second rate. With data storage, it could provide a total transmission of 10^8 bits, if used as a fly-by.

Planetary Entry Probes

By these are meant probes that would penetrate the atmosphere and permit direct sampling of the atmospheric profile and a demonstration of vehicle entry effects. Such a probe would not be expected to survive impact with the surface. Such missions become possible with the utilization of the Atlas-Centaur or any of the larger launch vehicles. Missions of this kind were suggested for the 1966 opportunity as part of a fly-by experimental payload. At that time, both a spherical and a non-spherical probe were suggested. The spherical probe had a diameter of about 3-4 ft and a weight of approximately 100 lb. The minimum instrumentation included a telemetry transmitter and an integrating three-axis accelerometer. Other instruments were suggested, including pressure gauge, anemometer, densitometer, mass spectrometer, thermocouple and radar altimeter. Flight instruments have already been tested in rockets for these functions. Atmospheric constituents can also be studied with such probes by observing the plasma sheath through a sapphire window.

The use of the spacecraft bus to relay telemetered data from such probes to the Earth is often advocated. While such a relay gives an added possibility for failure, it is preferred because of the difficulty of obtaining sufficient power, antenna directivity, and probe stability for the direct link to Earth. Data rates for a minimum experiment would be of the order of 20 bits per second, and transmitter power (battery source) of the order of 20 watts. A possible difficulty with direct probe-to-Earth communications would be antenna voltage breakdown in the atmosphere at the high power levels required for this long transmission path.

A particular problem with a blunt-shaped probe is communication "blackout" due to the formation of a plasma sheath. Data could be stored during this time and then transmitted in the short time between blackout and impact. While such a procedure appears feasible, it is complicated by the fact that the onset and duration of the blackout depends upon the very atmospheric parameters that are to be investigated. The duration of the blackout has been estimated at 8 to 32 seconds and the interval between blackout and impact, during which transmission could take place, at 26 to 160 seconds.

A *non-spherical entry probe,* of shape similar to that of a soft-landing payload, could provide important vehicle entry engineering data. Rate gyros would be required for determining the angle of attack. Otherwise, the instrumentation could be as described for the spherical probes. Blackout problems would be essentially the same as for the sphere. In order to avoid the blackout problem, a slender body entry probe has also been pro-

TABLE 2. System Performance Summary

	Titan IIIC			Saturn IB SVI
	Bus-Lander	Orbiter	Orbiter-Lander	Orbiter-Lander
Injected Weight (lb)	2546	3600	3600	7030
Lander Weight (lb)	2042	—	1284	1450 + 1450
Lander Scientific Payload (lb)	387	—	110	211 + 211
Orbiter Weight (lb)	—	1815	1440	2059
Orbiter Scientific Payload (lb)	—	347	123	215
Orbit (n. mi.)	—	1000×2278	$1000 \times 19{,}000$	$1000 \times 19{,}000$

posed. Entry dynamics for such a probe are evidently not too well understood, however, and if large body oscillations occur, a plasma sheath would form and cause radio blackout in this case also.

Orbiter Missions

These missions become marginally possible with the utilization of the Atlas-Centaur launch vehicle. The JPL Mariner Mars 1969 Orbiter Feasibility Study considered the use of an Atlas-Centaur, improved by the addition of fluorine to the first stage oxidizer, that would have the capability of placing a 50-75 lb scientific payload in orbit about Mars with a lifetime of two to three months and a data rate of 33 bits per second. Under contract with the Jet Propulsion Laboratory, the General Electric Company completed on August 7, 1964, a study of an orbiting spacecraft for the 1971 Mars opposition utilizing the Titan IIIC launch vehicle. Orbiter-lander combinations and lander missions were also considered, and spacecraft performance was estimated for the 1973, 1975 and 1977 Mars opportunities. Table 2 gives a systems performance summary of these studies and compares them with earlier estimates of a three-stage Saturn IB orbiter-lander mission. Tables 3 and 4 give the scientific payloads that were considered possible for the all-orbiter payload and the orbiter of the orbiter-lander combination. The nominal transmission rates for the all-orbiter and the orbiter of the orbiter-lander were 12 and 6 kilobits per second, respectively. Storage capacity was 2×10^8 bits. The television cameras for the orbiter were designed to provide optical resolution of one km, 140 m (in color), and 20 m at the periapsis. Four bits per sample point were utilized in all cases; the number of lines was 512 for the low resolution vidicon system and 1024 for the other two systems utilizing image orthicons.

In 1962 and 1963 four studies were made (by General Electric Company, AVCO Corporation, Jet Propulsion Laboratory and Lockheed Missiles and Space Company) on the use of the three-stage Saturn IB configuration to perform a combination orbiter-lander mission to Mars. These have been referred to as the "Voyager Studies." The JPL and AVCO concepts included an orbiter and a single lander. The GE studies considered an orbiter accompanied by two landers. The Lockheed study emphasized the orbiter and included also two small landers. Weight summaries for the orbiters that were postulated in these studies are given in Table 5. The orbiters weighed about 2000 lb and were expected to function for three to six months. The total amount of data to be returned to Earth can be expressed in terms of the number of equivalent television pictures.

TABLE 3. Martian Orbiter Payload for Launch by Titan IIIC

Name	Weight (Pounds)	Power (Watts)
Magnetometer	5	5
IR Multi-Channel Radiometer	3	3
Solar Multi-Channel Radiometer	3	3
Television: 4 Image Orthicons, 2 Vidicons	115	(140)
Geiger Tubes & Ion Chamber	55	1
Far UV Radiometer	6	3
Micrometeroid Flux	8	1
Bi-Static Radar (Ionospheric Profile)	13	2
Polarimeter-Skylight Analyzer	4.5	4.5
IR Spectrometer	29	7
Retro-rocket & High-Resolution Package	146	
Mass Spectrometer	6	6
Langmuir Probe	3	3
	347	179

Assuming 800,000 bits per picture, the orbiter would have a capability of about 10,000 pictures or a total of 10^{10} bits.

The Saturn IB-Centaur spacecraft system, now under study, would allow for orbiters with a total weight in Martian orbit in the 2-4,000 lb range. In December, 1964, the General Electric Company completed a study of spacecraft systems compatible with the much larger Saturn V launch vehicle. The emphasis in these studies was on large landers. However, the use of orbiters as part of the payload was considered throughout, although no effort was expended to provide a specialized design for an orbiter. The method adopted involved the modification of the mid-course "bus" to make it suitable as an orbiter by adding subsystems, such as the necessary retro-propulsion and scientific instrumentation. These considerations would have resulted in a 1971 payload in orbit of 2633 lb with a scientific instrumentation payload of 350 lb. The amount of scientific payload that could be landed on the surface of Mars from an orbiter was also considered. With an entry velocity of 15,000 fps and a Mars orbit of 1000 nautical miles periapsis altitude and 19,000 nautical miles apoapsis altitude, the

TABLE 4. Martian Orbiter Payload for Launch by Titan IIIC in
Conjunction with a Lander

Name	Weight (Pounds)	Power (Watts)
2 Vidicon Cameras 3 Image Orthicon Cameras	83.0	25.0
IR Radiometer	3.0	3.0
Visible Radiometer	3.0	3.0
Magnetometer	5.0	5.0
Far UV Radiometer	3.0	3.0
Micrometeroid Flux	3.0	0.5
Charged Particle Flux	5.5	1.0
Polarimeter	4.5	4.5
Bistatic Radar	13.0	2.0
	123	47.0

TABLE 5. Martian Orbiters for Launch by Saturn IB with Upper Stage
Summary of Estimated Weights (lbs)

	JPL	AVCO	GE	Lockheed
Structure & Thermal Control	345	324	506	351
Power Supply	388	461	218	506
Guidance & Control	348	186	226	326
Communications & Data Handling	332	283	321	284
Harnessing	150	128	106	45
Scientific Instruments	257	135	215	493
	1820	1517	1592	2005

total weight that could be put in Martian orbit for the 1971, 1973, and 1975 opportunities, respectively, was approximately 27,500 lb, 25,600 lb, and 22,400 lb. The potential of orbiter missions can only be estimated from these numbers. Since the point of these studies was to maximize the landed weight, the orbiter was incidental and became inert after separation of the very large lander. No extensive studies have been made of the potential yields from orbiters with scientific payloads in excess of 250 lb.

Lander Missions

As with orbiter missions, the Atlas-Centaur is the smallest launch vehicle that can land a survivable scientific payload on the surface of Mars. A Jet Propulsion Laboratory technical feasibility study of a Mariner Mars 1969 lander led to the conclusion that payloads could be landed weighing 10 to 20 lb, or as much as 100 lb, depending upon the assumptions that were adopted about the atmospheric profile. The previously referenced General Electric report on the utilization of the Titan IIIC launch vehicle included the study of a bus-lander mission for the 1971 opposition. In these missions the main purpose of the bus is to deliver the lander to its impact trajectory. Bus functions include propulsion guidance, attitude control and communication during interplanetary transit. During these studies some consideration was also given to missions that combined in one payload an orbiter and a landing capsule. In the studies of the bus-lander system, the model atmospheres assumed were characterized by an 11-30 millibar surface pressure. These studies also estimated spacecraft performance for the 1973, 1975 and 1977 Mars opportunities. The diameter of the Titan IIIC shroud of 120 inches would allow a lander entry weight of only 1380 lbs. Either the development of larger shrouds, or some other means, such as extensible flaps, were required to use the Titan IIIC energy. The GE studies required the development of a 144-inch-diameter shroud, although they point out that further study of movable flaps might permit the same payload to be used with the standard shroud diameter. Again referring to Table 2, one finds a system performance summary comparing the Titan IIIC missions with the three-stage Saturn IB missions. Tables 6 and 7 give the scientific payloads that GE considered possible for the 2042 lb lander and the lander of the orbiter/lander combination. These studies showed that the lander could include a vehicle with some capability for independent movement on the surface. This is in addition to the other experiments listed for the lander. Very little detail on the Rover and its capability is presented in these studies. The nominal data transmission rate for the lander would be 800 bits per second. This would be reduced to 400 bits per second after 62 days. A storage capability of 10^7 bits is

TABLE 6. Scientific Payload for 2042-pound Lander for Launch by
Titan IIIC

	Weight (Pounds)	Power (Watts)
Temperature	0.3	0.07
Sounds	0.5	1
Pressure	0.3	0.10
Density	1.5	2
Multiple Chamber	4.0	2
Surface Penetration Hardness	4.5	0.1
Photoautotroph	3.0	1
Light Intensity (Sun Sensor)	0.5	0.1
Composition, H_2O	1.5	1
Composition, O_2	1.5	1
Turbidity & pH Growth Detector	4.0	1
Wind Speed and Direction	2.0	0.5
Gas Chromatograph	7.0	4.5
Composition, N_2	1.0	1
Composition, CO_2	1.0	1
Soil Moisture	2.0	25
TV Camera, Panorama TV	20.0	20
Radioisotope Growth Detector	6.0	3
Composition, O_3	1.5	1
Composition, A	1.5	1
Precipitation	1.0	1
Electron Density (Langmuir Probe)	3.0	3
Surface Gravity	3.0	3
Radar Altimeter	15.0	25
TV Microscope and Subsurface Group	75.0	200
Seismic Activity	8.0	1
	168.6	299.37

TABLE 7. Scientific Payload for Lander of Lander-Orbiter Combination,
for Launch by Titan IIIC

	Weight (Pounds)	Power (Watts)
Temperature	0.3	0.77
Sounds	0.5	1
Pressure	0.3	0.10
Density	1.5	2
Multiple Chamber	4.0	2
Surface Penetrability/Hardness	4.5	0.1
Photoautotroph Detector	3.0	1
Light Intensity (Sun Sensor)	.5	0.1
Composition, H_2O	1.5	1
Composition, O_2	1.5	1
Turbidity & pH Growth Detector	4.0	1
Wind Speed & Direction	2.0	0.5
Gas Chromatograph	7.0	4.5
Composition, N_2	1.0	1
Composition, CO_2	1.0	1
Soil Moisture	2.0	25
TV Camera, Panorama	20.0	20
Radioisotope Growth Detector	6.0	3
Composition, O_3	1.5	1
Composition, A	1.5	1
Precipitation	1.0	1
Electron Density (Langmuir Probe)	3.0	3
Surface Gravity	3.0	3
Radar Altimeter	15.0	25
Seismic Activity	8.0	1
	93.6	100.07

TABLE 8. Martian Landers for Launch by Saturn IB with Upper Stage
(Voyager Studies) Summary of Estimated Weights

	JPL	AVCO	GE	Lockheed
Adaptor, Separation, Propulsion, etc.	316	210	187	82
Heat Shield & Structure	499	450	489	
Retardation & Deployment	195	320	273	42
Communications & Data Handling	145	200	143	36
Power Supply	402	300	112	33
Thermal Control	20	55	91	15
Scientific Instruments	121	200	155	28
	1700	1735	1450 ($\times$ 2)	236 ($\times$ 2)

also provided. A total of 8350 television frames would be transmitted during the total mission time of 180 days. These frames would have approximately 4×10^5 bits per frame, with 256 lines and 6 bits per sample.

The four Voyager studies undertaken in 1962 and 1963 (GE, AVCO, JPL and Lockheed) considered three-stage Saturn IB launch vehicle configurations in connection with Mars lander missions. These studies were initially based on the Schilling model of the Mars atmosphere ("Limiting Model Atmospheres of Mars," G. S. Schilling, *R-402-JPL:* A report prepared for JPL by the Rand Corporation.)

Late in these studies, the possibilities of very low surface pressures were introduced. The design limits were 11-30 millibars with a mean of 15 millibars. Since this possibility was introduced late in the studies, its effect was not considered in great depth. The JPL and AVCO concepts included an orbiter and a single lander. The GE studies considered an orbiter with two landers. While the Lockheed study emphasized the orbiters, they also included two small landers. Weight summaries of the landers considered are shown in Table 8. Table 9 gives an over-all summary of the results of these Voyager studies. The JPL, AVCO and GE studies divided the total spacecraft weight between the orbiter and lander in about the same way. The lifetime at the planet for these payloads was 3-6 months. Assuming 800,000 bits per television picture, the lander would have a capability of about 1000 pictures or a total of about 10^9 bits.

TABLE 9. Voyager Characteristics

Spacecraft Weight—6,000 to 7,000 lb
    Orbiter—2,000 lb
    Lander(s)—2,500 lb

Instrument Weight—450 to 550 lb

Lifetime at Planet—3 to 6 mos

Communication Capability—
    Orbiter 10,000 TV Pictures
    Lander(s) 1,000 TV Pictures

Landing Accuracy—Dispersion about Aiming Point 250 to 500 KM

All of these studies indicated an additional technical factor to be of importance for long lifetime landers: the need for radioisotope thermo-generator power sources. It is through the utilization of such power systems that the long lifetimes were achieved. Solar cells on the surface of Mars were thought not to be attractive for many reasons. The development of these radioisotope thermo-generator (RTG) units, at power levels adequate for such applications, is not now in progress and would represent a long lead-time development item. The amount of radioisotopes required represents a significant fraction of the whole available national supply.

Because of the considerable interest in large landers, NASA supported the General Electric Company in a study of the Saturn V as a launch vehicle for such missions. This study was completed December 9, 1964. The objectives were "to define landers capable of carrying scientific payloads of 250, 500, 1000, 2500 and 5000 lb. The study was not intended to define the makeup of the scientific payload, but a range of required electrical power and communication bit rates was assumed for each payload size. . . . The range of surface pressures considered in this study was 11 to 30 millibars. The entry angle corridor used in the basic study was from 20° to 35°, which was consistent with the guidance accuracy used in previous Saturn IB and Titan IIIC studies." The primary retardation was achieved by parachutes. With the limitations implied by system designs that do not involve carrying the landers into orbit, the shroud volume limitation is encountered before the weight limit is reached. The total launch energy available from the Saturn V booster could be used to provide considerable flexibility in the conduct of the mission. Wide launch windows and short trip times could be achieved. Control of these parameters allows a degree of choice over the season of arrival at Mars. The system configurations used in the study are shown in Table 10, and the important characteristics of the lander and payloads are given in Table 11.

TABLE 10. Saturn V Lander System Configurations

Midcourse Bus	Midcourse Bus	Midcourse Bus	Midcourse Bus	Individual Bus
Cluster Bus	Cluster Bus	Individual Bus	Individual Bus	Lander
Cluster Bus	Cluster Bus	Lander	Lander	
Cluster Bus		Individual Bus	Individual Bus	
		Lander	Lander	
		Individual Bus		
		Lander		
A	B	C	D	E

System	Landers Per Cluster	Total Landers	Weight Per Lander	Scientific Payload Per Lander
A	4	12	1400	150
B	3	6	2000	370
C	—	3	6200	1760
D	—	2	13,100	3100
E	—	1	26,200	5000

The procedure used to carry out the parametric studies was to assume a nominal and a maximum and a minimum power level and communication bit rate required as a function of payload size. Figures 10 and 11 give these values. From these numbers, and based on an Earth-to-Mars separation of 1.4 AU, Figures 12 and 13 are derived, giving the communication subsystem power and weight requirements.

The comment previously made about RTG power sources in connection with three-stage Saturn IB missions applies also here.

The large capabilities of the Saturn V launch vehicle generate an indefinitely large array of possible missions. The choice of missions characterized as optimum by any particular study becomes a very sensitive function of

TABLE 11. Saturn V Lander and Payload Summary Tabulation

	Unit						
Scientific Payload	lb	250	500	1000	1760	2500	5000
Gross Payload	lb	739	1138	1850	2842	3978	7235
Lander Gross Weight (W_G)	lb	1675	2396	3846	6192	10,400	24,260
Entry Weight (W_E)	lb	1563	2231	3576	5900	9850	22,800
Base Diameter (D_B)	ft	10.30	12.33	15.60	20.00	25.70	39.35
Nose Radius (R_N)	ft	2.42	2.90	3.67	4.70	6.04	9.25
Scientific P/L Nominal Power	watts	60	162	345	576	805	1425
Communication Nominal Data Rate	bps	1100	2000	3700	6000	8000	15,000
Antenna Dish Diameter	ft	4.90	5.70	6.70	7.55	8.10	9.50

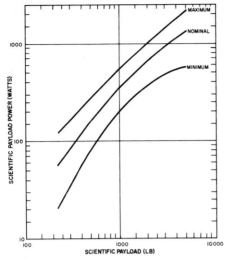

Figure 10.
Scientific payload power versus weight for Saturn V landers

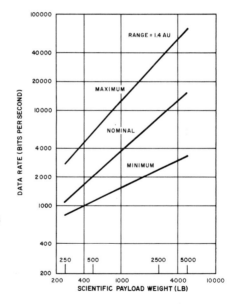

Figure 11.
Scientific payload bit rate versus weight for Saturn V landers

the initial assumptions. For example, assumptions concerning guidance accuracies and method of retardation lead to a maximum in the curve of gross payload weight as a function of lander gross weight, so that if the entry angle were less than 23°, the total payload on Mars with all

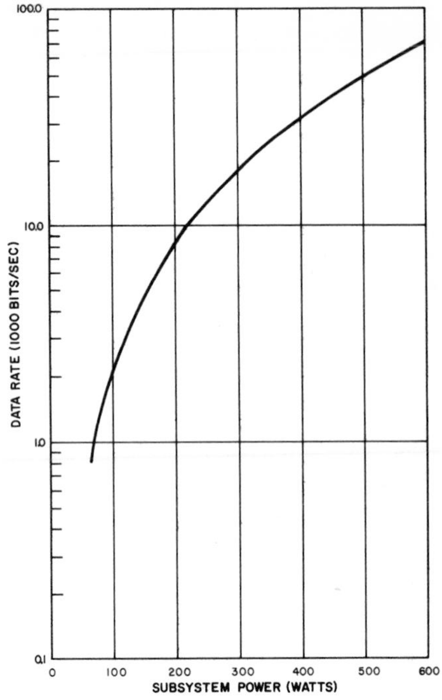

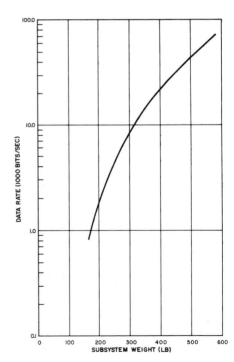

Figure 12.
Communication subsystem data rate versus subsystem power for Saturn V lander

Figure 13.
Communication subsystem data rate versus subsystem weight for Saturn V lander

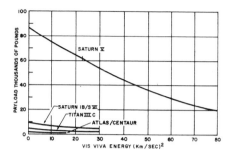

Figure 14.
Comparative launch capabilities

other assumptions remaining the same could be increased by about a factor of 3. An alternate approach would be to eject the landers from orbit about Mars. Ordinarily this would be considered inefficient due to the energy required to place the payload in orbit. However, entry from orbit would allow a tighter entry corridor with the same guidance accuracies and a significant reduction in the entry velocities. Both these effects allow significantly higher ballistic coefficients and thus a much higher payload weight for a given total lander weight. This more than doubles the possible scientific payloads landed per mission. Figure 14 shows the comparative capability of the Saturn V launch vehicle as a function of the "vis-viva energy", or C_3, the injection energy of the Earth escape hyperbolic trajectory. This points up the fact that the use of this launch vehicle opens up a new regime of mission opportunities and problems.

The potential of the Saturn V for the biological exploration of Mars can perhaps be exploited even further. According to H. H. Koelle, Director of the Future Projects Office, MSFC, 7200 lb of the 50,000 lb a Saturn V could deliver to a Mars transfer trajectory would be required to return a 600 lb capsule from Mars to Earth on a minimum energy mission of about 950 days duration. This simply shows that such a mission is possible with the Saturn V and, for that matter, even with the three-stage Saturn IB. A detailed study would be required to establish the technical feasibility of such a mission. Because of the hazards of back contamination, one might want to impose additional requirements on such a study, such as the delivery of the return capsule to a scientific station on the Moon or to an Earth-orbiting space station. On the Moon, man could study at first hand the interaction of terrestrial and Martian biota without the dangers of contamination of either Earth or Mars. Concern with planetary contamination could prevent the use of orbiting laboratories for this purpose.

Table 12 gives a comparison of the estimates of cost, weight, data transmitted and lifetime for many of the planetary missions discussed above.

TABLE 12. Estimates of Costs, Weights, Data Transmitted and Lifetimes for Planetary Missions

Spacecraft	Spacecraft Costs (in $ millions) First Opportunity (2 spacecraft)	Repeat (2 spacecraft)	Launch Vehicle Costs (in $ millions) Per Opportunity (2 launch vehicles)	Instrument Weight (lbs)	Scientific Payload Data Transmitted (bits)	Lifetime
ATLAS-CENTAUR						
Orbiter				50-75	33 per sec	2-3 mos
or						
Lander	210	150	22	10-20	10^5	1-5 hrs
TITAN IIIC COMBINED PROGRAM (3 landers, 2 orbiters)						
Orbiter	450	250	40	347	PER ORBITER 5×10^{10} at 12,000 per sec	3 mos
Lander		250		386	PER LANDER 2×10^9 at 600-800 per sec	6 mos
SATURN IB						
With S-6 Stage	450	250	60	100-500 20-200	10^{10} (orbiter) 10^9 (lander)	6 mos
With Centaur Stage	450	250	60	200-300 100-600	10^8 (orbiter) 10^7 (lander)	6 mos
SATURN V	1500	900	200	5,000	3×10^{10} to 7×10^{11} per yr at 3,000-70,000 per sec	2 yrs

COMMENTS

The excitement of the search for extraterrestrial life, which extends well beyond the domain of science, need not be reiterated here. The strategies suggested for implementation of this search arise in a context of engineering constraints—mainly those of weight, power and communications. When it was felt that there were opportunities for one- to ten-pound instruments and communication rates of a bit per second in the early 1960's, and that a significant relaxation of these constraints would not occur for approximately a decade, the strategic debate focused on the selection of the "best" "life detector". One argued that growth was a "riskier guess" than metabolism and that a single step functional test for a ubiquitous enzyme had more generally than a multi-step metabolic degradation. The morphologists, on either a macroscopic or microscopic scale, could not sharpen their criteria to justify the utilization of the total communication channel required for one picture of even a modest combination of field of view and spatial resolution.

This debate has not been fruitless, for it has served as a reminder that the unambiguous recognition and characterization of life requires a diversity of experimental investigations.

An examination of the instrumentation developments that have been completed or are under way gives the conviction that a sufficient range of specific experimental techniques can be exploited with an instrument payload of thousands of pounds and perhaps even several hundred. The requirement for thousands of pounds becomes necessary when one makes the essential inclusion of the non-specific technique of visual observation on any scale. Its singular value is its non-specificity. The full benefit of this value is achieved only by the transmission of an enormous amount of data. Ten minutes of microscopic observation represent more than 10^9 bits of data presentation. It is the interaction of these data with the collective store of scientific intelligence represented by the observers viewing the images at Goldstone that gives power to the specific instruments situated in a laboratory on Mars. A Saturn V lander makes possible video transmission at high rates during a good deal of the mission.

It is continually necessary to face the task of evaluating whether or not a mission is "possible". What is "possible" is determined by many kinds of constraints in addition to those imposed directly by technological matters. There are financial considerations having to do with total costs, and the phasing of costs with the motion of the planets and fiscal budgets. There are manpower problems and political considerations that concern the scientific community, the Government, Congress, and the country at large.

To avoid the danger of circular reasoning with regard to what is "possible," it is important that scientists and engineers separate and identify the various considerations that affect their judgments about the possibility or desirability of a mission.

It has been generally true so far, that the constraints of size and weight have been so overriding on planetary missions that there have been unrelenting pressures to push miniaturization to "state-of-the-art" limits and to maximize the number of different scientific objectives a mission could achieve. This has led to a certain comparability in some of the parameters of different scientific payloads, such as cost per pound, development costs and development time per pound, the dependence of cost on bits transmitted and dependence of reliability on weight or size. Statements or implications that these are generally invariant parameters of space missions and that they cannot be radically changed should be examined quite carefully. It is possible that with larger launch vehicles, good engineering and scientific management of the opportunities presented by large payloads could lead to more favorable levels of performance, economy and yield than would be expected by extrapolation from past experience with smaller rockets and smaller payloads. Similar precautions are required with regard to "learning" or "success" curves of previous missions or vehicles. It has been suggested that data on failures as a function of experience show that one arrives best at a successful large payload by means of a series of modest steps. A more careful examination should be made to be sure that the contrary is not true. In attempting a radical departure in size and capability for a planetary mission the number of failures that must be expected before achieving success may be an insensitive function of the number of launch experiences with different missions of much smaller scale. If this is true, and a large mission is thought to be necessary in any case, the greatest effectiveness and economy may be achieved by starting in the first place with a large mission.

These remarks suggest a compromise: the mission strategy is based on the use of a large launch vehicle, spacecraft, power source, and data capability but the initial scientific objectives are kept simple in order to maximize reliability. The mission could then have a large potential for growth in scientific yield. The scientific yield or objective is then the parameter that changes with time or experience, rather than the "basic" mission hardware. Such a procedure could lead to a different and improved dependence of scientific yield on cost.

Acknowledgements

In addition to the utilization of material from the referenced reports, material was also abstracted from memoranda prepared by Mr. J. W.

Haughey, NASA representative to the Exobiology Summer Study; the talk to the Exobiology Summer Study, June 17, 1964, by Mr. Donald P. Hearth of NASA Headquarters; and material prepared by Professor Von Eshleman of Stanford University on planetary entry probes.

BIBLIOGRAPHY

Atlas-Centaur

1. General Electric Re-Entry Systems Department; Mariner B Entry Vehicle, Nov. 26, 1963; submitted to Jet Propulsion Laboratory.
2. Goddard Space Flight Center; Experiments from a Small Probe which Enters the Atmosphere of Mars; NASA Technical Note D-1899, Dec. 1963.
3. Ames Research Center; Use of Entry Vehicle Responses to Obtain Measurement of the Structure and Composition of the Mars Atmosphere.
4. General Electric; Mariner B Entry Vehicle—Vol. 1: Technical Study; Nov. 26, 1963.
5. General Electric; Mariner Mars 66 Capsule, Vol. 1: Technical Proposal; Jan. 17, 1964.
6. Lockheed; Proposal for Preliminary Mars Atmospheric Probe Design; Dec. 18, 1963.
7. Goddard Space Flight Center; Measurement of Upper Atmosphere Structure by Means of the Pitot-Static Tube; J. E. Ainsworth; NASA Technical Note D-670, Feb. 1961.
8. Jet Propulsion Laboratory; Mariner Mars 1969 Orbiter Feasibility Study; EDP-250, Nov. 16, 1964.
9. Jet Propulsion Laboratory; Mariner Mars 1969 Lander Feasibility Study; EDP-261, Dec. 28, 1964.

Three-Stage Saturn IB

1. Jet Propulsion Laboratory; Study of Mars and Venus Orbiter Missions launched by the Three-Stage Saturn CIB vehicle; EPD-139, Vol. 3, Dec. 31, 1963.
2. Research and Advance Development Division; AVCO Corporation, Wilmington, Mass.; Voyager Design Studies; AVCO RAD-TR-63-34, Oct. 15, 1963; prepared under contract NASw697.
3. General Electric Missile and Space Division; Voyager Design Study; Document 63SD801; Oct. 15, 1963; prepared under contract NAS W-696.
4. Lockheed Missiles and Space Co., Sunnyvale, Calif.; Voyager Program Study; LMSC-5-53-63-4; Oct. 4, 1963.

Titan IIIC Launch Vehicle

1. General Electric Spacecraft Department; Voyager Spacecraft Systems Study (Phase I - Titan IIIC Launch Vehicle) Document 64-SD933; Aug. 4, 1964; prepared under contract 950847 for Jet Propulsion Laboratory.

Saturn V

1. General Electric Re-Entry Systems Department; A Study of Advanced Voyager/Beagle for Saturn V; GE-RSD70036; March, 1964.
2. General Electric Space Department; Voyager Spacecraft System Study (Phase II-Saturn V Launch Vehicle) Final Report, Volume 1 Summary. Document No. 64SD4376; Dec. 9, 1964; prepared under contract 950847 for Jet Propulsion Laboratory.

PART VII

MARTIAN LANDINGS: UNMANNED

BIOLOGICAL OBJECTIVES AND STRATEGY FOR THE DESIGN OF A SPACE VEHICLE TO BE LANDED ON MARS

D. A. GLASER

INTRODUCTION

The age-old question of the existence of extraterrestrial life has been given new and more specific meaning by the remarkable development of molecular biology during the last two decades. The question also has a new immediacy because of the rapid development of space vehicles capable of sending instrumentated packages to the neighborhood of Mars and other planets and of landing them on their surfaces. Our new knowledge of the detailed molecular mechanisms of genetics and of biochemical physiology has led us to delineate our interest in extraterrestrial life in the form of two specific questions:

1. Is it highly probable that living systems will arise in any planetary environment capable of supporting a complicated biochemistry?
2. Is the terrestrial form of life, based on nucleic acids and protein chemistry, unique in the sense that all living systems that can arise in an environment similar to that on Earth share the same biochemistry?

These questions have particular interest because biologists want to know if their science is characterized by the same universal causal necessity that has been found in chemistry and physics as they apply to the solar system

325

and the remote regions of the Universe as we know them from astronomical observations. It would be an extremely important new scientific fact if it were found that living systems arise with high probability in favorable environments and that they are always based on approximately the same biochemistry that characterizes terrestrial life.

It is probable that the majority of biologists today believe that life will arise and evolve to some stage with high probability in a favorable environment and that it will be based on a biochemistry not very different from that found on Earth. In designing instruments to be sent to Mars on a spacecraft, therefore, they would like to include a variety of instruments that would be capable of establishing the presence of biochemical substances, such as amino acids, proteins, nucleic acids and a variety of other substances found in terrestrial organisms. It is generally agreed among most biologists, however, that one should not overlook the use of detectors that could identify the presence of life even if its chemistry were quite unfamiliar to us and if we had no method for making a detailed chemical study of the strange organisms. Detectors for such unusual forms of life would have to depend on more general properties of living systems such as morphological, dynamical, thermodynamical, or ecological properties. Certain kinds of morphological complexity and symmetry are extremely improbable in non-living systems. Arguments that such unusual shapes are the products of living systems would be much strengthened if many similar copies of such shapes are discovered. Another class of properties possessed by living systems that could be the basis for a detection system is that they exhibit motion of a type that would not be expected for non-living systems. One might imagine a system to detect the presence of bacteria among a large number of non-living particles of about the same size and shape if they were motile and exhibited rapid swimming motions sufficiently vigorous to be distinguishable from the Brownian motion characterizing all particles of small size. The motion of larger systems might exhibit a response to a stimulating signal not expected of non-living systems. One can imagine the Martian spacecraft to be equipped with means of making a noise or flashing a light and observing whether any of its environment begins to move in response to these stimuli. A third characteristic of living systems that might be used to establish their presence on Mars are thermodynamic properties having to do with reaction rates and entropy production. In particular, there have been very speculative arguments that the reaction rates in biological systems must be significantly greater than the reaction rates in their non-living environment in order that the organisms be able to grow, reproduce, and maintain their integrity at a greater rate than the erosive or degradative processes that act on the environment in the weathering of rocks and other such processes. A general characteristic of terrestrial organisms is that they go through a stage of exponential increase in numbers under favorable conditions. In the case of terrestrial microorganisms, such kinetics have been detected calorimetrically. On Mars one can imagine that the spacecraft can be instructed to scoop up a handful of frozen soil and install it in a sensitive calorimeter. When the soil has been warmed up to growth conditions, an exponentially increasing evolution of heat could indicate the multiplication of microorganisms, if other autocatalytic processes can be discounted. Another possible basis for detection of unfamiliar life-forms would be generation by them of various signals not expected to be emitted by objects in their non-living environment, such as bursts of light or sound. If it can be established that optical activity is produced only rarely by inorganic processes, its detection is another fairly non-specific signature of life.

In general, the detection of living systems by observations that do not depend on detection of a biochemistry similar to that of terrestrial organisms depends on observing some phenomenon that cannot be explained by the laws of physics and chemistry as they are ordinarily applied to phenomena not resulting from a long history of sequential events. In this view a living organism is, to be sure, a product of physical and chemical phenomena, but has achieved its "living" status through a long evolutionary history of interaction with its environment. To the extent that a phenomenon can be established as being an exceedingly improbable result of short term physical and chemical events, it can be called a living system. An obvious and necessary requirement for the evolution of living systems is the invention of a memory or genetic mechanism that allows the system to retain and use selectively the information corresponding to its successful historical variations.

EXPERIMENTAL STRATEGY AND INSTRUMENTATION

Many specific instruments and measurements have been suggested for the use of known biochemical and biological techniques for detecting life on Mars. The decision concerning which instrument to incorporate in the actual package involves a balancing among the biological importance of the result to be obtained, the weight of the apparatus, its power requirements, its volume, its likelihood of successful operation or failure, its data rate requirements, and perhaps still other factors that would be part of an engineering feasibility study. Present policy also requires that the entire spacecraft and all of its equipment be sterilizable in order to minimize the probability of contaminating Mars and thereby destroying possible Martian organisms or modifying the biochemical environment so as to reduce the usefulness of Mars for biological study or utility at some future time. In addition to the need for choosing among the possible experimental packages, it is important to outline some sort of experimental strategy by which the logical relationships of the instruments are defined. Let us remark about the practical requirements simply that we want to do whatever is possible to maximize the rate of data acquisition, power resources, experimental versatility, reliability, sterility, etc. One important way to attain several of these objectives simultaneously is to use a compact general purpose computer aboard the spacecraft to correlate, organize, and program the sequence of experimental operations and the transmission of data to Earth. This computer could replace a large number of relays or other switching elements that would normally be used in each separate experiment to turn the equipment on and off and to operate motors, light sources and other active and passive elements in the proper sequence to carry out the desired measurements. The use of a computer to serve these various programming functions would probably eliminate much duplication and have the overriding advantage that changes could be made in the sequence of experiments, and sequence of operations within a given experiment, so that newly gained knowledge using improved laboratory techniques can be incorporated into the experimental strategy of the space laboratory until rather late in its engineering development and construction. In fact, the complexity of the total possible answers that the space laboratory might discover in response to various questions it would ask of the Martian environment is so great that it is unlikely that it will be possible to foresee all exigencies and to program the built-in computer for them in advance. It will, therefore, be necessary to envision a constant dialogue between the computer on the spacecraft and much larger computer facilities on earth. These terrestrial computers can be used to increase the effective data rate from Mars to Earth by a system of logical interrogation in which the computer on Earth asks "multiple choice" questions and the Martian computer has only to tell which alternative is correct rather than transmitting an explicit answer. A great advantage of having a fairly flexible computer aboard the spacecraft to control its operations is that new experiments and new ideas can be inserted into its experimental program by biologists who can have programs written on short notice to send for the instruction of the spacecraft.

Since it seems unlikely that biologists will be able to develop a system of experimental designs radically different from the customary, we will probably want to design the strategy of operation of the Mars spacecraft along the same general logical lines as those used for a well-designed experiment in a terrestrial laboratory. Perhaps it would go something as follows: On first landing or perhaps while the descent is being made, if that is a practical engineering feat, the spacecraft can be recording the temperature, pressure, perhaps chemical composition of the atmosphere, noise level and spectral light intensity. On the basis of these physical observations it would be possible to make a decision concerning which of the various instruments aboard the spacecraft are capable of carrying out their special measurements at the ambient conditions on the planet. It may well be that some of the unexpected forms of life on Mars will live under conditions that are inappropriate for use of the instruments in the package. In particular, if some of the living systems operate at temperatures below the freezing point of water, those parts of the Martian spacecraft devoted to water-based chemistry will not be useful at first. Probably, we should first attempt to apply our life detection techniques to materials as we find them in the normal Martian environment, to the extent that our physical measurements have told us that our instruments will work under those conditions. The second stage would be to collect a sample of the Martian surface or of objects or materials that are close to the spacecraft and gradually begin to change the conditions of the collected samples in the direction of the range of usefulness of our life detection systems. If one knows enough by that time of the cycle of the Martian environment between day and night and among the seasons, perhaps the environmental changes during the experiment should be chosen to follow the normal Martian ones as closely as possible, particularly if that route leads in the direction of making a larger fraction of the spacecraft's instruments useful. Thus if we land on a frozen Martian tundra at a temperature of $-30°C$ we would first try to detect optical activity, to measure infrared spectra, to look at the neutron albedo with a neutron source in seeking hydrogeneous materials, make mass spectroscopic and electromagnetic spectroscope and fluorescence measurements, etc., in the materials under their normal Martian conditions. After that we would try to take some of the material into the spacecraft laboratory and gradually raise its temperature or humidity or perhaps add a small quantity of oxygen or other gases in order to make studies of enzyme activity, or ultraviolet absorption in aqueous solution, and others of the biochemical techniques normally used in assaying terrestrial biochemicals and their reactions. It is very likely that the most efficient use of the facilities of the spacecraft will be made by terrestrial control of the experimental sequence in which the decisions at each time are based on previous findings. The intellectual task of making all these decisions in advance for every possible constellation of results is virtually impossible. One can imagine a team of perhaps 20 biologists sitting at a number of small individual consoles which feed a large central computer in constant contact with the computer on the spacecraft. Each of them will be responsible for a certain problem or a set of instruments. Since the round trip for information to flow from Earth to Mars is from 5 to 25 minutes, there will be a certain amount of time between the making of a decision and the receipt of the result of the measurement performed by the spacecraft in response to that decision. Thus, carrying out the experiments by the spacecraft will be rather like the actions of a chess master who plays 20 opponents simultaneously, walking from board to board, making his move, and coming back only after half an hour to see what results his move has produced. The individual players, in this case the individual biologists, will have opportunity to consult their colleagues at other universities to ask for expert advice, to go to the library, to make calculations, and in other ways to carry on their usual scientific intellectual activities as they would do if they were carrying out an individual experiment. One can imagine a large scoreboard, showing the participating biologist the state of each of the sensor and motor functions of the spacecraft at any moment, so that he can see what moves are possible for him at every moment and can have in front of him a summary of the kinds of results his colleagues are getting, for these will certainly be factors on which he will base his decisions and desires as the investigation proceeds.

It should be emphasized that this procedure is not necessarily committed to delivering all-or-nothing answers concerning the existence of life on Mars but instead is a program aimed at studying the physical, chemical, biochemical and biological condition of that planet. It may well be that Mars is at an early stage or an arrested stage of biological development and will contain on its surface a rich mixture of organic and biochemicals without displaying any of the features of systems that we would call "living". On the other hand, there may be living systems, but this first attempt may not be able to prove that they are living, but only that the biochemical environment allows the possibility of life. Proper design of the instruments themselves and of the logical procedure for their operation and interpretation is bound to yield much knowledge of importance to geologists, physicists, planetary scientists, and biologists.

CHAPTER 19

THE AUTOMATED BIOLOGICAL LABORATORY

D. A. GLASER, JOHN MCCARTHY, AND MARVIN MINSKY

INTRODUCTION

The state of evolution of the Earth is very complex to describe, let alone to discover. Mars may be in a much simpler state, but we cannot count on it. Even if Mars is in a much simpler evolutionary state than the Earth, there is much work to be done before Mars is nearly so well understood as our own planet.

We are now considering what can be done with a single unmanned lander weighing several thousand pounds. Our present ability to make small scientific equipment already permits us to include a wide variety of techniques within our weight limit. The problem we shall face in this chapter is to suggest how the various devices can be coordinated into an automated biological laboratory (ABL) that will give us a good chance of determining whether there is life on Mars, and in any case, of giving an estimate of the state of its chemical evolution.

In our opinion, the key to making the automated laboratory effective is to make it a computer with sensors and effectors rather than a collection of isolated experiments. It should be possible to use a piece of apparatus such as a television camera or a mass spectrometer in a number of different ways in experiments aimed at answering different questions. Moreover, we want to maintain as much control of the experimental program from the Earth as the 5 to 25 minute round-trip time for signals between Earth and Mars will allow. Only the maintenance of this control will give us much chance of getting a reasonable picture of Martian evolution from a single mission or even from a small number of missions.

Few biologists have thought much about the computer control of experiments, and there is a temptation to put the idea aside as too complicated for an early mission and settle for adapting to predicted Martian conditions a few experiments that would be simple if performed on Earth. This puts a heavy burden on our ability to predict Martian conditions, and we must face the fact that many of the experiments planned would turn out to be inappropriate. A much greater chance of success is offered by a co-ordinated laboratory that can be ordered to change the experiments from the Earth after the first results are returned.

Computer Programs for Controlling Experiments

A computer program is a sequence of instructions in the memory of the computer. The ABL computer should have room in its main memory for, say, 50,000 instructions, and substantial secondary storage, such as magnetic tape. It executes instructions one after another. Some of these instructions do arithmetic operations involved in computing the next value of the magnetic field for the mass spectrometer, some compute where to point the television camera, or when to end a titration. Other instructions select the instructions to be executed next according to whether an experimental operation is complete or whether an iterated computation has been carried out the right number of times, or whether a signal has come from Earth indicating that a new program is being transmitted. Other instructions turn on or off experimental apparatus such as the motor that rotates the camera in azimuth or the motor that extends the sample collection arm. Other instructions cause information to be transmitted to the Earth after it has been edited into a compressed form that will make best use of limited transmission bandwidth.

Time Scales

It is important to understand the time scales involved. The computer executes an instruction every few microseconds. A simple mechanical operation involving the experimental apparatus takes between one tenth and ten seconds. The round trip time for a signal from Earth is between 300 and 1500 seconds. Thus the computer can execute about 10^5 instructions in the time required for a mechanical operation, and we can perform, say, 2000 mechanical operations in the time required to look at the result of some complex of operations and decide what to do next. When the ABL is on the opposite side of Mars from the Earth it will be on its own for 12 hours and could be shut off if we cannot program a useful strategy. These times are the key to understanding the possibilities and problems of computer control of the automated biological laboratory.

First of all, 10^5 computations in a mechanical operation time means that the computer can control, say, 100 mechanical devices at a time and still execute an average of 1000 operations in deciding what each device is to do next. This means that the procedure for deciding what each device is to do next may be quite elaborate, if this is desirable. Secondly, if we want to use our device with full effectiveness, we must delegate to the computer program control of up to 2000 elementary actions of each device while we decide on the next compound action. Thus, we should program complex actions such as: a complete sequence of separation actions such as solvent extractions, titrations, and scans of the mass spectrum, including the decisions about endpoints or when the mass spectrometer has been at a given charge-to-mass ratio long enough. More elaborately, if we can, we should program the computer to collect objects of a kind we are interested in.

Kinds of Experiments

Let us try to classify the experiments that might be performed in the following way:

a) Observations. Most important will be pictures on scales ranging from telescopic panoramas to photomicrographs. Also there may be temperature, pressure, atmospheric chemical content, sound, and radiation measurements.

b) Analysis of samples. For example, we may use a computer-controlled shovel to pick samples, grind them, dissolve them in chemicals, use solvent extraction and chromatographic methods to concentrate fractions of high optical activity, finished off by mass spectrometer analysis of the final concentrate. The remaining concentrate may have to be stored while scientists on Earth decide what further tests shall be performed.

Physical as well as chemical analyses will be made.

c) Growth experiments. A specimen may be put in a variety of environments, and effects of growth, or other signs of life, looked for periodically.

Limitations of Programming

The limits of what can be programmed for the ABL are not easily set. A large class of useful operations is well within the state of the art. For example, it is not difficult to program a fractionation process to select for further analysis the fraction that shows optical activity or shows fragments at given mass numbers on the mass spectrometer. It would also be easy to program the machine to transmit only the parts of pictures that differ from previously stored pictures of the same scene.

It is fairly easy to program a computer to make a hardness map of a mineral specimen by poking it with a needle and transmitting this together with a picture of the specimen.

It is difficult, but probably possible, to take pictures of a desert scene and, after looking at them, program the computer to transmit pictures of cacti that differ from the already classified types of cacti, as these are encountered in the ABL's travels. If biologists are to be able to ask for this kind of performance, they will need the support of extensive earth-based computer facilities and programming groups.

It is not now within the state of the computer art to program a computer to control the dissection of a mammal, much less to perform an operation on a mammal such as might be involved in a physiological experiment. By 1971 this situation may change if a determined effort is made, but it would be unwise to count on it. It would also be unwise to make decisions that preclude it.

When we cannot program a kind of decision, the experiment is slowed up because we must send a picture of a tray of samples, or mass spectrograms of fractions to Earth for decision as to what objects should be ground up or what fractions should be further treated and how. Fortunately, the automated biological laboratory can provide us with complete flexibility in this respect. If a particular decision that has to be made on Earth is slowing our progress, we can test on Earth suitable programs for making the decision, and when we think they are correct transmit the programs to Mars.

Danger of Thinking too Small

We must confess to the following fear: At present, the art of programming computers to select objects of a given kind by looking at a picture of collection of objects against a background, is in a rather primitive state. On this basis, it might be decided that although the ABL is to be provided with the ability to take pictures and transmit them to Earth, the Mars computer will not be able to look at the pictures. (The computer looks at a picture by having an instruction that allows it to read the optical density at a point on the picture with given co-ordinates; programs can be written, using this operation, that track the light-dark boundaries and recognize objects). We believe that it is extremely important to make the ABL completely flexible. This requires that all apparatus be subject to computer control, and that all information collected by the sensors be readable by the computer. It is also important that the necessary computer programming and checkout facilities be available on Earth to allow the quick changing of computer programs to meet changed experimental conditions.

If our view of what we will be able to program and of the benefits of flexibility proves over-optimistic, little will have been lost. The computer is still the best way to control even relatively simple processes, as industrial experience is showing. On the other hand, if through lack of imagination a decision is made for a preprogrammed system, or even if the computer and its programming are set up in a way that makes changes difficult or risky, or if not all sense information is available to the programs, a tremendous opportunity will be lost.

Summary

In the succeeding sections of this chapter we shall treat the following topics: the state-of-the-art in computer control; description of a simple automated laboratory; control of the laboratory from the Earth; television systems, transmission of pictures, and the problems and uses of computer picture pattern recognition; sample collection and the computer controlled hand; the advantages and the problem of making the ABL mobile; some recommendations for research and development projects that may be undertaken now to provide support for the ABL.

The automated biological laboratory provides a marvelous focus for research and development in computer control systems. The potential technical benefits for the control of scientific experiments and other processes on Earth seem as great as that for any other aspect of the space program. By itself it may repay the cost of the entire Mars exploration.

THE STATE OF THE ART OF COMPUTER CONTROL

The art of computer control of external devices is advancing rapidly. If this were 1955, what we propose in this report would be almost impossible, and if it were 1975, what we have to say would be regarded as obvious by every scientist. We are now at the point where the tools are comfortably available, but we shall have to work fast to make good use of them.

Computers in Airplanes and Spacecraft

Modern fighter planes contain computers for navigation and fire control. They are usually magnetic drum computers, and their programs are rarely changed. They are reliable enough for their present use and compact enough, even for the Mars mission. However, they are not fast enough, they are not easily programmed, they do not have sufficiently large memories, and they are probably not sufficiently reliable for use in the ABL. The M.I.T. Instrumentation Laboratory has designed, and IBM is building, a computer to be carried on the Apollo spacecraft. This computer is probably fast and reliable and small enough for the ABL, but it uses a read-only memory for programs and does not have enough memory. The proposed supersonic transports are to be controlled by digital computers. Several American companies have designed computers for inclusion in spacecraft, but we believe that the ABL computer can and should be more powerful than these.

Computer Control of Industrial Processes

Chemical plants, bakeries, atomic power plants, and nuclear particle accelerators have been controlled by computers. Most of these programs have been rather simple, certainly simpler than we shall want for the ABL.

Time-Sharing

The ABL computer must be able to manage many pieces of apparatus at the same time. This is possible because the computer is nearly 100,000 times faster than the apparatus it controls. The art of making a computer carry out a large number of separate tasks at the same time without confusion is called time-sharing. Systems that allow a computer to interact simultaneously with tens of people and external devices are in use today. They have the property that an error in one user's program cannot result in interference with the programs of any other user. This property is essential for the ABL if we are to dare to allow scientists to change programs after the machine is on Mars.

Picture Recognition

Some work has been done on programming computers to classify pictures into a number of categories. These programs even learn the categories from examples. The number of categories and their complexity are quite limited so far. Other work has concentrated on the more relevant problem of picking out objects of given categories from a background and measuring their positions and dimensions. The work in recognizing nuclear events in bubble chamber and spark chamber pictures is relatively advanced. The apparatus for this recognition work is just becoming available, and rapid advances may be expected because the problem is being pursued energetically.

Artificial Intelligence

This is the problem of making computers perform tasks which, when performed by people, are considered to require intelligence. Modest successes have been achieved, but progress is likely to be slow. This work has led to an ability to identify those tasks that are readily assigned to a computer and those that still require human intervention.

Computer Performance

In our opinion the ABL can profitably use a computer of large scale by present standards. Great advances are being made in minaturizing computers. However, we do not yet know whether a large scale computer (with, say, 2^{16} words of one microsecond memory) can be reduced to 200 lb, in time, or whether we will have to compromise in this area. The result of a compromise would be to reduce the complexity and number of processes that can be controlled simultaneously and to increase the time required to change the course of the experiments.

A SIMPLE AUTOMATED LABORATORY

In order to clarify the problem of automating a biological laboratory, we shall consider a simple one. We mention specific apparatus not to express an opinion about what should be included—much more can be included than is listed here—but merely to make the control problem concrete.

Let us assume the following equipment:

1. A television camera and a storage tube. The camera has a variety of lenses for magnifications from telescopic to microscopic. An arm permits the camera many positions: on a tower for looking at the landscape; attached to a microscope for looking at slides; overlooking the immediate foreground for controlling an arm used for picking up samples or for

controlling the motion of the ABL over the ground; and a position that allows the camera to look inside the ABL in order to see the positions of movable parts. Several cameras may be taken if the workload or reliability requires it. The computer can transfer information from the storage tube into its memory either *en masse* or point by point. Computer programs compress picture information for digital transmission and use the same information to make decisions.

2. One or more mechanical arms like those used for handling radioactive materials are under the control of the computer. They can be positioned to computed positions when the computer knows the precise sequence of motions desired, or can be controlled via the picture information by the computer when a servo-mechanical type of operation is required. The arms can use tools such as shovels, coring drills, and a variety of clamps for holding objects of various shapes.

3. A wet chemical laboratory. Reagents may be added to samples, and operations such as titration, centrifuging and filtration may be performed.

4. Optical spectrometry.

5. Mass spectrometry.

CONTROL FROM THE EARTH

The ABL will be carrying out simultaneously a wide variety of experiments in a number of different fields. Many of these experiments are of kinds that, on Earth involve continuous supervision by the experimenter. The round trip signal time precludes continuous supervision and so we have emphasized computer control. Nevertheless, we want to make human supervision as effective as possible, and this requires very sophisticated Earth-control.

We envisage the following kind of system:

1. There are several groups of scientists, each pursuing its own line of investigations.

2. Each group has consoles for the display of information coming from Mars, and for transmitting instructions to that part of the computer program on Mars carrying out the group's investigations. They have computer facilities on Earth for analyzing data and for correcting new programs to be sent to Mars.

3. The consoles are attached to a computer on Earth that coordinates their communication with the experiment on Mars.

The allocation of resources among the groups is decided by directorate and administered by programs in the Earth computer and to a lesser degree in the Mars computer. These decisions include:

a. The rate of which each group can obtain pictures and other data from Mars.

b. Allocation of expendable supplies.

c. Decisions about when and where the lander will move.

d. Allocation of the services of the arm, the chemical analyzer, and the cameras.

One might argue that it would usually be better to do one experiment at a time, and this might be true if we could program all decisions for the Mars computer. However, if a particular experiment has to be carried out in such a way that a short operation is first performed, and then the result sent to Earth for decisions, there will be much time wasted if only one experiment is done at a time.

4. Each group will strive to program the decisions needed to carry out its experiments. For example, suppose an experiment requires the selection of objects from a shovelful for subsequent chemical analysis. At first, it may be necessary to have a television picture of the shovel returned to Earth in order to select the objects. However, the experiment will go faster once the selection criterion can be programmed for the Mars computer. The programs to do this will be verified on Earth-bound copies of the Mars computer operating Earth-bound copies of the ABL.

5. Because of the limited time the lander will operate, the results obtained up to a given time should be available in raw form to the whole scientific community. This will enable suggestions to be made and even new groups to start new research programs using the ABL, if their proposals seem to warrant it.

THE CHEMICAL LABORATORY

It is too soon to say what the chemical analysis facilities should be in detail. However, some general remarks can be made. A chemical analysis procedure is a strategy involving the following kinds of operations.

1. Physical preparation of the sample. Grinding, etc.

2. Mixing reagents with the sample.

3. Controlling the physical environment. Temperature, pressure, illumination.

4. Separation. Filtration, centrifuging, solvent extraction, chromatography.

5. Physical measurements. Presence (e.g., did anything precipitate), weight, color, reflection spectrum, form (flocculent precipitate; if we want the criterion, we need a computer program to recognize it); spectrum; mass spectrometry; optical activity; density; viscosity.

6. Storage. Some fractions may be put aside for later use.

In general, the results of the physical measurements determine what mixing and separation operations will be performed next and what fractions will be put aside or discarded. Besides reliability, the following considerations should determine the methods made available:

1. Generality. As few assumptions as possible about the chemical environment of Mars should be made. Some long shot guesses can be accommodated by including special reagents.

2. Economy. The consumption of expendable supplies per experiment should be very low.

3. Speed. Automated mechanical movements can be very fast; five operations per section are readily achieved. This means 3×10^8 elementary chemical operations may be performed in the life of the ABL. If one milligram of supplies is consumed per operation we will need 300 kg of supplies. The above figures represent our guess as to the order of magnitude of the quantities involved, and perhaps they suggest that expendable supplies will be the limiting factor on how much chemistry can be done. Much present chemistry depends on having large excesses of certain reagents, especially water. Perhaps, in order to get by with milligram amounts of reagents one should use microgram amounts of sample. It should be pointed out that the mechanical movements can be speeded up to 100 per second, if small enough masses have to be moved.

One may ask whether there would be any use for 3×10^8 chemical events. Would not some smaller number, say 3×10^4, do? We believe that the larger number is quite likely to be wanted because the reactions will be combined into procedures, and each procedure may involve hundreds of chemical events.

The reactions themselves should usually proceed on the 1/10 second time scale although one second reaction times can be tolerated if one vessel can be put aside to react, while others are manipulated.

The problem of cleanliness is a large one. Perhaps disposable liners for the reaction vessels will solve the problem. Difficult-to-clean vessels like stills, and perhaps continuous processes generally, may turn out to be impractical.

PICTURES AND VISUAL CONTROL OF EXPERIMENTS

In discussions of research techniques one takes vision for granted. However, the beginner in biology is often bewildered by the expert's sure identification of the important object in what appears to be a very complicated or indistinct picture. We are all beginners so far as Mars is concerned, but we would like to become experts.

In this section we deal with two topics:

1. Returning pictures to Earth to develop our understanding of what things on Mars look like.

2. Programming the identification of objects by the ABL computer so that it can avoid obstacles, select samples of desired kinds for analysis, send back pictures of previously unseen objects, etc.

What is there to look at?

Much more of Mars will be visible from the ABL than can be inspected with any other sense. A camera boom on the ABL, and the ability to move the ABL to scenic lookouts will increase what can be seen. What can be seen may be divided into topography and objects.

Some general information about topography will already be available from the environmental flights required to assure the safe landing of the ABL. The additional topographical information obtained by the ABL will be useful, if correlated with the objects.

The possible varieties of objects are too numerous to catalog. They include craters, vegetation, mineral outcroppings and many objects that may be difficult to classify when first seen.

In order to extract the maximum information from distant objects, the ABL needs telescopes of various magnifications, with emphasis on the maximum usable magnification. Color information may provide useful clues about the composition of the surfaces seen. This suggests that we include the ability to photograph a scene through an arbitrary spectral window and that we develop the ability to infer composition from such reflection spectra.

The near scene also requires photography at various magnifications.

Next we come to photography of objects that we can manipulate. Here are some examples:

1. Lichen on a rock.

2. Objects under an over-turned rock and the bottom of the rock.

3. The stratification of a hole we have made.

4. Fragments of a broken or breakable abject.

5. Sections of a sectionable object.

6. A precipitate or polymer resulting from a chemical process.

The picture handling system should include the following:

1. Optical instruments—telescopes, microscopes.

2. A television camera with a storage tube.

3. A picture storage system, e.g., video tape in the ABL.

4. The ability of the computer to look at points in pictures on the storage tubes.

5. Computer programs for digitizing and compressing picture information.

6. Computer programs for recognizing objects of various kinds.

7. Transmission facilities for sending the pictures to Earth. Pictures are likely to require more bandwidth than any other information transmitted.

Programming Computers to Recognize and Handle Objects

First we shall list the relevant research.

1. H. A. Ernst programmed the TX-O computer to control a mechanical hand to pick up blocks and stack them. (1961 M.I.T. Sc.D. Thesis in Electrical Engineering).

2. L. Hodes and T. Evans at M.I.T., while working under Minsky, programmed the IBM 7090 to find geometrical objects when partially overlaid with other objects.

3. A number of physics groups have programmed computers to find events of given sorts in pictures of spark chambers. The group at Argonne National Laboratories has used their system to count the number of chromosomes of each of several types occurring in a picture.

4. A programmable film reader that reads radar traces and graphs from film and writes magnetic tapes with the information in digital form is marketed by Information International.

5. A large amount of work has gone into the classification of whole pictures. This is not very relevant for the present purpose that requires the identification of objects in a picture in a manner that will allow the manipulation of the objects.

6. A system called FIDAC has been developed by R. S. Ledley (*Science,* Oct. 9, 1964) that scans pictures and reads about 10^6 bits of information into the memory of an IBM 7090 computer for analysis. A programming system for picture analysis has also been developed, and is being used to classify chromosome pictures.

Much of the work on picture recognition uses the following technique: The computer controls the position of a spot on the face of a cathode ray tube, i.e., there is a computer instruction that says position point of light at image coordinates (x,y). An optical system projects the light point through a photographic transparency and onto a photomultiplier cathode. An analog-to-digital converter makes the photomultiplier cathode current, which is proportional to the transparency of the photograph, available to the computer. Thus the basic computer instruction is to determine the optical density at a point on the film with given co-ordinates.

Several variants of this apparatus have been used or proposed to increase the speed of various recognition schemes. The "PEPR" apparatus for measuring bubble chamber pictures displays a bar whose length and orientation, as well as position, are controlled by the computer. This is useful for detecting tracks of particles. The Argonne apparatus scans a rectangle chosen by the computer and returns the co-ordinates of all points where a change in density occurs from one level to another (64 levels are used in this case).

Given this basic facility, the computer can be programmed to find objects of various kinds, for example by tracing their outlines. The apparatus is only now beginning to be available, and all the present facilities are dedicated to very specific applications.

Besides the above-mentioned work, much attention has been given to apparatus and programs that classify pictures as a whole, e.g., this is a picture of an A. It is difficult to see how these methods can help with the present problem, but the advocates of perceptions, and adelines, etc. will speak for themselves when the time comes.

All the above-mentioned work, except Ernst's which used photocells and mechanical sensors, has been concerned with photographs. Direct recognition of objects requires a television system, in which the computer can ask for the intensity at a given point on an electrical image of the scene. Systems of this kind have been designed, but are not yet built. A number of additional techniques have been proposed, such as using the magnitude of the high frequency component of the intensity in a scan as a measure of whether the camera is in focus and using focus to measure distance.

We believe that a useful capability for recognizing and manipulating objects can be available in time for the ABL if a prompt and serious effort is made.

Mechanical Manipulation

We believe it is reasonable to consider basing much of the ABL's mechanical activities upon a set of general purpose computer-controlled manipulators.

Each manipulator would consist of a fast, firm positioner, with several degrees of freedom, and an attachment that can hold a variety of special tools, graspers, or sensors. Interchangeability would mean much more flexibility and capability than could be obtained by the same number of actuators installed in particular experiments for fixed purposes.

The most straightforward design would have motions of the positioner based on a fixed coordinate system relative to some points on the ABL vehicle. We should also study the possibility of making the manipulator along the general lines of the human arm and hand. With computer control and visual monitoring (by computer) this may be practical.

Computer-controlled manipulation exists today chiefly in the form of automatic machine-tool control systems. Visual control of manipulators has not been developed, but we believe the state-of-the-art is just ready for such a development. The computer-controlled, human-like arm, developed by H. A. Ernst, used only simple tactile sensors, but it could find a number of scattered blocks, stack them up in a tower, and then put them in a box that it had to find.

The advantages of general-purpose manipulators include:

Reduction in weight, as compared to many special activators.

Great flexibility in programming sample-collection and material transfers.

Adjustment of physical layouts of experiments.

Assembly of parts into many configurations.

Adjusting parameters of experiments.

Some possibilities of repairs on site, or at least replacement of parts.

In particular, a manipulator could serve to control TV cameras, outside and within the spacecraft. It might be feasible to use it to lay out and phase a large, efficient, outside antenna. It could operate micro-tools, through a reduction device.

It is possible that basing operations on a few reliable manipulators could yield a substantial gain in overall reliability, since it would then be possible to simplify most experiments. It may be preferable to adjust the mechanical parameters of an experiment by moving a simple stud or tab, instead of installing and depending on a special motor or actuator for that task. It is not possible to say now which system would be most reliable and compact.

We shall want arms of several sizes. Very small arms can move very quickly.

MOBILITY

We believe that the effectiveness of the ABL can be greatly enhanced by making it mobile. There is a substantial chance that it will land in an unsuitable place such as a small crater, and there may be very little to observe. A negative conclusion about the existence of life would be quite suspect, if based on a single site or even a few sites.

The problem of providing mobility has three aspects:

1. The power available will be quite small. For example, the Beagle

study estimates that a total 300 watts will be available for all activities of a 5000 lb package. Other studies estimate up to 2 kilowatts.

2. The terrain is unknown.

3. Step-by-step control from the Earth is hampered by the signal round-trip time.

The answer to the power problem is to go slowly. A velocity of one meter per second, the maximum that could be hoped for, would permit covering 60,000 km in two years. This amounts to two circumnavigations of Mars. Even one cm per sec would permit 600 km of travel. If the ABL could find vantage points along its route, permitting 10 km of side visibility, this allows the exploration of 12,000 square kilometers in the sense that a number of visually interesting objects could be approached and examined in detail.

A one meter per second velocity means that the ABL would cover about one kilometer in a round trip signal time. This precludes detailed control from Earth and requires a computer program that can use television information to steer a course. On the other hand the one cm per second rate permits only 10 meters to be covered, so instructions to the vehicle can be based on a human look at the terrain to be covered.

The decision on what mobility system is best is a complicated one. In this chapter we shall mention only two complementary systems that suit the low power available.

The first system is to have a long arm that can extend a drill that can make a hole and that can attach an anchor. A winch is then used to haul the ABL with whatever power can be spared. Three cable-anchor combinations are needed. This system can deal with almost any solid terrain, including cliffs.

More suitable for flat ground with unavoidable obstacles not more than one meter high is a system of eight legs, two at each corner. One set of legs is lifted, advanced and set down, the second is lifted, advanced and set down, and finally the body of the ABL moves forward. The legs can extend to different lengths and are as light as possible. We minimize up-and-down motion of the ABL in order to reduce the power used.

Research and Development Projects

The purpose of this section is to identify some research and development projects that should be started soon if the ABL is to be maximally effective.

1. Identification of substances by reflection spectra. The ABL will be

able to see much more than it can touch.

    2. Computer recognition and manipulation of objects.

    3. Computer controlled wet chemistry on as small a scale as possible.

    4. Computer control of a vehicle. One should work towards systems that have at least the human ability to tolerate variations in terrain.

CHAPTER 20

ANALYTICAL METHODS FOR LANDERS

D. G. Rea, Editor

INTRODUCTION

The scientific motivation and goals of exobiology have already been discussed at some length. To achieve these goals, biological laboratories must be landed on the surface and used to provide answers to the initial questions. Although the detailing of such an instrumental package is still in the future, it is of value to consider the various techniques that could be used in tackling the analytical problems. This section is intended to fulfill this function within the following framework.

The outstanding subjects for exobiology can be grouped into three general categories:

(1) The detection of the presence of life, and its characterization if present.
(2) The characterization of any existing organic matter, with particular reference to those molecules and functional groups of importance to terrestrial biology.
(3) The characterization of the inorganic and physical environment, including both the surface and atmosphere.

The most important question, of course, concerns the existence of life on the planet. The investigator approaching this must consider the possibility of different levels of evolution of the Martian biota, and of varying

347

degrees of divergence from the terrestrial system. Because of its lack of definition, this question may be the most difficult to answer, an unfortunate circumstance in view of its importance.

A more tractable problem is the characterization of any organic matter present on the surface or in the atmosphere. Any data will be of interest, since, even if life has never existed on Mars, their analysis will be of immense value in studying the chemical development of a sterile planet, and this relates in turn to the origin of life itself. However a complete analysis would be beyond the scope of the biological landers that can be foreseen for the next decade or two. Accordingly, in view of the basic goal of the search for life, the methods discussed here will of necessity be oriented towards compounds and functional groups of known biological interest. Falling in this category are, for example, the amino acids, proteins, purines, pyrimidines, carbohydrates, nucleic acids, liquid water, the secondary amide and the phosphate linkages. It is doubtful whether the presence of such molecules and functional groups would ever be construed as an unequivocal sign of life. But they would be very suggestive and of the most direct interest if they were found in objects that had already been characterized as living by other means.

Finally there is the problem of determining the nature of the physical and inorganic environment. Experiments designed to elucidate this are the most likely to produce results and such results will be important in interpretations of direct observations of any biological activity. Despite the lower priority accorded these "non-biological" measurements some space in the landers must be devoted to answering some particular questions relevant to the overall problem. These cover such topics as the flux of ultraviolet radiation and of charged particles at the surface, the partial pressures of water vapor and oxygen, the principal mineral components of the top few centimeters of the surface and any minor elements which may play a biological role.

In approaching this project the study enumerated the analytical techniques that appeared to be the most fruitful for the task. Requests were then made of a number of outstanding scientists, asking them to write a brief note on the applicability of the technique in which they were particularly competent. They were asked to stress the methodology and not to concern themselves unduly with the engineering aspects. Points to be emphasized were the interpretability or ambiguity of the method's indications and quantitative statements on the limits of sensitivity, constraints on type and size of samples and requirements for sample preparation and treatment.

The resulting contributions were edited by a subcommittee of the study and details on some existing flight instruments added. They were subsequently examined by the entire group and final amendments made. In view of the editing process the consulting scientists who contributed the working papers should not be held responsible for the final versions that appear below. This is not intended to minimize their contributions, which were of the utmost value in lending authority to the discussions. Their willingness to expend valuable time, often on short notice, is acknowledged with the most sincere appreciation.

The topics that were treated in this fashion are listed below, together with the names of the contributors; a brief note on morphological criteria is also appended.

1. Separation Methods and Sample Preparation, R. Bock, S. R.Lipsky, F. J. Stevenson and M. J. Johnson.
2. Atomic Spectroscopy, J. Conway.
3. Neutron Activation Analysis, H. Mark, J. Waggoner and C. D. Schrader.
4. Electron and X-Ray Fluorescence, C. C. Delwiche, K. Fredricksson and A. Metzger.
5. X-Ray Diffraction, H. H. Hess, R. C. Speed, D. B. Nash, N. J. Nickle, R. Pepinsky, I. Barshad and C. C. Delwiche.
6. Sensitivity of Fibers to the Physical and Chemical Environment, H. P. Lundgren.
7. Gas Chromatography, J. Oró, S. R. Lipsky, V. I. Oyama, G. R. Shoemake and A. Zlatkis.
8. Mass Spectrometry, K. Biemann.
9. Gas Chromatography—Mass Spectrometry, J. Oró, K. Biemann, R. S. Gohlke, S. R. Lipsky, J. E. Lovelock, F. W. McLafferty, W. G. Meinschein and R. Ryhage.
10. Infrared Spectroscopy, R. C. Lord, N. K. Freeman and C. Sagan.
11. Ultraviolet and Visible Spectroscopy, G. A. Crosby.
12. Fluorimetry, L. Stryer.
13. Optical Shifts in Dye Complexes, D. F. Bradley.
14. Nuclear Magnetic Resonance and Electron Paramagnetic Resonance, J. Shoolery and J. D. Roberts.
15. Colorimetry, A. D. McLaren and A. Novick.
16. Optical Microscopy, P. S. Conger.
17. Electron Microscopy and Electron-Optical Techniques, H. Fernández-Morán.
18. A Note on Morphological Criteria for Recognizing Life, D. Schwartz.

The list of methods presented, although rather lengthy, is not to be construed as definitive. Some techniques, such as optical activity and the use of isotopes, are discussed elsewhere in this report. Of the other omissions, wet chemistry stands out as having real possibilities but since any treatment of it would almost necessarily be encyclopedic, and since its applications are widely appreciated, it was not included. Our intention in compiling this section was to be provocative and stimulating, not exhaustive.

Accordingly, the possibilities discussed range from those readily achievable even now, to those that will require very extensive development before they are ready for incorporation in lander payloads. Equipment ready for flight or of the "breadboard" type has already been constructed to carry out several kinds of measurements, for example, neutron activation analysis, x-ray diffraction, gas chromatography, mass spectrometry, infrared spectroscopy, electronic spectroscopy in the visible and ultraviolet and optical microscopy. Some of these have been designed to analyze the lunar surface, while others have been intended for studying the terrestrial atmosphere or for remote observations. All are at such a stage that adaptation or development into equipment capable of performing on the Martian surface is straightforward. In other cases, however, such as nuclear magnetic resonance and electron microscopy, major technological developments are required before they can be considered seriously. Both methods, under the limits of weight that will probably apply for the first several missions, are dependent on the development of techniques for operating superconducting magnets on the Martian surface after a 6-months' flight time. Such developments will consume many years of intensive work, but this should not stand in the way of examining their potentialities.

An important constraint that has been generally omitted from the various papers is that of the data transmission capacity. Early missions may be able to send data back at a rate of only 1 bit per second. To send a picture taken by a camera, optical microscope, or electron microscope, and containing, say 10^7 bits of information, would require about 120 days. This is inordinately long and would pre-empt the majority of the telemetering capacity to the detriment of other experiments. It is to be hoped that more extensive knowledge of Martian surface conditions will permit the use of more efficient antennas and, with improved power supplies, allow a rapid increase in data transmission rates. The sending of pictures of high quality might then become a reality.

A final word must be said about what is probably the most critical problem facing us at this time—the acquisition and preparation of a sample. Some of the techniques do not require a sample, e.g., inelastic neutron scattering, but the majority do. Moreover, to make the output data meaningful a certain amount of sample processing is demanded. These problems are treated briefly in the section on Separation Methods and Sample Preparation. They are of such importance, however, and are in such an elementary stage of solution, that a major effort must be expended in the immediate future to solve them. The scientific goals of the mission will never be satisfied by the most sophisticated and ingenious collection of experiments if the sampling device is ineffective or if the necessary sample treatments are not properly applied.

After reading the Analytical Techniques section it should be clear that the problems are many and that they range from the trivial to the profound. At the same time it is hoped that the feasibility of resolving them has been demonstrated and that scientific observations of the greatest significance can be carried out on the Martian surface and its components, whether organic or inorganic, biogenic or abiogenic.

1. SEPARATION METHODS AND SAMPLE PREPARATION

Physical and chemical processes for separation of Martian solids, gases and solutes into simple, convenient or better defined sub-classes will find utility as necessary sample preparation before examination by sophisticated analytical methods. If the results of simple separation processes are also observed, useful data can be accumulated about the Martian environment. Examples of suggested questions and methodology are given in this section. Many of the elegant analytical techniques discussed in other sections of this report are less definitive or inapplicable if the sample provided them is an extremely complex mixture or if the class of components to be detected is a minor constituent of the sample. Many other methods require that the sample be subdivided physically into thin sections, small uniform granules, volatile components or soluble components. These sampling problems are closely related to those of separation and will be discussed in the last half of this section.

Specific Questions Answerable By Separation Methods

1. What is the distribution of particle size and particle density found in Martian soils?
2. What is the electrostatic charge of solutes extracted from Martian soil or putative biological objects? Can they exist as polyelectrolytes and as ampholytes with charge dependent upon the acidity of the solvent?
3. What are the fractional solubilities or volatilities of Martian soils or other objects of interest?

It is evident that answers to these questions will aid in design of future chemical experiments needed for detailed studies of Martian chemistry and biology. These data are essential for any description of the Martian environment.

The first question can be probed by simple dry sieving, membrane filtration or gel filtration of soil extracts, and by flotation in solvents of differing density. Each of these methods permits simple sample acquisition, miniature apparatus, and quantitation of the materials separated. The results can be relayed economically in terms of numbers of bits to be transmitted. None of these methods will give so complete a description of the sample as does the automatic particle sedimentation analyzer [*Ziegler et al.*, 1964]. In this device, a pressure transducer in a settling tube transmits digitized values of accumulated sediment at predetermined times of settling. If two of these devices contained solvents of differing density the data could be analyzed for particle size distribution and density distribution. Direct microscopic observation and Coulter counter size distribution analysis should be evaluated as competing methods for obtaining these data. The density of selected macroscopic objects can be determined in a gas pycnometer. The density range of Earth objects of biological origin is distinctive and in contrast to objects of geological origin.

If the limitation on number of data bits transmitted does not rule out video observations at the macro- and microscopic level, the video description of particle sizes would be preferred.

The second question can be probed by ion exchange adsorption, dialysis through ion exchange membranes or electrophoresis. In each of these approaches the electrolyte or polyelectrolyte behavior of the Martian solutes would be examined in polar solvents (water, formamide and dimethylsulfoxide) in the presence and absence of added acids and bases. Each of these methods can be adapted to simple, durable and miniature devices but the ion exchange adsorption process appears to be both simplest in application and capable of extension to yield the greatest selectivity. The ways of applying this technique are so varied that considerable study and testing on known soils should be conducted. The equilibrium distribution of soil solutes among a set of differing ion exchange papers immersed in the same medium can be a very simple but informative experiment. The quantitative uptake of solutes by a single exchange material will vary as the pH and ionic strength of the solvent is altered. This phenomenon can be observed in an array of batch adsorptions or in a single adsorption followed by an array of batch elutions. The latter can be designed to give data of higher information content because it is a higher resolution separation process.

The third question can be probed by sealing the Martian samples in a set of containers and then breaking a vial of solvent previously enclosed in that container. The group of solvents chosen should be of low melting point, known to be good solvents and should include representatives of low, medium, and high dielectric constant. After the sample and solvent have been held at a known temperature for a considerable period of time, the connection between an evacuated vial and a porous Teflon filter in the bottom of the solution chamber could be established by breaking a seal. After the vial has filled, it should be separated from the filter, the solvent allowed to evaporate and the mass of the previously weighed vial determined. Alternative methods for detecting the amount and identity of material dissolved should be considered. Devices of this type may be needed for sample processing for such diverse operations as gas chromatography, optical rotation or infrared spectroscopy.

Fundamental Principles and Limitations of Selected Separation Methods

The separation methods likely to be utilized in the Martian lander experiments are widely used in chemistry and biology and their power and limitations have been explored. Sedimentation, extraction, electrophoresis, chromatography and other wet separation methods share the limitation that no single solvent is applicable to a wide range of materials. Experiments that depend on dissolving the test substance may have to be designed with multiple sets of solvents or as multiple packages each with a different solvent. Vapor phase experiments usually have a wider range of applicability in that a broad scan of temperature can successively vaporize or pyrolyze—or both—most chemical species. As will be discussed under sample preparation, this thermal volatilization process is a broad range method of preprocessing for many experiments that require a sample in the vapor phase.

Theoretical studies have indicated that liquid phase chromatographic systems have potentially higher resolution than gas chromatographic procedures. This resolution has not been obtained in practice and the properties of sensitive detection, applicability to a wide range of substances with a single solute (carrier gas)—adsorbant combination and convenience of sample introduction and regeneration of supplies (carrier gas) make gas chromatography the method of choice for separation of complex mixtures.

Procedures for Sample Acquisition and Preparation

Any sample acquired for analysis should be taken from a definable region of Mars, a known depth of penetration into the soil or height above the soil and should be acquired at a prescribed time of day and season.

The range of temperatures and pressures during sample acquisition and the intensity of chemical operations during any processing should be known so that judgment may be made on the probability of melting, destruction of morphology, or racemization of optical activity. Video observation of the region from which samples are taken will be a powerful aid to any subsequent interpretation of results. While many Earth sampling techniques collect large samples, comminute them and mix to randomize before taking a small portion for analysis, the variability thus obscured is an important datum for exploration of Mars and any improvement in statistical weight should be obtained by repeated sampling rather than mixing. Selection of a single object after video or tactile perception can be a powerful means of obtaining a sample of great interest, even though it is apparent that the object is not to be considered representative of the properties of the landscape in general.

Certain processes are of general applicability in that they permit acquisition of a sample of limited size range, density range, of minimally disturbed morphology or in an appropriate vapor or solution phase. Drilling a simple core sample followed by extrusion, possibly with simultaneous sectioning, can lead to a good definition of place of acquisition. If the soil is friable, it may be necessary to fix the soil with plastic or low melting waxes which are infused into the core and permitted to harden before sectioning.

Particle size selection can be accomplished by using a Venturi tube for sample pickup so that large aggregates are not acquired. The sample size can be narrowed further by passing the pickup gas stream through a cyclone cone dust collector or through a small gas centrifuge with impeller vanes to accelerate dust particles so that they leave the gas stream. Dry sieving of bulk samples or of objects that have been crushed may be useful. Micro-coring and surface sectioning or grinding may be found to be more precise and controllable operations than crushing and sieving.

Section by flotation and sedimentation is dependent on density alone if equilibrium methods are used, but on density and shape if rate of sedimentation is allowed to influence the fractionation. A simple, equilibrium flotation separation can be effected by dispersing the sample in a low density solvent, allowing ample time for sedimentation and drawing off the liquid including all objects floating in it. A new solvent of significantly higher density is now added and the process repeated until the density range of interest has been covered.

Components from a crude sample or from one simplified by any of the above processes may be made volatile by simple slow heating. The vapors produced can be introduced directly into a mass spectrometer, infrared spectrometer [*Bartz and Ruhl*, 1964] or a specific detector designed to search for certain vapors (water, CO_2, NH_3), or may be condensed in a form appropriate for convenient application to other analytical techniques. If the vapors are condensed on the surface of a thermoelectrically cooled film or plate, the condensate can periodically be transferred to an infrared spectrometer or a polarimeter for observation. If the sample vapors are passed through an indium capillary chilled over a small region, the capillary may be crushed (swaged) periodically to entrap the condensate in a container convenient for transfer to a gas chromatogram or mass spectrometer. The indium capillary is placed in a heatable receptacle and melts at 153°C to release a concentrated sample for analysis [*Wilkins Instrument Co.*, 1964]. If the vapors are condensed on a chilled silica rod, the rod may be transferred to an attenuated total reflectance device for ultrasensitive qualitative detection of its infrared spectrum [*Harrick*, 1963]. The same sample trapping devices may be employed on the effluent stream of a gas chromatogram.

The thermal volatilization and pyrolysis experiment gains value if it can be coupled with measurement of the change of mass of the sample as the temperature increases (thermogravimetry) and of the heat input needed to cause the temperature rise and volatilization [*Watson et al.*, 1964]. A detailed discussion of these techniques is given in another section of this chapter.

Samples that are later to be examined for optical rotation need additional care in that the temperature, acid and base strength of solvents and surfaces of contact should be chosen to minimize the degree of racemization of any optically active compounds present. This is not difficult to manage but is a precaution which must be borne in mind during design of separation processes.

The problem of introduction of samples into an evacuated chamber is shared by several analytical procedures. Design of simple, efficient ports for entry into vacuum chambers will be essential for the Mars mission. Because of its simplicity, the condensation of vapors into a swagable indium tube should be considered for atmospheric sampling and subsequent infrared or mass spectral analysis.

The finely divided samples, thin sections of fixed soil cores or of objects and microobjects discussed above can be examined by x-ray fluoroscopic, x-ray diffractometric, electron microbeam [*Buhler*, 1964] and electron microscopic methods. Of these methods, only electron microscopy conventionally uses samples which have been stained or shadowed. These operations can now be avoided if the Westinghouse or Argonne versions of scanning electron microscopes [*Westinghouse Electric Corp.*, 1964] are employed. The simplification of sample processing should be considered as a reasonable exchange for the slightly more complex instrumentation in the newer electron microscopes.

Apparatus for Spacecraft

A vacuum aerosolizer with dust collection impeller action has been designed and constructed in a form near that for flight testing. It is now a component of the Multivator project under Lederberg at Stanford. The vacuum cleaner method of sample collection is employed in the breadboard models now constructed for the Wolf Trap biological probe developed by Vishniac at the University of Rochester. A sampling device has been built at flight scale breadboard stage for the Gulliver project under Horowitz at California Institute of Technology. In this device a chenille string is ejected from the landed probe and upon dragging across soil, entraps small particles and drags them back into the probe when the string is rewound. This principle can also be used for collecting samples to be pyrolized if the chenille is fabricated from stainless steel or glass fibers.

Design of an atmospheric gas collector for infrared spectroscopy of Martian atmospheres is under investigation by Pimentel at Berkeley.

Core drilling devices have been designed and constructed for the Surveyor moonshot. The sampling device is near flight capability for simple coring operations.

REFERENCES

Bartz, A. and H. Ruhl (1964), Rapid Scan Infrared Spectrometer. *Anal. Chem. 36*, 1892.

Buhler, J. (1964), The New Era of X-ray Analysis and Control. *Instruments and Control Systems, 37*, 77.

Harrick, N. J. (1963), Attenuated Internal Reflectance Spectroscopy. *Ann. N. Y. Acad. Sci. 101*, 928.

Watson, E., M. O'Neill, J. Justin and N. Brenner (1964), A Differential Scanning Colorimeter for Quantitative Differential Thermal Analysis. *Anal. Chem. 36*, 1233.

Westinghouse Electric Corp. Tech. Bull. (May 1964), A Scanning Electron Microscope. Box 8606, Pittsburgh, 99-362.

Wilkins Instrument Co. (1964), An Indium Capillary for Introduction of Samples into Heated Zone of Column. *Previews and Reviews for Gas Chromatography*, Box 313, Walnut Creek, Calif.

Ziegler, J., C. Hayes and D. Webb (1964), An Automatic Particle Sedimentation Analyzer. *Science 145*, 51.

....

.. 357

2. ATOMIC SPECTROSCOPY

Atomic spectroscopy would be able to analyze the atmosphere and surface of Mars for most of the elements present. Of the 103 elements presently known, all but six have observed spectra. The great majority of these elements has lines in the easily available regions of the spectrum. The sensitivity of detection varies according to the accessibility of the most sensitive lines to observation, but a good working estimate of sensitivity for most of the elements is between 0.1 and 0.01 micrograms. In methods, such as those using the arc, where one commonly uses a milligram or so of sample, this is a ratio of 10,000 to 1 (of matrix to detectability limit). In spark methods, where the sample is at most 100 micrograms, the ratio is 1000 to 1 and with laser excitation where the sample is between ½ and 1 microgram the ratio is from 10 to 1, to 100 to 1. In cases where the sample is 50 micrograms or less, there is usually no interference of one element with another, or rather, there are almost always some sensitive lines of an element that do not interfere with lines of other elements.

There are several methods to record the spectrum which would be then transmitted to Earth. One possible method is to record the spectrum on photographic film although the problems of developing the film may be severe. This film is then read at fixed intervals (5 or 10 microns) and the distance and intensity transmitted. These data can be used as input to a computer which constructs the entire spectrum, finds the peak position of the lines and by comparison with standard wavelengths gives the wavelength of every line on the plate. The corresponding relative intensity is also obtained.

A second method is to have a number of photomultipliers fixed on preselected lines. The phototubes are read out in order and an intensity for a given position recorded. In large commercial installations 50 to 70 tubes have been used. However, if more than 15 tubes are used, maintenance of optical alignment is difficult.

A third method which has not been very extensively investigated is that of using TV cameras to record the spectrum. Considerable work would be required but this method is promising.

Sampling is one of the greatest problems in spectrochemical analysis. In the laboratory, much handling of the sample is usually required to prepare it for analysis. In most cases the sample is weighed and transferred to electrodes, but a standard volume sample could also be used. The spectrum is excited by passing electrical discharges between the electrodes. Recently, lasers have been used to excite spectra. In this case the sample does not have to be placed in an electrically conducting electrode; it has merely to be held in position so that the light enters the spectrograph. The limitation here is that only small amounts of sample are consumed, giving a low ratio of matrix to detectable limit. Standardization of such small amounts of sample is proving to be difficult. However, because of the small size of the sample (20 microns deep and 50 microns in diameter) the laser method is very good for probing across a sample for segregation. Any spot on a sample could be analyzed and should something different appear near to the spot analyzed, it too could be checked. This type of analysis is useful in work on minerals.

One can also analyze for the composition of the atmosphere. The lines of both the sample and electrodes plus the atmosphere surrounding the discharge appear in the spectrum. So if electrodes of known purity are used, the additional lines would be from the atmosphere. Two sources could be used: (i) a spark source with pure graphite electrodes so that the composition of the atmosphere could be determined; (ii) a laser source to analyze the solid samples. For recording spectra, the photographic method with the necessary reading equipment seems preferable. By these means one could think of analyzing on the order of 50 to 100 samples.

The method of data reduction of spectra on photographic films has been worked out by Steinhaus and Engleman at Los Alamos. Recently D. W. Mann Company has marketed an instrument with these features.

BIBLIOGRAPHY

Harrison, G. R., R. C. Lord, and J. R. Loofbourow (1948), *Practical Spectroscopy*, Prentice-Hall, New York.
Nachtrieb, N. H. (1950), *Spectrochemical Analyses*, McGraw-Hill, New York.

3. NEUTRON ACTIVATION ANALYSIS

Three important types of neutron interactions produce gamma rays. Although all the reactions have inherent advantages and disadvantages, all are useful for analytical work. The important point is that each type of reaction has a different time dependence—a fact that enables the reactions to be separated. This results in three independent series of gamma-ray spectra, all of which must combine to give a self-consistent final analysis. In practice the time separation is accomplished by pulsing the neutron source and by properly gating the detection system. The three reactions are:

Inelastic scattering: Here the neutron is scattered from the unknown nucleus with a loss of energy to the nucleus. The nucleus de-excites promptly (in $< 10^{-12}$ sec) with the emission of a gamma ray. Since inelastic scattering does not change the nuclear composition, the emitted gamma rays are characteristic of the original material and therefore introduce no ambiguity. The cross sections for gamma-ray production in the ten or so most abundant elements in rock are in the useful range ~ 1 barn. In most of the rare elements cross sections are too small to be useful for trace analysis.

Radiative capture: If a neutron becomes thermalized (in microseconds to milliseconds), it is usually captured. For example, an important reaction is the capture of a neutron by hydrogen to form deuterium with the emission of a 2.2-MeV gamma ray. In ordinary sand or rock, however, only the capture gamma rays from hydrogen and silicon are prominent.

Activation: Here the neutron is absorbed to form a new nucleus that can decay with the emission of a gamma ray characteristic of the new nucleus and with a characteristic lifetime. The decay time of each nuclide allows one to discriminate in favor of certain species by appropriately selecting activation periods and intervals between them. Very small amounts (as small as parts per million) of certain elements can be detected. For activation a larger neutron flux is needed than for inelastic scattering.

The gamma rays that are produced by these reactions will also interact (by photoelectric, Compton and pair-production processes) in both the unknown material and the detector. Moreover there are undesirable gamma-ray backgrounds that must be eliminated or minimized and determined. It is a problem of design to take advantage of the best features of all these interactions while keeping within the limits of practical equipment and the restrictions of the over-all space mission.

Because it is the nuclei with which the neutrons interact, no information on the nature of the compounds present can be obtained. Thus this technique is restricted to providing information only on the elemental composition of the surface. It is also essentially restricted to the inorganic portion since the most important elements in biochemistry (carbon, oxygen, nitrogen and hydrogen) are relatively difficult to detect by nuclear methods.

A problem which is very similar in many respects to the analysis of the Martian surface is the analysis of the lunar surface. After considering different possibilities for applying the method to this analysis it was concluded that the inelastic scattering approach was superior for the following reasons: 1. Reduced neutron requirements. The ready availability of tubes that will provide necessary flux for inelastic scattering and the power, weight and complexity of auxiliary equipment to operate the larger tubes required for activation analysis are very important. 2. Less sensitivity to background from natural causes. 3. Uniform cross sections for various elements. 4. No ambiguity in results. 5. No requirement for neutron flux determination or stability. 6. No mechanical operations required to perform the analysis, i.e., no sample preparation is required. (This is required for activation analysis and capture radiation analysis.) Laboratory studies give the following estimate for minimum detectable abundances: Fe, 0.1 per cent; Si, 0.5 per cent; Mg, 0.3 per cent; Al, 2.0 per cent; O, 3.7 per cent; K, 1.0 per cent; Ca, 1.2 per cent; Na, 1.3 per cent; Ni, 1.0 per cent. These estimates are approximate only, since interference by other elements in the matrix can change them.

No sample preparation is needed to apply the inelastic scattering method. A beam of energetic neutrons is directed at the surface by a suspended source and the rays arising from the inelastic collisions are detected and analyzed by a gamma ray spectrometer. The latter consists of a scintillation crystal, photomultiplier tube and a pulse-height analyzer. The latter provides the energy or spectral analysis and the total number of pulses gives the abundance.

An instrument to apply the technique to lunar surface analysis has been constructed and developed to the prototype stage. It consists of an accelerator which accelerates deuterons to 80 keV and impacts them on a tritium target. The d-t reaction produces 14-MeV neutrons which are used to activate the target material. The emitted rays are analyzed in a conventional spectrometer. During accelerator operation the total instrument uses about 10 watts of power. The prototype weights ~15-18 pounds depending upon telemetry requirements. A determination can be made in about 20 minutes.

BIBLIOGRAPHY

1. Palm, A. and R. G. Strom, Research Report of Elemental Abundances of the Lunar Crust According to Recent Hypothesis, Space Sciences Laboratory, University of California, Series 3, Issue 5.
2. Schrader, C. D. and R. J. Stinner, Remote Analysis of Surfaces by Neutron-Gamma-Ray Inelastic Scattering Technique. *J. Geophys. Res., 66,* 1951, 1961.
3. Benveniste, Mitchell, Schrader, Zenger, Gamma Rays from the Interaction of 14 MeV Neutrons with Beryllium. *Nuclear Physics 19,* 448-452, 1960.
4. Benveniste, Mitchell, Schrader, Zenger, Gamma Rays from the Interaction of 14 MeV Neutrons with Lithium. *UCRL-6074,* Rev. 1, Univ. Calif. Rad. Lab., 1962.

5. Caldwell, Mills, Hickman, Gamma Radiation from Inelastic Scattering of 14 MeV Neutrons by the Common Earth Elements. *Nuc. Sci. & Eng. 8* (3) 173, 1960.
6. Metzger, A. E., Some Calculations Bearing on the Use of Neutrons for Remote Compositional Analysis. *JPL Tech. Rept. No. 32-286,* 1962.

4. ELECTRON AND X-RAY FLUORESCENCE

Electron and x-ray fluorescence are grouped together because they differ only in their means of excitation. The bombardment of a sample by electrons, or irradiation by white x-rays, produces excited atoms which fluoresce with emission of x-rays. The wavelengths of the x-rays are characteristic of the elements present in the sample, so that the x-ray fluorescence spectrum can be used for both qualitative and quantitative elemental analysis. Some spectral broadening results from chemical combinations, but not enough to enable one to identify the compounds present.

If the collimation is good and a crystal is used to analyze the spectrum, overlapping of lines is not a problem. Line interference may exist when L transitions from heavy elements are concurrent with K transitions of light elements. However, these heavy elements are not abundant geochemically and this should pose no problem for extraterrestrial measurements. There is also the possibility of complications because, in matrices of low atomic number, some Compton or incoherent scattering does occur. This can result in some masking of fluorescent lines and could produce spurious peaks. Energy discrimination in the detector would be of some help in avoiding confusion due to these phenomena. Energy discrimination would be desirable on another count since the analyzing crystal will show second order diffraction, and energy discrimination could distinguish second order from first order lines where there was overlap.

The choice between electron and x-ray excitation is a tactical one. Since the electron beam is strongly attenuated by air molecules, the pressure in the excitation chamber must be less than 0.01 millibar. Accordingly, if used for Mars, an auxiliary vacuum pump would be required. However, this is not required for an x-ray source since the attenuation by an atmosphere in the pressure range estimated for Mars is insignificant for the paths used in practice. Moreover, electron beam bombardment of a sample, particularly if it consists of organic matter, can produce a large space charge which can disintegrate the sample. This can be alleviated by the admixture of 5-15 per cent graphite, but the heating which is also produced can be excessive and result in sample decomposition.

The facility with which elements can be detected is a function of the wavelength of their emitted x-rays, which decreases with increasing atomic number. For elements above silicon ($Z = 14$), there are no serious problems. For these elements the x-rays are short and are only slightly absorbed by the ambient atmosphere. For elements with $Z = 11\text{-}14$ special instrumentation is needed, but this now exists. Light element analysis down to $Z = 5$ has recently become possible in the laboratory, but it requires special methods which have not yet been adapted to space instrumentation.

The sensitivity of the method is dependent on the required resolution and resulting collimation of the fluorescent x-rays. This is not a very restrictive condition since, with reasonably good collimation, elements in the middle and upper parts of the periodic table can be detected at concentrations in the range of parts per million. At the low end of the table the elements such as calcium, potassium and magnesium probably would be determinable if present to the extent of 1-2 per cent.

Sample preparation is straightforward since the only requirement is that it be powdered, a particle size of 200 mesh or finer being desirable. The sample should be compacted into a pellet at a fixed pressure to make a reproducible matrix. This is not important for the higher energies, but in the lower half of the periodic table, and particularly below $Z = 20$, sample preparation becomes quite important since the energies involved penetrate only the very skin of the sample (an estimated 10 microns at $Z = 20$ calcium).

A combined dispersive and non-dispersive electron fluorescence "breadboard" apparatus for analyzing the lunar surface has been built and is currently being tested. The instrument weighs about 20 pounds and consumes about 15 watts of power. It has 13 dispersive channels which can be set for detecting any 13 elements of interest. The sample is powdered and fills a graphite cup, of diameter 1⅛ in. and depth 1/16 in. The sensitivity is 0.1 per cent for most elements, and the experimenters hope to lower this to 0.02-0.05 per cent for rock-like materials.

BIBLIOGRAPHY

1. Birks, L. S., *X-ray Spectrochemical Analyses,* Interscience, New York, 1959.
2. Clark, G. L., ed., *Encyclopedia of X-Rays and Gamma Rays,* Reinhold, New York, 1963.
3. Johnson, C. M. and P. R. Stout, Fluorescent X-ray Spectrometry; Inferences from Compton Scattering from Matrices of Low Atomic Number. *Anal. Chem. 30,* 1921-23, 1958.

5. X-RAY DIFFRACTION

With the exception of cellulose, x-ray diffraction is not promising as an identifying method for large organic molecules *in situ* in plant or animal tissues. Cellulose is accessible since its diagnostic x-ray spacings fall in a region of the x-ray diagram that is nearly devoid of spacings characteristic of the aluminosilicate minerals which are normally formed in rock or soils. Despite this limited application to biochemical analysis the technique is of potentially great value for biological exploration because of the information it provides on the mineralogical composition of the planet. The object in the examination of rock and dust specimens on Mars is to determine their composition. This is an important environmental parameter and is also essential in attempting to estimate the physical conditions (temperature, solid pressure, fluid pressures) under which the rocks formed. From data of this type taken at different places on the planetary surface, planetologists can reconstruct the processes operative in and on the body and derive its history.

X-ray diffraction is the analytical method which, by itself, can provide the most information required for such interpretations. A diffraction analysis of surface and subsurface rock specimens comprises:

1. identification of the solid phases in the specimen
2. determination of the relative abundance of each solid phase in the specimen
3. determination of the composition and degree of ordering of each phase.

Complete data on these three topics would give the composition and conditions during crystallization of the specimen as well as the approach to equilibrium of the assemblage of solids and the rate at which the system crystallized. For instance, it may be possible to show that melting occurred within Mars, that vertical mechanical movements are a factor in rock distribution, that meteorite impact has occurred at a point, that hydration has occurred, etc. Given other data on the geometry and spectral reflectivity of the surface surrounding the point where the diffractometer sample was taken, the processes interpreted from the x-ray data may be extrapolated beyond the sample source.

In view of the postulated significance of large bodies of water for the origin of life it is of great importance to determine whether or not such bodies have existed on Mars, and if so, when. An x-ray diffraction analysis would be critical in settling this question since it could determine the presence of mineral assemblages indicative of marine sedimentation.

It is fairly well established that specific clay minerals and associated oxides, carbonates and salts are products of weathering of specific environments characteristic of certain climates. Therefore the identification by means of x-ray analysis of particular clay minerals could shed information on the present or past climatic conditions of Mars. The problem of identifying the various clay minerals by x-ray analysis is facilitated by the fact that the x-ray spacings that identify each of the major clay minerals occur in a region of the x-ray diagram devoid of spacings of the minerals commonly found in rocks, namely between 18Å and 7Å.

The ability of an x-ray diffraction experiment to obtain data of sufficient quality and quantity for optimum interpretability as discussed above depends, in general, on three variables summarized below and discussed in more detail later.

Instrumental and Operational Parameters.—The quality of diffraction is judged by the conventional terms: resolution (or line width), peak height or area precision, and signal-to-noise ratio. These functions are governed by many variables among which are: radiation wavelength, source geometry, and intensity, monochromaticity of radiation, collimation in vertical and horizontal planes, sample transparency, sample curvature relative to focus circle curvature, beta filter, deviation of refocus of diffracted x-rays from focusing circle, travel of after-slit on focusing circle, scattering angle, detector efficiency, dead time, pulse discrimination, and scan rate.

Specimen Source.—There are two general types of Martian materials which can be sampled: Martian bedrock and dust. Bedrock is part of the solid body of Mars, and this material is formed by processes originating within Mars. Dust consists of a particulate surface layer formed by deposition of materials of diverse sources. Analytical data on Martian bedrock will indicate the nature of Martian processes. Dust, however, is almost certainly a disequilibrium assemblage, and analyses of the dust will be exceedingly difficult to interpret in terms of the processes by which it was formed or, more importantly, the nature of Mars.

Sample Preparation.—The resolution and reproducibility of diffraction data are strong functions of the way in which the specimen has been prepared. The parameters are particle-size distribution, contamination, fractionation, surface geometry, porosity, and preferred orientation.

The Surveyor-type diffractometer (developed by W. Parrish of Phillips Laboratories and intended for lunar analysis) described below employs a simple bedrock sample acquisition and presentation device. The specifications given for sample preparation by this device will provide a degree of precision in peak intensities which will allow only a crude estimation of relative mineral abundances. A sample spinner can be incorporated in the diffractometer, however, for improvement of peak statistics.

The present Surveyor diffractometer system consists of: (1) a scanning goniometer with side-window proportional counter, fixed Cuk_a conduction-cooled x-ray source, beryllium-window sample holder; (2) fully transistorized electronic and power components consisting of detector pre-amplifier, minimum pulse-energy threshold circuit, main signal amplifier, binary count-down circuit (reduction of $\times$ 8), 25 kV — 1.0 ma x-ray source power supply, 2000 V detector supply, and goniometer drive-motor supply; (3) logic circuit with command control of 3-step scan rate, 2-position threshold control, and power on-off mode. Goniometer para-meters are as follows: scanning radius 8.5 cm, scan rates ½ and 4 deg 2θ per minute forward and 8 deg 2θ per minute reverse, scan range 7-90 deg 2θ; curved specimen holder with focus at 30 deg 2θ; 8 deg take-off angle, 3 deg divergent slit, 0.006-inch receiving slit; 0.0006-inch nickel beta filter, mica detector window; detector filled with xenon with a methane quench.

The focal circle is vertical in order to simplify specimen mounting. The speciment mount, conceived by W. Parrish and M. Mack of Phillips Laboratories, is made of an aluminum frame upon which 0.002-in. beryllium foil is cemented. The upper surface of the foil is in contact with the powdered specimen and is curved to fit a focusing circle at 3 deg 2θ. This curvature was chosen to provide maximum resolution in the angular region where the majority of diagnostic peaks occurs for the common rock forming minerals. The beryllium "cup" arrangement allows a powdered specimen to be tightly pressed into the cup without a binder; a smooth surface of the powder against the Be foil is therefore automatically presented to the x-ray beam.

The beryllium used in the specimen mount is prepared by cold-rolling in a single direction. The (002) spacing forms parallel to the plane of the foil and provides a strong reflection at 50.97 deg 2θ. Each lunar diffraction pattern then, will have its own reference line from which angular measurements can be made.

The performance characteristics of the instrument for the (101) quartz reflection are: peak intensity 4000 cps, background 40 cps, ½ height peak-width 0.18 deg 2θ. It is noteworthy that this instrument gives resolution and intensity comparable to a laboratory diffractometer consuming 26 times the power. The entire diffraction system, less the sample acquisition system, weighs 18 pounds and occupies 0.9 cubic feet. The electronics, including the power supply, consume 56 watts. Ground support equipment consists of telemetry decoding systems, tape-recorders, real-time strip-chart display, and computer support for automatic spectra interpretation. A typical Martian operational scheme would be: acquisition and preparation of bedrock and surface-dust specimens, pulverizing and size fractionation of specimen particles and insertion into sample-cup, preliminary fast scan of specimen at 4 deg/min, reverse scan at 8 deg/min, and a final slow-scan at ½ deg/min.

Particle Size.—The statistical precision of x-ray diffraction peak intensities increases with the abundance of fine (1 to 20 μ) particles in the sample. For quantitative mineralogical analysis on Mars, samples must have at least 90 per cent of the particles in the above range, and the preparation apparatus must provide particle-size distributions that are reproducible within small limits.

In the interests of simplicity in early diffraction experiments it is desirable to reduce greatly the particle size specifications for the combined diffractometer-sampler system. A proposed specification is simply that the maximum particle size be 0.1 mm in greatest dimension; the granulation will occur simultaneously with acquisition of the sample.

This specification is based on results of empirical grinding tests of natural materials in the literature and on experiments at Princeton University and Jet Propulsion Laboratory with reproducibility of diffraction peaks as a function of screen-sized fractions. The particle-size distribution of granulated silicates depends on grinding apparatus, time of grinding and grain size of the initial material. The size-frequencies generally form a skewed Gaussian distribution, but the reproducibility in these distributions is not sufficient for calculation of the percentage of particles in any selected size increment. The data show, however, that a large percentage of particles an order of magnitude or smaller than the maximum particle size is formed during grinding of these brittle materials. Accordingly, it is reasonable to assume that the maximum particle size in the specifications could be raised to a value where the percentage of fine particles decreases to the point where the data reproducibility approaches some minimal allowable limit.

The actual distribution will depend on the apparatus chosen for the sampler. One can approach the desired distribution, however, by varying the time of the granulation process according to empirical test data with the selected apparatus. Further, if it is found that the sample prepared by this system tends to be coarse or if granulation time must be limited due to a tendency to overgrind, a sample spinner can be incorporated in the diffractometer to improve peak statistics.

It should be remembered that the peak reproducibility affects only the accuracy of determination of mineral abundances and to a lesser degree, the sensitivity level of minerals. It does not, however, affect our ability to identify minerals in major abundance which is the prime objective of a diffraction experiment.

Performance of the Surveyor Prototype.—The sample size demanded is only 2-3 milligrams. On the lunar surface it is planned to use 2-3 grams in order to facilitate sample preparation. Sample handling problems are more severe for the lunar experiment than for Mars due to the hard vacuum on the Moon; thus the sample size required on Mars should be less than 2 grams.

Pattern overlap can make the interpretation of the results from multi-component mixtures uncertain. However laboratory studies of some 500 rocks and an equal number of artificial samples indicate that percentage compositions can generally be determined with errors not greater than $\pm$ 10 per cent if the number of components does not exceed five. Under ideal conditions the composition can be determined to $\pm$ 2 per cent. The minimum detectivities fall in the same ranges. For some mineral groups such as the pyroxenes a fairly good description of their chemical composition can be given. Moreover, the proportion of glass in a sample can also be estimated fairly satisfactorily.

BIBLIOGRAPHY

1. Barshad, I., Chemistry of Soil Development. In: *Chemistry of the Soil,* F. E. Bear (ed.), Reinhold, New York, 1964.
2. Frei, E. and R. D. Preston, Cell Wall Organization and Wall Growth in the Filamentous Green Algae Cladophora and Chaetomorpha. *Proc. Roy. Soc. 159B,* 70, 1961.
3. Keller, W. D., Processes of Origin and Alteration of Clay Minerals. In: *Soil Clay Mineralogy,* C. I. Rich and G. W. Kunze (eds.), Univ. of North Carolina Press, Chapel Hill, 1964.
4. Parrish, W., Lunar Diffractometer Geometry. In press.
5. Speed, R. C., D. B. Nash and N. L. Nickle, A Lunar X-Ray Diffraction Experiment. In: *Advances in X-Ray Analysis 8,* W. Mueller, G. Malin and M. Fay (eds.), Plenum Press, 1964.

6. SENSITIVITY OF FIBERS TO THE PHYSICAL AND CHEMICAL ENVIRONMENT

Fibers offer a simple means for obtaining information on the physical and chemical environment while consuming only a small number of data bits. This can be accomplished by monitoring the physical state of the fiber on exposure to the environment. For instance, collagen fibers are compared by measuring their times to break in solutions containing proteolytic enzymes. For a Mars experiment the procedure would be reversed: the time for a known collagen fiber to break being a measure of the unknown concentration of proteolytic enzymes. The only datum to be telemetered to Earth is the break time so that the experiment's demands on the data link are negligible.

There exist alternate methods of detecting changes in fibers due to the environment, for example the vibroscopic technique in which the resonant frequencies of the fiber are measured. This method is based on vibrating string considerations and can be used to measure small changes in fiber diameters (weight or density). Changes in fiber stiffness, either in bending or torsion, can be sensitive indicators of secondary as well as primary bond breakage.

These fiber techniques could be used for measuring a wide range of parameters. The latter include not only specific enzymes, but also water, ozone, ultraviolet flux, etc. Such an approach has the advantages of simplicity in experimental design and minimal demands on the data transmission system. On the other hand the specificity may, in certain cases, not be very high since several possible environmental factors may be acting on the fiber. Still these techniques can provide a unique means for obtaining significant data and should receive serious consideration.

7. GAS CHROMATOGRAPHY

Gas chromatography [*James and Martin,* 1952] is a procedure whereby the individual components of a mixture of gas molecules (derived from a gaseous, liquid or solid sample) are separated by gas-liquid partition or adsorption processes during the forced flow of such a mixture through suitably prepared packed or capillary columns. The separated gaseous components emerging from the column are quantitatively measured by means of appropriate detectors.

In the exploration of Mars by means of a soft-landing spacecraft, gas chromatography can be used for the analysis of the gaseous components of its atmosphere and of any volatile compounds found in its soil. Furthermore, using appropriate pretreatments, gas chromatography can also be used to determine the presence or absence in the Martian soil of monomeric or polymeric organic substances. These studies would provide basic knowledge of the physical conditions and chemical composition of the planet's atmosphere and lithosphere.

Analysis of the Atmosphere

A specific objective to be accomplished by gas chromatography in one of the first soft-landing Martian missions could be to separate directly and determine accurately certain individual constituent gases (carbon dioxide, nitrogen, oxygen, water vapor and other gases) which may be present in the Martian atmosphere. The gas chromatographic apparatus which could be used is similar to instruments previously described [*Lipsky; Oyama, 1963b*] and consists essentially of a carrier gas supply system, a sample injection system with a known-sample chamber, an oven, a set of columns and detectors (with several possible configurations) and the necessary auxiliary electronic equipment for general operation and for the detection and registration of data signals.

This instrument (in one of its possible configurations) is capable of detecting the presence of carbon dioxide, argon, nitrogen, oxygen and hydrogen in about 1 minute after sample procurement. Moreover, if gases or vapors other than these are present, such as H_2O, CH_4, NH_3, CO, C_2H_6, the instrument (in another configuration) has the capability of carrying out the complete analysis of all 10 components in a few minutes. With appropriate modifications, the nitrogen oxides, N_2O, NO and NO_2, could also be determined. All compounds with the exception of ammonia may be detected at a level of 10 ppm or higher within the Martian atmosphere.

Identification is based on the precise time required for a component band to emerge from a selective column system when compared with a known calibration sample analyzed under similar conditions on Earth, and in moments prior to entry into the Mars atmosphere. Quantitative determination of a component is based on the amplitude of the detector signal as the detector senses the component after it emerges from the column. Sampling cycles of 1 to 5 minutes may be selected depending on the time allowed (in-flight analysis or analysis after landing) and other requirements. Over-all accuracy is better than 5 per cent.

By an appropriate arrangement of columns the analytical separation of the four most obvious atmospheric components (CO_2, A, N_2, and O_2) can be accomplished in about one minute. Another arrangement in series of the four major columns has been considered as an effective configuration for the separation of the above four components plus H_2, CO, CH_4, C_2H_6, NH_3 and H_2O. This analysis could be performed in about 4 or 5 minutes. In this configuration a charcoal column is used to adsorb oxygen irreversibly in effecting the argon–oxygen differentiation, a special silicone oil column to elute NH_3 and H_2O, and a silica gel and a molecular sieve column to resolve all the other compounds. A small calcium carbide column could also be used instead of the silicone oil column to determine water by transforming it into acetylene. The columns may be operated at any one temperature from 0°C to 50°C. Injection of a reference gas sample should be used for standardizing the system after prolonged flight.

Two detection devices can be used in the gas chromatographic instrument. They are the small volume ionization cross-section detector and the electron capture detector.

Small volume ionization cross-section detector [*Lovelock et al., 1964*]. This detector has been selected because of its predictable response to a wide range of concentrations of sample gas components. The response to any given substance can be calculated from the simple addition of the cross-sections of ionization of the constituent atoms of its molecules. The source of ionizing radiation is a beta emitter (either 200 mc of tritium embedded in titanium foil as titanium tritide or 20 mc of Sr^{90} embedded on a gold plated, stainless steel foil) which produces a saturation current of 10^{-9} amperes in helium when a potential is applied to the chamber. The response of this detector is precise and linear to 100 per cent gas concentration. It is a simple and rugged device which is insensitive to changes in carrier gas flow rate and does not require a precisely regulated source of polarizing potential.

The electron capture detector [*Lovelock, 1963*]. This detector is exceedingly sensitive to any compound which has the capacity for capturing free electrons. It is an ion chamber which is maintained at a potential just sufficient to collect all the free electrons produced in the carrier gas. The source of ionizing radiation is similar to that employed in the cross-section detectors. The detector responds only when an electro-negative gas sample, such as oxygen, passes into it. Under these conditions, oxygen accepts free electrons to form slow moving stable negative ions. This causes a decrease in the flow of current from the chamber. This detector responds to O_2, CO, N_2O and to other gases or vapors containing electro-negative atoms (O, S, halogens, etc.) which may conceivably exist in the Martian atmosphere. (Minimal detectable quantities of oxygen are in the order of 10^{-14} moles per second.) Therefore it would serve a dual function in providing qualitative as well as quantitative analysis.

Although the quantitative determination of the gaseous components emerging from the gas chromatographic columns can be done efficiently and accurately with the above described detectors, the use of a simplified mass spectrometer as a detector is possible and should not be excluded from consideration. However, the potentialities of such an analytical instrument would be better used for the determination of more complex substances. The application of a combined gas chromatographic-mass spectrometric technique to these studies is described elsewhere in this report.

Analysis of Soil Organic Matter

In a general way three major groups of organic compounds possibly present in the Martian soil can be analyzed by gas chromatography: liposoluble (soluble in organic solvents), hydrosoluble, and polymeric substances. These three groups of substances can be analyzed independently or in a systematically programmed sequence from the first to the last. They will be treated separately in this order. Discussion of gas chromatographic instrumentation will be limited to aspects not covered in the previous section.

Analysis of Liposoluble Organic Substances. It is possible to design an automatic extracting and fractionating device to perform the extraction from the soil of liposoluble substances and the fractionation of this extract into alkanes, aromatic hydrocarbons and other liposoluble organic compounds with functional groups (e.g., fatty acids and steroids). The analysis of the components in each one of these three fractions can be carried out by gas-liquid chromatography using miniaturized conventional equipment. Packed or capillary columns with silicone oil, apiezon or high molecular weight wax as stationary phases are efficient for the separation of these compounds. Single column configurations (in series or parallel arrangement) are capable of resolving most of the isometric components usually found in these fractions. In addition special columns can be used to effect more selective separations. For instance a short molecular sieve column can be used to adsorb essentially all of the normal alkanes allowing the subsequent separation analysis of the branched paraffins.

Because of their chemical inertness alkanes of relatively high molecular weight are some of the most stable molecular biological indicators [*Meinschein, 1963*]. The finding of saturated isoprenoid hydrocarbons such as farnesane, pristane, phytane, squalane, steranes, etc., would be a strong indication for the existence of terrestrial-like biosynthetic mechanisms leading to the formation of such compounds. It should be pointed out that not only the products of contemporaneous Martian life but also the fossilized remains of a life long extinct could be evidenced in this manner.

It is reasonable to assume that the conditions for the existence of life on Mars were more favorable in the past than at present. Therefore the analytical determination of characteristic alkanes by the method described above would tremendously increase the probability of success of the over-all space mission aimed at detecting the possible existence of past or present life on Mars.

The determination of aromatic hydrocarbons and of other liposoluble organic substances such as steroids and fatty acids by established gas chromatographic procedures [*Horning and Van den Heuvel, 1963*] could provide additional evidence for the biogenic or abiogenic origin of these organic substances.

Analysis of Water Soluble Organic Substances. L-Alpha amino acids are some of the most characteristic water soluble organic substances of terrestrial living organisms. The determination of these compounds by gas chromatography is possible after their transformation into aldehydes by a short ninhydrin column [*Zlatkis et al.,* 1960] or after their transformation into *N*-trifluoroacetyl methyl esters [*Hagan and Black,* 1964; *Cruikshank and Sheehan,* 1964]. The adaptation of such procedures for operation in a soft-landed space probe should not pose any particularly difficult problems. Separation from salts and non-amphoteric ionic organic substances can be carried out by electrolytic desalting; methylation and acylation can be carried out automatically in a short time. Preparation of derivatives containing at least two asymmetric carbon atoms could also be accomplished using for instance 2-fluoropropionic anhydride instead of trifluoroacetic anhydride. With the help of an asymmetric stationary phase it should be possible to resolve the resulting diastereoisomers obtained from the D and L forms of alpha amino acids. Although it is not completely certain that optical asymmetry is an absolute requirement for living organisms a differentiation and quantitative measurement of D and L amino acids by formation and separation of diastereoisomers would provide much wanted basic chemical information. (The sensitivity of present optical polarimeters is relatively low.) This gas chromatographic method would also provide information if amphoteric compounds other than alpha amino acids (beta amino acids, etc.) prevailed on Mars.

Polymetric Substances. Organic macromolecules constituting perhaps the bulk of the organic matter in the Martian subsurface can be analyzed before or after separation from the other components of the soil (by extraction and precipitation). Such analyses require a pretreatment of the sample, either chemical (hydrolysis by enzymes or bases) or thermal, so that the resulting small molecular weight compounds can be separated and measured by gas chromatography.

Chemical degradation. Techniques are presently available for the automatic hydrolysis of proteins and the subsequent separation of their component peptides and amino acids [*Catravas,* 1964]. Undoubtedly this method is capable of providing a wealth of biochemical data and its further development using the gas chromatographic techniques just described would make it a very powerful means for achieving present goals.

Thermal degradation. Even though the thermal degradation method may provide less information about the nature of the individual original components of the macromolecules, this technique is simple, reliable and potentially applicable to the characterization of many different types of macromolecules. The application of this method as a means of "life detection" on Mars was advanced some time ago by *Oyama* [1963*a, b*] and preliminary investigations on terrestrial materials have confirmed the validity of this concept as applied to terrestrial life.

According to *Oyama* [1963*a*] the premise on which this concept is based originates from the fact that terrestrial life is an ordered aggregate of carbonaceous macromolecular structures as well as of smaller amounts of monomeric organic substances, the latter arising as intermediates in the syntheses of the macromolecules or by-products of metabolic processes. The proteins, polysaccharides and nucleic acids which represent biological macromolecular structures are composed of sub-units such as the amino acids, monosaccharides, purine and pyrimidine bases. These constituent substances are distributed universally among living materials and the essential composition of protoplasm requires that critical proportions of them be maintained either by assimilation from the environment or manufacture by the organism.

The simple technique of thermal degradation has been applied with success to the analyses of chemical structure of synthetic polymers. However, in a complex organic aggregate of biological origin, the pyrolysates obtained by thermal degradation present us with a relatively difficult task of determining the original contributing structures. Nevertheless, it is possible to obtain a chromatographic pattern (comparable in a way to a paper chromatographic two-dimensional display of peptides for the elucidation of protein structure) which could similarly be used to indicate the presence of biological matter.

The pyrolysis chamber consists essentially of a stainless-steel loop attached to a linear 6-way valve, that permits initial evacuation of the sample loop, filling of the pyrolysis chamber with inert helium atmosphere, pyrolysis under closed system and sweeping the contents of the pyrolysis chamber into the flowing gas system directed into the gas chromatographic column. The valve and tubing between the pyrolysis chamber and column are maintained at 125°C during the course of the analysis. A heat pretreated Fiberglas cordage is inserted into the sample loop to prevent particulate matter from entering the critical valving area. Optimum temperature and residence time are 450–500°C for 2 minutes. Detectors: Micro cross-section or flame ionization.

Packed columns, approximately 3 mm × 3m, of 15 per cent S. E. 30 on chromosorb W have given good results. With gas flow of about 100 ml/min they may be operated isothermally, at 200°C, or by temperature programming.

The accumulated volatile products of thermal decomposition represent only the thermal products that are measurable at the instant that the vapors are swept into the column. Variations can be expected if the pyrolytic conditions are changed. Therefore once fixed it is important to repeat exactly the pyrolytic conditions. Under reproducible conditions (and using linear temperature programming) the chromatographic peaks corresponding to the volatile thermal degradation products occur with a periodicity common to essentially all the organisms examined. Similar patterns from proteins whether they be of plant or animal origin have also been observed. Variations in relative peak heights of some components appearing in different chromatograms may indicate differences in the relative amounts of precursor organic substances in the corresponding biological samples.

Capabilities and Limitations of Gas Chromotography

1. Because of the efficiency of the gas-liquid partition process few analytical methods, if any, can be compared to gas chromatography with regard to separation capability and rapidity. More work should be done on efficient columns for the gas chromatographic separation of water and other polar substances.

2. The simple rugged detection systems employed (particularly the micro cross-section detector) possess several unique properties of great value. They provide a readily predictable response at any known temperature or pressure. They possess a wide linear dynamic range and thus are capable of measuring sample component concentrations from parts per million to 100 per cent within the detector. Under these circumstances such detectors cannot be "overloaded" following the unexpected admission of an unusually large volume of gas into the sampling system. (This may result from errors in the calculations of the theoretical density of the atmosphere or organic content of the soil.) In summary the detectors are reliable, sensitive and have an extremely wide dynamic range, the last applying mainly to the micro cross-section detector.

3. Since this detector response is absolute, additional information other than the separation and determination of the atmospheric gases, such as the density of the atmosphere or the approximate concentration of organic matter in the soil, may be provided with this system.

4. Calibration runs with known samples can be performed before entry into the Martian atmosphere, which in addition would provide the necessary check on the working conditions of the instrument. Individual internal standards can be run at any time.

5. The complete instrument has reasonable volume, weight, and power requirements. It can be designed to withstand shock, vibration and broad variations in temperature. Telemetric requirements are also relatively small.

6. A partial limitation exists in the fact that gas chromatography provides only relative identification as a function of retention times. However, for light gas molecules (atmosphere) the number of different possibilities having the same molecular weight is sufficiently small so that, using a multiple column configuration as described earlier, the identification by retention time offers little ambiguity. In the case of organic compounds from the soil the treatment carried out before gas chromatography (extraction, chemical reaction or thermal degradation) causes a selection in family groups of the compounds to be analyzed, making their identification quite specific. This is further enhanced by use of the electron capture detector.

7. Another limitation may also exist in the instability of some of the column organic stationary phases. However this can be partially avoided by using mainly columns with inorganic adsorbing materials and with the most stable organic stationary phases presently available. Fundamental work in the area of thermally-stable inorganic and organic stationary phases should be undertaken not only from the point of view of the present aims but mainly because progress in this area would greatly expand the horizons of gas chromatography.

REFERENCES

Catravas, G. N. (1964), *Anal. Chem., 36,* 1146.
Cruickshank, P. A., and Sheehan, J. C. (1964), *Anal. Chem. 36,* 1191.
Hagen, P., and Black, W. (1964), *Federation Proc. 23,* 371.
Horning, E. C., and Van den Heuvel, W. J. A. (1963), *Ann. Rev. Biochem. 32,* 709.
James, A. T., and Martin, A. J. (1952), *Biochem. J. 50,* 679.
Lipsky, S. R., Analysis of Mars' Atmosphere, unpublished.
Lovelock, J. E. (1963), *Anal. Chem. 35,* 474.
Lovelock, J. E., Shoemake, G. R., and Zlatkis, A. (1964), *Anal. Chem. 36,* 1410.
Meinschein, W. G. (1963), *Space Sci. Rev. 2,* 653.
Oyama, V. I. (1963a), *Nature 200,* 1058; Oyama, V. I., Vango, S. P., and Wilson, E. M. (1962), *ARS J. 32,* 354.
Oyama,, V. I. (1963b), *Lunar and Planetary Exploration Coll. Proc. 3* (2), 29.
Zlatkis, A., Oró, J., and Kimball, A. P. (1960), *Anal. Chem. 32,* 162.

8. MASS SPECTROMETRY

While mass spectrometry is not able to "detect" life in any specific manner, it is a method that would permit us to learn much about the products of life, namely organic molecules. Within the last decade, it has become an important method for the organic chemist interested in the detection, identification and structure determination of substances, not only those produced by man synthetically, but also—and with even more obvious success—of those produced by nature on Earth.

Reasonably complex molecules (of molecular weight below 1000) have had their structure determined in part or wholly by mass spectrometry, frequently revealing subtle details in their structure [*Beynon*, 1960; *Biemann*, 1962; *Budzikiewicz et al.*, 1964a, b].

As a technique in organic chemistry, mass spectrometry occupies a place between the other spectroscopic techniques—ultraviolet, infrared, nuclear magnetic resonance on the one hand and color reactions and bioassays on the other. The first three yield detailed, characteristic and structurally interpretable data but require samples ranging from a fraction of a milligram to a few milligrams (if conventional laboratory techniques are employed). The least specific method—ultraviolet—occupies the lower part of this range; nuclear magnetic resonance (perhaps the most specific) lies at the other extreme.

Mass spectrometry requires at present between a few tenths of a milligram and a few nanograms; its potentialities for further increase in sensitivity are still largely unexplored. The specificity of the data obtained by mass spectrometry is extremely high and our knowledge concerning the correlation of these data with the structure of the molecule has grown rapidly during the last decade and will continue to do so because more and more research laboratories are becoming engaged in this field.

If one would take the mass spectrum of that fraction of organic matter which contains compounds exhibiting both acidic and basic properties one could easily ascertain whether any of the common terrestrial amino acids were present. If so, it would be possible to identify them and estimate roughly the molar ratios. If the spectrum did not indicate the presence of these known compounds one would still be able to interpret it in terms of the probable structures of the compounds present—which might as well be β-amino acids or α-amino-phosphonic acids or even more exotic and more unexpected molecules. The mass spectrometric determination of the structure of new amino acids and detection of unexpected ones in complex mixtures have been accomplished [*Biemann*, 1962, Ch. 7]. While the conditions in terrestrial laboratories are, of course, much more favorable than those to be expected in space research, the structural problems that have been resolved in the laboratory were sometimes quite complex.

Thus the amount of detailed information obtainable per unit weight, say per microgram, is probably greatest for mass spectrometry, if compared with any other method presently used in organic chemistry. There are, of course, some complicating factors in its application to the study of extra-terrestrial life, especially if this study is to be undertaken on the spot, i.e., on another planet. Although one can successfully interpret the spectra of multicomponent mixtures, the sample should not be a complete "mess" as this would lead to a non-specific spectrum with peaks at each mass indiscriminately. Some preliminary separation is required, e.g., thermal fractionation, controlled pyrolysis or gas chromatography.

A second problem is the ultimate sample size. While the mass spectrometer is quite sensitive, it cannot be used directly for the detection of traces in liquids or solids by using a very large sample. The substance to be investigated has first to be separated from the matrix or solvent and for this purpose one could use one of the above mentioned processes.

Aside from the determination of structure, the major subject of the above discussion, two other aspects of mass spectrometry would be of interest. First: study of the composition of the atmosphere on the planet might give some clue about the possibility that it would be favorable for metabolic activity and the type of chemistry that might be involved. Second: precise determination of the abundance ratios of stable isotopes of the elements of the atomic number would be of great interest, not only to the study of extraterrestrial life, but also to geophysics and cosmogeny.

In conclusion it may be said that any reasonably elaborate scientific payload soft-landed on another planet, such as Mars, should incorporate a mass spectrometer with a mass range and resolution permitting the determination of spectra of compounds up to a molecular weight of at least 250. The telemetry requirements would be rather high, as one would wish to monitor each single mass (with very few exceptions) and the corresponding abundance over a dynamic range of at least 1:100, or, preferably, 1:1000. Sampling systems need to be developed, but existing laboratory techniques and methods for remote control could be adapted.

REFERENCES

Beynon, J. H. (1960), *Mass Spectrometry and Its Applications to Organic Chemistry,* Elsevier, Amsterdam.

Biemann, K. (1962), *Mass Spectrometry, Organic Chemical Applications,* Mc-Graw-Hill, New York.

Budzikiewicz, H., C. Djerassi and D. H. Williams (1964a), *Interpretation of Mass Spectra of Organic Compounds,* Holden-Day, San Francisco.

Budzikiewicz, H., C. Djerassi and D. H. Williams (1964b), *Structure Elucidation of Natural Products by Mass Spectrometry I: Alkaloids,* Holden-Day, San Francisco.

9. GAS CHROMATOGRAPHY—MASS SPECTROMETRY

Leaving aside the discussion of weight, electrical power and telemetering requirements, the combination of gas chromatography and mass spectrometry by means of molecular separators, as described mainly by *Ryhage* [1964; 1962] and *Watson and Biemann* [1964], provides an ideal method for the rapid separation, detection and precise identification of organic compounds on planetary surfaces. Moreover, such a system can be designed also to provide a complete chemical analysis of the atmosphere of a planet not only at the surface but also during descent of the spacecraft.

A sample component vapor eluted from a gas chromatographic column by means of a carrier gas is concentrated many times via one or several molecular separators and fed directly into the ion source of a mass spectrometer. Here the compound is ionized, the ions accelerated and deflected and the ion masses of the parent molecule and its characteristic molecular fragments are measured and recorded.

Brief Technical Description

In the molecular separator constructed by *Ryhage* [1964; 1962] according to the principles given by *Becker* [1961], the molecules emerging from the gas chromatographic column pass straight on through two holes of small diameter that are very close together while the lighter carrier gas (helium or hydrogen) diffuses to the side and is pumped away. To increase the separation effect of carrier gas and compound two identical molecular separators are connected in series. This allows the rapid effusion of relatively large quantities of carrier gas producing in a very short time an increase of the sample-to-helium ratio of at least 100 times. The high enrichment coefficient, the short time operation constant and the small effective volume of the concentrated gas sample provide optimal conditions for the operation of the mass spectrometer.

The line from the molecular separator is connected by means of a vacuum valve directly into the ion source of the mass spectrometer, where the sample is ionized. About 10 per cent of the total ion current generated by the ionization is continuously registered on a potentiometric recorder which serves as a detector and provides a permanent record of the gas chromatographic separation.

At any time (usually when the total ion current is at a maximum, or at an inflection point) the magnet current regulator and the oscillograph recorder are started to obtain the mass spectrum of the sample that is being ionized. The energy of the electrons is kept constant at 20 eV and the acceleration voltage at 3,000 volts. The mass spectrometer is equipped with a high speed recording system which can scan and register the mass range m/e 12 to 500 in 1 to 2 seconds. Since the partial pressure remains essentially constant during this short time, the scanning can be repeated immediately and no disturbance of the cracking pattern results.

With this system it is possible to procure mass spectra in less than 2 seconds of each of the bands emerging from a gas chromatographic column consisting of less than 1 μg of a compound of molecular weight 12 to 500. If necessary it could be modified for lower and higher molecular weights. A more recent version of this technique that uses capillary instead of packed columns, a single molecular separator instead of two and registers the total ion current instead of 10 per cent of the total, allows the determination of nanogram amounts of individual components emerging from the gas chromatograph [*Ryhage et al.*, 1965].

Advantages of the Gas Chromotography–Mass Spectrometry (GC–MS) System

The combination of gas liquid chromatography and mass spectrometry offers all the advantages inherent in either of these techniques alone with additional advantages that result from the combination of both instrumental methods.

In essence, gas liquid chromatography offers an excellent method to separate volatile organic substances (it also allows relative identification by measurement of retention times) and mass spectrometry is perhaps the best method presently available for the complete identification of a compound by determination of its molecular weight and characteristic cracking pattern (from which the structure of the compound can be deduced). The combination of both instruments by means of molecular separators offers the following additional advantages:

1. The possibility of rapid separation and identification in a single operational step of essentially all the individual components of a complex mixture.

2. It permits continuous operation of the mass spectrometric identification process, making it unnecessary to break the vacuum of the mass spectrometer to introduce a sample. In fact samples (gases, liquids or solids if sufficiently volatile or appropriately pretreated) can be continuously analyzed by introducing them successively through the gas chromatographic inlet. This can be done automatically as fast as allowed by the rate of the chromatographic separation, which is the rate-limiting step of the over-all analytical process.

3. The fact that each of the components of a mixture does not need to be isolated allows the determination of certain compounds, which would be impossible to identify otherwise, particularly if they are present only in trace amounts.

4. Components which are poorly or practically not resolved on the gas chromatographic column can also be identified, since the mass spectrum can be taken every 1 or 2 seconds and observations of mass spectra can be made almost continuously during the time the effluent passes the ion source. In this way what sometimes may appear to be a single chromatographic peak or band may be resolved into 2 or 3 compounds.

5. Until now, the use of combined gas chromatographic–mass spectrometric techniques for the characterization of individual component bands as they emerged from the gas chromatographic column has been fraught with difficulties. Satisfactory results were confined to the analysis of highly volatile hydrocarbons. In studies involving more complex substances, samples eluted from the column were trapped out and then introduced into the mass spectrometer. As noted by some investigators [*Ryhage*, 1962, 1964; *Becker*, 1961; *Ryhage et al.*, 1965] this method was exceedingly time consuming and had many disadvantages associated with the collection, handling, and introduction of the sample. With the availability of efficient molecular separators these difficulties are a thing of the past and the analytical horizons of this dynamic system have been greatly extended.

Identification and Structure Determination of Organic Compounds

As an identification technique the GC–MS method occupies, with mass spectrometry, a privileged position in analytical organic chemistry because a single mass spectrum determination secured in seconds or minutes from a very small sample provides more information about the molecular weight and structure of the compound than any other method. Since this information is derived from the masses of the whole and different parts of the molecule it requires no previous knowledge, or very little, of the nature of the compound analyzed. A discussion of this point is given by Dr. Biemann in this report and additional information and data may be found elsewhere [*Beynon*, 1960; *Reed*, 1962; *Biemann*, 1962; *Elliott*, 1963; *McLafferty*, 1963a, b; *McDowell*, 1963; *Budzikiewicz et al.*, 1964a, b; *Reese and Harllee*, 1964].

Potentialities of the Gas Chromotography-Mass Spectrometry (GC-MS) System for the Detection of Extraterrestrial Life*

Typical Chemical Composition. Whereas the gas chromatographic-mass spectrometric system will not be able to "detect" life in any definitive way,

---

* For simplification, "extraterrestrial life" is considered to have the same attributes as terrestrial life.

it is a method that will allow us to obtain accurate information about the typical composition and nature of the organic compounds and other molecules of biological significance which may be present in the atmosphere, on the surface or in the subsurface of another planet.

Molecular Order and Structure. Both gas chromatography and mass spectrometry are good methods for the detection of molecular order in the analyzed sample. In fact they complement each other in this respect for while gas chromatography can reveal intermolecular order (order in the distribution of components in a mixture or population of molecules) mass spectrometry can determine intramolecular order or structure. Moreover, by providing a complete analysis of a mixture by the combined GC–MS system more reliable information about the biological significance of the whole sample can be obtained than it is possible to secure otherwise.

Molecular Biological Indicators. Compounds like the alpha amino acids present in the proteins that are characteristic of terrestrial life may be referred to as molecular biological indicators. With the new methods available for the quantitative transformation of alpha amino acids into volatile *N*-trifluoroacetyl methyl ester derivatives [*Hagan and Black,* 1964; *Cruickshank and Sheehan,* 1964] it should be possible to analyze amino acid mixtures quantitatively by the GC–MS system. Other such molecular biological indicators which could be identified by the GC–MS technique include, for instance, hexoses, pentoses and deoxypentoses and their derivatives, steroids and related compounds, even-carbon-number fatty acids, odd-carbon-number normal hydrocarbons, hydrocarbons with periodic branching such as farnesane, pristane, phytane and squalane and cyclic hydrocarbons derived from steroids and other biological molecules [*Horning and Van den Heuvel,* 1963]. These compounds are present not only in living organisms but also in other terrestrial products such as petroleum —indeed, their presence in petroleum is considered today the best evidence for its biological origin.

Typical Degradation Patterns. Many scientists acquainted with the problems inherent in the detection and identification of organic compounds on planetary surfaces agree that one of the most feasible approaches involves the use of controlled pyrolysis of surface samples (polymeric or nonvolatile) with subsequent separation of degradation products by means of high resolution gas chromatographic columns. With the GC–MS technique a complete mass spectrum of each individual degradation product that can be separated in this manner can be made available for positive structural identification in a matter of seconds. With this information at hand it should be possible to predict with a high degree of certainty the chemical nature of the organic moities originally present in the sample.

Isotope Fractionation. A knowledge of the abundance ratios of stable isotopes of the elements carbon, nitrogen, oxygen and sulfur as determined by mass spectrometry is also of important biological significance, since it is known that low temperature chemical processes such as those catalyzed by enzymes lead to characteristic fractionation of isotopes (as a result of slightly different rates). The assumption made here is that, in the absence of life, the natural abundance ratios of isotopes are more or less uniform throughout the solar system.

Instrumental Capabilities and Limitations

1. The interpretability and specificity of data obtained with the GC–MS instrument is high compared with other current analytical techniques such as ultraviolet, visible and infrared spectroscopy.

2. Sensitivity. Nanogram to microgram amounts of individual components can give interpretable spectra. About 10^{-14} moles sec^{-1} of a sample give a good signal and in theory the sensitivity can be considerably increased. However, it is felt that a further increase in sensitivity is neither necessary, because the expected samples would be of sufficient size, nor desirable, since a point of diminishing returns is reached in instrumental techniques when sensitivity is carried beyond certain limits.

3. Mass range and resolution can be selected at any desired level. Current GC–MS instruments allow the determination of mass spectra of compounds with a molecular weight (M) of 500, M and $M + 1$ being completely separated at this mass value. Of course, a much simpler instrument, with less mass range $(M < 100)$ and resolution would be required for the determination of atmospheric gases.

4. There is no severe limit on the type of sample (gas, liquid or solid) so long as a vapor pressure of the order of 10^{-10} mm Hg can be obtained. If such a vapor pressure is not given directly by the sample it can be produced indirectly by pyrolytic procedures.

5. Miniaturization is possible and reasonably small values for weight and power consumption have been indicated by some authors.

6. Telemetering requirement would in general be high if one wishes to monitor all the ions from a given compound. However, the telemetering requirements would be greatly reduced by selecting for transmission to Earth only the parent molecular ion and the major maxima of the molecular-fragment ions. In some simple cases an adequately "informed" computer should be able to transmit to Earth the names of the compounds detected.

7. Of course a number of problems remain to be solved before such an instrument could reliably operate after a long interplanetary flight and a

rough "soft-landing" on the surface of a planet. In particular, attention should be given to the development of a trouble-free pumping system capable of operating efficiently under non-optimal conditions.

Complementary Instrumentation

The complete instrumental design of a GC–MS probe should include:

1. An automatic sensing and sampling device for all kinds of samples, solid, liquid or gas;

2. An automatic pretreatment device for preliminary testing and fractionation (if needed) of the sample. This may include differential thermal analysis, controlled pyrolysis, adsorption, solubilization, reaction, etc., depending on the nature of the sample;

3. A computer for overall operational control of the instrument and for the reduction [*Lederberg, 1964*] and storage of data to be fed to the telemetering system.

REFERENCES

Becker, E. W. (1961), *Separation of Isotopes,* p. 360, George Newnes Ltd., London.

Beynon, J. H. (1960), *Mass Spectrometry and Its Applications to Organic Chemistry,* Elsevier, Amsterdam.

Biemann, K. (1962), *Mass Spectrometry,* McGraw-Hill, New York.

Budzikiewicz, H., Djerassi, C. and Williams, D. H. (1964a), *Interpretations of Mass Spectra of Organic Compounds,* Holden-Day, Inc., San Francisco.

Budzikiewicz, H., Djerassi, C., and Williams, D. H. (1964b), *Structure Elucidation of Natural Products by Mass Spectrometry, I: Alkaloids,* Holden-Day, Inc., San Francisco.

Cruickshank, P. A., and Sheehan, J. A. (1964), *Anal. Chem. 36,* 1191.

Elliott, R. M. (ed.) (1963), *Advances in Mass Spectrometry,* Pergamon, London.

Hagen, P., and Black, W. (1964), *Federation Proc. 23,* 371.

Horning, E. C., and Van den Heuvel, W. J. A. (1963), *Ann. Rev. Biochem. 32,* 709.

Lederberg, J. (1964), *The Computation of Molecular Formulas for Mass Spectrometry,* Holden-Day, Inc., San Francisco.

McDowell, C. A. (ed.) (1963), *Mass Spectrometry,* McGraw-Hill, New York.

McLafferty, F. W. (1963a), *Mass Spectral Correlations,* American Chemical Society, Washington, D. C.

McLafferty, F. W. (ed.) (1963b), *Mass Spectrometry of Organic Ions,* Academic Press, New York.

Reed, R. I. (1962), *Ion Production by Electron Impact,* Academic Press, London.

Reese, R. M., and Harllee, F. N. (1964), *Anal. Chem. 36,* 278R.

Ryhage, R. M. (1963), *Arkiv Kemi 20*, 185.
Ryhage, R. M. (1964, *Anal. Chem. 36*, 759.
Ryhage, R. M., Wilkstrom, S. and Waller; G. R. (1965), To be published (See also references to other GC–MS combination systems listed therein).
Watson, J. T., and Biemann, K. (1964), *Anal. Chem. 36*, 1135.

10. INFRARED SPECTROSCOPY

Information Provided by Infrared Spectroscopy

If we restrict ourselves at first to the mid-infrared wavelength range (2.5–50 microns), this information consists mainly of the vibrational frequencies of atoms within molecules. Since these frequencies are determined by the masses of the atoms and by short-range interatomic forces, they are characteristic of small groups of atoms. They are less sensitive to forces extending over distances greater than, say, five times a typical interatomic distance. Thus the mid infrared spectrum of a substance is quite sensitive to, and provides information about, the kind and arrangement of atoms in small groups. It enables one to make specific identification of small molecules (containing, say, no more than 100 atoms) and of groups of atoms within large molecules (the organic chemist's "functional groups"). Not being sensitive to molecular weight, it can rarely be used to measure this quantity.

In addition to such qualitative identification, quantitative determination of volume concentration of molecules and functional groups is possible. The information needed consists of a quantitative measurement of the infrared absorption of the unknown sample at appropriate wavelengths, a knowledge of the quantitative infrared absorption spectrum of each constituent of the sample under conditions comparable to those under which the sample was measured, and a value for the optical path length of the infrared radiation within the sample. To the extent that this information is inaccurate or incomplete, the quantitative precision of the measurement will deteriorate.

In both qualitative and quantitative applications, absorption coefficients in the mid infrared are such that workable absorbances ($\log_{10} I_0/I$) are obtained when the thickness of a solid or liquid sample lies in the range 0.01–1 mm. If the sample area is 0.1–1.0 cm^2, this thickness range corresponds roughly to a sample weight range of 100 micrograms to several hundred milligrams. The latter figure is almost always more than is necessary, while the lower limit set by the former may be further reduced under favorable circumstances. For gaseous samples the product of pressure times path length for an appropriate absorbance corresponds to values estimated from the above figures with the help of the perfect gas equation, the molecular weight and the absolute temperature. Typically for a 10-cm vapor path, the required pressure ranges from 0.01 to 1.0 atmosphere at 300°K.

Gaseous samples require no special preparation for measurement other than introduction into an absorption cell of appropriate size and optical characteristics. Liquid samples, whether pure or mixtures, also offer no difficulty if they can be introduced into thin cells ($\sim$ 0.1 mm thick) and do not attack the windows chemically. Transparency and homogeneity to visible radiation are unimportant. Solid samples offer more difficulty. If the material is a fine powder, it can be suspended in a viscous oil chosen for its infrared transparency, such as mineral oil or hexachlorobutadiene. If the solid can be made into a thin self-supporting film or slab, such a form is suitable for spectroscopic study.

The foregoing statements imply that infrared absorption is the quantity to be measured. If necessary, reflection or emission of infrared radiation may be employed, though these properties are usually less specific than absorption. A further characteristic of infrared spectra in the gas phase of possible utility is the rotational structure accompanying the vibrational absorption. This structure, especially if it is widely spaced enough to be resolved, can be used to determine the dimensions of the molecule and the temperature of the gas.

Finally the other two infrared regions, the near (0.8–2.5 microns) and the far (50–1000 microns), may be mentioned. The near infrared is sometimes called the overtone region because the overtones and combination tones of vibrations involving the stretching and bending of CH, NH, and OH bonds occur in the near infrared, whereas the fundamental vibrations of all molecules (except H_2) correspond to wavelengths above 2.5 microns. Certain low-lying electronic levels in molecules also give rise to absorption in the near infrared. One advantage of the region is that extremely thin sample paths are not required because the absorption coefficients for the overtones are 10–100 times less than those of fundamentals. Conversely, larger amounts of sample material are needed.

The far infrared region contains only those molecular bands that correspond to very low vibrational frequencies and to the rotational frequencies of small molecules in the gas phase.

At the present stage of discussion it would appear that neither the near infrared nor the far infrared offers significant added utility over the mid infrared region and the discussion below will deal with the latter only.

Possible Uses of Infrared Spectroscopy in Detecting Signs of Life on Mars

From the preceding section it can be inferred that infrared methods alone are not able to discriminate between living and non-living matter. It appears that the role infrared spectroscopy might play is that of helping to establish the nature of the chemical environment on and above the surface of Mars.

It is therefore suggested that consideration be given to the following in deciding whether infrared equipment would pay its way on a mission and if so what the design of the equipment should be:

Infrared analysis of the Martian atmosphere at various altitudes. It appears feasible to sample the atmosphere at intervals during a descent to a soft landing and to perform a gas analysis of the samples. Monatomic and symmetrical diatomic molecules such as A, N_2 and O_2 do not absorb infrared radiation significantly but all other molecules do. Identification and semiquantitative measurement of CO_2, H_2O, N_2O, NO_2, HCN, NH_3, CH_2O and C_2N_2, for example, would show the extent to which such basic small molecules are available for the synthesis of more complex molecules. In addition, the concentration of these gases in the atmosphere would indicate something about their quantitative availability on the surface.

Infrared analysis of solid samples acquired at the surface. By various means, solid samples from the terrain near a landing might be acquired for spectroscopic study. If the inorganic materials in these samples do not obliterate extensive areas of the spectrum, it would be possible to identify, in addition to small molecules like those mentioned above, more complex compounds of low molecular weight and perhaps even simple carbohydrates, amino acids and pyrroles, for example.

However if the organic matter is a minor component of a mixture such as a random sample of soil there is serious doubt as to the degree of certainty with which an identification could be made or that it could be made at all. This is especially true of carbohydrates for which some of the major absorption bands fall in the same range as those of silicate minerals (direct). Furthermore the organic matter might contain other types of compounds as a result of degradation and decay (humus?).

However "soil" is likely to be the most readily accessible kind of sample unless some means of selection can be developed. Therefore it seems probable that it will be necessary to prepare from it an organic concentrate, relatively free of inorganic material, which can be presented to the spectrometer with the hope of obtaining a meaningful spectrum. The final sample might be deposited on a suitable plate for either transmission or reflection measurement or perhaps collected on a plastic filter (millipore, polyethylene).

As an alternative to examining the organic matter in its native form various chemical or other treatments might be considered. Some possibilities are those which yield gas samples as products, e.g., CO_2 from combustion, NH_3 from Kjeldahl, or some other procedure.

Attenuated total reflectance (ATR) may be useful for certain types of samples. Although it is more complicated optically, it obviates the necessity for controlling sample thickness within rather narrow limits. This could conceivably simplify sample preparation.

A possibility that bears investigation is the coupling of a microscope with a spectrometer to obtain spectra of small, single particles, a technique that has been extensively used in fiber and biochemical studies. In general the microscope is placed in the dispersed radiation coming from the exit slit in order to minimize heating of the sample that would occur if it were exposed to the undispersed incident beam. On Mars similar procedures would be used since it is organic samples that are of the greatest interest, and these could be altered drastically by excessive heating. In application one might use the technique to select particles of particular interest, the system being told to retain only those particles possessing particular spectral features. These particles could then be examined by the various techniques available without the inclusion of the possibly more numerous particles of little or no interest. This selectivity would be invaluable in taking full advantage of the limited data transmission rate available.

Instrumental Considerations

It is apparent that considerable thought will have to be devoted to the design of light-weight, reliable spectroscopic and sampling equipment that will function adequately under the expected extremes of acceleration, temperature and ultraviolet irradiation. It does not seem impossible to cope with these complications, however, and the present remarks will be limited to generalities about what the block diagram of the system might be. (The notes below refer to the numbered stages in the diagram.)

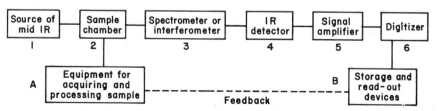

1. Since it is unlikely that infrared emission of the samples to be studied would be useful, and that the solar infrared could be employed without serious complications, a source of mid infrared would be needed. This would increase the power and load requirements but would provide a controllable amount of continuous mid-infrared radiation.

2. The radiation from the source is usually passed through the sample prior to its dispersion by the spectrometer. This order can be interchanged if there are compelling reasons for doing so. The sample chamber can be designed to accommodate different kinds of sample cells for gases and solids, with liquid samples also, if this is necessary. The sample chamber would be supplied by devices indicated by block A. These devices would be of critical importance, since the quality of the spectra obtained would depend on their effectiveness. For the intake of gas samples, they could be relatively simple, but for solid samples they would necessarily be more complex. Apparatus for acquisition of solid materials from the terrain and for their preparation for spectroscopic study by grinding, pressing, milling and similar treatment would have to be developed.

3. The spectroscopic device would be either a grating spectrometer or some sort of interferometer. The latter makes better use of limited radiation but cannot produce spectrophotometric information so easily or reliably. In any case the state of the art here is advanced and no design difficulties would be expected. It would be relatively easy to provide spectral resolution of 1–5 cm^{-1} and photometric accuracy of 0.1 absorbance unit in the usual working range of about 0–2 units.

4. The state of the art in thermal detectors is also good. Probably a thermistor bolometer would be the most reliable kind of detecting element for present purposes.

5, 6. The signal would be amplified and digitized by standard electronic methods, and fed to storage and read-out devices B. These latter would be determined by the nature of the communications system between the probe and terrestrial receivers. However, it might well be possible, and would certainly be desirable, to have feedback from the system B receiving and storing the spectral data to the system A for acquisition of samples. The purpose would be to monitor the spectra and to instruct system A to repeat the sample acquisition procedures if the digitized spectral data were devoid of information.

BIBLIOGRAPHY

1. "Spectroscopie dans l'infrarouge", J. Lecomte, *In: Handbook der Physik 36,* Springer-Verlag, Berlin, Göttingen, Heidelberg, 1958. This article of seven

hundred pages and 555 illustrations is the most recent truly comprehensive survey of the subject. It is especially complete for its reference to the literature up to the date of publication.

2. *Detection and Measurement of Infrared Radiation,* R. A. Smith, F. E. Jones and R. P. Chasmar, Oxford Press, 1957. A thorough discussion of the instrumental aspects of infrared measurements.

3. *Infrared Spectra of Complex Molecules,* L. J. Bellamy, John Wiley and Sons, Inc., New York, 2nd Edition, 1958. The standard work on characteristic infrared frequencies of organic functional groups.

4. *Infrared Spectroscopy of High Polymers,* R. Zbinden, Academic Press, Inc., New York, 1964. An authoritative recent treatment.

5. "Symposium on Biological Applications of Infrared Spectroscopy", *Ann. N. Y. Acad. Sci. 69,* 1957.

6. *Molecular Spectra and Molecular Structure: 1. Spectra of Diatomic Molecules,* G. Herzberg, D. Van Nostrand Company, Inc., New York, 2nd Edition, 1950; *2. Infrared and Raman Spectra, ibid.,* 1945. These two volumes are the standard monographs on the theory of infrared spectra of molecules.

7. *Chemical Infrared Spectroscopy, 1. Techniques,* W. J. Potts, Jr., John Wiley and Sons, Inc., New York, 1963. An elementary discussion.

8. "Molecular Spectroscopy of Planetary Atmospheres", D. G. Rea, *Space Science Reviews 1,* 159-196, 1962. Contains a considerable bibliography.

11. ULTRAVIOLET AND VISIBLE SPECTROSCOPY

Absorption Spectrophotometry

The technique of ultraviolet and visible absorption spectrophotometry offers a sensitive method for the proof of the existence of large molecules and the partial identification of their functional groups. One of the salient features of large organic molecules, whether based on carbon chemistry, nitrogen chemistry, or indeed phosphorous chemistry, is that the electronic transitions occur in the lower energy range of the spectrum and therefore become detectable in the visible or near ultraviolet with the aid of standard photomultiplier tubes. Carbonyl, carboxyl, and aldehyde groups, for example, have bands between 2000–4000 Å [*Kasha,* 1960]. Aromatic rings have prominent UV bands which have been extensively studied. Benzene, toluene, and pyridine all show the typical "benzene 2650 Å transition" modified slightly depending upon the heteroatom or the presence of side chains. This transition is accompanied by a second one near 2000 Å. Though less specific, it is indicative of π-conjugated systems [*Jaffe and Orchin,* 1962]. Visible and near infrared bands are shown by molecules that are sufficiently complex to have extended conjugated systems. Examples are chlorophylls a and b with prominent bands at $\sim$6600 Å (molar extinction coefficient $\sim$93,000) and at $\sim$6400 Å (molar extinction coefficient $\sim$53,000) respectively [*Kamen*, 1963, p. 95]. In the near infrared, absorption bands are displayed, for example, by bacteriochlorophyll ($\sim$8000 Å) and bacteriopheophytin ($\sim$7500 Å) [*Kamen*, 1963, p. 103].

Presupposing that the Martian environment has led to the development of some plant life with a respectable degree of organization and consequent molecular complexity, one could imagine a series of experiments involving spectrophotometry as the primary technique, preceded by proper chemical preparation of samples, which could give results having important bearing on the degree of complexity of the molecules on the planet. After suitable sampling procedures have been carried out and a portion of the Martian soil has been brought into a module, several important kinds of investigations could be made such as listed below:

Presence of Organic Degradative Products in Martian Soil. A core of the Martian soil could be extracted with small amounts of solvents in a prescribed order to maximize the possibility of sequentially extracting molecules of various organic types. The resulting series of extracts could then be fed into a spectrophotometer and scanned in the ultraviolet and near UV for characteristic absorptions due to functional groups. Beginning with water and working down through solvents which have affinities for different kinds of molecules, it is not inconceivable that the Martian humus would yield many types of organic compounds whose electronic absorption spectra would be sufficiently rich to give important information about constituent groups. A selected group of solvents would probably pull out one or two major components each time and therefore a certain amount of simplicity would arise from the possibility of obtaining absorption spectra as a function of the solvent. (Cf., *Bear* [1964], Chap. 5 for extraction methods and results for terrestrial soils.)

Except for linear and branched saturated molecules and simple alcohols, most organics have UV or near UV spectra; some, even visible absorption spectra with high molar extinction coefficients ($\epsilon_{max}\sim$10,000). The rich spectra, however, only come forth in molecules with some types of extended conjugated systems, such as those containing metal atoms like iron, manganese, calcium, etc.

The size of the sample required to detect an electronic band depends upon the molar extinction coefficient. For electronic transitions in the near ultraviolet–visible region one can assume $\epsilon\sim$10,000. This would require 10^{-4} molar solutions of material in a 1 cm path length. For a unit absorbance (a prominent absorption band) one could therefore obtain a very strong signal using only 1/10 of a micromole of material. (Cf., *Kasha* [1960]; *Jaffe and Orchin* [1962]; *Kamen* [1963]; *Hershenson* [1955-59]; *Lang* [1961] for tabulation and interpretation of UV and visible spectra.) Automatic techniques based on feed-back mechanisms could be used to monitor the spectra until the maximum amount of information was obtained before proceeding to the next extraction phase.

Presence of Large Molecules By Detection of Pyrolysis Products. A sample of Martian soil, if subjected to rapid heating in the absence of any kind of solvent, would probably yield a variety of degradative pyrolysis products, if the sample contained organic molecules built on carbon chemistry, or even on other chemistry, so long as the complexity was reasonably great. One would expect bond rupture and the rapid vaporization of molecular fragments of sufficient size to give rich electronic spectra. The spectral analysis, although not definitive, would indicate the degree of complexity. It is even conceivable that the Martian environment could have highly colored molecules that would absorb in the green, red, or near infrared portions of the spectrum (compare chlorophyll a and b, bacteriochlorophyll, and bacteriopheophytin above). It is also possible that these molecules would be easily vaporized at a moderate temperature above say, 200 or 300° C. One might even obtain condensates with the molecules intact. The scanning region of the spectrophotometer, in this instance, should at best be chosen to cover the near infrared as well as the UV and visible. The performance of commercial photomultipliers is good at wavelengths extending to 9000 Å.

Complex Formation as a Means of Detecting Soil Constituents. Another interesting analytical method for obtaining information on the composition of the Martian soil and its capacity for supporting life involves the use of organic precipitants as color developing reagents. These could be used to detect extremely small amounts of trace metals. Highly selective reagents are available for complexing metallic ions into compounds which are very highly colored and which have easily identifiable spectra. Molybdenum, for example, can be detected in quantities ranging from .05 to 1 ppm using 4-methyl-1,2-dimercaptobenzene. Of course, common elements such as aluminum and iron can be measured also. Iron can be detected, for instance, with 1,10-phenanthroline in water after a one-step reduction in amounts of 0.5 to 5 ppm [*Boltz and Schenk,* 1963]. (See below for detection by fluorescence.)

A second method of complex formation which could yield interesting information, if the Martian plant life is quite well developed, would be first to extract the samples with selected reagents and then to inject agents into the solutions to complex the extracted substances. By monitoring specific wavelengths fixed primarily by the agents, which show strong absorptions in the UV and visible when complexed by various organic materials, certain organic moieties such as amines and amino acids could show up. Primary amines, for example, can be detected in quantities of 10–40 ppm using copper salicylaldehyde [*Boltz and Schenk*, 1963]. The special appeal of this method is the possibility of monitoring only a few wavelengths. Since the frequencies of the characteristic absorptions for the agents complexed with various organic groups are known, the spectrometer output could be monitored at certain selected wavelengths and a maximum amount of information thus be obtained with a minimum of telemetry. (See below for fluorescence methods.)

Chemical Treatment of Soil Samples Followed by Selective Reagents and Spectrophotometry. Rather than limiting oneself to the extraction by solvents or to pyrolysis, techniques amenable to the detection of well-developed plant life, one could focus attention on chemical treatment of the soil with subsequent treatment by selective reagents in order to bring out the existence of certain constituents in the soil which are necessary for terrestrial plant life. Treatment of soil samples before extraction by harsh chemical methods, such as acid digestion or fusion, could lead to the formation within the soil of soluble fractions which could be developed with selective reagents and monitored by the methods of spectrophotometry [*Bear*, 1964, Chapter 12]. This technique could lead to sound information on the types of minerals contained on the planet and whether it would show promise of supporting life transferred from Earth. The sample size would vary, depending upon the number of tests made, but the sensitivity to visible and UV light of most complexes is unusually high and milligram quantities of original material could suffice for some procedures.

Presence of Cellular Material. If one supposes that the life cycle on Mars is well developed and that it is quite similar in nature to that on Earth, then an important method of looking at such a material would be to sample and monitor a water extract for the nucleic acid band occurring at 260 mμ for most materials. The purine and pyrimidine components of the nucleic acids strongly absorb ultraviolet radiation, with a maximum absorption at about 2600 Å. "For this reason the nucleic acids also absorb radiation with a maximum at this wavelength and indeed the intensity of this absorption may be used as a quantitative measurement of the amount of these substances in nucleoproteins *in vitro* or in the cell" [*Greenstein*, 1944]. (The ultraviolet absorption curve of sodium thymus nucleate is reproduced in *Greenstein* [1944].) Proteins have a maximum which lies at approximately 2700–2900 Å which is largely due to the content of tyrosine, phenylalanine, and tryptophan. The presence of a band in these regions would be strong indication that some plant molecules similar to the ones that we have here are already developed on the planet.

Emission Spectroscopy

The use of molecular emission spectroscopy as an analytical tool is rapidly developing and offers an interesting and extremely sensitive method for obtaining information on large molecular species on extraterrestrial bodies. The possible presence of a substantial ultraviolet component in the light falling directly on the Martian surface leads to the conjecture that, if life is present on the surface, there may be some sophisticated mechanism for losing the energy, after the absorption of UV light, fast enough such that the molecules are not photochemically degraded. If the previous climatic conditions are not too much different than the present ones, then we must conclude that the molecules have developed a mechanism for getting rid of the high energy from UV photons. A common method for molecules to do this is to convert the radiation into heat or secondly, a more esoteric mechanism is to re-emit the radiation as fluorescence, thereby degrading the excitation energy harmlessly.

It is well known that many organic molecules fluoresce at room temperature. When they are subjected to low temperatures the efficiency increases; in near rigid solutions the efficiency maximizes. A fluorescence capability is possessed by *most* molecules with any degree of complexity. The possibility presents itself of taking extracts from the Martian environment and irradiating them with UV light at some cycle of the operations described above. If large molecules of an organic nature do exist, it is highly probable that some of them would absorb the energy and re-emit it as fluorescent radiation at a much longer wavelength than the absorption. This would give one an extremely sensitive technique which could be applied on very small samples for detecting the presence of complex molecules and for yielding information on their structures. Another intriguing variation stems from the fact that the natural ultraviolet flux on the planet may be high enough that one could conceivably use solar radiation as a source and the ultraviolet spectrophotometer setup as a detector for a fluorescence assembly. The same electronic components could be used for fluorescence as would be used for spectrophotometry. The complications which would arise from the fluorescence of inorganic materials would be virtually nonexistent and, especially if organic extractors were used, any fluorescence seen in the region between 4000 and 7000 Å would be most indicative of large organic molecules having extended and sophisticated electronic structures. For example, chlorophyll a, when pumped with UV light, emits at

6800 Å and can be detected in microgram quantities [cf., *Becker and Kasha*, 1955]. When excited at 3650 Å flavinoids from pollen emit fluorescent light (wavelength varies) and can be detected in 0.1 microgram quantities [*Weissler and White*, 1963].

Common elements, and trace elements too, can be identified by fluorimetry. Instead of relying only upon absorption spectroscopy, complexing agents could be selected for detecting materials by fluorescence methods. Magnesium, using *bis* salicylidene-ethylenediamine, can be detected in amounts as low as 2×10^4 microgram per milliliter. Using leucofluorescene, free oxygen gas shows up in approximately 0.1 microgram quantities [*Weissler and White*, 1963].

REFERENCES

Bear, F. E. (1964), *Chemistry of the Soil*, Reinhold Pub. Corp., New York.

Becker, R. S., and M. Kasha (1955), Luminescence Spectroscopy of Molecules and the Photosynthetic System. *The Luminescence of Biological Systems* (F. H. Johnson, Ed.), Am. Assoc. Adv. Sci., Washington, D. C.

Boltz, D. F., and G. H. Schenk (1963), Visible and Ultraviolet Spectrophotometry. *Handbook of Analytical Chemistry* (L. Meites, Ed.), McGraw-Hill, New York.

Greenstein, J. P. (1944), Nucleoproteins. *Advances in Protein Chemistry, 1,* Academic Press, New York, p. 223.

Hershenson, H. M. (1955-59), *Ultraviolet and Visible Absorption Spectra, Index for 1930-54,* Academic Press, New York.

Jaffe, H. H., and Milton Orchin (1962), *Theory and Applications of Ultraviolet Spectroscopy,* John Wiley and Sons, New York.

Kamen, M. D. (1963), *Primary Processes in Photosynthesis,* Academic Press, New York.

Kasha, M. (1960), Paths of Molecular Excitation. *Radiation Research,* Supp. 2, 243.

Lang, L., Ed. (1961), *Absorption Spectra in the Ultraviolet and Visible Regions,* Academic Press, New York.

Weissler, A., and C. E. White (1963), Fluorescence Analysis. *Handbook of Analytical Chemistry* (L. Meites, Ed.), McGraw-Hill, New York.

12. FLUORIMETRY

Fluorimetry is a highly versatile and sensitive instrumental technique [*Förster*, 1951; *Udenfriend*, 1962; *Pringsheim*, 1949] which could be employed in a variety of ways in exobiological studies: (1) to detect molecules containing a fluorescent label; (2) to identify molecules; (3) to investigate macromolecular structure and interactions. Fluorescence spectroscopy enjoys a broader scope than absorption spectroscopy because it involves relaxation processes as well as the initial absorption event. The manner in which the excited molecule returns to the ground state provides a wealth of information concerning the structure of the fluorescent molecule and the nature of its environment.

There are five basic fluorescence parameters:

(1) the excitation spectrum [*Weber and Teale*, 1958]: the relative intensity of emission as a function of the wavelength of exciting light, for equal numbers of incident photons;

(2) the emission spectrum [*Parker and Rees*, 1962]: the relative number of photons emitted as a function of the wavelength of emission;

(3) the polarization spectrum [*Feofilov*, 1961]: the ratio of the intensities of the x- and y-polarized components of the emission as a function of the wavelength of the exciting light which is x-polarized;

(4) the absolute quantum yield [*Weber*, 1957]: the fractional number of photons emitted per photon absorbed;

(5) the excited state lifetime [*Steingraber and Berlman*, 1963]: the time interval in which the intensity of emission falls to $1/e$ of its initial value.

Detection of a Label

The high sensitivity of fluorimetry makes it a suitable method for the detection of molecules containing fluorescent moieties. If the fluorescent portion has an appreciable quantum yield, say, greater than 0.1%, then fluorescence spectroscopy is a far more sensitive analytical method than absorption spectroscopy for a number of reasons. In absorption, the ratio of the light intensities through a blank and through a weakly absorbing sample is nearly 1, while in fluorimetry, the ratio is typically high, of the order of a thousand or more. It is the markedly reduced photon flux from the blank that gives rise to this favorable ratio. By observing at right angles to the incident light, the blank reading is due only to the scattered light from the sample cell walls and to the Raman and Rayleigh scattering of the solution. A second advantage is afforded by the choice of wavelengths at which the emission is observed. The fluorescence peak is always shifted to longer wavelengths with respect to the excitation peak, but the interval between the two depends upon the particular fluorescent species and its environment. By appropriate choice of the emission filter, it is possible to reduce the blank reading by eliminating most of the Tyndall, Rayleigh and

Raman scattering. Furthermore, if there are several fluorescent species in the material, it will usually be feasible to optimize the assay for the particular one of interest by choosing both an appropriate excitation and emission wavelength.

Some molecules of biological interest, such as chlorophyll, are sufficiently fluorescent in themselves to be "self-labelled." Most need to be labelled by an exogeneous fluorescent tag. Perhaps the best example of the use of a fluorescent tag is the fluorescent antibody technique developed by Coons [1960]. The localization of the green-emitting fluorescein-labelled antibody is readily followed by fluorescence microscopy. The liberation of low-molecular-weight peptides containing a fluorescent tag has been used to follow the action of fibrinolytic enzymes on rhodamine-labelled fibrin [Lüscher and Käser-Glanzmann, 1961]. The recent work of Hartley and Gray [1964] on the use of dimethylaminonaphthalene sulfonyl chloride to label the terminal α-amino group of proteins is an excellent demonstration of the very high sensitivity of fluorescent methods. The resulting naphthalene sulfonamide derivative is stable to acid hydrolysis and can be readily detected at levels of 10^{-9} moles by fluorimetry. In contrast, the dinitrophenyl derivatives produced with Sanger's reagent are nonfluorescent, and at least 10^{-6} moles are required for detection by absorption spectroscopy. This 1000-fold difference in sensitivity is a conservative estimate, and may be regarded as typical of the gain to be anticipated in shifting from absorption to emission detection.

In these examples, the fluorescent tag could well have been replaced by a radioactive label, with perhaps some loss of convenience or sensitivity, but in principle they both serve much the same role. There is a second category in which the fluorescent label is not interchangeable with a radioactive one. An example is given by the biochemically important molecule diphosphopyridine nucleotide which is fluorescent in the reduced state (DPNH) but non-fluorescent when oxidized (DPN+). Thus this molecule is self-labelled in only one of its oxidation states, and it is this feature which makes it possible to use fluorescence to follow the numerous enzymatic reactions that involve DPNH. The change can also be detected by absorption spectroscopy since DPNH absorbs strongly at 340 mμ, where DPN+ does not absorb, but again, the sensitivity is a thousand-fold lower [Ehrenberg and Theorell, 1962].

This "on-off" type of fluorescence has been used to advantage in a number of synthetic substrates which incorporate a fluorescent label. α-Naphthol emits in the blue, while the phosphate ester of α-naphthol is virtually non-fluorescent at those wavelengths. The action of phosphatases on these phosphate esters can be readily followed by monitoring the emission at 450 mμ [Moss, 1960]. Similarly, 7-hydroxycoumarin is highly fluorescent, while its glucoronide is non-fluorescent, permitting ready assay of the enzyme β-glucoronidase [*Mead et al.,* 1955]. Rotman has shown that the use of fluorogenic substrates is sufficiently sensitive to detect single enzyme molecules such as β-D-galactosidase [*Rotman,* 1961]. The galactose and phosphate esters of fluorescein are non-fluorescent, while the hydrolysis product fluorescein is of course highly fluorescent.

These fluorogenic substrates require a bond cleavage adjacent to the fluorescent moiety which alters its capacity to ionize. It would be desirable to have available a second type of fluorogenic substrate in which the bond break occurs at a distance from the fluorescent moiety [*Stryer*]. A substrate of this type would have the structure F-b_1-b_2-b_n-Q, where F is the fluorescent tag, which has been rendered non-fluorescent due to the proximity of a quencher Q located within some 20 Å. The mechanism of this quenching would be a dipole-dipole one [*Förster,* 1951]. If any of the susceptible bonds b_1, b_2 .... b_n are broken, F and Q are released, and in solutions of less than 10^{-4} M, they will be sufficiently far apart to preclude quenching by dipole-dipole transfer. The synthesis of a large number of fluorogenic substrates employing this principle should be feasible. The converse, the quenching of fluorescence upon chemical combination, has been demonstrated in the studies of Weber and Teale on fluorescent naphthalene derivatives of apomyoglobin. When the heme group recombines with the apomyoglobin, the emission of its attached naphthalene derivatives is virtually completely quenched.

Identification of Molecules

Suppose that a preliminary chemical investigation of a molecular species on Mars suggests that it might in fact be identical to one with which we are familiar. Under these circumstances, fluorimetry is well suited to determining whether they are in fact identical. If the molecule under scrutiny is not sufficiently fluorescent, then it will usually be feasible to convert it to a derivative possessing greater fluorescence.

The first parameters to compare are the excitation and emission spectra. The excitation spectrum, under appropriate conditions, is equivalent to the absorption spectrum in most pure organic compounds. If these spectra are identical for the compounds under scrutiny, then additional fluorescence parameters should be examined. The polarization spectrum is particularly sensitive to any alterations in structure, especially for excitation at wavelengths corresponding to the weaker electronic transitions. Finally the absolute quantum yield and the excited state lifetime of the emitting species should be determined. It should be noted that the latter three fluorescence parameters are hardly ever utilized in the characterization of fluorescent compounds, primarily because they have been experimentally less accessible. The parameters should be studied in a number of solvents at several temperatures. Then, the equivalence of these five parameters for a pair of compounds would constitute strong evidence for the identity of the fluorescing chromophores. However, this would not preclude the possibility that the pair might differ in a region of the structure somewhat removed from the chromophore, as in a long saturated alkyl side-chain attached to an aromatic nucleus.

Fluorimetry would be far less useful in elucidating the structure of a new molecule encountered in extraterrestrial studies. A determination of the basic fluorescence parameters would not ordinarily point to a particular family of organic compounds. Of course, if the emission had its maximum in the red, it would suggest a rather highly conjugated molecule, more akin to a porphyrin than to a benzene derivative. If the emission were centered in the blue, however, it would bring to mind too many possibilities to be of any real help. However, there is one fluorescence parameter, the polarization spectrum, that is of general utility since it reveals something about the symmetry of the molecule [*Feofilov, 1961*]. In particular, it distinguishes between the following types of molecules [*Gouterman and Stryer, 1962*]: (a) isotropic, $x = y = z$ (no examples in organic chemistry); (b) "circular," $x = y \neq z$ (e.g., benzene); (c) x and y are distinct, and are symmetry axes (e.g., phenol); (d) there are no symmetry axes in the plane of the chromophores (e.g., o–cresol). The interpretation requires no assumptions concerning the molecular structure. Again, the inferences hold strictly only for the chromophoric portion of the molecule.

A Probe of Macromolecular Structure and Interactions

Fluorescent molecules can be used as probes of molecular structure. The fluorescence polarization, for example, provides an estimate of the rotational relaxation time of the portion of the macromolecule to which the fluorescent group is attached, as was first shown by *Weber* [1952]. If the fluorescent label is firmly attached to a rigid molecule whose molecular weight is known, then it is possible to infer something about the shape of the particle, primarily its axial ratio or departure from spherical symmetry. These estimates require a knowledge of the lifetime of the fluorescent species, which is now directly obtainable by nanosecond flash techniques. The degree of fluorescence polarization can be used to follow structural transitions in proteins, such as those that accompany changes in pH or temperature, for example, *Steiner and Edelhoch* [1962].

The polarity of the dye binding region of serum albumin has been investigated by the use of an anilinonaphthaline sulfonate [*Weber and Young*, 1964], which has a very low quantum yield of fluorescence in water (.004) but which increases in nonpolar solvents [*Bowen and Seaman*, 1962]. Furthermore, its emission maximum shifts from the green to the blue as the hydrogen-bonding capacity of its environment decreases. When the dye is bound to serum albumin, its quantum yield is 0.75, while its emission maximum is at 465 mμ, indicating that the binding site is highly non-polar.

The binding of a number of small molecules to proteins has been studied by fluorescence methods. Velick investigated the interactions of diphospho-pyridine nucleotide with a number of dehydrogenase enzymes [*Velick*, 1961]. The increased polarization of the DPNH emission is one index of binding. A second measure is the increase of DPNH emission upon excitation at 280 mμ, which is mainly absorbed by the protein, due to energy transfer from the protein to the DPNH. A concomitant change upon binding is the decrease in the tryptophan emission from the dehydrogenase. *Teale* [1959] studied the kinetics of heme-protein combination in apomyoglobin and in apohemoglobin containing a fluorescent label. Binding of the heme led to quenching of the emission of the label through dipole-dipole transfer. A similar use of fluorescence quenching was made in studies of hapten-antibody combination, in which the hapten acted as the quencher. Both the equilibria [*Velick et al.*, 1960] and kinetics [*Day et al.*, 1963] of combination were investigated in this way.

Other Aspects of Emission Spectroscopy

In this discussion, fluorescence has been emphasized to the exclusion of phosphorescence only because its potential has been more fully realized. There is need for a good deal more exploratory work on phosphorescence in biologically important systems. One promising area is the nucleic acids, which are virtually non-fluorescent but do display considerable phosphorescence [*Longworth*, 1962]. Furthermore, certain dye complexes of nucleic acids show particularly interesting delay-emission characteristics [*Isenberg et al.*, 1964].

Emission arising through chemical reactions rather than initial light excitation is well worth looking for in an exobiological survey. The luminescence we observe in fireflies and various marine organisms and bacteria is probably a characteristic that originated early in the evolution of life on Earth [*McElroy and Seliger*, 1962]. It has been postulated that the early stage of life on Earth was primarily anaerobic, and in fact, that oxygen was toxic. Under these conditions, oxygenases were probably prevalent, and it is thought that the emission of visible light was an incidental by-product of the reduction of oxygen. Since the environment of Mars is anaerobic, a search for such oxygenases and in particular, for bioluminescence, would therefore seem worthwhile.

REFERENCES

Bowen, E. J. and Seaman, D. (1962), The Efficiency of Solution Fluorescence. In: *Luminescence of Organic and Inorganic Materials,* Kallman and Spruch, eds., Wiley, New York, pp. 151-160.

Coons, A. H. (1960), Immunofluorescence. *Public Health Reports, U. S. 75,* 937.

Day, L. A., Sturtevant, J. M. and Singer, S. J. (1963), The Kinetics of the Reactions Between Antibodies to the 2, 4 Dinitrophenyl Group and Specific Haptens. *Ann. N. Y. Acad. Sci. 103,* 611.

Ehrenberg, A. and Theorell, H. (1962), Fluorescence. In: *Comprehensive Biochemistry, 3,* Florkin and Stotz, eds., Elsevier, New York, pp. 169-188.

Feofilov, P. P. (1961), *The Physical Basis of Polarized Emission,* English translation, Consultants Bureau, New York.

Förster, T. (1951), *Fluoreszenz Organischer Verbindungen,* Vandenhoeck & Ruprecht, Göttingen.

Gouterman, M. and Stryer, L. (1962), Fluorescence Polarization of Some Porphyrins. *J. Chem. Phys. 37,* 2260.

Gray, W. R. and Hartley, B. S. (1964), A Fluorescent End-Group Reagent for Proteins and Peptides. *Biochem. J. 89,* 59.

Isenberg, I., Leslie, R. B., Baird, S. L., Jr., Rosenbluth, R. and Bersohn, R. (1964), Delayed Fluorescence in DNA-Acridine Dye Complexes. *Proc. Natl. Acad. Sci. U. S. 52,* 379.

Longworth, J. W. (1962), Luminescence of Purines and Pyrimidines. *Biochem. J. 84,* 104.

Lüscher, E. F. and Käser-Glanzmann, R. (1961), Determination of Fibrinolytic Activities Band on the Use of Fluorescent Fibrin as a Substrate. *Vox Sang 6,* 116.

McElroy, W. D. and Seliger, H. H. (1962), Origin and Evolution of Bioluminescence. In: *Horizons in Biochemistry,* Kasha and Pullman, eds., Academic Press, New York, pp. 91-102.

Mead, J. A. R., Smith, J. N. and Williams, R. T. (1955), The Biosynthesis of the Glucoronides of Umbelliferone and 4-Methylumbelliferone and their use in Fluorimetric Determination of β-Glucoronidase. *Biochem. J. 61,* 569.

Moss, D. W. (1960), *Clin. Chim. Acta 5,* 283.

Parker, C. A. and Rees, W. T. (1962), Fluorescence Spectrometry: A Review. *Analyst 87,* 83.

Pringsheim, P. (1949), *Fluorescence and Phosphorescence,* John Wiley & Sons, New York, 794 pp.

Rotman, B. (1961), Measurement of Activity of Single Molecules of β-D-Galactosidase. *Proc. Natl. Acad. Sci. U.S. 47,* 1981.

Steiner, R. F. and Edelhoch, H. (1962), Effect of Thermally Induced Structural Transitions on the Ultraviolet Fluorescence of Proteins, *Nature 193,* 375.

Steingraber, O. J. and Berlman, J. B. (1963), Versatile Technique for Measuring Fluorescence Decay Times in the Nanosecond Region. *Revs. Sci. Instr. 34,* 524.

Stryer, L., Unpublished.

Teale, F. J. W. (1959), Haem-globin Equilibrium Studies by Fluorimetry. *Biochim. Biophys. Acta, 35,* 289.

Udenfriend, S. (1962), *Fluorescence Assay in Biology and Medicine,* Academic Press, New York.

Velick, S. F., Parker, C. W. and Eisen, H. N. (1960), Excitation Energy Transfer and the Quantitative Study of the Antibody Hapten Reaction, *Proc. Natl. Acad. Sci. U.S. 46,* 1470.

Velick, S. F. (1961), Spectra and Structure in Enzyme Complexes of Pyridine and Flavin Nucleotides. In: *Light and Life,* McElroy and Glass, eds., Johns Hopkins Univ. Press, pp. 108-143.

Weber, G. (1952), Polarization of the Fluorescence of Macromolecules, *Biochem. J. 51,* 155.

Weber, G. (1957), Determination of the Absolute Quantum Yield of Fluorescent Solutions. *Trans. Faraday Soc. 53,* 646.

Weber, G. and Teale, F. J. W. (1958), Fluorescence Excitation Spectrum of Organic Compounds in Solution. *Trans. Faraday Soc. 54,* 640.

Weber, G. and Young, L. B. (1964), Fragmentation of Bovine Serum Albumin by Pepsin. *J. Biol. Chem. 239,* 1415.

13. OPTICAL SHIFTS IN DYE COMPLEXES

It has long been known that organic dyes bind to biopolymers and in doing so change their optical properties. Shifts in the wavelength of maximum absorption or emission, in integrated absorption or emission intensity, and in optical rotatory dispersion may occur in a dye when it forms a dye-polymer complex. Although there is yet no unified, quantitative theory of all of these effects, they have been used for many years on a semi-empirical basis to locate, identify and characterize biopolymers both in solution and *in situ* by physical chemists, molecular biologists, and histologists.

The statistical mechanical and quantum mechanical studies which have been carried out on these systems show that, in order to explain the observed optical shifts, one must take into consideration the direct interaction of dye with polymer (binding), the statistical distribution of dyes among available dye-binding sites on the polymer, and the thermodynamic and exciton interaction (stacking) between neighboring, bound dyes [*Bradley,* 1961].

It is important to realize that the dyes show these shifts only when they bind to polymers. The elements of which the polymers are composed do not possess the ability to bind or stack dyes and these two properties only begin to appear when about four to six elements are covalently linked to form short chain polymers (oligomers). Optical shifts in the dyes can therefore be used to detect even small amounts of oligomers or polymers in the presence of relatively large amounts of monomeric organic compounds, including the very elements of which the polymers are composed. Thus if an aqueous extract of Martian "soil" were to cause shifts when added to appropriate dye solutions the existence of polymers of chain lengths four to six or greater would be established.

Optical shifts in the elements of the polymers themselves occur upon polymerization. Changes in the magnitudes of these shifts upon suitable treatment of the polymer (e.g., by measurement of hyperchromism-temperature profiles), are widely used to study polymer conformations and conformational changes. However, for most polymers the optical shifts occur in the ultraviolet region of the spectrum, in sharp contrast to those of the dyes which occur in the visible. In general, most organic compounds absorb light much more strongly in the ultraviolet than in the visible. Organic, non-polymeric impurities in Martian soil extract would therefore be much more likely to obscure, by creating a high background absorption, shifts in the polymers than shifts in the dyes. Conversely, less extensive purification of soil extract would be required to achieve the same sensitivity with measurements on dye-polymer complexes than with measurements on the polymers themselves.

Optical shifts in dye complexes are also quite sensitive: in the laboratory samples of the order of 4×10^{-8} monomoles of polymer are analyzed quantitatively and characterized structurally on a routine basis. For a polymer with 10^4 elements, this corresponds to only 2×10^{12} molecules, and this sensitivity could be increased one hundredfold without difficulty.

It has been well established [Bradley and Wolf, 1959; Stone and Bradley, 1961] that the extent of the shifts (e.g., degree of hypochromism, $\Delta\epsilon$) depends upon the ratio (D/P) of bound dyes (D) to the total number (P) of available binding sites on the polymer. Each dye-polymer complex exhibits a characteristic $\Delta\epsilon$ vs. D/P curve: the curve for the acridine orange-deoxyribonucleic acid complex (AO-DNA) is highly specific for DNA [Stone and Bradley, 1961] and can be easily distinguished from the same curve for AO-denatured DNA [Bradley and Felsenfeld, 1959], AO-ribonucleic acid [Bradley and Felsenfeld, 1959] and complexes of AO with many other polyanions [Bradley and Wolf, 1959]. Such curves could be obtained by the automated continuous addition of Martian soil extract to a standard dye solution, since D/P is inversely proportional to the volume of extract added. Absorbance of the solution at a given wavelength ($\Delta\epsilon$) could be measured by a simple photometer assembly and the $\Delta\epsilon$ *vs.* extract volume data telemetered to Earth for interpretation.

The optical activity of biopolymers and other biological molecules is often cited as one of the most characteristic signs of life at work. Dyes show optical activity when bonded to optically active biopolymers in asymmetric conformations [*Stryer and Blout, 1961; Neville and Bradley, 1961*]. This induced rotation [α], in the dyes appears in the form of oddly shaped Cotton effects [*Tinoco et al., 1963*], and, as with other shifts, depends on D/P in a manner characteristic of the dye-polymer complex: The [α] *vs.* D/P curve for AO-DNA [*Neville and Bradley, 1961*] is easily distinguishable from that of AO-denatured DNA [*Neville and Bradley, 1961*], AO-RNA, and complexes of AO with other polyanions [*Stryer and Blout, 1961*]. An [α] *vs.* extract volume curve could be obtained automatically and telemetered back to Earth. With luck, it would be possible to decide from such a curve what types of helical polymers, if any, exist in the Martian soil.

In summary, optical shifts in dye complexes show promise of providing a valuable, purely instrumental technique for systematically searching other planets for polymers created by life.

REFERENCES

Bradley, D. F., and G. Felsenfeld (1959), Aggregation of an acridine dye on native and denatured DNAs. *Nature 185,* 1920-22.

Bradley, D. F., and M. J. Wolf (1959), Aggregation of dyes bound to polyanions. *Proc. Nat. Acad. Sci. U. S. 45,* 944-52.

Bradley, D. F. (1961), Molecular biophysics of dye-polymer complexes. *Trans. N. Y. Acad. Sci. 24,* 64-74.

Neville, D. M., Jr., and D. F. Bradley (1961), Anomalous rotatory dispersion of acridine orange-native DNA complexes. *Biochem. Biophys. Acta 50,* 397-399.

Stone, A. L., and D. F. Bradley (1961), Aggregation of acridine orange bound to polyanions: The stacking tendency of DNAs. *J. Am. Chem. Soc. 83,* 3627-3634.

Stryer, L., and E. R. Blout (1961), Optical rotatory dispersion of dyes bound to macromolecules: Cationic dyes: Polyglutamic acid complexes. *J. Am. Chem. Soc. 83,* 1411-1418.

Tinoco, I., Jr., R. W. Woody and D. F. Bradley (1963), Absorption and rotation of light by helical polymers: The effect of chain length. *J. Chem. Phys. 38,* 1317-1325.

14. NUCLEAR MAGNETIC RESONANCE AND ELECTRON PARAMAGNETIC RESONANCE

Nuclear Magnetic Resonance

In view of the fact that the sensitivity to detection of hydrogen nuclei is greater than that of any other nuclei, and the high probability that detection of extraterrestrial life will involve organic substance containing hydrogen, the discussion will be restricted to proton magnetic resonance. In order to achieve any significant degree of specificity, it would be necessary to use the high resolution approach that would depend for its success upon the ability to resolve chemical shifts characteristic of protons in organic environments from other constituents of the sample. The method would require extraction of the organic material, preparation of a solution in a suitable solvent—preferably proton-free, and transfer to the sensing head of the instrument. The sensitivity for detecting protons in a specific molecular environment, i.e., corresponding to a single line in the high resolution NMR spectrum, is about 10^{16} protons. To achieve this sensitivity requires highly stable instrumentation and accumulation of data over periods of several hours. Sensitivity of high resolution NMR techniques would more normally be limited to detection of approximately 10^{17} protons in a single spectral region.

For the detection of small molecules where sensitivity would be reasonably high, NMR is not particularly competitive with other techniques such as gas chromatography, infrared or mass spectroscopy, all of which are considerably more sensitive and are specific for small molecules. The main advantage of high resolution NMR would be in the characterization of relatively complex mixtures where it could give some insight into the *average* composition of the mixture. For example, the NMR spectrum of a protein does reflect the average distribution of protons in aromatic rings, protons on carbon atoms adjacent to nitrogen or carbonyl groups, and purely aliphatic protons. Macromolecules typical of living organisms generally give very poor NMR spectra in aqueous solution due to the coiling effects and consequent insufficient molecular motion. Solvents such as trifluoroacetic acid tend to uncoil these polymers and permit better measurements.

Certain types of compounds, such as aldehydes, are quite specific in the NMR spectrum. Also, certain classes of complex compounds such as steroids give very characteristic spectra.

Another way to use NMR would be to analyze for organic substances in rock or soil pyrolyzates. If anything resembling coal, peat, lignite, etc., were present, even a small sample could well give ample material for analysis. Hopefully such pyrolysis experiments could be combined with fractional distillation to increase the amount of information obtained.

Instrumentation for high resolution NMR is relatively heavy and complex; however, it is not out of the question that lighter and simpler apparatus could be designed for space probes if this were given sufficient priority. It would be particularly fine to be able to use a superconducting magnet with a field of 45,000–75,000 gauss since it would give enhanced sensitivity, chemical shift differences four to five times greater than are now normally used, and a much lighter weight system.

Electron Paramagnetic Resonance

It would appear that electron paramagnetic resonance or electron spin resonance would offer somewhat better possibilities. The sensitivity of electron spin resonance is considerably greater than that of proton magnetic resonance due to the much higher moment of the unpaired electron. Commercial instruments have sensitivities in the range between 5×10^9 and 2×10^{11} unpaired electrons. However, it should be noted that in life processes the concentrations of unpaired electrons are seldom more than mere traces, and samples involving milligrams of living matter usually yield EPR signals on the threshold of detectability. Consequently, a serious sensitivity problem would almost certainly still exist with electron spin resonance techniques.

From the point of view of specificity, electron spin resonance offers two interesting avenues. 1) Many enzyme substrate reactions which occur in living organisms are accompanied by unpaired electrons due to their free radical mechanism. 2) The photosynthetic process appears to involve unpaired electrons and consequently the combination of an EPR signal with irradiation by light of the appropriate frequency would give a very specific response.

One advantage of electron spin resonance compared to nuclear magnetic resonance is the ability to work with either a liquid or solid sample. It is probable that some extraction and concentration procedures would be called for but the final form of the sample could be either a solution or a minute solid residue.

Electron spin resonance equipment would be smaller, lighter and less complex than nuclear magnetic resonance equipment and should present no particular problems to a space probe. Some development work would be required, however, in particular regarding the feasibility of using superconducting magnets on the Martian surface.

BIBLIOGRAPHY

Blois, M. J., Jr., and E. C. Weaver (1964), Electron Spin Resonance and Its Application to Photophysiology. In: *Photophysiology 1*, A. C. Giese, ed., Academic Press, New York.
Jackman, L. M. (1959), *Applications of Nuclear Magnetic Resonance Spectroscopy in Organic Chemistry*, Pergamon Press, London.
Marling, J. *et al.*, eds. (1960), *Nuclear Magnetic Resonance and EPR Spectroscopy* [*Varian's 3rd Annual Workshop*], Pergamon Press, London.
Roberts, J. D. (1959), *Nuclear Magnetic Resonance: Applications to Organic Chemistry*, McGraw-Hill, New York.
Nuclear and Paramagnetic Resonance (1955-1964), *Ann. Rev. Phys. Chem. 6-15.*

15. CALORIMETRY

A necessary manifestation of living organisms is the heat they must dissipate while they are engaged in the conversion of materials from the environment into their substance. This heat production can be used as the basis of a life detection experiment. It has the advantage of providing a signal no matter what the chemical basis of the living system, and under some circumstances it can yield almost certain indication of life, i.e., a heat release which rises exponentially with time.

The sensitivity of calorimetric devices, as can be estimated from the next section, is such that the heat released by 10^4 bacteria per ml, growing with a one hour doubling time, is detectable. The only physical technique used by microbiologists with potentially equivalent sensitivity is nephelometry, but it is faced with a serious technical difficulty, the high noise level due to other suspended materials. Thus, as a general technique useful for the detection of all organisms, calorimetry is probably unequalled for potential sensitivity and accuracy.

Calorimetry also offers the hope of obtaining a specific as well as sensitive indication of life. It is very frequently observed that in the presence of conditions which allow growth, the number of organisms present rises exponentially until some factor begins to limit growth rate. Autocatalytic phenomena which might mimic the exponential growth of a population of organisms are not very probable.

One can visualize the possible consequences of providing water, perhaps the limiting nutrilite, to a sample of Martian soil. At first there would be thermal changes associated with the solution and chemical modification of substances in the soil. Hopefully, these changes would become very small after an hour or two, and one would have the low noise level which would

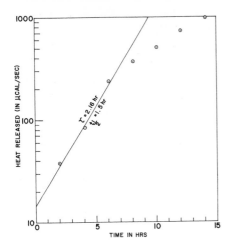

Figure 1.
Metabolic heat released by micro-organisms in a soil sample added to a nutrient broth.

allow the detection of the exponential growth of a relatively small mass of organisms.

In the next section such an experiment is described with a terrestrial soil sample, and the results are plotted on a semi-log scale in Figure 1. Note that the exponential rise does not persist long in this instance, as a consequence of the fact that the number of organisms initially present is so large (1/20) compared to the limiting level, *viz.*, terrestrial soil is very rich with bacteria. At 2 hours, the heat release corresponds to the presence of about 6×10^7 bacteria, of wet weight 10^{-12} g consuming their wet weight of glucose per generation (2.2 hr). This growth curve, therefore, represents the rise of bacteria starting from about 10^7/ml and stopping at about 2×10^8/ml (probably because of oxygen limitation which would occur at this point in a non-aerated culture). The curve is about as precise as would be obtained with standard laboratory procedures with clear solutions, and would not even be measurable by standard techniques in the face of the high soil concentration (2g/ml).

It thus appears that calorimetry is one of the most promising methods for the detection of the growth of organisms. Its sensitivity is excellent and it provides the possibility of detecting an almost unique manifestation of life, the exponential growth of a population.

Experimental Procedure

Beckman Instruments (Spinco Division, 1117 California Avenue, Palo Alto, Calif.) now makes a very sensitive instrument, which is being tested with soil microorganisms by Dr. Jack Ohms of the Spinco Division and Dr. Glenn E. Pollock of the Life Detection Branch of NASA (Ames Research

Center), and some exciting preliminary results have been obtained. Through the courtesy of Dr. Pollock, one may say the following:

A soil sample containing an estimated 10^6 microorganisms per gram was submitted for the series of experiments. Two experimental approaches were used: (1) a measurement of the exothermic reaction during the metabolism of a bacteriological nutrient medium and (2) a measurement of the differential thermal response between a "live" sample and a control sample in which the microorganisms were killed with $HgCl_2$.

The nutrient medium used in the first experiment was a trypsin-digest of soybean protein with added constituents such as glucose.

The experiments indicated that thermal reactions of low magnitude can be monitored for long periods of time. It appears that the thermal response of the metabolism and growth of an initial culture with as few as 10^3 soil microorganisms can probably be monitored with trypticase soybroth nutrient.

A typical experiment (1, above) in which the heat from contents of the right thermopile chamber were read against the left is as follows.

Reaction vessels—stainless steel with stainless steel center wells.

Right thermopile—10 g dry "live" soil + 200 mg trypticase; center well—5.0 ml. distilled water.

Left thermopile—10 g dry "live" soil; center well—5.0 ml distilled water.

The results were as follows:

Time after mixing	$\mu cal/sec$
2 hr.	38
4	84
6	240
8	370
10	508
12	746
14	989
16	1176
17.4	1210
18	1202
20	991
22	396
24	—

The integrated area of the curve is equivalent to 47.6 cal. It may be noted that the heat output reaches a maximum within one day.

In another experiment (2, above), soil was tested without the addition of any nutrient other than water. It is well known that a dry soil will, upon the addition of water, begin to metabolize, give off CO_2, and show an increase in numbers of microbes. This is mirrored by the following results.

Reaction vessels—Stainless steel jacket and Teflon center well
Right thermopile—8.9 g of "live" soil + 4 ml 1 per cent $HgCl_2$
Left thermopile—Soil + water
This reaction, either endothermic in the $HgCl_2$-treated soil sample or exothermic in the H_2O-treated sample, reached a magnitude of 46 $\mu cal/sec$ within 1 hour after mixing. This reaction fell to 12 $\mu cal/sec$ within the next hour. During the interval of 2 to 11 hours post-mixing there was a slow drift to 45 $\mu cal/sec$. This peak then declined to the baseline at 20 to 24 hours post-mixing.

The baseline drift between 24 and 31 hours post-mixing was 0.17 ($\mu cal/sec$)/hr. In an 8 hour interval prior to mixing the instrument drift was 0.25 ($\mu cal/sec$)/hr.

If this is an exothermic reaction due to the metabolic processes in the wet soil sample, the signal-to-noise ratio is about 20. Thus, the metabolism of 10^5-10^6 organisms could probably be detected without addition of nutrient.

16. OPTICAL MICROSCOPY

Life on another planet, however different or primitive, should possess certain recognizable attributes. If still extant and advanced to a macroscopic stage its detection should be positive and amenable to the easy techniques of unamplified photography. If not yet advanced beyond a "molecular" level, life detection could hardly be positive, and could perhaps be recognized only by indirect methods.

Between these two extremes falls the possible, and not altogether unpromising, utilization of microscopy. Its various adaptable techniques and applications would seem to present a number of decided advantages, as well as disadvantages and difficulties, and its potentialities are worthy of exploration.

Its advantages, in general, are:
1. Adaptability to some degrees of miniaturization.
2. Providing means for the lowest limits of visualization of fragmentation of form.
3. Ability to deal, within limitations, with materials and application under adverse conditions.

Inherent disadvantages are:
1. Great restriction of materials that can be examined, except under immediate and favorable conditions.
2. Great operational difficulties of manipulation under remote automated or telemetered control.

3. Great uncertainty in securing life-remains, even though they may be abundant.

Much of the limitation in applying microscopy to this objective depends intrinsically upon successful planetary landing of equipment, ability to explore terrain and select samples, and necessity of remote or automatic instrumental manipulation. In this application of microscopy, the following would seem the desirable approach:

1. To use the simplest possible low-power microscopy (100 to 500 ×, or even less), unless high power (with much more difficult techniques) is needed.
2. To direct attention to the simplest methods and types of sampling expected to yield plant or animal remains of rugged and indestructible character.
3. To attempt discovery of and place reliance upon such organic remains as could be known to be free of contamination from space vehicle or other-planetary sources.
4. To concentrate upon the most numerous and smallest conclusive objects or fragments.
5. To avoid contamination.

In discussing procedural approaches, we will move from the more advanced and sophisticated to the more simple, by elimination; procedures being relative in degree of sophistication to versatility of space-flight success.

The most satisfactory and positive procedure for recognizing life-remains would involve searching the terrain, selective sampling, returning the samples to Earth, and subjecting them to conventional microscopic examination in the laboratory. Haphazard sampling and examination could result in thousands of sterile field pictures and might lead to failure to detect rare objects that the more systematic laboratory procedures would discover. Even objects that were relatively abundant might be overlooked unless systematic procedures were adopted. The outlook may, however, not be so discouraging as this suggests, for many microscopic organic forms, or fragments, are so abundant and widely distributed over any terrain as to be likely of discovery, and immediately revealing when seen.

If a planetary flora and fauna are encountered that have evolved no further than the one-celled microorganism or very simple algal-type stage, the microscope is called for and can probably offer the best means for life detection. Or, if a once abundant, highly-developed and diversified biota has been obliterated, except for fragmentary resistant hard parts, the microscope is again needed. Even in the case of an abundant diversified macroscopic biota of elusive character, difficult of differentiation from its surroundings, or of extremely strange and unfamiliar type, the microscope might once more prove the superior means of detection.

For its use in these connections, as is the constant experience of a microscopic analyst on Earth, there is needed a knowledge, familiarity, and good interpretive sense of characteristic attributes of organic structure, even of the merest fragments of material that must sometimes be determined. In all such work experience is obviously invaluable, and, in general, the larger the sample, specimen, or fragment, the more likely and confident its recognition would be.

Some of the more generally characteristic microscopic attributes of organic structure are listed below.

Microscopically Detectable Attributes of Living Matter

The most elemental attributes of organic morphology, above the molecular level, by which organic origin might be differentiated from inorganic, are:

1. A certain regularity of structure and "design" with subordinate or contained degrees of irregularity; as contrasted with true duplication.
2. Sequential repetitiveness, but with orderly progressive change.
3. Varying degrees (in larger units or fragments) of symmetry and harmony of parts.
4. Basically amorphous, nonrotatory properties; as contrasted with rotatory effects and birefringence.
5. Heterogeneous, atypical diffraction image; as contrasted with rigid pattern.
6. Reduplication, but with individuality of pattern.
7. Micro-pore and reticulate, as contrasted with solid and interface structure.
8. Variably striate; as contrasted with smooth and rigid, or chaotic cleavage.
9. Growth by accretion and reduplication; as contrasted with proliferation by aggregation.
10. Morphological differentiation, and continuity of generative substance.
11. Rounded and blended transition of parts; as contrasted with sharp, chaotic or angular and straight abutment of interfaces.
12. Superficial adherence to certain conventional, mathematical patterns of form.

13. Compensatory deviation from, and recovery of, pattern; as contrasted with linear divergence.
14. Freedom and nonconformity within limits, as contrasted with rigidity, of pattern.
15. Some sort of consistent, though diversified, cellular structure.
16. A suggestively teleological morphology.

(If only a few of these characteristics are found in isolated cases, organic origin cannot be inferred with certainty. The dependability of the inference will, of course, improve with the number of positive findings.)

For sake of argument, and to anticipate all possible contingencies, it may be suggested that life on another planet, arising and developing independently of our Earth or any other system, might give rise to an organic form completely unfamiliar to us and not remotely resembling any known or imagined organisms. Still, fundamental concepts of form and structure must necessarily require in any living entity, for their sustenance and perpetuation, certain of the following attributes: some sort of pore structure for intake of materials for growth, some membrane structure for selective absorption and retention, some skeletal or shell framework for support of these structures and their protection, some design or arrangement of this framework to permit of growth and expansion (a natural effect of life activity), and some periodic mechanism for division and reassembling of this material into smaller and similar continuing units. Such a structural system, however divergent from things familiar to us, is necessarily committed to certain real and *a priori* geometrical patterns, whatever complicated variation may elaborate and embellish them. Form and substance are inseparably related, and, in living systems, function is, if not teleologically, at least intimately associated with them. With a consciousness of these principles, and an experienced awareness of the natural attributes of living form, it should be possible for us to recognize *a priori* in unknown objects form of living derivation.

Thus certain structural attributes, with varied degree of elaboration and application, are not particular expressions of specific form, but of life itself.

Although these can be, as above, rather categorically listed, they are hardly traits that can be instrumentally determined, or applied very confidently by one who has merely read them; the more experience and familiarity with such presentments the more likely their fruitful employment. Even the most versatile and widely experienced microscopist is often baffled in the identification of fragments. On the other hand, on the basis of certain of these attributes (characteristics of living form) the merest fragment and almost microscopically indivisible speck of organic structure *can* frequently be determined immediately, and with utmost confidence, not only as to its living character, but even as to species, or part of a structure whence it came, by one thoroughly familiar with the forms and the principles. Obviously, there is no substitute for experience.

There is ever-present danger in these practices, of carelessly or mistakenly assigning identity to obscure fragments, and of failing to recognize artifacts. In all such determinations, and certainly in one so significant as a positive or negative determination of the existence of planetary life, complete conservatism must be the inviolable rule. However, rightly circumstanced, one almost visibly indivisible microorganic fragment could give a positive answer. The microscopic part of such an assignment is relatively simple. It would depend wholly upon the success of the array of vast and seemingly insurmountable problems of encompassing the space barrier that could make possible the obtaining and examining of samples. The recovery of a single, positively identifiable organism, or organic fragment, could leave no question of life's existence.

The well-developed "Atmospheric Dust" sampling techniques, static precipitation on a microscope slide, and micrographic television telemetering of the field would seem one microscopic technique of some promise, both as to implementation and as to picking up some objects of life-revealing conclusiveness. Two great difficulties would be (1) elimination of contamination possibilities (amenable to control), and (2) scarcity or absence of forms sought. It could be, contrarily, that an abundance of some life-form would settle the whole question in a matter of seconds.

As on Earth, any planet's atmosphere capable of supporting life would probably contain a great miscellany of objects and particles, microorganisms and fragments of organic structure, as well as inorganic. On Earth, such an assemblage may be expected to include (in addition to bacteria) such an assortment as: pollens, fungal and other plant spores, plant and animal hairs, fibers, stomatal epidermis of leaves, feather fragments, butterfly wing and other scales, and the tests of diatoms.

As indicated previously, whether the planet in question had evolved any of the above-named forms familiar to us, a favorable environment and generatively active C-H-O chemistry should very likely have developed some comparable organic species, bearing attributes of living matter recognizable to us, and the more representing its special planetary biota. All the types of microscopic forms mentioned above have the distinct advantages of:

1. Production in great numbers, and of being almost universally present in an atmosphere.
2. Great durability.
3. Sturdy composition, and retention of form when dry.
4. Characteristic and ready recognition under low-power (100×) microscopy.
5. Providing varying degrees of ecological information.

The Problems of Bacteria

With bacteria, elaborate precautions for sterile entry into a planetary environment, and measures against contamination by any part of an entering vehicle or its load, must be observed; difficult high-power microscopy is needed; and the results may be made unreliable and difficult to interpret. Should they indicate or prove an exclusive or best detectable clue, well and good, but otherwise much painstaking labor, cost, and difficulty can be avoided by concentrating upon other forms not so endowed, and possessing more determinative features.

17. ELECTRON MICROSCOPY AND ELECTRON OPTICAL TECHNIQUES

Introduction

Within the framework of the stated problems relating to the diagnosis of the presence of life on Mars and its characterization, we shall try to discuss the possible contributions of electron microscopy and related electron optical techniques, centering on experiments *in situ,* with telemetry back to Earth. Essentially, this approach is based on the fundamental role of microscopy in its broadest sense as a central unifying discipline of the natural sciences, which has immeasurably augmented man's dimensional span in the scale of living systems. It represents a logical complement and extension of the comprehensive automatic light microscope system for use on a planet as proposed by *Lederberg et al.* [1961].

Electron microscopy extends the range of resolution of the light microscope several hundredfold, scanning the whole range of submicroscopic structures down to the molecular and atomic level. Beyond this, electron microscopy and related techniques possess certain inherent specific advantages and capabilities which are uniquely suited to the space environment and to exobiological studies in general.

The nature of life is literally writ small, in the submicroscopic domain, and electron microscopy permits us to read directly all variants of the sculpture of living forms at the molecular level. Thus, within *Lederberg's* [1964] comprehensive evolutionary scheme of chemogeny, biogeny, and cognogeny, an electron optical scan would ideally supplement the chemical scan and radiation probes to integrate automatically relevant information pertaining to life at the various hierarchical levels of subcellular, viral, macromolecular, and molecular organization. In this quest the electron microscope, and the microscope in its broadest sense, may prove to be the prime analytical tool both for the detection of "entropy pockets" in an alien planetary environment, and for subsequent operational interaction and controlled modification of this domain. Since the fundamental definition of biogeny involves the well-ordered, information-carrying macromolecule, electron microscopy appears to be one of the most promising direct approaches to its detection. In this connection, detection of any type of ordered macromolecules or their derivatives—which can only be accomplished directly by electron optical techniques—would provide invaluable information relevant to the origin of life, giving clues to the related cognogenic, biogenic or chemogenic processes. As *Lederberg* [1961] has pointed out, we can reasonably expect to find evidence of microscopic life in any "drop of water," "pinch of soil," or "gust of wind." All the more reason to suppose that extension of this microbiological analysis by electron microscopy through the macromolecular domain may well prove to be the most reliable diagnosis for the presence of life on Mars or any planet. Imagine, for example, how much we would miss today if electron microscopy had not disclosed the sophisticated morphology of virus particles (bacteriophages, etc.) in which, quite literally, resides the combined information on their structure and function. In turn, how much would we not miss if our analytical scan of the environment on Mars were not to encompass the whole spectrum of submicroscopic organized forms which may well prove to be particularly well represented under the peculiar ambient conditions of Mars.

From these considerations stem the basic concepts of miniaturized and mobile electron microscope "stations" embodying appropriately miniaturized componentries for an integrated collection and transport of specimens, physico-chemical and physical processing of the samples remotely controlled by servo systems, and coupled with a vidicon-transmitter telemetry chain. Such a miniaturized electron microscope station would not only serve as a powerful analytical tool for detection of life on Mars, but also for exobiological studies in general.

Methodologically, electron microscopy and related electron optical techniques have the significant advantage of being able to extract the maximum of information from samples which are several orders of magnitude smaller than those required for light microscopy. This economy or optimized parsimony of the ratio of information output referred to submicroscopic sample size is of critical importance when dealing with automated exobiological experiments *in situ* which have to be relayed back to Earth by telemetry. In many ways, one can invoke a revealing example quoted by *Lederberg* [1961; 1964] when pointing out the extremely cumbersome automatic instrumentation that would be needed to catch a hare and then to determine its nutritional requirements. By analogy, one could point out

416

MARTIAN LANDINGS: UNMANNED

that a systematic electron optical survey can be carried out on an ultrathin section only 100Å in thickness and not more than a few square microns in area, which is several orders of magnitude smaller than the requisite light microscopy samples of several hundred thousands Å thickness and scores of square microns in area. This is particularly relevant to the problem of being able to sample not only the atmosphere and surface of Mars, but perhaps more importantly, the subsurface and deeper strata of Martian soil, where we may expect to find the most valuable clues on the evolution of life. An electron microscope equipped with a miniaturized ultramicrotome incorporating a diamond knife [*Fernández-Morán, 1962; 1964; 1953*] or a diamond drill for production of ultrathin sections, which can be read off directly with the attached electron microscope, would serve all of these required functions in a practical and efficient way. As will be described later on, these systems would not in any way replace, but in fact ideally supplement, the light microscope systems now contemplated.

In the following, a brief outline will be given of the distinctive methodological features of electron microscopy in terms of the relative interest that this approach should attract in dealing with the basic problems. Only the essential engineering details will be presented of the specific project embodying a miniaturized electron microscope with coupled preparative devices for sampling, preparing, sorting, and telemetering of specimen data. Finally, some of the promising approaches in the development and implementation of these proposals will be surveyed, with particular emphasis on the priority assigned to this project which merits a determined effort.

Miniaturized Electron Microscope—Vidicon Systems

Methodologically, electron microscopy and related electron optical techniques are of unique operational value in exobiology and space investigations in general, for the reasons discussed below.

The conditions under which a sample is examined in electron microscopy—high vacuum, electron-beam and ion irradiation, thin specimens (100–1,000 Å), and in some instances low temperatures, are very similar to conditions encountered in space.

Successful application of the high spatial resolution of the order of 6 to 8 Å reproducibly attainable with modern electron microscopes, now permits direct visualization of structural organization down to the molecular level, and in favorable cases of the array of atoms in crystalline lattices. In fact, this unique possibility of obtaining data, which is directly related to a limited number of atoms or molecules only, and is thus well above the level of statistical uncertainty commonly associated with indirect analytical methods, is of particular importance in the study of the structure and composition of submicroscopic particles, such as those of interstellar matter with diameters of a few tenths of a micron down to 10 to 100 Å. Moreover, electron optical and related microprobe analytical techniques are at present the only adequate methods for examination of gaseous and solid components as they occur in the extremely high dispersion, ultrahigh vacuum and low temperatures encountered in outer space, and in certain planetary environments.

The special techniques that have been developed for electron microscope studies of specimens are actually readily adaptable to examination of extraterrestrial matter, because we are dealing essentially with the same problems. Thus, the use of thin graphite or single-crystal, stable coherent films, of plastic films, replication, shadow-casting, etc., are suitable for these purposes. In this way, and despite the numerous unsolved technical problems, it should be possible to obtain and examine, as well as perform chemical analysis (electron microprobe analysis, electron diffraction, correlated physico-chemical and mass-spectrometric analysis, etc.) of material from space, and from lunar and planetary probes in a way that cannot be achieved by any other known technique. It should be pointed out that most of the relevant fine structures of the specimen materials would be well below the resolving power of present light and x-ray microscopes.

Electron microscopy and related electron optical devices are essentially extensions of television techniques. They can, therefore, be readily adapted directly to television cameras such as those used on Surveyor or Ranger spacecraft adapted for use in the exploration of Mars. A television survey camera essentially contains the same basic elements (electron source, electromagnetic focusing lenses, vidicon tubes, etc.) as an electron microscope. It would only be necessary to add certain components in order to convert such a television survey camera into a simple type of electron microscope which would considerably extend the range of resolution of such a camera from the present meter range to the sub-micron range. In fact, the proposed use of miniaturized electron microscopes represents a logical supplement and extension of the "Vidicon Microscopes" for planetary exploration as suggested by Dr. Joshua Lederberg of Stanford University, and now being developed in Dr. Gerald Soffen's laboratory at the Jet Propulsion Laboratory of the California Institute of Technology [*Quimby,* 1964]. Even a simple miniaturized electron microscope (coupled directly and preferably in the same vacuum system with the television survey camera) would have a resolving power of the order of a few hundred Angstrom units, which is well below the useful resolving power (of about 3,000 to 2,000 Å) of the best light microscopes presently available. Moreover, instead of using a vidicon tube which works on a photoconductive principle, the electron image of such an electron microscope can be converted directly by suitable image intensifiers [*Haine and Casslett,* 1961] into electrical signals which, when highly amplified and converted to a frequency-modulated signal, can be sent and received on Earth. Alternatively, as discussed further on, the electron microscope image could be recorded directly on special high-resolution and ultrathin photographic emulsions, suitably demagnified by a factor of several thousand times. In this highly condensed form the electron microscope image could be either read out and telemetered back to Earth, or conceivably sent back directly in suitably packaged form for retrieval on Earth (see supplement to this report).

It is of course possible and actually advisable to combine the automatic light microscope system proposed by Lederberg and his associates with this type of miniaturized electron microscope system, in order to achieve a mutually supplementary, step-wise analytical processing of the samples. In many ways both systems complement each other and can be used either combined or singly in appropriately designed planetary missions.

Although all present commercial electron microscopes are considerably larger, weighing over a ton with attached power supply cabinets, it is considered feasible to reduce substantially the size and weight of microscopes with advanced techniques. Thus, by appropriate scaling down of the lenses, including the possible use of permanent magnet lenses which do not require a separate lens power supply, it should be possible to reduce the column to about 1 foot length or perhaps even less; and to combine this with appropriately miniaturized high-voltage pointed-filament electron sources and controlled power supplies. It should be pointed out that there have already been several successful attempts to produce commercially small, extremely compact electron microscopes, such as the RCA type EMT permanent-magnet electron microscope. The small table-model microscope designed by *Reisner and Dornfeld* [1950] has permanent magnet lenses and attains a resolution of about 100Å. Electron microscope lenses have a very small useful numerical aperture (of the order of 100th radian), and their depth of field is therefore extremely large compared with that of light microscopes of high resolution where the numerical aperture is large (1 to 1.6). This large depth of field of electron microscopes is of particular interest because it makes possible the recording of "stereoscopic" views of objects having considerable extent in the axial direction. This would also considerably facilitate recording of sharp images by remotely controlled servo systems.

General Design Features of a Simple Miniaturized Electron Microscope

The schematic diagram (Figure 1) illustrates some of the general design features which can be incorporated into a miniaturized electron microscope

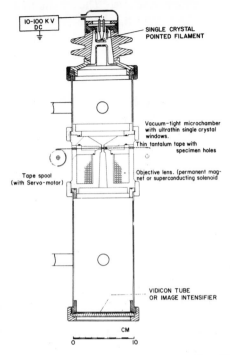

Figure 1.
Schematic diagram of miniaturized electron microscope for exobiology studies.

for detection of extraterrestrial life. The microscope column (with a length of 6 to 12 inches approximately) comprises a pointed filament source (of tungsten, or preferably rhenium for longer life) with a Schottky type of gun for T-F emission at accelerating voltages of 10 to 50 kV. One objective lens of the permanent magnet, standard electromagnetic, electrostatic or superconducting type is shown here. However, it may be necessary to use an objective and projector gap in series to obtain higher magnifications. The image is recorded either directly onto a vidicon tube with fluorescent screen, or onto an image intensifier of the solid state or scanned type [*Haine and Cosslett,* 1950]. Alternatively, the special type of ultrathin photographic films on tapes could be used for recording of the image either at high magnification or after appropriate demagnification. The whole column assembly can be made very rigid and attached directly onto the television survey camera, or be a supplementary element to the vidicon microscopes currently being designed at the Jet Propulsion Laboratory.

At present, two basic approaches are being pursued in trying to solve the difficult specimen mounting and preparation problems:

(1) There is a possibility of effecting a continuous scan of ultrathin specimens (fine particles in aerosol suspensions, atmosphere samples, etc.) by sandwiching them between vacuum-tight, 200 to 1,000 Å thick, single-

crystal mica, graphite, aluminum or beryllium windows. These windows would be transparent to electrons and, in this case, the microscope itself would be constantly kept under high vacuum which does not have to be broken in order to examine the specimens. This would also permit a continuous sampling of wet or partially hydrated specimens, and the use of very fine "ultratape" reels of indefinite length.

The envisaged miniature objective pole pieces with a bore of 1 mm or less would be ideal for this approach. In the rarefied atmosphere of Mars this type of approach to specimen examination may prove to be particularly useful. A variant would involve the use of an impaction plate (as in the case of the vidicon microscope being designed in Dr. Soffen's laboratory [*Quimby*, 1964]) which can be periodically cleaned by suitable electrostatic filtering devices.

(2) Specimens could be collected on a traveling ultrathin ribbon of tantalum or rhenium foil about 100 to 1,000 Å thick and about 1 mm wide, with appropriate reinforcements and suitably etched slits or holes (1 to 20 microns in diameter). These thin metal tapes can be fed automatically into the microscope after having been exposed to the environment, in the same way as the transparent tape first proposed by *Lederberg et al.* [1961] or by the Gulliver biochemical probe device being developed by Dr. Norman H. Horowitz of California Institute of Technology and by Dr. Gilbert V. Levin of Haselton Laboratories, Inc. [*Quimby*, 1964]. The advantage of these rhenium or tantalum foils would be that no direct specimen substrate film is required, and that they can be re-used many times by appropriate heating to destroy old specimens. This practice of heating to incandescence in a vacuum has proved to be very effective in eliminating contamination. The "ultratapes" would be mounted on shields which can be operated by remotely controlled servo systems. A similar type of reel could also act as a substrate for the ultrathin, very fine-grained photographic emulsions used in recording electron microscope micro-images as described later.

The miniaturized electron microscope would be equipped with an appropriately miniaturized ultramicrotome (e.g., of the Fernández-Morán type with "V-shaped diamond or sapphire bearings without lubrication" equipped with a diamond knife [*Fernández-Morán*, 1953]) for automatic production of ultrathin sections of the specimens which would be automatically fed to the microtape specimen reel and examined directly by electron microscopy. It is also interesting to consider the possibility of using a similar device to produce an "aerosol" of very fine particles, by using a diamond knife revolving at high speeds, of even the hardest materials. These particles could then be examined in the previously described impact device. Alternatively, a miniaturized diamond drill with a servo-controlled motor would be used to prepare samples of the different strata of Martian soil. All of these specimen preparation devices would automatically convert the sample into appropriate ultrathin sections or fragmented specimens suitable for electron microscopy. In analogy with the ingenious design first proposed by *Lederberg et al.* [1961], one could combine ultrathin sectioning and ultrasonic dissociation of the specimens with a suitable centrifugal or ultracentrifugal separator. It should be possible to miniaturize these separators to permit use of density gradient techniques which would be of key value in sampling the environment and in obtaining specimens of the size range of virus particles and larger macromolecules (DNA, nucleo-proteins, etc.). The required high ultracentrifugal forces could perhaps be generated by a modified design of the Beams magnetic suspension ultracentrifuges suitably scaled down for this purpose.

In its simplest form, such a miniaturized electron microscope should not be more difficult to operate than are any of the other contemplated devices for detection of extraterrestrial life. Since all of its components are of rugged construction and are readily adaptable to the already tested television cameras for spacecraft, these devices can be expected to perform reliably, without the need for sophisticated techniques. This point deserves particular emphasis, since it is generally accepted that high resolution electron microscopy does indeed require considerable sophistication and experience in experimental technique. Here we would not be dealing with high resolution electon microscopy, but rather with electron microscopy in an intermediate range of resolution which could yield a vast fund of useful information which is well beyond the limits of light microscopy. Moreover, this type of electron microscope can serve as a prototype for the special demagnification electron microscope, described in Appendix II, which could be used to condense information on ultrathin films for subsequent retrieval.

Design Features of More Advanced Miniaturized High-Resolution Electron Microscopes

With present advances in the generation of stable superconducting electromagnetic fields and progress in low-temperature electron microscopy, etc., it is conceivable that the contemplated design of new types of high resolution "cryo-electron microscopes" immersed in a liquid helium cryostat using superconducting electromagnetic lenses [*Fernández-Morán,* 1953; 1962; 1964; 1965] and related types of miniaturized electron microscope systems may find direct application in the examination *in situ* of lunar and planetary matter by electron optical techniques.

It is readily conceivable that such a cryo-electron microscope could be miniaturized. By being of smaller size and invested with a far greater resolving power, with useful magnifications on the order of 10^5 to 10^6 times that of a light microscope, it would permit a greater range of applications, and thus supplement and extend the usefulness on a planet of the presently contemplated automatic light microscope systems proposed by Lederberg and associates.

By further development of the concepts embodied in our earlier low-temperature electron microscopy techniques [*Fernández-Morán, 1962; 1964*] it has been possible to design a new type of miniaturized high resolution electron microscope totally immersed in liquid helium. These "cryoelectron microscopes" operating at temperatures of 1 to 4°K would embody the following significant features:

(1) Highly stable superconducting electromagnetic lenses, with very ripple-free magnetic fields when operated in the persistent current mode;

(2) Operation in ultrahigh vacuum and low temperatures resulting in decisive advantages of minimized specimen contamination, specimen damage and thermal noise;

(3) Improved single-crystal pointed filament sources, with optimum conditions for both low voltage (i.e., 1 to 10 kV) and high voltage electron microscopy. In addition, the use of high efficiency viewing (single-crystal fluorescent screens, fiber optics, etc.) and recording devices operating at optimum low temperature would make it possible to use high speed cinematography and stroboscopic recording (e.g., obtained through pulsed T-F emission from pointed filament sources) for attainment of high temporal resolution combined with high spatial resolution.

The described combination of optimized instrumental design parameters, operative under conditions of minimized specimen perturbation represents one of the most promising coherent experimental approaches towards attainment of the theoretical resolution limit (about 2 Å) in direct examination of organic and biological structures. At present an instrument of the type shown in Figure 1 is currently being developed at our laboratories in the University of Chicago, as part of a comprehensive research program in the field of low-temperature electron microscopy [*Fernández-Morán, 1965*].

Potential Applications of Electron Microscopy in Combination with Other Techniques for the Detection of Extraterrestrial Life

Based on the extensive background of classic terrestrial biological observations, both with the light and electron microscopes, the direct observation of structural detail at the various levels of dimensional hierarchies lends considerable support to the morphological approach. While it is likely that certain structural attributes may be specific expressions of life, it is recognized that many other criteria derived from biochemistry, physical chemistry, and the physical sciences are, in fact, indispensable in characterizing biogenic origin.

With this in mind, it is interesting to note that an electron microscope can be readily used in combination with other techniques to carry out correlated biochemical and biophysical studies. Thus, by introducing certain modifications in the design of the miniaturized electron microscope, the following procedures could be adopted:

(1) X-ray microscopy [*Engstrom and Finean,* 1958], particularly in the use of microabsorption x-ray spectrometry;

(2) X-ray microdiffraction, which would be of particular use in examining larger bulk samples of fossil or other material. This could lead to the detection of the characteristic small-angle, x-ray diffraction pattern, for example, of collagen and other fibrous proteins which appeared to be uniquely specific for biogenic origin.

(3) Different types of scanning microscopes (Nixon, Westinghouse) [*Haine and Cosslett,* 1950] could be used and these would be of particular value in the rarefied Martian atmosphere, since they could permit the use of microprobe analysis outside the microscope itself.

Other conceivable applications would be in connection with mass spectrometry, micro-spectrophotometry, micro-histochemistry, micro-fluorometry, radio-isotope biochemical probes, and devices like the Wolf Trap of Professor Wolf Vishniac for detecting the growth of microorganisms. This latter combination is of particular significance in connection with the detection of submicroscopic organisms like viruses, which may be potentially dangerous to man. It is, for example, conceivable that single-cell cultures could be kept frozen in special microchambers, then infected or otherwise placed in contact with extraterrestrial material and the subsequent changes in the thawed-out cell observed both by light and electron microscopy as well as by biochemical techniques. In fact, the Wolf Trap optics lend themselves readily to adaptation to electron optical techniques.

All of these analytical systems complement each other and should be used in combination in appropriately designed planetary missions. Electron microscopy is particularly suitable for the study of certain features of biological systems when adequately supplemented by the results of parallel biophysical and biochemical investigations. One of the most challenging problems that can be approached with electron microscopy in combination with x-ray diffraction techniques would be the detection on Mars of the presence of highly organized, repetitive, periodic but asymmetric fibrous and other anisodiametric structures at the macromolecular level. These have been hitherto found on Earth to be characteristic of life, although admittedly no single criterion is acceptable. Thus, for example, the repeating pattern of 660 Å observed in collagen both by x-ray diffraction and electron microscopy has been found to hold true even for fossil specimens. Such patterns are not explicable solely by statistical combination of random asymmetric elements, but imply at least some form of replication, self-assembly and self-checking, which are quite distinct from the epitaxial growth of crystals. Although much work remains to be done in this area, it remains a fundamental problem to ascertain what morphological criteria at a given level of morphological organization are characteristic of biogenic origin.

Once a given type of specimen has been thoroughly worked out and understood, it would be possible to program these microscope systems to "react" specifically to a given submicroscopic entity of predetermined configuration. This latter possibility would be of special interest in the case of electron microscope sensor and contamination monitoring devices. The merits of this approach are manifest when taking into consideration the example already discussed by *Lederberg* [1964]: assuming capture of a dust sample of about 100 milligrams, containing at most 100 micrograms of organic matter, perhaps 1 μg (about 10 nanomoles) of a particular species. Appropriate diffusion, differential ultracentrifugation techniques, etc., could be devised to separate such species and the various steps monitored by light microscopy until the enriched molecular species can be examined directly by electron microscopy. In the envisaged science of metrology, the orderly study of methods of measurement [*Lederberg*, 1964], the described electron microscopy, and electron optical techniques are bound to play a key operational role. Implementation of the described experimental approaches appears to be well within the present capabilities of technology and applied scientific research.

REFERENCES

Engstrom, A. and Finean, B. (1958), *Biological Ultrastructure,* Academic Press, New York.

Fernández-Morán, H. (1953), A Diamond Knife for Ultrathin Sectioning. *Exptl. Cell Res. 5,* 255-256.

Fernández-Morán, H. (1962), New Approaches in the Study of Biological Ultrastructure by High-Resolution Electron Microscopy. *In: Symposia of the International Society for Cell Biology 1,* R. J. C. Harris, ed., Academic Press, London, 411-427.

Fernández-Morán, H. (1964), New Approaches in Correlative Studies of Biological Ultrastructure by High-Resolution Microscopy. *Roy. Microsc. Soc. 83,* 183-195.

Fernández-Morán, H. (1965), Electron Microscopy with High-Field Super-conducting Solenoid Lenses. *Proc. Nat'l. Acad. Sci. (U. S.) 53*, 445-451.

Haine, M. E., and V. E. Cosslett (1961), *The Electron Microscope*, Interscience, New York.

Lederberg, J. (1961), Exobiology: Experimental Approaches to Life Beyond the Earth: *In: Science in Space*, L. V. Berkner and H. Odishaw, eds., McGraw-Hill, New York, 407-425.

Lederberg, J. (1964). Signs of Life: A Survey of the Detection Problem in Exobiology. Exobiology Summer Study 1964.

Newberry, S. P., Buschmann, E. C. and Klotz, T. H. (1963), *Advanced Electron Beam Recording Techniques: Final Report*, RADC-TDR-63-234, Rome Air Development Center, Griffiss AFB, New York.

Quimby, F. H., ed. (1964), *Concepts for Detection of Extraterrestrial Life*, NASA SP-56, Washington, D. C.

Reisner, J. H. and E. G. Dornfeld (1950), A Small Electron Microscope. *J. Appl. Phys. 21*, 1131-1139.

18. A NOTE ON MORPHOLOGICAL CRITERIA FOR RECOGNITION OF LIFE

When considering morphological criteria, by which the existence of extraterrestrial living forms may be recognized, it is necessary to concentrate on those criteria that should be characteristic of any form of life, however it evolved and whatever its nature. It is useless to compile, even into broad classes, the forms of organisms with which we are acquainted on Earth. If pictures of earthly forms were transmitted back to us from Mars they would be recognized as living without much difficulty. I feel that it is also useless to try to set out criteria for recognizing "organisms" that are very low on the evolutionary scale and are just making the change from the chemogenic to the biogenic stage. The classification of such forms as living or non-living, on the basis of morphology, would be most difficult, even if they could be investigated in our laboratories here on Earth with the best microscopes and microtomes available. Rather, we should concentrate on general criteria that we feel would apply to any forms of life regardless of its evolutionary history, genetics and energy transport system. The following is a list of criteria that I believe are applicable:

1. Motility—this is self explanatory.
2. Change in form—demonstration of change in form would be most compelling evidence for life. Under this heading I would include both spontaneous change such as pulsation or amoeboid movements and as changes induced by alterations in the environment as, for example, irritability, or shrinkage and expansion of microscopic particles in re-

sponse to change in osmotic pressure. This would be strong evidence for a semi-permeable membrane enclosing the particle and I cannot conceive of living organisms without such a membrane.

3. Complexity of Structure
   a. Macroscopic
      1. Evidence that larger forms are comprised of discrete smaller units (cells).
      2. Non-random association of the sub-units.
   b. Intracellular—existence of organelles, membranes, vacuoles, etc.

Tests that would be useful for the recognition of some of these morphological characteristics include:

   a. Differential staining.
   b. Impermeability—this would indicate the presence of a membrane surrounding a particle.
   c. Histochemistry—this would be a powerful method because it combines the morphological approach with a functional or chemical assay.

CHAPTER 21

THE USE OF MARTIAN MATERIALS IN THE SEARCH FOR MARTIAN LIFE

ALEXANDER RICH

The exploration of Mars will involve both a search for possible life as well as a chemical characterization of the planet. It is possible that these two activities can be carried out jointly in that the procedures developed for chemical characterization can also be usefully employed in the detection of living systems.

One of the problems we encounter in the search for extraterrestrial life is the question of its similarity to life as we know it on this planet. Conditions on Mars are such that they probably could support terrestrial life. Accordingly, experiments have been designed to be used in conjunction with a soft landing on Mars in which samples of potentially life-containing Martian matter are inoculated into reaction vessels filled with nutrients which would support growth of a wide variety of terrestrial organisms. The rationale of these experiments is that the detection of growth would certainly lead us to the conclusion that life does exist on Mars. These experiments should be carried out but we should also consider a different class of experiments in which we make no presuppositions about the nature of Martian life. In these experiments, we do not try to speculate about the type of metabolism or the nature of Martian materials which have been utilized by Martian life, but instead we utilize the materials available on the planet directly in an attempt to detect life.

An example of the danger of presupposing something about the Martian

427

environment is the natural tendency which we have to think of life and its chemical reactions in an aqueous medium. The possible hazard of this is illustrated by some recent work from Pimentel's laboratory. They have found that it is possible to match the reported infrared bands in the Martian atmosphere with a 1:1 mixture of D_2O and HDO. It was suggested that there is a large amount of deuterium relative to hydrogen in the Martian environment, and much greater than that which prevails in the terrestrial environment. While it eventually developed that the disputed infrared spectrum was of terrestrial and not of Martian origin, it raised the possibility that Martian life might exist in an environment with a different isotopic composition from that found on Earth. If this is indeed the case, then the use of terrestrial H_2O would poison these organisms. It has been shown in experiments carried out by J. J. Katz that simple organisms are unable to adapt to very drastic changes from H_2O to D_2O or vice versa even though these organisms can be induced to grow on pure D_2O if the transition is made very gradually. In the experiments proposed here, we would not supply terrestrial water. Instead we would collect an appropriate solvent from the Martian environment, concentrate it by one of the techniques described below and then attempt to detect Martian life directly in a medium supplied from Martian material.

LIFE DETECTION METHODS

Any experiment designed for the detection of life is carried out by perturbing the system in some manner and then making measurements to detect metabolism or multiplication. The perturbation in the experiment discussed above consists in inoculating Martian matter into a reaction vessel filled with terrestrial nutrients. Following this, turbidity is measured, or the incorporation of radioactive material is detected associated with metabolic activity. Since we must acknowledge the possibility of destroying Martian life by using terrestrial materials (and terrestrial assumptions about life) we should ask what is the minimum perturbation that we can apply to a life detecting system that is consonant with the actual detection of life.

The simplest experiment of this type would be one in which a portion of Martian matter is heated slightly and then a thermal analysis carried out to detect subsequent metabolic activities by Martian microorganisms which are now subjected to a higher ambient temperature. Experiments of this type have been described elsewhere in this document.

Another type of minimum perturbation experiment is one in which a sample of Martian matter is sterilized, for example, by raising it to a very high temperature adequate to kill terrestrial organisms and therefore presumably also Martian microorganisms. This cooled Martian material could then be reinoculated with unheated, unsterilized Martian matter and the sample observed for signs of increased metabolic activity. This might occur because of the presence of more metabolic nutrients in the sterilized sample of Martian material which could be utilized by the organisms of the inoculum.

A common problem in all of these analyses is the type of perturbation that we must introduce into the system in order to carry out the detection of metabolic activity. The simplest type of detection might be that obtained by thermal analysis as mentioned above. Another method for detecting metabolic activity might involve neutron activation of "sterilized" Martian material which is then exposed to Martian organisms. Detection in this case may involve looking for the end products of metabolic activity. Alternatively, another type of detection system might involve the utilization of $C^{14} O_2$, C^{14}-glucose or P^{32}-phosphate or other radioactive materials that are of terrestrial origin, supplied by the lander. This tracer material may then participate in the metabolism of Martian organisms even though the bulk of the nutrients themselves are not supplied by the lander but rather are obtained from Martian material itself as described below.

THE CHEMICAL PROCESSING OF MARTIAN MATERIAL TO COLLECT NUTRIENTS

An important type of experiment is one that would involve the isolation and concentration of chemicals from the Martian terrain that could then be fed to samples of Martian matter that we suspect are contaminated with Martian microorganisms. In short, Martian matter would be subjected to chemical purification processes in the hope of concentrating nutrients that would then enable Martian microorganisms to proliferate in such a way that a positive answer could be obtained in a life detection experiment. In the execution of this project we may imagine that we have developed, for example, ten small chemical extractions modules that serve to process and concentrate Martian matter in various ways. For example, one might simply filter the materials and accumulate smaller particles, and exclude larger particles. Such a simple screening by size would select finer particles which have larger surface areas and this may represent a type of primitive chemical fractionation. Another method might use a flotation technique in a non-aqueous solvent followed by the isolation of the lighter materials. This might lead to the accumulation of oil-like Martian constituents. Another process might involve solubility in water or other solvents, followed by an extraction of the material from the solvent with subsequent drying. This would be a simple chemical extraction procedure. Another technique might involve volatilization and then condensation to collect the more volatile Martian components. Various techniques for chemical purification might then also be associated with a subsequent chromatographic isolation that might then produce materials beginning to approach chemical purity. The chemical techniques that can be employed are numerous. For example, another process might involve the acid hydrolysis of Martian matter followed by the concentration of a hydrolysate. This would tend to convert polymeric material into monomers that might be readily utilized by microorganisms. The net result of all of these chemical fractionation and extraction procedures would be the accumulation of semi-purified Martian materials. These could be used in a double manner, on the one hand to test their value as potential nutrients for Martian organisms and, alternatively, the chemical analysis of these components would be a useful step in beginning the chemical characterization of the Martian environment.

With these ten different types of chemical concentrates as described above, it would then be possible to add these materials into samples of Martian matter suspected of containing microorganisms and then to assay for the signs of metabolic activity. It would, of course, be possible to program a system to use mixtures of various products of the purification process to see whether they may be more effective than some of the components extracted singly. Finally it would be possible to construct, very simply, a program that would optimize the effect of adding these various constituents. Analysis of these materials thus gives us some primitive information concerning Martian biochemistry. One could think of a fairly simple automated laboratory that could carry out this kind of experiment and would, in effect, carry out logical checks to determine whether positive results were consistent.

Another significant consequence of this type of system is that chemical analysis could be carried out on each of the products isolated by these various techniques. In some cases, the material could be analyzed by infrared spectroscopy, gas chromatography or mass spectrometry. This information would be of direct importance itself, independent of its effect on the biological experimentation since it would contribute to a knowledge of the chemical state of the planet. A positive result in the biological experiment would, however, give us direct information about some parameters of Martian life and allow a comparison with what we observe in terrestrial life.

In summary, it may be possible to detect life on Mars through the use of chemical nutrients extracted on the planet by the landing apparatus. This type of experiment allows us to minimize our assumptions regarding the nature of Martian life and, at the same time to obtain some direct information regarding the chemical composition of the planet.

PART VIII

MARTIAN LANDINGS: MANNED

CHAPTER 22

THE IMPACT OF MANNED SPACEFLIGHT ON THE EXOBIOLOGY PROGRAM

N. H. HOROWITZ

It seems self-evident that the study of Martian life, assuming it exists, could be most effectively carried out by human investigators working in terrestrial laboratories on returned Martian samples. The resources of brains, of equipment, and of human intuition and judgment that could be brought to bear on the problems of Martian biology would, under such circumstances, be virtually limitless. By comparison, the information that could be obtained from automatic instruments landed on Mars and trans- mitting data by radio would be far inferior—not only in quantity and rele- vance, but also in reliability. It might well take many years of Martian exploration by automated spacecraft to discover what could be learned in a few months of study of returned samples in laboratories on the Earth.

Until recently, the prospects of returning Martian samples to the Earth appeared so remote that it did not seem necessary to take these prospects into account in planning exobiological programs. Rather, the emphasis was on ingenious and ever more complicated machines. Recent engineering studies sponsored by NASA have changed the picture, however. It now appears that the sending of a manned mission to Mars and back will be technically feasible in the near future. For example, one estimate suggests that six or seven men could make the round-trip to Mars in the early 1980's if the current rate of NASA funding remains constant, or earlier if the funding is increased. It should be noted that forecasts such as this are based on anticipated rocket capabilities and assume that men are physiologically capable of making such a journey. Whether, in fact, the latter is correct or not cannot be decided until we have had more experience with prolonged manned space flights.

The possibility of manned missions to Mars obviously has great significance for the exobiology program, since it implies that Martian samples may become available for terrestrial study in the foreseeable future. One of the major tasks is to arrive at a recommendation regarding the direction that the exobiology program should take in the light of this possibility; to wit, should it orient itself exclusively toward an unmanned sequence of missions, or should it prepare for the possibility that we may have Martian samples in our hands within twenty years? This question is not an academic one, since long-range plans have to be made, and the manned and unmanned programs will eventually be in direct competition for funds and priorities. In some ways, this competition has already begun.

Although the advantages of returning Martian samples for study at home are very great and quite obvious, there are also possible disadvantages which the study has to evaluate. Among these are the risk of contaminating Mars with terrestrial microorganisms, a risk that is presumably greater with manned missions than with unmanned ones, and the risk of contaminating the Earth with returned Martian organisms. As regards the former, we do not have sufficient information to decide whether any terrestrial species could, in fact, take hold in the Martian environment and infect the planet in competition with whatever native organisms may exist there; present knowledge of the Martian environment indicates that it would be unreceptive to terrestrial species. As regards the risk of back contamination, the probability of finding organisms on Mars that are dangerous to man or other terrestrial species appears to be very remote, especially when one considers the fact that the pathogens we know have evolved in association with their hosts, or with a closely related species. In any case, precautions could be observed in introducing Martian samples to the Earth, with, for example, special facilities for quarantining such samples until an assessment of the actual hazard had been made.

In any case, it is highly probable that if men can go to Mars, they will do so whether we like it or not. The path of wisdom, it seems to me, is therefore to anticipate the possibility of round-trip flights to Mars and to plan the exobiology program so that it can take full advantage of such missions in case they prove feasible; but also so that it will not be left high-and-dry if they prove to be impossible. The details of such a program cannot be stated here, but some general points can be made:

1. Whether manned missions are undertaken or not, the initial observations of Mars will be by unmanned probes.

2. The first objective of these probes would be to determine whether or not life exists on the planet.

3. If life is detected, the next tasks of the unmanned probes might be to discover the geological and ecological distribution of the organisms, i.e., where they are to be found in the greatest numbers. Also, information as to the size and gross morphology of the Martian biota, and some estimate of their numbers and variety would be among the first objectives.

4. The foregoing determinations and possibly others would be common to both the manned and unmanned programs. At some point, however, these two programs would diverge in interest. The long-range objective of both programs would be to obtain a detailed description of the chemistry and biology of the Martian biota, but whereas one unmanned program would attempt to accomplish this *in situ,* the manned program would set about gathering the kinds of information necessary to insure the success of the anticipated manned landing. Meteorological and geological data, atmospheric and soil analyses, radiation flux measurements, etc., are some of the kinds of information that might be required.

In summary, the technology of space flight is rapidly developing and changing. Goals that seemed out of the question a few years ago are now within the realm of possibility. The exobiology program should retain enough flexibility so that it can take full advantage of new advances in the art of space flight as they come along. Among these developments, none will be more significant for exobiology than the development of the means for prolonged manned missions.

CHAPTER 23

PROSPECTS FOR MANNED MARS MISSIONS

ELLIOTT C. LEVINTHAL

Studies called "EMPIRE" (standing for Early Manned Planetary-Inter-planetary Roundtrip Expeditions) were initiated early in 1962 by the Future Projects Office for the Marshall Space Flight Center. These and related studies by other NASA centers were intended to bring to light the technical problems associated with such missions. The emphasis of these studies was on single and multiple planetary fly-bys, with some considera-tion given to planetary orbital and landing missions. The time period con-sidered was the early 1970's. The contractors were Aeronutronic Division (Philco-Ford Motor Company), Lockheed Missiles and Space Company and General Dynamics/Astronautics. Studies relating to the time period 1975-85 were initiated in early 1963, by contracts with General Dynamics/ Fort Worth and Douglas Aircraft Company. Follow-on EMPIRE studies were carried out by Lockheed and General Dynamics/Astronautics. In addition, studies were made of a Mars Excursion Module by Aeronutronic, a Mars Mission Module (MMM) by North American Aviation's Space and Information Division, and an Earth Return Module (ERM) by Lock-heed under the direction of the Manned Spacecraft Center. Complementary to these efforts were studies initiated by the Ames Research Center early in 1963 for a Manned Mars Landing and Return Mission. These studies were conducted by North American Aviation and by the TRW Space Technology Laboratories.

The complete reports or summary volumes of all the above except the General Dynamics/Fort Worth and Douglas Aircraft Company studies were reviewed. This review was not penetrating or critical but was intended to survey the types of missions considered, the time period during which they might occur, a rough estimate of their costs, and their realtionship to other NASA programs.

Three classes of manned planetary missions have been considered: manned round-trip planetary fly-bys; orbiters; and landers. All of these would have the capability of including small and medium-sized unmanned orbiting, hard or soft landed probes as part of the mission. Unmanned, survivable landers containing instrument payloads on the order of 2500 kg could not, however, be included as part of the "minimum" manned fly-by mission described below.

All the systems considered consisted of surface launch vehicles and orbital launch vehicles. The surface launch vehicle places the spacecraft and orbital launch vehicle in Earth orbit. From this orbit, the orbital launch vehicle provides the excess velocity for the particular transfer trajectory chosen. Many trajectory studies have been carried out. The trajectories fall into two main classes: high energy trajectories, which can provide either light side or dark side Martian fly-bys; and low energy trajectories, which provide light side Martian fly-bys. The high energy trajectories, besides being characterized by the requirement for higher energies from Earth orbit and shorter trip times for fly-bys, dip within the Earth's orbit. (Because of their increased exposure to solar flares, compared to the low energy trajectories that are never within the Earth's orbit, the high energy trajectories are known as "hot" and the low as "cool".) The trajectory studies show that on the basis of energy requirements, a dual planet fly-by (Venus and Mars) is not much harder to accomplish than a Martian fly-by. The use of trajectories that pass near Venus, either inbound or out-bound, increases the number of possible departure dates for flights between Earth and Mars. Trip times range from 400 days for high energy fly-bys to 630 days for low energy fly-bys and depend upon the year of launch, distance of nearest approach to Mars and the escape propulsion system. All of the Martian missions studied required either the use of several Saturn V's as Earth launch vehicles or the development of a post-Saturn launch vehicle. These studies considered several orbiting launch vehicles, including those using either chemical or nuclear propulsion stages. The fly-by mission described below requires a two-stage nuclear booster for the orbital launch vehicle.

MANNED FLY-BY

"The Saturn V appears incapable of launching a single nuclear stage into orbit with sufficient propellant to accomplish the Mars low energy fly-by" [*Lockheed, 1964*]. The total trip time for this flight is 650-680 days. Assuming the development of a two-stage nuclear booster, a multi-Earth launch mode utilizing three Saturn V launches reasonably assures Mars fly-by capability. At the level of fiscal 1965 funds, it was estimated a "minimum" fly-by mission could be accomplished by 1975. The estimates of Lockheed of the cost were, in their Follow-On Study, $3.5 to 3.8 billion plus $2.3 billion for nuclear engine development for one flight in 1975. *General Dynamics/Astronautics* [1963], by subtraction from a much more elaborate mission, estimates the cost of a fly-by which might be launched in 1975 at about $12 billion. *Aeronutronic* [1962] estimates a dual planet fly-by at $12.6 billion. These cost estimates are given solely to indicate range. In many of these studies they are presented simply as extrapolations from general cost surveys appearing in McGraw-Hill's *Handbook of Astronautical Engineering* [1961], with no pretensions to precision.

Photographic observations could be made during the course of a manned fly-by mission. In one such case, it was estimated that about a hundred overlapping photographs could be taken during a period of about an hour and a half, when the spacecraft would be relatively close to the planet. The reconnaissance and scientific instrumentation carried on board would include, in addition to a 120-inch focal length camera, an infrared camera, a small radar set of moderate resolution, and scientific instruments representing an extension of Mariner/Centaur experiments, weighing 204 kg. In addition, there is the possibility that a 105 kg probe could be launched from the manned fly-by vehicle.

One report characterizes the mission as follows:

> "The flyby is a limited, one-shot, narrow-swath reconnaissance tool, subject to continuous scale and angular-rate variation detrimental to optimum sensor design and to data interpretation. Its best use may be for operational test of future-mission equipment and possible for accurate insertion of a reliable unmanned reconnaissance orbiter and/or lander" [*Lockheed, 1964*].

MANNED ORBITER MISSION

Missions that remain in orbit about Mars for 30 to 50 days and last for a total of 400 to 450 days require orbital departure weights of the order of 10^6 kg. Based on a 90 per cent probability of the success of a single Saturn V launch—with the capability of 150,000 kg in Earth orbit, refueling requirements, and the number of different modules to be assembled in orbit—one would need to be prepared for twenty or more Saturn V launches to assure an 80 per cent probability of mission success (assuming operational nuclear engines). This has led to the conclusion that a launch vehicle much more powerful than the Saturn V is required for these missions—one with a capability of placing about 500,000 kg in Earth orbit.

The following estimates are pertinent to reconnaissance missions. To map the planet with a resolution of 10 meters, a 4-bit grey level scale, and a factor of π for overlapping, requires 1.44×10^{13} bits [*General Dynamics, 1963*]. Assuming a storage capacity of 1000 lines/mm of film, the storage weight for data would be 8,000 kg (compared to total estimated weights of 50,000 kg for a Mars orbiter module and 25,000 kg for a Mars manned lander module). For complete transmission within 100 days at 2 cycles/bit, it would require a bandwidth of 3.22×10^6 cycles. This suggests the use of the crew for on-board data evaluation and selection. The following quotation from a Lockheed report enumerates some of the engineering difficulties that this, in turn, presents:

> "Feasibility studies on the system requirements for implementing onboard crew evaluation must include sophisticated estimates of requirements for rapid data-processing; storage and retrieval of reference-frames (both pre-mission and post-orbit); automatic aids to the comparison of past and current reconnaissance shots and the correlation of many-source data; display/control techniques to integrate the crew into the man-machine loop; computer size to perform the access and retrieval function, as well as more complex calculations. Feasibility studies of the rapid reconnaissance-evaluation function— still problematic for giant ground systems—are still in the embryonic stage for onboard space-vehicle application" [*Lockheed, 1964*].

MANNED MARS LANDERS

While some of the first studies indicated that manned landings would be feasible from the engineering point of view in the 1970's, the follow-on studies predicted a time period in the 1980's. These predictions require a post-Saturn launch vehicle with a capability of placing about 500,000 kg in Earth orbit, nuclear vehicles, and the development of improved multi-start rocket techniques. The cost estimates range from an $18.5 billion calculation of *General Dynamics* [1963], which allows about $1 billion for a Mars excursion vehicle, to an *Aeronutronic* [1964] estimate of $40 billion. This last represented an extrapolation from a detailed study of a Manned Excursion Module with a 10 to 46 day capability for surface exploration and a two-man, 1000 kg scientific payload. The excursion module was estimated at a total cost of $6.16 billion for development and production and was projected as 10 to 15 per cent of the cost of total mission—giving $40 billion as the total mission cost.

RELATIONSHIP OF MANNED MARS MISSION TO OTHER MISSIONS

Disregarding any other issues, it is generally agreed that the engineering success of the Mars Manned Lander Mission demands extensive reconnaissance. In most reports this task is presumed to be carried out by unmanned spacecraft. *Aeronutronic* [1962] states:

> "... *It is essential* that probes be flown into the Mars atmosphere, that experiments be landed on the Mars surface, and that pictures of Mars be obtained with higher resolutions than currently available from the Earth. These efforts should use unmanned spacecraft and be conducted at the earliest opportunity. The availability of more precise data on Mars and the near Mars environment was presumed in the planning for MEM, but was not included in the estimated funds to accomplish the over-all MEM program."

We have also the following statement from the *TRW Space Technology Laboratories* [1964]:

> "A vital precursor for manned Mars stopover missions is the unmanned probe mission, which will obtain crucial data about the Mars environment, particularly the properties of the atmosphere. This information is urgently needed in establishing design criteria and functional requirements for the follow-on manned missions. In view of the rapidly expanding program of manned Mars planning studies, which is indicative of the increasing interest in interplanetary exploration, steps should be taken to accelerate the precursor probe missions."

The General Dynamics report, while emphasizing the need for reconnaissance, also points to the technological objective of "demonstrating the feasibility of manned flight from the activity sphere of our planet into that of the other" as another prerequisite for planetary *surface* exploration (Mars is considered the only planet for which this can now be seriously planned). These two objectives can be combined, which ties the manned capture (non-landing) missions to Mars. This has the disadvantage of postponing until the 1980's any extensive reconnaissance for any purposes— technological or scientific. As *General Dynamics* [1963] notes, by not combining them, "one is free to consider demonstration of the feasibility of a planetary capture mission by a flight to Venus. If this flight is successful, a repetition in the form of a fast capture mission to Mars appears not warranted." This has the advantage that the manned feasibility mission to Venus requires considerably less mass in Earth orbit and would be possible to implement at an earlier date than a Mars mission. It also frees early reconnaissance from the restrictions man imposes on these missions (for example, long stays in orbit or on the surface over several Martian seasons).

An extensive general consideration of the Manned Missions and their utilization is included in Lockheed's Follow-On Study:

"Deeper considerations . . . will raise additional serious doubts as to the usefulness of contributions expected from the manned nonstop trips. In fact, the fly-bys viewed in relation to other schemes of planetary exploration are seemingly characterized by their transient usefulness, and hence appear to be of sufficiently low import that their alleged contributions may be easily provided by the automatic probes" [*Lockheed*, 1964].

Nevertheless, they find need for a fly-by mission as a realistic "training" flight to serve as a bridge reaching from unmanned probes and manned near-Earth missions to the first manned planetary stopovers. They feel the fly-by should be considered in the mid-1970 time period to prepare for manned stopovers in the mid-1980's.

In conclusion, unmanned automated orbiters and landers should be planned that can carry out the scientific exploration of Mars. Any desire for manned missions makes this more, rather than less, urgent. The reconnaissance requirements for manned missions are not likely to be incompatible with the scientific objectives of unmanned missions and they impose similar requirements for sophistication.

REFERENCES

Aeronutronic Division, Philco, Ford Motor Company, *EMPIRE Final Report,* Dec. 21, 1962.

Aeronutronic Division, Philco, Ford Motor Company, Summary Report: Study of a Manned Mars Excursion Module (U). *Publ. No. U-2530,* May 13, 1964.

General Dynamics/Astronautics, A Study of Early Manned Interplanetary Missions. Final Summary Report *No. AOK 63 0001*, Jan. 31, 1963.

Lockheed Missiles and Space Company, Summary Report: Early Manned Interplanetary Mission Study, Volume 1. *No. 8-32-63-1*, March 1963.

Lockheed Missiles and Space Company, Manned Interplanetary Missions; Follow-On Study, Final Report; Volume 1—Summary *No. 8-32-64-1*, Jan. 28, 1964.

McGraw-Hill Book Co. *Handbook of Astronautical Engineering*, H. H. Koelle (Ed.), 1961.

TRW Space Technology Laboratories, Manned Mars Landing and Return Mission, Volume 1 (Summary). *No. 8572-6011-RU-000*, March 28, 1964.

CHAPTER 24

"BACK CONTAMINATION" AND QUARANTINE PROBLEMS AND PERSPECTIVES

A. H. Brown

The possibility and consequences of transferring to the Earth organisms that are indigenous to another planet or to the Earth's Moon have not been a focal point of discussion by this Study. Nevertheless, the participants have been variously concerned about such a contingency. If exotic life forms are introduced into our own biosphere, would they survive, propagate, infect terrestrial organisms, or bring harm directly or indirectly to our ecosphere? If there is a real danger of this so-called "back contamination" we should evaluate the seriousness of the threat and assess the means we ought to employ in our own protection.

This general topic was the subject of a two-day conference on the Potential Hazards of Back Contamination which was held during the period of this Study but drew on specialists outside the ranks of the regular Study participants. The report of the conference on Potential Hazards of Back Contamination from the Planets (Space Science Board, 19 Feb. 1965) should be consulted for more detailed arguments, but the conclusions are summarized here as they have some bearing on the general topic of the Summer Study.

The problem is not one of great urgency in the case of Martian round trip missions, as they will not be feasible for one or two decades. In the case of lunar missions, whatever risk may be involved is of immediate concern.

The existence of life on the Moon or on some planets cannot rationally be precluded. At present it seems quite impossible to estimate reliably the probability of life existing on any of several possible sites (the Moon, the Venus cloud layer, the Martian surface, possibly others). Thus some chance, however small, of back contamination must be presumed.

There are various lines of reasoning which argue either for or against the seriousness of back contamination. The danger of direct infection of man with resulting disease manifestations is unlikely but possible. The harmful infection of terrestrial plants or animals other than man is far more likely. The introduction of non-pathogenic organisms seems more probable than that of agents that could cause disease. These might or might not proliferate but, if they should do so, they might bring about severely adverse effects on our environment by any of several mechanisms. Again, the chance seems remote but the possibility exists, nonetheless.

In our ecosystem, where the biota has very great diversity, engendered over billions of years of evolution, clearly, no living agent has brought about a biological catastrophe of such proportions that terrestrial life was eliminated. It is true that many species (and for that matter even entire phyla) have evolved, flourished, then declined and disappeared in the long history of life on this Earth. In a few instances the decline can be ascribed to a specific, harmful, biological agent—either a pathogen, predator, or agent that altered the environment in some critical fashion. By and large, however, organisms have not developed the potency to inflict catastrophic harm on the rest of the biota, perhaps because the harmful has evolved along with the susceptible and evolution has provided for defense as well as for vulnerability. If a truly exotic organism were to be introduced, what are the chances that it would prove harmful? What are the chances that existing defenses would not suffice to keep it in check? What are the chances that its introduction would have disastrous consequences?

Patently we have no way to supply precise estimates, but in a qualitative sense we know that an exotic species—if it can be harmful at all—will not likely be checked effectively by defense mechanisms built by evolution into our terrestrial species. Also, if a biological disaster is possible from back contamination, the chances of it becoming of catastrophic proportions seem enormously greater because the causal agent is so foreign to our living world. While the risks cannot be calculated, concern is based not on irrational fear of the unknown, but on appreciation of how very serious the consequences *may* be. It is this awareness that prevents us from dismissing the danger as trivial, just because the risk of disaster from back contamination—even though we cannot compute it—must surely be very small. It was the well-considered, unanimous judgment of the participants at the Conference on Potential Hazards of Back Contamination that the

United States should take leadership in the study and implementation of protective measures against back contamination.

Specific protective measures would include retention of returned samples behind absolute bacteriological barriers where they should be examined under conditions of rigid biological and chemical isolation. Tests should be made on returned samples to reveal any living components and to determine the pathogenicity to plants, animals, and man, of returned sample material. Only after thorough testing should the samples be certified as safe to distribute to other scientific laboratories.

The preparation for lunar and planetary roundtrip missions should include the development of techniques for minimizing contamination of astronauts and equipment while on the lunar or planetary surface. Astronauts should be trained in procedures to reduce inadvertent transfer of material and the effectiveness of such procedures should be tested on Earth in a "dry run" with non-pathogenic, tracer organisms.

Upon return from the mission, spacecraft, astronauts, and all persons who come in contact with them should be received into an isolation environment and remain there for a period of strict quarantine which was recommended provisionally as three weesks in the case of a Martian mission. The spacecraft, suits, and other equipment should not be decontaminated until study of the returned samples indicate they may be certified as biologically safe.

It seems imperative that a continuing committee or other agency be established to develop plans for quarantine, for detailed operational procedures of sample collection, handling, and study, for utilizing the experience of persons and organizations who have carried out relevant research, and to insure that we do our best to reduce the dangers of back contamination without impairing unnecessarily the primary operational responsibility of NASA for the exploration of space.

PART IX

AVOIDING THE CONTAMINATION OF MARS

CHAPTER 25

STERILIZATION AND CONTAMINATION:
THE NATURE OF THE PROBLEM

K. C. ATWOOD

The sterilization of objects that may land on extraterrestrial bodies is an accepted feature of any responsibly planned attempt at planetary exploration. It will require vigilant and resourceful persons and substantial facilities and will definitely add to the cost and difficulty of the program. Contamination with terrestrial microbes must be avoided since it may confound future studies of the planetary history, surface characteristics and biota. On the other hand, the requirement that spacecraft withstand sterilization procedures may not always be met without sacrifice of advantages in materials and systems. As to the relative emphasis appropriate to these two considerations, it may be noted that the kinds of difficulties caused by sterilization, e.g., systems failures, launch cancellation or design problems are postponements; they do not preclude ultimate attainment of the scientific goals. In contrast, the conceivable difficulties, real or unreal, that sterilization is intended to prevent may be permanent. They include major uncertainties in regard to the natural state of affairs on the planet, destruction of as yet unforeseen resources and irretrievable forfeit of important objectives of planetary exploration.

So far as can be foreseen at present, planetary exploration will be confined to the solar system. It is possible that Mars may provide our only chance to study life-forms of entirely separate descent. The importance of this opportunity outranks every prospect; the effect on world thought of the

449

discoveries to be made on Mars may compare with that of the works of Copernicus or Darwin. A careless blunder could destroy the opportunity. The reasons for the sterilization of spacecraft are clear: we do not know enough about Mars to predict with confidence the outcome of microbial contamination of its surface. Regrettable and irreversible results can be imagined. The means of avoiding these results are known; hence we must employ such means.

The importance of sterilization of spacecraft, as well as the technical aspects, have been the subject of several prior reports. Phases of the subject that have not been emphasized elsewhere will be given disproportionate attention here. In particular an attempt is made to assess the consequences of contamination of Mars on the basis of the very limited information we now possess and to suggest what information would be most valuable from the standpoint of assessment of these consequences as the exploration of the planet proceeds.

PROSPECTS FOR SIGNIFICANT CONTAMINATION OF MARS

A lander that carries life detection devices may be the source of contamination of its own experiments. More remote consequences of biological contamination would be significant only if the organisms are subsequently recovered, particularly in samples taken at some distance from the point of inoculation, or if their growth measurably alters the chemical constitution of the planetary surface, or if they affect indigenous life forms, e.g., as pathogens. If the organisms do not multiply or if they remain localized, their presence will be irrelevent to subsequent studies of the planet. This statement is based on the dilution factor provided by the Martian surface area, which is about 10^{14} square meters. Suppose, for example, that a landing capsule deposits 10^8 viable and environment-resistant organisms (an obvious overestimate) on the Martian surface. If these are distributed uniformly, the probability of detection by a device that exhaustively samples one square meter is only 10^{-6}. If they remain localized, the probability is even less. The detection probability will increase only if the contaminants stay localized *and* subsequent devices are superimposed. Thus we may confidently expect that significant contamination would require both multiplication and dispersion of the introduced organisms.

In order to appreciate the bearing of the contamination problem on future scientific investigation and to offer conjectures based on present evidence concerning the likelihood that the introduction of organisms would result in significant contamination, we consider three cases which should, when all their variations are comprised, exhaust the possibilities with regard to the stage of planetary evolution to come under investigation: (1) Primary abiosis, (2) Autochthonous biota present, and (3) Postbiotic stage. We ignore the possibility that the planet is in a biopoietic stage since available evidence points to surface conditions far advanced beyond those conducive to origination of life. It will be assumed from the outset that the surface presents more or less drastic local departure from the average environment.

In the present context the important thing about condition (1) is that life *may* be absent even though the chemogenic prerequisites for biopoiesis were established approximately as they were on Earth. The example provided by the origination of Earth's biota does not tell us how probable such an outcome may be, given a comparable prebiotic opportunity; for reasons discussed elsewhere we cannot dismiss the possibility that the opportunity for prebiotic chemical evolution on Mars during some period in its history was comparable to that on Earth. Thus Mars and Earth may be taken hypothetically to represent independent trials with roughly similar probabilities of success. If no replicating and evolving forms arose on Mars during favorable times, the Martian surface may now contain relict deposits of the presumably rich and varied chemical *mélange* which, with the advent of life on a planet, would soon be recycled and changed beyond recognition. Experiments have shown that substrates utilizable by terrestrial organisms would be abundant in such mixtures; hence, in physically favorable local environments, the stage would be set for explosive multiplication of contaminants. Theoretically the consequences could be drastic indeed. Given a generation time of one month (a thousandfold submaximal) the population resulting from a single bacterium after eight years would be sufficient to cover the entire surface of Mars with one gram of bacteria per square centimeter. Such catastrophic potentialities are not mentioned here to suggest that they are possible on Mars, but rather to illustrate the magnitude of the effect given extensive though suboptimal conditions for microbial growth.

If the origination of a system capable of indefinite evolution were completed and refined on Mars, the history of such systems on Earth permits the surmise that condition (2) is more likely than (3); that is, that life has persisted until the present. Earth organisms have evolved to inhabit environments just as remote from those that are believed to have been favorable for biopoiesis as is the average Martian environment. In at least one particular, the oxygen tension, the Earth conditions are more extreme than Martian. It is curious in the light of current concepts of biopoiesis and evolution that the presence of molecular oxygen should persist in many minds as an indispensible condition for advanced life.

In any case, if rapid environment change or catastrophe has not brought an end to previously established life, the organisms must have evolved to keep pace with the progressively more extreme departure of the external environment from that present during the period of biopoiesis. Again, if we follow the example of Earth the modifications to accommodate to such environmental changes would have to be superimposed on certain ubiquitous and primitive characteristics such as the chemical identity of the genetic material itself and the specification of functions analogous to our genetic replication, transcription and translation. The internal environment of cells provides the conditions under which the elementary molecular copying processes can occur much as they have from their early beginnings. Thus the internal conditions may be regarded as much closer to those of the biopoietic environment than are the conditions outside the protective enclave of the organism. Further adaptations involve the maintenance of a special environment beyond the boundaries of the organism itself.

Despite the strong possibility that the detailed chemical basis will be unique for each system that has had a separate origin, we expect the evolution of elaborate mechanisms for the maintenance of primitive conditions within, or in the immediate neighborhood of, organisms to be a general feature of life on any advanced planet. On Earth and Mars these primitive conditions may have much in common. The relevance of these considerations to the sterilization question is that the expected physiological and ecological adaptations of organisms to the conditions on an advanced planet are likely to provide local opportunities for the multiplication of adventitious contaminants within or around the indigenous forms.

In case autochthonous life has at some time in the past been exterminated, the planet could not offer the afore-mentioned biogenically maintained habitats. Suitable microenvironments could, however, be maintained around special surface features such as fumaroles, warm springs, or buried chemical deposits. The establishment of steady-state populations of contaminants in such localities might temporarily confound investigations more than would the coexistence of authochthonous and adventitious forms.

Significant contamination of Mars appears to be a distinct possibility irrespective of the presence or absence of life there. The experimental assessment of the significance of contamination will remain incomplete until the range of different environments is known so that appropriate simulation experiments can be performed. Even then, the interactions with Martian biota will remain a major uncertainty. Since we may assume, however, that large areas of the surface have the average environment, the question of the likelihood of dispersion of contaminants can be discussed in a preliminary way.

THE SPREAD OF CONTAMINANTS

Experiments with simulated average environments cannot answer the question whether contaminants would become established on Mars. Such experiments can, however, be helpful in evaluating the possibilities for spread of contaminants; hence—and especially important—the condition that would be found by future explorers of the planet in case contamination from earlier landers had become established.

Preliminary studies in environments simulating average Martian conditions with a diverse though limited number of microorgansims have revealed none which continue to multiply under those conditions although some have remained viable. We shall make the reasonable but unproven assumption that some terrestrial species will be able to survive on Mars but that none can multiply under *average* Martian conditions. On this assumption the establishment of an adventitious population would require the introduction of the landed organisms into a suitable microenvironment. Thus, the multiplication of contaminants would be more or less delayed, perhaps indefinitely, depending on the circumstances of the landing and the accessibility of the special environments. No matter how direct the initial introduction, it will be to some extent selective; we cannot expect the local environment to support all of the species that are potential contaminants.

Subsequent spread from an established growing population might take place by direct extension, by wind, or by transport on (or in) mobile Martian macroorganisms. Spread by direct extension would be limited by topographic barriers unless the relevant microenvironments form an interconnected unit. Experienced observers represent the dark surface features of Mars as a single network. A similar contiguity of hospitable microenvironments would be especially surprising in view of the scarcity of liquid water; so much so that one would be tempted to consider a cognogenic origin for such a system. In short, it seems impossible on the basis of present knowledge of the average conditions that terrestrial microbes could become widespread on Mars through direct extension of their range unless a stage of cognogeny has been reached, in which case the contamination would not preclude the recognition of Martian organisms, although it might have other undesirable effects. Similarly, the presence of indigenous vectors would imply a Martian biota that could not possibly be confused with any recent terrestrial introduction.

Aeolian dispersion remains as a more general basis for planet-wide distribution of contaminants. A primary limitation on this form of transport is the rate at which organisms become windborne. On Earth the frequency of organisms in the air varies enormously from place to place, but is only a very small proportion of the source populations. The occurrence of dust storms on Mars gives ample evidence of the transport of surface materials from dry areas, but these areas are not the ones in which we should expect contaminants to be concentrated. In the moist microenvironments that would allow multiplication of contaminants, organisms would be much less likely to be lifted by wind, and drying of the region would probably be a prerequisite for rapid or extensive dispersion of its organisms. Windborne organisms and those deposited on the surface would be exposed to the rigors of the Martian environment; thus, dispersion would be selective for species that can withstand desiccation and the freeze-thaw cycles. Solar ultraviolet, which is believed to reach the surface with little atmospheric attenuation, would certainly have a deterrent effect on aeolian spread. While it is true that association with opaque particles will shield the organisms, only a fraction will be completely surrounded by opaque material and hence able to survive indefinitely in fully exposed locations. On the whole, it seems likely that the obstacles to the spread of contaminants on Mars are formidable.

CONTAMINATION AS A SOURCE OF CONFUSION

A great deal has been made of the confusion that would result if contamination occurred before or near the beginning of a program of biological exploration. A summary of the possible conditions following multiplication and spread of contaminants suggests that the extent to which they would obfuscate scientific investigation has been exaggerated in the context of very thorough studies, but perhaps correctly assessed in the context of preliminary observations. If the planet were barren up to the time of contamination, the biota found later would have three distinctive features. First, few different kinds would be present; second, they would all be classified in Earth taxons and, finally, their distribution on the planet would be superficial. If it were feasible to apply these criteria, they would serve to identify the organisms as adventitious with absolute certainty.

It is obvious that the number of species effectively introduced would be small. The sources of contamination during assembly of the vehicle are non-random with respect to species, and further selective attenuation would result from the incomplete sterilization and the Martian environment. Autochthonous biota, on the contrary, would comprise many types. Mutation and selection are necessary for any form of life, exobiota included; hence the presence of any evolved organism implies a variety of forms appropriate to the variety of ecological opportunities. An absence of autotrophs would be a very suspicious feature. Terrestrial autotrophs would be unlikely contaminants and the indigenous biota of an advanced planet is expected on thermodynamic grounds to include a larger biomass of autotrophs than of heterotrophs.

The identification of an ostensible exobiont as a member of an Earth taxon would prove not only that it was adventitious, but that the introduction was relatively recent in the time scale of planetary evolution. If a major portion of the evolutionary history of an organism had occurred on Mars it could not fit into any *lower* taxonomic category now extant on Earth. Evidence of common ancestry would be present, however, if the introduction had been made after ubiquitous Earth biochemistry was established, say in the Precambrian. Statements such as the foregoing are not prejudgments of the issues we hope to resolve by exobiological studies; they are substantiated by terrestrial experience. It may be added, parenthetically, that the principles adduced in this hypothetical case of transplanted Earth biota are also generalizable to exotic life because they do not depend on the chemical basis of life, but only on its capacity to evolve by mutation and selection.

Autochthonous organisms and their remains would be present in undisturbed subsurface locations and permafrost in striking contrast to the superficial distribution of recent contaminants. Reliable evidence of the absence of dormant forms in cryptic locations, while they are present superficially, would be a strong indication of their recent advent.

Having considered the problem of mistaken identity of biota, we turn attention to other changes in the planetary surface. The surface composition of a planet on which life could have arisen, but did not, might be completely obscured by the growth of contaminants if the physical conditions were everywhere favorable. On Mars, however, the average conditions are such that if the contaminants significantly changed the composition of their local environments, examples of the original surface composition would still be preserved by having been dried, frozen, or buried during the history of the planet.

The question remains of the feasibility of applying these criteria in case an initial confusion should arise. The taxonomic criterion would be rather easy in an Earth-based laboratory and could be confirmed beyond doubt by means of molecular hybridization. The decision between a recent and a remote introduction might remain equivocal for some time unless return of the organisms could be arranged, with appropriate precautions against back contamination. The other two criteria would require investigations on the planet approximately as elaborate as those now visualized for the automated biological laboratory. By means of still more prolonged investigations, contamination could not only be proved, but dated with a fair degree of precision. We may conclude that contaminants on Mars, if it is now in a condition of primary abiosis, could under certain circumstances be mistaken for exobionts. The true condition would become evident upon detailed study of the organisms and their surroundings, but the necessary studies would probably be as lengthy and difficult as those for the characterization of *bona fide* exobionts.

If Mars is in secondary abiosis, evidences of prior life would probably be found. These evidences might preclude an easy decision on the question of whether the living examples were survivors or adventitious forms, and the extreme improbability of this scenario would only serve to render the erroneous interpretation more plausible. The special difficulty here would be to rule out the possibility that the extinct life, very likely autochthonous, had the same primitive components as the living forms, erroneously suggesting that identical systems of macromolecular specification and synthesis had evolved on Mars and Earth. If as seems likely, no decisive differences were apparent from fossil chemistry the alternatives would remain of a terrestrial origin of the living forms versus a common Martian origin for both. Since the latter alternative would indicate unforeseen severe restraints on the variety of solutions to the problem of biopoiesis, an important issue would be confounded. The taxonomic criterion, although powerful, would have to stand alone. The confusion could be resolved, but this would require thorough characterization of the organisms.

In this, as in other instances, an adequate series of precontamination tests for *terrestrial* organisms would be of decisive value. After the distribution and means of dispersion of the contaminating organisms had been studied, it would be possible to interpret prior negative results of these tests more confidently than before, and establish that the organisms found later were indeed contaminants. A positive result at first, on the other hand, would have initiated the study of the *bona fide* exobionts without delay.

If living exobionts are present, they will tend to be better adapted than contaminants to the conditions. Even if terrestrial microbes could ultimately compete with Martian counterparts, this would require time for the evolution of special ecotypes. The recognition of contaminants in the presence of exobionts seems feasible and it is difficult to see how their presence would prevent the isolation and study of exobionts. The interaction of terrestrial microbes with Martian macrobionts, however, is open to any conjecture, including the possibility of various degrees of pathogenicity. It is true that on Earth the host-pathogen relation always involves special adaptations that would have essentially zero probability of preexisting in mutually exotic forms. We cannot be sure, however, that pathogenicity between mutually exotic forms may not have some basis entirely unanticipated from our experience with monophyletic biota. If this were true, it might or might not confound scientific investigations, but we can imagine many reasons why a pandemic would be regrettable; suffice it to say that the risk should not be taken inadvertently. An early search for macrobionts is essential and the credibility of their presence should not be underestimated. The suggestion of large, complex organisms on Mars is often ridiculed in accordance with the popular belief that inhospitable environments should support only simple or primitive forms. In actuality the opposite is true. Increasing hostility of the environment tends to exterminate both primitive and inappropriately specialized forms, and to select increasingly elaborate adaptations to the new conditions. Some of the most successful adaptations that can be imagined, or are known on Earth, can occur *only* in complex organisms.

We may conclude that contamination of Mars would probably not cause *permanent* confusion in any of the contemplated scientific investigations. The one serious consequence that cannot be evaluated is pathogenicity of terrestrial microbiota for Martian macrobiota. Hence proof of the absence of macrobiota, or proof of non-pathogenicity would be a necessary—but not sufficient—prerequisite to relaxation of sterilization practices.

In the foregoing arguments a great deal of confidence has been placed in the uniqueness of each genetic lineage at the level of primary sequence in polypeptides and polynucleotides, and the consequent certainty with which genetic relationships can be established. Clearly, an organism not possessing the ubiquitous molecular components of terrestrial biota would be identified as an exobiont. On the other hand, an organism that did possess these components could be subjected to detailed comparisons with known taxa. Amino acid sequences can be determined analytically and nucleotide sequences compared by the techniques of molecular hybridization. The probability of common ancestry approaches unity as the length of common sequence increases. On reasonable assumptions, the coincident sequence required for strong proof of genetic relationship is surprisingly short. Perhaps current opinion on the likelihood of confusion among contaminants and exobionts has not taken the possibilities of molecular taxonomy properly into account.

Strong reliance has also been placed on the ecological argument that if life exists at all on Mars, some forms of it will have a practically ubiquitous distribution. The selective advantage of dispersion capability is very strong and is tantamount to selection for prolonged survival in the average, presumably inhospitable areas. This prognostication cannot be proved except by experiment, but it provides a reasonable *a priori* basis for the belief that the distribution of indigenous and adventitious bionts would differ for a long time following the introduction.

STANDARDS FOR SPACECRAFT STERILIZATION

Bacteriological sterility can be expressed as an all-or-none attribute, or as a probability, depending on the criterion employed to ascertain sterility. The all-or-none criteria are tests performed after the sterilization procedure; for example, we inoculate a medium and if nothing grows it is sterile (at least with respect to organisms capable of growth on that medium). Alternatively, the surviving fraction of organisms can be determined in separate experiments under the sterilizing conditions and a probability obtained that the treated population contains one or more viable organisms. Since in typical cases the surviving fraction declines exponentially with time of treatment, the required probability is usually simple to estimate from experimental points, and an estimate of the size of the initial population. The testing of spacecraft for sterility is not feasible; therefore the sterility of a spacecraft can be expressed only as a probability.

Standardization of the permissible number of viable organisms per spacecraft is a matter of judgment. No particular value can be rigorously defended by appeal to fact or logic, and all attempts to do so turn out upon close scrutiny to be specious. The mechanism by which such values are actually derived can be reduced to two steps. First an all-or-none decision is made by means of the same criteria that would apply if the sterility of the spacecraft could be confirmed experimentally. Second, if by these criteria sterilization is required, then the permissible probability of contamination is fixed at a level which is, in the judgment of the responsible person, indistinguishable from zero. Such values, reflecting individual temperament, range from 10^{-3} to 10^{-6}.

Sagan and Coleman (Chapter 28) point out that the probability of contamination of Mars during a program of scientific investigation is different from the probability of contaminating it in any given mission. They show how the theory of waiting times can be used to compute a standard for spacecraft sterilization such that the risk of contamination prior to completion of the program will not exceed some predesignated value. Required parameters are the number of experiments that must succeed to complete the program, the probability of success per experiment, the number of experiments per mission, the probability of failure of a mission as a whole, and the probability of effective contamination per organism deposited. In practice, these values would be extremely uncertain, and changeable during the program. The calculation of the standard for individual missions from predesignated program characteristics should not obscure the fact that the permissible risk of contamination for the entire program is an arbitrary figure to be assumed *a priori* for the purpose of computation. This approach does not supply a basis for selection of a standard; its value is in transferring the point of subjective judgment from the individual mission to the anticipated series.

Various rationales can be conceived that obscure the arbitrary nature of the standard. For example, the probability is greater than zero that Mars has already been contaminated with organisms from Earth; hence, a risk of contamination no greater than that which has already been sustained might be acceptable. To derive a number on this basis we begin by rejecting the Arrhenius hypothesis having to do with spores, or particles of equivalent size, on the ground that such particles would be insufficiently protected against solar ultraviolet and ionizing radiation to survive the traverse. Macroscopic chunks ejected from the Earth's surface, however, would effectively shield included organisms. It has been estimated that fragments with sufficient velocity to reach Mars are ejected by meteoritic impacts about once in 10^7 years; that is, about 10^3 such instances may have occurred since the Cambrian. If they are ejected in random directions then the probability that a given one impacts on Mars is about 10^{-9}, the ratio of the area of the disk of Mars to the area of the sphere of orbital radius. On these assumptions the expectation that Mars has been contaminated since the Cambrian is 10^{-6}. The mechanism also suffices for Mars to Earth transport, or contamination of both planets by fragments from a common parent body. No such rationale is relevant to the problem, however, and none but an arbitrary standard can be specified.

If an arbitrary standard is prescribed, its maintenance in practice may require a more or less reliable estimate of the size and composition of the microbial population in the spacecraft prior to the terminal sterilization. This problem would not arise if the terminal sterilization procedure remained harmless to components at arbitrarily low levels of microbial survival. In that case, a fictitious but safe upper limit of the microbial load could be assumed (e.g., the weight of the spacecraft) and the terminal sterilization adjusted accordingly. Such fictitious upper limits are not useful if the damage to components tends to increase with the effectiveness of sterilization. It has been suggested that the bacterial load can be approximated by means of experimental determination of the steady-state populations on representative surfaces, and sampling of components for internal contamination. Estimates obtained in this way would be useful provided that the sources of major fluctuations in number of bacteria per spacecraft can be recognized and controlled. These considerations should make it obvious that a set of procedures will ultimately have to be prescribed, rather than a standard of contamination probability. Such procedures may be designed with an approximate upper limit of contamination probability in mind. Only the procedures themselves, however, can be standardized.

STERILIZATION METHODS

The elaboration of useful details pertaining to methods of spacecraft sterilization would require a degree of engineering sophistication beyond the scope and intent of this discussion, or the competence of the author. Methods cannot be discussed intelligently unless the effects of heating and other procedures on different spacecraft components are known. No attempt will be made, therefore, to recommend specific procedures. Principles of redundancy and flexibility are generally applicable, however, no matter how the problems may differ in detail from time to time. As much redundancy should be incorporated into the sterilization program as is feasible from an engineering standpoint. Modules, sub-assemblies and separate components should be sterilized when feasible even though they will later be sterilized again as parts of a larger ensemble, or even though they will be joined to other components that have not been treated in the same way. Reundancy is desirable because it increases the probability that complete sterilization is achieved by some terminal procedure, and because it is a safeguard in case of accidental failures. Even in a complete failure of terminal sterilization the prior measures would not have been in vain, since an innumerable variety of situations can be imagined in which the probability of effective planetary contamination would depend strongly on the *number* of organisms introduced. The entire process of spacecraft production should be reviewed continuously in an effort to discover opportunities for reduction of bacterial load. Such opportunities should be exploited as they arise, even though a predesignated standard is already being met.

The terminal heat soak is a preferred method because it is simple and reliable in principle. No single method, however, is a *sine qua non* of effective sterilization. Where questions of feasibility arise they can be approached either by rendering existing methods feasible or by finding new methods, and the choice of these approaches should be based on calculable merit rather than on preconceived dogmatism. Given that a sterilization method can be made effective, its figure of merit must also be influenced by its effects on the functioning of spacecraft systems. At present it seems possible that the terminal heat soak can be made feasible even for large and complex spacecraft.

ADJUNCTIVE STRATEGEMS

Despite all efforts at a prevention the possibility remains that because of an improbable event, or a blunder, Mars will be contaminated at some time during the program of exploration. Accidental impact of an unsterilized object may occur. It is also possible that the decision to deliberately allow contamination (e.g., by manned landing) will turn out to be premature, or based on some error of judgment. It would be wise therefore to plan the biological exploration in such a way as to minimize the harm done by such an eventuality. One measure that has been suggested is the early collection of samples in sterile sealed containers. This may be a valuable procedure. Small samples taken at many different locations would be more valuable than one or few large samples. Means would have to be devised to make these samples easy to locate at some indefinite time in the future. The method has the disadvantage that it would not yield information in time to be useful in planning subsequent missions, since the samples could not be examined until much later.

Another stratagem is the early landing of life detection devices designed to detect *terrestrial* microorganisms and biochemical activities. This would immediately yield evidence concerning the presence or absence of organisms having a superficial resemblance to Earth biota. These would be the important types in case of later confusion. They are also the types expected to inhabit the same microenvironments in which contaminants would thrive. If such exobionts exist it is almost certain that they possess at least as effective dispersion capabilities as those of the putative contaminants; moveover, they have been present since an indefinite time in the past. Therefore some evidence of their presence—dormant forms, microscopic fragments and remnant biochemical activities and materials—would be found everywhere on the planet. If such exobionts are present they would have a very high probability of being detected by means of a few rather imprecisely placed devices, some in light and some in dark areas. Various devices that make use of the criteria of growth, metabolic and biochemical activities would permit deductions concerning the background against which future contamination would have to be interpreted. Negative results with devices that detect growth in various media, for example, would strongly suggest that no Martian microbionts can multiply under conditions favorable for contaminants. It would also suggest, less strongly perhaps, that if Martian microbionts are present (a presence perhaps confirmable by one of the other criteria) favorable microenvironments for contaminants are rare or absent, for otherwise some exobionts would have evolved to utilize this opportunity and hence would be able to grow on some of the test media in common with some terrestrial forms.

The devices should perform a sufficient variety of tests to give a fairly distinctive pattern in case of a positive result. They should remain sealed following the experiments, so that examination of their contents may be meaningful if they are recovered. The inclusion of such devices on the earliest missions is important, since any result, negative or positive, will be valuable for future reference and a much needed guide to action.

CRITERIA FOR DISCONTINUANCE OF STERILIZATION

The decision that spacecraft landing on Mars need not be sterilized may be based on observational data, experiments, and theory. The necessary observations relate to the range of physical environments, the surface composition at different sites, and the presence of macrobiota. The purpose of the observations is to permit the accurate simulation of the environments in Earth-based experiments. The experiments concern the fate of terrestrial microbionts in the special Martian conditions known from the foregoing observations.

Theoretical estimates of the probabilities of different degrees of evolutionary convergence at the molecular level, e.g., *Spetner* [1964], may permit a decision on whether confusion as to phylogenetic origin could result from contamination.

SUMMARY

1. The results of projected scientific investigations on Mars are potentially so important that even a remote possibility of invalidating such results should be avoided. Hence a sterilization program is necessary until it becomes more certain that contamination would not have undesirable effects.

2. On the basis of current beliefs concerning average Martian conditions, contamination with terrestrial microbes does not seem likely to have significant effects. This fact in no way relieves us of the responsibility to avoid contamination of the planet for the present.

REFERENCE

Spetner, L. M. (1964), Natural Selection: An Information-transmission Mechanism for Evolution. *J. Theor. Biol. 7*:412-429.

CHAPTER 26

THE OBJECTIVES AND TECHNOLOGY OF
SPACECRAFT STERILIZATION

LAWRENCE B. HALL

Man's ability and intent to travel in space is increasing with irresistible force. The Apollo project will take man to the Moon. Instrumented flights will be the forerunners of manned flights to the planets. A most urgent, perhaps the most urgent, question to be answered by instrumented flights relates to the existence of life on the planets. An affirmative answer to this question has biological, medical and even religious implications that far transcend the results to be obtained by mere geographical and physical exploration of the planets.

The major efforts of engineers and allied scientists who have made the opportunities of space flight possible must shortly turn from the struggle to obtain a successful flight to maximizing the use of a flight as a tool to obtain valuable scientific return. The first such missions, in which the requirements for successful scientific return may be more exacting than those of the flight itself, will be found in the first flights to Mars. In these flights, the necessity for preserving the planet as an uncontaminated subject for life detection experiments must take precedence, even at the expense of missing one or more launch opportunities. Other opportunities will follow, the geology and geography of the planet will remain for future examination, but any flight that infects Mars with terrestrial life will compromise forever a scientific opportunity of almost unequalled proportions. There will be no second chance.

Terrestrial life has survived and multiplied in simulated Martian environments. Should it do so on Mars itself, it could result not only in competition with any Martian life, but in drastic changes in the geochemical and atmospheric characteristics of the planet. To avoid such a disaster, certainly the first, and probably many succeeding landers on Mars, must be sterile—completely devoid of life. Since the space environment will not in itself kill all life on board, the lander must leave the Earth in a sterile condition.

Macroscopic life can be readily detected and kept or removed from the spacecraft, but the detection and removal of microscopic and submicroscopic life is a much more difficult task. The National Aeronautics and Space Administration is approaching this problem in four stages:

1. Develop flight hardware that will withstand the sterilizing agent employed without significant loss of reliability;
2. Reduce the biological loading of the lander to a low level during manufacture and assembly;
3. Achieve surface and internal sterilization of the completely assembled lander;
4. Protect the spacecraft from recontamination during testing and launch.

The development of hardware that will withstand sterilization is a major problem in itself. Sterilizing agents have been evaluated not only for their ability to kill both microbial life on surfaces and that sealed inside components, but for the agents' effect on spacecraft reliability as well. Of the available agents, only radiation and heat will penetrate to the interiors. Radiation is expensive, hazardous, complex and damages many materials more than does heat. Heat, therefore, has been selected as the primary method and will be used, except in specific cases where radiation may prove to be critically less detrimental to reliability.

A qualification heat cycle has been established for materials and components at 145° C for 36 hours, repeated for three cycles. Following this heat application, the component must be proven to be capable of operating within established tolerances for a lifetime compatible with mission requirements. Some spacecraft components are subjected to even higher temperatures during manufacture and test. A number of components are already being made of materials and in configurations that make them resistant to the maximum temperatures required. Other components, of which batteries and tape recorders are examples, cannot at present withstand the qualification cycles without subsequent failure. The problem of batteries has narrowed down largely to one of separators. The problem with recorders is largely one of the plastics used for belts and tapes. Based on results to date, no reason has been found to believe that a full complement of heat-sterilizable hardware cannot be available when needed. Every effort is being made to improve the state-of-the-art to a point where spacecraft can not only withstand sterilization temperatures, but will be even more reliable than present state-of-the-art hardware that is not heated.

Control of the quantity of biological loading on the spacecraft is necessary for the success of sterilization since the greater the number of organisms on the spacecraft, the longer heat must be applied, or the higher must be the temperature. Viable organisms can be kept from the spacecraft by the use of modern clean room methods. Engineers and mechanics understandably are not anxious to work under surgical constraints, but recent data suggest that good vertical laminar flow clean room practice may limit the biological contamination to acceptable levels and concurrently increase reliability.

In another decontamination technique now under study, components may be manufactured under normal factory conditions without special regard to contamination. Then before the component is used, it would be decontaminated, i.e., the biological population would be drastically reduced, though not necessarily brought to zero, by the application of a modified heat cycle. Components decontaminated in this way and made into more complex assemblies would have to be handled under clean room conditions or the assembly must again be decontaminated. The adverse effect upon reliability of the application of extra heat cycles will vary with the materials being treated. Until these adverse effects can be fully evaluated, heat decontamination will not be considered as an operational concept.

Those familiar with operational problems will point out that, despite clean assembly, the spacecraft will be heavily contaminated during necessary tests in facilities that cannot be kept up to clean room standards. This contamination, however, will be on surface only, not in interiors. It can therefore be reached by gaseous decontaminants such as ethylene oxide that will be used to reduce the viable contamination to a low level.

By the use of clean techniques and decontamination by heat or ethylene oxide, it should be possible to bring a spacecraft to the point of sterilization with not more than 10^8 organisms on board.

Sterility of any object is a concept that implies the complete absence of life. The presence of life, or the lack of sterility, may be proven, but the absence of life, or sterility, cannot be proven, for the one viable organism that negates sterility may remain undetected. Certification of sterility, based on experience with the process used, knowledge of the kinetics of the thermal death of organisms, and computation of the probability that no life exists on the spacecraft may be combined to produce the closest possible approach to sterility.

The actual goal established for Mars landers is a probability of less than one in ten thousand, or 10^{-4}, that a single organism will be on board.

Laboratory studies of the kinetics of heat kill of resistant organisms show that at 135° C the number of organisms can be reduced one logarithm (or 90 per cent of those remaining) for every two hours of exposure. The reduction in microbial count needed is the logarithm of the maximum number of organisms on the spacecraft—10^8, plus the logarithm of the reciprocal of the probability of a survivor—10^4, or a total of twelve logarithms of reduction in microbial count. Thus a total of twelve logarithms of reduction in count has been accepted as a safe value which can be achieved by a heat treatment of 135° C for 24 hours. This is the heat cycle that has been adopted and is being used in all studies. However, other heat treatments are under study at temperatures as low as 105° C for periods of time of 170 hours or longer. Such cycles, when developed to the extent that full reliance may be placed upon them to produce sterility, would provide the reliability engineer with a choice of heat treatments so that the cycle selected can be the least damaging to the reliability of the particular equipment involved. The possibility of error in the definition of an adequate heat cycle rests largely upon the possibility of radically increased heat resistance for organisms encased in solids. This potential problem is under investigation.

Proposals have been made to insert into the sterilized lander, by aseptic techniques, heat-sensitive components that have been sterilized by other means. While this is recognized as a possibility, present National Aeronautics and Space Administration policy will not permit its use, unless evidence can be developed proving the technique to have reliability comparable with heat sterilization.

Once sterilized, the lander must be protected from recontamination until it reaches outer space. Ideally, the spacecraft should be sterilized inside a hermetically-sealed canister and remain therein until the canister is opened in outer space. Other concepts would permit the spacecraft to be heated outside the canister. It would be encapsulated after sterilization by mechanics working through glove ports set in the wall of the oven or by remote control actuators.

CHAPTER 27

SPACECRAFT STERILIZATION

N. H. HOROWITZ

The chance that a spacecraft will contaminate Mars with terrestrial microorganisms is a function not only of the number of bacteria carried to the planet, but also of their location in the spacecraft. Bacteria on exposed surfaces will obviously have a better chance of infecting the planet than those which are sequestered within electronic or other components. Fortunately, exposed bacteria are also accessible to bactericidal agents such as ethylene oxide and can easily be destroyed. Sequestered cells, however, can be killed only by heat or other drastic treatments the use of which would seriously jeopardize the mission. This note is a preliminary attempt to assess the magnitude of the risk that would be involved if interplanetary spacecraft were subjected only to ethylene oxide sterilization.

THE BACTERIAL LOAD

Data on the extent of internal contamination of electronic components have been published by Phillips and Hoffmann (*Science 132:* 991, 1960). These authors determined the number of items with internal contamination among 150 assorted electronic components: transistors, capacitors, resistors, etc. The surfaces were first sterilized with ethylene oxide, and each component was then pulverized aseptically and used to inoculate a flask

467

of broth. After incubation, the flasks were scored for growth or no growth. In this way, it was determined that 21, or 14 per cent, of the items were contaminated. The remainder carried no detectable microorganisms. If the plausible, but unproven, assumption is made that bacteria are distributed in a Poisson distribution in electronic components, it becomes possible to estimate the average number of bacteria per component. This number is 0.15, an intuitively obvious result. If it is assumed that the average weight of the components was 3 grams, then there is one bacterium per 20 grams of electronic apparatus, or 1000 bacteria per 20 kilograms.

RELEASE OF SEQUESTERED BACTERIA

Bacteria carried to Mars inside electronic components do not constitute a contamination hazard so long as the components remain intact. If the spacecraft is broken up, as in a crash landing, then there is a certain probability of release (P). An estimate of P as a function of the extent of fragmentation has been made, based on the following model: Bacteria are assumed to be spherical cells of diameter 1 μ. Spacecraft components are assumed to be fragmented into spherical particles of radius r. A bacterial cell is considered to be released if it comes to lie within 5 μ of the surface of any fragment; thus, for example, a bacterium contained anywhere in a 10 μ diameter particle is considered released.

The probability that a bacterium will lie within 5 μ of the surface of a spherical particle is equal to the volume of the spherical shell of thickness 5 μ, divided by the volume of the particle:

$$P = \frac{4/3 \; \pi r^3 - 4/3 \; \pi (r-5)^3}{4/3 \; \pi r^3}$$

where r is the radius of the particle. Some representative values of P are shown in the following table:

r (in microns)	P
5	1.000
10	0.875
50	0.37
100	0.14
150	0.1
200	0.07
500	0.03
1000	0.015
1500	0.011

It can be seen that fragmentation to millimeter size liberates only a few per cent of the sequestered bacteria; fragmentation to the micron range is necessary to free more than 50 per cent.

CONCLUSIONS AND RECOMMENDATIONS

The limited data at hand suggest that electronic components are very clean from a bacteriological viewpoint. Furthermore, the organisms which are the most dangerous from a cosmo-ecological point of view are those which, being located on exposed surfaces, are most easily killed by gaseous sterilants such as ethylene oxide. Organisms that are located within components can be released only by considerable fragmentation of the components. These considerations suggest the possibility that reasonable sterility levels might be attained without terminal heat-sterilization of spacecraft. In order to make a judgment of this possibility, further information is urgently needed on the following points:

1. More extensive studies like those of Phillips and Hoffmann, covering the complete range of spacecraft materials and components, should be carried out.

2. A determination is needed of actual numbers of bacteria in contaminated components, so that the statistical distribution can be calculated. It is possible that a Poisson distribution describes the situation for some types of components, but not others.

3. Also important is knowledge of the kinds of microorganisms prevalent in spacecraft materials and components. Is the population a typical sample of soil or air organisms, or does it show special features? Particular attention should be paid to the proportions of aerobes vs. anaerobes, and nutritionally exacting vs. nutritionally unexacting species.

4. Manufacturing processes should be examined with a view toward suggesting changes that would reduce the bacterial contamination to minimal levels.

5. Data should be obtained on how spacecraft components fragment under impact. Possible methods of minimizing fragmentation in the event of hard landings should be studied.

6. A soft-landed spacecraft on Mars will eventually be broken up by weathering, although this may be very slow in the dry, anaerobic Martian environment. The diurnal temperature change is very great, however, and the effect of this variable on the integrity of spacecraft materials should be studied under simulated Martian conditions.

CHAPTER 28

DECONTAMINATION STANDARDS FOR MARTIAN EXPLORATION PROGRAMS

CARL SAGAN and SIDNEY COLEMAN

It has recently been established that typical samples of terrestrial soil contain populations of microorganisms capable of surviving the rigors of simulated average Martian environments [*Scher, Packer, and Sagan,* 1964; *Packer, Scher, and Sagan,* 1963]. Growth of microorganisms in simulated microenvironments having moisture and organic-matter contents higher than the anticipated mean values of Mars has also been demonstrated [*Young, Deal, Bell, and Allen,* 1964]. These results give experimental credibility to the concern, repeatedly expressed, that the landing of unsterilized space vehicles on Mars may obscure subsequent attempts to detect, in a pristine state, indigenous life on that planet. To avoid possible biological contamination of Mars, it is clear that entry vehicles should be carefully and conscientiously sterilized. This recommendation is in accord with others previously made by the COSPAR Committee on Contamination by Extraterrestrial Exploration [*CETEX,* 1958; 1959], *Lederberg* [1960], the Space Science Board [*Brown et al.,* 1962], and *Imshenetsky* [1963].

A policy governing the decontamination of spacecraft landing vehicles has been adopted by the National Aeronautics and Space Administration (see *Brown, et al.* [1962]); this policy is being carried out. If contamination is to be avoided, the Soviet Union must also implement a sterilization policy for Mars entry capsules. Methods for space vehicle sterilization are being actively developed in the United States, and there is a good indication that there are adequate sterilization procedures which do not compromise the engineering and scientific requirements of the mission [e.g., *Phillips and Hoffman*, 1960; *Posner*, 1961; *Swift*, 1961, 1963; *Brown et al.*, 1962; *Hall and Bruch*, 1964].

At present, the most reliable procedure for insuring a high degree of sterility is to heat the entire landing capsule. In one scheme, the capsule is heated in three spaced cycles to temperatures above 135°C for 36 hr. Longer exposures to lower temperatures may possibly be equally effective. If heat sterilization is to be employed, the initial design of capsule components must, of course, be made with the necessity of subsequent heat sterilization in view. This seems to be a feasible objective; indeed, the reliability of some components—for example, certain transistors—can be enhanced by the heat-sterilization procedure. Nevertheless, sterilization introduces serious engineering problems, especially by decreasing component reliability. The type and duration of sterilization procedure must depend on some estimate of what constitutes an acceptable risk of planetary contamination. Our intention here is to provide a means of computing the level of spacecraft sterility as a function of this acceptable risk.

One early study [*Davies and Comuntzis*, 1960] arbitrarily concluded that the probability of landing one viable microorganism on Mars should be kept below $\sigma = 10^{-6}$ per mission. A recent reestimate by *Jaffe* [1963] places $\sigma \simeq 10^{-4.6}$. However, Jaffe's computation neglects the facts that large numbers of biological experiments will be desirable on Mars, before a significant risk of contamination can be allowed; and that not every microorganism carried to Mars will be able to contaminate a significant fraction of the planet. In the following discussion, we undertake the derivation of a general expression for σ by summing the probabilities of all conceivable scenarios of scientific successes and biological contaminations.

It is important to distinguish between two different strategies for the biological exploration of Mars. In a *mission-centered strategy*, it is decided to send a fixed number of unmanned missions to Mars, after which, independent of the number of experiments successfully completed, biological contamination of the planet (e.g., by manned exploration) is allowed. In an *experiment-centered strategy*, it is decided to conduct a fixed number of experiments, independent of the number of missions accordingly required. Biological contamination is permitted only after a satisfactory survey of Mars and its indigenous organisms, if any, is completed. In the bulk of the following discussions we assume an experiment-centered strategy, and undertake to derive an expression for the probability that Mars will be biologically contaminated in an extended series of experiments. This probability will be a function of σ and other relevant parameters. We will use the following notation:

v is the mean number of viable microorganisms within the landing capsule at the time of landing;

σ is the mean number of viable microorganisms per capsule which are distributed outside the capsule, on the Martian *surface;*

N is the total number of experiments that must be performed successfully before the experimental program can be considered completed;

χ is the mean number of experiments per capsule;

L is the probability that a capsule lands successfully, if it lands at all;

E is the probability that an individual experiment will succeed, assuming that the capsule containing it has landed safely;

M is the probability that a viable microorganism landed on Mars will subsequently multiply, and contaminate a significant area of the planet within the duration of the total experimental program and, finally,

p is the probability that the program of N experiments will be completed without biological contamination of Mars. We will require p to be very close to unity.

We will assume throughout that all parameters are constant during the experimental program. If our mean values of the above parameters are chosen properly, this assumption will introduce no significant errors into the final results. For all cases of interest, the product of σ and M is much less than unity, and thus, the probability that a given capsule contaminates the planet is approximately σM. On the average, N/E experiments must be attempted for N to succeed, and $m = N/\chi EL$ missions are required.

To obtain an initial orientation, we will first assume that $\chi = 1$. The calculation of p may then be performed exactly by elementary methods. It is possible to write down the result immediately, using standard techniques (e.g., see *Feller* [1957]). However, for the benefit of the reader unfamiliar with probability theory, the result will be derived from first principles. We will then show that an excellent approximation to the exact expression may be obtained through an approximate method. We will then use this approximate method to derive an expression for the case $\chi > 1$.

Since it is unlikely that every mission will be successful in its search for and characterization of life on Mars, there will be a number, $Q > N$, missions to Mars before the desired information is obtained. Consider the $(N + j)$th mission, and assume that it is the final in the series of N experiments. Thus, the $(N + j)$th experiment must be successful, because, by hypothesis, we are content to risk a probability p that biological contamination of Mars occurs after $N + j$ missions. The remaining missions may be arranged in any order whatever. Thus there are $(N + j - 1)!$ permutations of the remaining missions. Of these, $N - 1$ will be experimentally successful, where again, the order, for which there are $(N - 1)!$ possibilities, is immaterial. At the same time, j missions will be failures, and once again the ordering of the failures is unimportant. Further, there must be no contamination events in $N + j$ missions. The total number of ways of obtaining such scenarios of successful experimentation before contamination will then be

$$p = \sum_{j=0}^{\infty} (LE)^N (N+j-1)! \; \frac{(1-LE)^j (1-\sigma M)^{N+j}}{(N-1)! \, j!}. \qquad (1)$$

Thus, p is the probability that biological contamination does not occur until N experiments are performed. From the power series expansion for $(1-y)^{-N}$, we find

$$p = \left[\frac{LE(1-\sigma M)}{1-(1-LE)(1-\sigma M)} \right]^N. \qquad (2)$$

Taking the Nth root of each side, we find

$$\frac{LE(1-\sigma M)}{1-(1-LE)(l-\sigma M)} = p^{1/N} \simeq 1 + (\ln p)/N, \qquad (3)$$

since $(\ln p)/N$ is a small (and negative) number. Since σM and $\sigma M/LE$ are also expected to be $\ll 1$, we may expand the lefthand side of (3), finding it to be approximately $1 - (\sigma M/LE)$. Equation (3) then becomes

$$\sigma = \frac{LE}{MN} \ln p^{-1}. \qquad (4)$$

We will always wish to arrange the over-all experimental program so that p is very close to unity. In this case,

$$\sigma \simeq \frac{LE}{MN} (1-p). \qquad (5)$$

We may obtain the approximate equation (5) in a less rigorous, though more direct manner by making our approximations at the beginning of the calculation rather than at the end. We argue as follows: We wish to obtain the probability of scientific success in N experiments before biological contamination occurs. Because σM is very small, the probability of non-contamination is a very slowly varying function of the number of missions landed. Also, because N is fairly large, the probability distribution for the total number of experiments landed—successfully or otherwise—will cluster sharply about its mean value, N/LE. Therefore, to a good approximation, we may replace the average probability of noncontamination by its value at the mean—that is to say,

$$p \simeq (1 - \sigma M)^{N/LE}. \tag{6}$$

Taking the logarithms of both sides, we obtain an expression which is equivalent to Equation (4).

Our argument leading to Equation (6) can now be easily generalized to the case that $\chi > 1$. N is then replaced by N/χ and the remainder of the argument is unchanged. Thus, we obtain

$$\sigma \simeq \frac{LE\chi}{MN} (1 - p). \tag{7}$$

Up to this point, we have discussed only vehicles intended for planetary landings. There is a category of spacecraft, however, intended for planetary fly-by and orbit that may, nevertheless, accidentally impact the planet. If landers are sterilized but fly-bys and orbiters are not, the probability of planetary contamination from the latter spacecraft may be higher than from the former.

The number of microorganisms on a typical unsterilized spacecraft may be $\nu \sim 10^{-10}$. A significant fraction F of these escape from the vehicle upon impact. Therefore, the impact of one such spacecraft has a good chance of contaminating the planet, provided, as seems to be the case, that $FM \gg 10^{10}$. The heat and deceleration of impact will not kill all the contained microorganisms. Thus, the probability of contamination from an intended fly-by or orbiter will be I, the probability of accidental planetary impact, a parameter ordinarily computed in the planning of interplanetary trajectories.

We assume that, *in the long run,* the contribution to our knowledge of Martian biology from fly-bys and orbiters will be negligible, compared with the contribution from landers. Then, if n is the number of fly-bys and orbiters launched towards Mars in the same period as the landers, our previous arguments can be extended to give

$$p \simeq 1 - \frac{\sigma MN}{LE\chi} - n\,I. \tag{8}$$

The division of effort between sterilizing landers and controlling trajectories of unsterilized fly-bys and orbiters is a problem in operations research appropriate to national space agencies. However, to visualize the numerical constraints on σ and I, let us arbitrarily require that the contamination risk from fly-bys and orbiters equal that from landers. We then have, finally, a requirement for landers:

$$\sigma < \frac{LE\chi}{2MN} \, (1-p) \tag{9}$$

and for unsterilized fly-bys and orbiters:

$$I < \frac{1-p}{2n}. \tag{10}$$

Some representative numerical values for σ as a function of N and p appear in the accompanying graph. We have assumed that the mean number of experiments per mission over the entire exploration program is $\chi \simeq 20$, and that the mean probability, over the entire program, of spacecraft failure resulting in no biologically significant information from an entire *mission* is $1 - L \simeq 0.1$. We have also taken the mean probability of scientific success of a given *experiment* to be $E \simeq 10^{-1}$. Estimating the value of E involves trajectory information, since presumably not all locales on Mars are equally likely to have detectable life-forms. It also involves an evaluation of the ability of biologists to design experimental packages to detect Martian life-forms in the face of almost complete ignorance of the biochemistry, morphology, or physiology of Martian organisms.

While every tested terrestrial soil sample has microorganisms capable of surviving simulated mean Martian conditions [*Scher, Packer, and Sagan,* 1964], the exact fraction that survives is very difficult to determine. The problem is complicated by the wide variety of microbial survival conditions and the fact that no culture medium is optimal for all microorganisms. There are many microbial types which do survive freezing and dessication [*Packer, Scher, and Sagan,* 1963]. We adopt a preliminary value of the fraction of survivors $\simeq 10^{-1}$, a value which, after the initial freeze-thaw cycle, is essentially independent of time. But we emphasize that the uncertainty is at least one order of magnitude; intercomparison of soil samples shows a fractional survival range of at least this order. Survival and growth are by no means equally easily achieved, especially under *average* Martian environmental conditions.

In the following discussion, we adopt $M \simeq 10^{-2}$. The graph shown in Figure 1 gives, for the choice of parameters just cited, minimum values of σ. From Equation (9) and the graph, the reader can easily make his own choices of these parameters and redetermine σ.

N is the desired number of experiments for a thorough survey of Martian

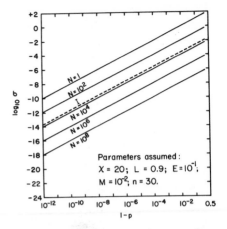

Figure 1.
Risk of planetary contamination. See text.

biology. If there *are* Martian life-forms, biologists will need adequate time to investigate their anatomy, physiology, biochemistry, genetics, ecology, systematics, and behavior. The wealth of desired information per variety of Martian organism, coupled with the potential variety of Martian organisms, indicates that the value of N must be large. However, it is relevant that no existing plans for manned landings are responsive to the contamination problem. There seems to be no immediate prospect of spacesuits with negligible contaminant leak. Indeed, the design difficulties involved may prove insuperable. The specification of a very large N in an experiment-centered strategy will be tantamount to requiring manned exploration of Mars in self-contained mobile vehicles entering and leaving the spacecraft through a sterilization lock.

An alternative and, from the present vantage point, much less desirable procedure will be to accept a mission-centered strategy; to accept planetary contamination after manned landings on Mars; and to maximize the efficiency of the preceding unmanned exploration phase. In the spirit of this alternative, let us adopt 1984 as the date of the first manned landing on Mars.

Assuming an average of three launches of landing vehicles at each opportunity before 1984 by each of two space-faring nations, we have about 60 possible missions, of which 54 land successfully. With $\chi \simeq 20$, this leaves 1080 possible experiments. With $E = 10^{-1}$, we have $N = 108$ successfully completed experiments, a number small compared with the range of biological prospects, but hardly insignificant. During the same period, a number $n \simeq 30$ launches of fly-bys and orbiters appears to be an upper limit.

Suppose it were concluded that $N = 108$ is consistent with an experiment-centered strategy. If we desire 99.9% probability that 1080 biological experiments can be attempted before contamination, the mean number of viable organisms deposited on the planet by each spacecraft must be less than $9.3 \times 10^{-4} \simeq 10^{-3}$. With a mission-centered strategy the analysis follows that preceding Eq. (6), and Eq. (9) is replaced by $\sigma < (1-p)/2Mm$, where m is the total number of missions. But we have seen that $m = N/\chi\ EL$. The equation is therefore identical to Eq. (11), and whichever strategy is used, the numerical results are the same. However, in the experiment-centered strategy N will almost certainly be larger than 120, and σ will be less than 9.3×10^{-4} by the same factor. Especially considering the conservative nature of the value of M in either strategy, a value for the sterilization parameter σ in the range between 10^{-3} and 10^{-4} would seem quite adequate for an extensive program of biological exploration of Mars.

Apart from the requirement that the planet as a whole be protected from contamination, it is necessary to sterilize landing packages containing life-detection experiments, so that there is no contamination of these experiments by terrestrial microorganisms carried to Mars with the package. Here again, a value of σ between 10^{-3} and 10^{-4} should suffice.

These values of σ are several orders of magnitude larger than some previous estimates, and may bring the required dry-heat-sterilization procedures within the thermal tolerance range of many space vehicle components. The results should provide some solace for the engineer, in his effort to maximize the reliability of the spacecraft components, and for the biologist, in his effort to minimize the possibility of biological contamination of Mars.

If we desire a 99.9% probability that the landing program be satisfactorily completed before contamination by accidental impact of a fly-by or orbiter, then from Equation (10), the probability of accidental impact must be $I < 4 \times 10^{-5}$. This is a probability consistent with fly-by trajectories passing within $\sim 2 \times 10^4$ km of Mars—i.e., distances from which significant planetary studies can be performed. Injection of spacecraft into Martian orbit should be made with care, so that the period of orbital decay will be more than the timescale required for the completion of the N biological experiments of the lander program.

We have now completed our objective of determining analytic expressions and preliminary numerical values for σ and I.

These values of σ and I are based on the assumption that we are willing to risk contamination after performing N biological experiments on Mars. It is conceivable that there are other reasons for preventing contamination of Mars besides interference or confusion with an indigenous biota. It is also possible that, in later times, we will think of entire categories of experiments which we are not clever enough to imagine today. In this respect, our values of σ and I may be considered upper limits. In any case, the parameters which were assumed for the computation of σ and I should be periodically reevaluated, especially in the light of new information obtained about Mars from early fly-bys, orbiters, and landers.

There are, however, other lines of work which, if properly pursued, might at some time in the future lead to an increase of the acceptable values of σ and I. We recall that σ is the probability that a single viable microorganism be deposited on the Martian *surface*. In the case of an intact soft landing, only those organisms near the exterior of the spacecraft have a high probability of being deposited on the Martian surface, a point recently emphasized by *Horowitz* [1965]. It would appear at first sight that organisms contained within sealed components, such as batteries or transistors, have no chance of escaping from the spacecraft. If this were rigorously true, the entire sterilization requirement would be greatly ameliorated, because the microorganisms likely to contaminate the planet would then be precisely those which can be killed by chemical surface sterilants. The necessity for heat sterilization would then be diminished.

However, microorganisms may diffuse through solid materials in time scales of the order of a decade [*Sneath*, 1964]. Also, there will always be a non-zero probability of accidental hard landing on Mars, in which case the fraction of the total load of contaminations which are distributed over the Martian surface will depend on the fragmentation size-distribution. If an impacting spacecraft fragments into spherical particles of characteristic radius r, the fraction of contained microorganisms of 5 μ dimensions which are sufficiently close to a surface to escape onto the planet will then be as follows:

$$P(r) \geqslant 1 - (1 - 5/r)^3, \tag{11}$$

where r is in microns [*Horowitz*, 1964]; e.g., if $r = 10$ cm, $P(r) > 1.5 \times 10^{-4}$. This expression gives a lower limit to $P(r)$, because it assumes a uniform fragmentation size. Small fragments make the greatest contribution to planetary contamination. In fact, $P(r)$ should be multiplied by $f(r)$, the frequency distribution of fragments of characteristic size r. Then, if we knew the probability that a given landing results in a particular fragmentation distribution $f(r)$, we could compute the probability of escape of a given organism due to an imperfect soft landing. If we also knew the specific probability that an organism migrates—by solid-state diffusion or through aeolian erosion—a distance r in time t, we could compute σ/ν, where ν is the total number of viable organisms aboard the spacecraft. In general, $\sigma < \nu$.

At the present time it is difficult to make even a fair numerical estimate of the relevant parameters. It is clear that substantial work is required on the fragmentation distribution of model spacecraft, on the diffusion of microorganisms through solids, and on the rate of aeolian erosion on Mars. Moreover, a good estimate of the probability distribution of accidental hard landing at various impact velocities would be useful. Until such information is available, it is premature to assume that $\sigma/v \ll 1$. For the present we must design space missions as if $\sigma/v \simeq 1$.

It should also be emphasized that any spacecraft designed to sample periodically the Martian environment will also provide at the same time some opportunity of egress for microorganisms contained in the spacecraft. Sampling procedures imply a route for microorganisms from the inside to the outside of the lander.

There are departures in spacecraft design which could greatly relax the standards on I and v. Precautionary terminal systems can be developed for assuming non-intercept trajectories in case of imminent accidental impact—for example, by extending the existing capabilities of midcourse-correction motors. Such systems must be failsafe. Possibly more promising, both for intended fly-bys and orbiters and for intended soft landers, would be the development of impact-actuated terminal-destruct sterilization procedures. These procedures can be low in weight and cost, compared with adequate sterilization before launch. Prelaunch sterilization of fly-bys and orbiters is also desirable. The problems attending microorganism solid state diffusion and aeolian erosion of soft-landed vehicles can similarly be circumvented—here, by development of destructive heat-sterilization techniques to be activated after a lander completes its experimental program. The reliability of the timer and sterilization would have to be demonstrated before such techniques could supplant prelaunch sterilization.

Several other decontamination requirements have been pointed out by *Brown, et al.* [1962]. These include provision for an independent authority to certify that the required values of σ are achieved; an emphasis on biological and chemical experiments with the first Mars fly-by, orbiter, and landing vehicles; the acquisition and retention of large numbers of sterile samples by the earliest missions; and an active program to continue sterility precautions after beginning manned exploration of Mars.

Future simulation studies can contribute to our evaluation of the probability of biological contamination of Mars, and therefore to a better specification of the vehicle sterilization parameter, σ. It will be important to determine the fraction of survivors of simulated Martian environments which also survive spacecraft sterilization procedures. It is possible that organisms which are fortuitously preadapted to survive heat sterilization are extremely maladapted to Martian regimes of freeze-thaw cycling. Certainly, there seems to be little selection pressure on Earth for survival of the same organisms both at $135\,°C$ and $-80\,°C$. Further characterization of the Martian environment and of the nature and modes of surviving microorganisms should permit a better understanding of this problem.

Summary. A significant fraction of terrestrial microorganisms survive the inclemency of simulated mean Martian conditions; a smaller fraction may be able to grow at favored times and places on Mars. To avoid biological contamination of Mars by terrestrial microorganisms on unsterilized landing vehicles, the number of viable microorganisms, σ, deposited on the *surface* of Mars by each entry spacecraft must be kept at a low value. We wish to specify a probability p, close to unity, that N biological experiments are successfully performed on Mars before biological contamination occurs, a straightforward probability theory problem whose solution is given in Eq. (9); numerical values are displayed in the accompanying graph. For the parameters chosen in the text $p = 0.999$ and $N \sim 10^2$ can be achieved for $\sigma \sim 10^{-3}$. Values of σ between 10^{-4} and 10^{-3} are provisionally recommended. Not all the viable microorganisms contained in a lander are distributed over the surface upon or after impact; but further study is required before the acceptable number of viable organisms per spacecraft can thereby be reduced below σ. So that accidental impact of unsterilized fly-bys or orbiters does not contaminate the planet, the probability of accidental impact should be kept less than 4×10^{-5}, for the same value of p. A number of experiments can be performed to better our estimates of permissible contaminant loads and impact probabilities. The development of emergency terminal sterilization and trajectory-control devices is recommended.

We wish to thank the members of the NASA Biosciences Subcommittee and of the COSPAR Study Group on Standards for Space Probe Sterilization for many stimulating conversations; Stanley Scher and Elliot Packer, for several discussions on the Martian simulation program and Eugene Titus and Robert E. Wheeler for a helpful discussion.

REFERENCES

Brown, A. H., *et al.* (1962), Report of the Working Subgroup on Space Probe Sterilization. *In: A Review of Space Research,* National Academy of Sciences—National Research Council Pub. 1079, Washington, D. C.

CETEX (1958), Development of International Efforts to Avoid Contamination by Extraterrestrial Exploration. *Science 128,* 887–889.

CETEX (1959), Contamination by Extraterrestrial Exploration. *Nature 183,* 925–928.

Davies, R. W., and M. C. Comuntzis (1960), Sterilization of Space Vehicles to Prevent Extraterrestrial Biological Contamination. *Proceedings of the 10th International Astronautical Congress 1,* Springer-Verlag, Vienna, pp. 495–504.

Feller, W. (1957), *An Introduction to Probability Theory and Its Applications,* John Wiley & Sons, New York, pp. 155–156.

Hall, L. B., and C. Bruch (1965), Procedures Necessary for the Prevention of Planetary Contamination. *In: Life Sciences and Space Research III,* M. Florkin (Ed.), North-Holland Pub. Co., Amsterdam.

Horowitz, N. H. (1965), "Spacecraft Sterilization." Chapter 27, this volume.

Imshenetsky, A. A. (1963), Perspectives for the Development of Exobiology. *In: Life Sciences and Space Research I,* R. B. Livingston *et al.* (Eds.), North-Holland Pub. Co., Amsterdam, pp. 3–15.

Jaffe, L. D. (1963), Sterilization of Unmanned Planetary and Lunar Space Vehicles—An Engineering Examination. *Jet Propulsion Lab. Tech. Rept. 32–325* (Rev.); also published in *Astronautics and Aerospace Engineering 1*(7), 22.

Lederberg, J. (1960), Exobiology: Approaches to Life Beyond the Earth. *Science 132,* 393–400.

Packer, E., S. Scher, and C. Sagan (1963), Biological Contamination of Mars, 2: Cold and Aridity as Constraints on the Survival of Terrestrial Microorganisms in Simulated Martian Environments. *Icarus 2,* 293–316.

Phillips, C. R., and R. K. Hoffman (1960), Sterilization of Interplanetary Vehicles. *Science 132,* 991–995.

Posner, J. (Ed.) (1961), Proceedings of Meeting on Problems and Techniques Associated with the Decontamination and Sterilization of Spacecraft, June 29, 1960, Washington, D. C. *NASA Tech. Note D–771,* Washington, D. C.

Scher, S., E. Packer, and C. Sagan (1964), Biological Contamination of Mars, 1. Survival of Terrestrial Microorganisms in Simulated Martian Environments. *Life Sciences and Space Research II,* M. Florkin and A. Dollfus (Eds.), North-Holland Pub. Co., Amsterdam, 352–356.

Sneath, P. H. A. (1964), Private communication.

Swift, J. (1961), Effects of Sterilizing Agents on Microorganisms. *Jet Propulsion Lab. Astronautics Information Literature Search No. 260;* and *Supplement* (1963).

Young, R. S., P. H. Deal, J. Bell, and J. L. Allen (1964), Bacteria Under Simulated Martian Conditions. *Life Sciences and Space Research II,* M. Florkin and A. Dollfus (Eds.), North-Holland Pub. Co., Amsterdam, 105–111.

CHAPTER 29

THE SPECIAL PROBLEM OF ENCAPSULATED CONTAMINANTS

A. H. BROWN

Viable contaminants lodged within the solid materials which make up a spacecraft pose a special operational problem when spacecraft sterilization is required. On the one hand, encapsulation of a living organism will prevent it from contaminating a virgin planetary surface as long as the organism does not escape from confinement. To assess the risk of contamination presented by encapulated organisms we must estimate their chances of escape. On the other hand, encapsulation *per se* introduces a large uncertainty into our estimates of viability for, although we have evidence that viability is enhanced by encapsulation, we are not yet able to put this on a thoroughly quantitative basis. The principal difficulty lies with the assay methods which are now available. Thus encapsulation is responsible for two effects which alter the risk in opposite directions.

If we could be sure that resistance to sterilization procedures would not be enhanced by encapsulation, we might relax the rigor of sterilization requirements to some degree because surface contaminants are more readily accessible to sterilizing agents. Moreover, ensured confinement of some of the spacecraft contaminants should effectively reduce the total hazard associated with their presence as long as the numbers remain relatively very small. We should then be most concerned with finding ways to reduce the probability of fragmentation of spacecraft components in the event of a hard landing, so as to reduce the likelihood of escape. If we could be convinced that our efforts to avoid planetary contamination would be rewarded effectively by progress in preserving structural integrity in the face of all contingencies, we should be well advised to introduce design requirements compatible with this philosophy into the basic planning and development of planetary mission landing capsules. To do so would, of course, impose restrictions on the design of scientific experiments to be included in the mission and at present it is difficult to be certain how serious such restrictions might become.

Great strides have been made in fragmentation design, and to construct a "fragmentation proof" spacecraft perhaps is not very far beyond the present state of the art. Nevertheless, our provisional conclusion has been that we cannot depend on such measures to provide the required protection; the interiors of spacecraft components must be sterilized as well as the surfaces.

When surface-sterilized solids (metals, plastics, circuit components) are crushed, ground up, and cultured, microorganisms are found to grow in many instances. The number that can be retrieved from a given solid varies greatly and we simply have no reliable assay method for determining the number of viable organisms present in any given solid component. Research on this topic is badly needed. Until we have a satisfactory, quantitative, assay method for encapsulated components we cannot expect to measure with desired precision the resistance of encapsulated organisms toward sterilization methods under consideration.

For a variety of reasons sterilization of the entire spacecraft by dry heat soak would be the method of choice if it can be accomplished. This of course depends on the designers' ability to employ none but heat resistant components. We are optimistic that this can be done. If not, then we must resort to clean assembly of sterile components. Possibly, most of the spacecraft can be heat sterilized and the few thermally sensitive components can be inserted by sterile techniques. Such components might be sterilized by other methods. In our judgment this is a possible, but not very desirable, alternative to a 100 per cent heat sterilizable spacecraft. The difficulties with using sterile insertion methods for many spacecraft components could be very serious and the risk of accidental breach of sterility correspondingly large.

If sterilization methods other than heat soak are required, penetrating ionizing radiation may be efficacious. However, for many types of components the dose of radiation needed to destroy all internal contaminants would impair function and reliability to a prohibitive degree. For only some components, it is likely that radiation will be the method of choice.

As we now assess the special hazard imposed by internal contaminants, we endorse strongly the policy of starting with components having the lowest achievable levels of contamination and of maintaining rigorous standards of cleanliness throughout spacecraft assembly. This will require an extensive program of component selection by biological criteria and an unusually ambitious program of training, supervision, and testing by a "sterility control group."

During July of 1964 a conference was held on the Hazards of Planetary Contamination Due to Microbiological Contamination in the Interior of Spacecraft Components. Salient points arising from this Conference are summarized above, although the Report of the Conference (title as above, Space Science Board, 15 February 1965) should be consulted for the detailed arguments. Perhaps the most significant recommendation made by the Conference was that research should be accelerated on the development of reliable assay methods for encapsulated contaminants. Only by use of such methods can design decisions be placed on a quantitative experimental instead of a conjectural basis.

APPENDIXES

INSTRUMENTATION FOR THE DETECTION OF EXTRATERRESTRIAL LIFE

CARL W. BRUCH

INTRODUCTORY NOTE

This paper contains a review of the characteristics and state of development of some of the instruments that have been devised under the auspices of the National Aeronautics and Space Administration.

The information given here is excerpted from a report prepared by the author for the present study. The instruments and experimental methods are reviewed in terms of the kinds of evidence of biological significance that they are intended to provide.

MORPHOLOGICAL EVIDENCE

One of the best ways to obtain evidence of macroscopic organisms or aggregations of microscopic forms is by means of a high-resolution television system. Such a device would enable us to view the surface with a resolution of 0.4 millimeters from a height of 4 meters with both wide and narrow angle fields between 25 and 45 degrees. Such an instrument is not now under development for biological purposes, but a related device has been considered for use in the program of lunar studies with the Surveyor spacecraft. Such a television experiment has limitations in that it requires large amounts of power and very considerable telemetry facilities.

Microscopes

Development of a vidicon microscope for detecting extraterrestrial life, suggested by Joshua Lederberg, is being carried out at the Jet Propulsion Laboratory of the California Institute of Technology.

The simplest model of such a microscope for space use is called the "abbreviated vidicon microscope." It is a fixed-focus, impaction, phase-contrast instrument. An aerosol sample is injected into the focal plane of the microscope through an orifice in the condenser lens. The lens system observes a 100 micron field with 0.5 micron resolution. The vidicon picture can be transmitted in digital form with eight levels of gray shading and 400 lines per frame. Transmission of this amount of data normally would require more than 500,000 bits per frame.

A second type of instrument, also under development, is the automated scanning, flying-spot, photometric microscope. This device has been used by the U. S. Army Biological Laboratories to distinguish viable organisms from dust particles in aerosol clouds. The principle of operation is as follows: particles are impacted on a clear plastic tape, which then passes through a staining solution; organic particles are differentially stained; and the tape, with adhering organisms, is passed under the flying-spot scanning objective, which monitors the opaque particles against the stained particles. A readout is obtained in terms of "dust versus organisms". The power requirements of this instrument would be much smaller than those of the vidicon microscope.

Both of these instruments have been brought in development to the stage of experimental breadboard models.

CHEMICAL EVIDENCE

Gas Chromatograph

Several chemical detectors for biological compounds are under development. The first of these, a gas chromatograph, is under development also at the Jet Propulsion Laboratory, with the assistance of Sanford Lipsky of Yale University and James Lovelock of Houston University. The basic principle by which the experiment works is the qualitative and quantitative separation and identification of pyrolytic products of organic compounds found in biological systems. This system is based on gas-liquid chromatography, which separates compounds by their variance in distribution coefficients and detects them by means of several sensitive devices. The present experiment is designed to reveal the presence of organic matter in soil samples obtained from the Martian surface. It can suggest the presence of life by producing fingerprint chromatograms of the pyrolytic products of known biochemical compounds, living organisms, their metabolic products, or the degraded products of dead organisms. Preliminary work on the gas chromatography of the volatile products from pyrolysis of microorganisms suggests that fingerprint chromatograms can be obtained that will identify proteins, lipids, carbohydrates, possibly nucleic acids, and other biochemical compounds. If chromatograms are obtained that are not indicative of any pretested terrestrial materials, interpretation of the data would be made by attempting to duplicate the chromatograms in the terrestrial laboratory under conditions identical to those existing during the performance of the experiment on Mars. Furthermore, preliminary data show that high sensitivity optical resolution of diastereoisomers of neutral amino acids can be achieved by gas chromatography. Controls include calibration samples of known organic materials that can be introduced into the instrument just prior to the performance of the experiment. Functional and environmental parameters will be monitored to verify the conditions of the experiment. The sensitivity of this device is in the range of 0.1 to 10 micrograms of organic sample and a single sample that can be acquired by a roving vacuum aerosolizer is adequate. In operation, the crude sample is subjected to pyrolysis and the volatile degradation products are introduced into the separation column of the chromatograph. The components of the instrument include a carrier gas storage tank, gas pressure regulator, separation column, ovens, ionization detector, and electronic circuit components. All instrumentation requirements are satisfiable within the present state-of-the-art; but some of the components need further development in order to be able to survive flight conditions.

The present status of the experiment is somewhere between a functional-feasibility breadboard and a flight-sized breadboard. A flight-sized instrument is estimated to weigh about 7 pounds, occupy a volume of 200 cubic inches (without apparatus for sample acquisition), and require 4½ watts of power. Data are taken for a 40 minute period and require special treatment in storage and transmission. Orientation of the instrument on the surface of Mars is not a crucial consideration, but the instrument must be protected against the temperature of the Martian night. It will survive within the temperature range of —50°C to +135°C. Radiation may affect the detector but it is small enough to be shielded. No pressure effects are anticipated.

It is believed that the instrument can be sterilized by dry heat, but the effects of this treatment have not been evaluated. Surface sterilization can be obtained with ethylene oxide.

Mass Spectrometer

A second instrument for deriving chemical evidence of the presence of extraterrestrial life is the mass spectrometer being developed by Klaus Biemann at the Massachusetts Institute of Technology.

At the present time the experiment is in the conceptual state. Standard mass spectrometers are being used to examine synthetic mixtures of organic compounds. The mass spectra of amino acids, peptides, nucleosides and carbohydrates have been investigated in detail to evaluate the potentiality of mass spectrometric techniques for the identification and structure determination of organic compounds of possible extraterrestrial origin. Complete groups of compounds obtained by breaking down an entire living organism have not yet been examined.

No reference controls are required except for machine operation. The sensitivity is in the range of 1 microgram to 1 nanogram. The projected miniaturized mass spectrometer will have a range of 0 to 250 mass units and may be operated in the range of 0 to 160 mass units.

Only one sample is required. To date, no sampling technique has been devised. The sample must be ground, placed on the tube filament, degassed and heated by the filament. The tube must be evacuated after the sample has been inserted.

The complete instrument includes a miniaturized mass spectrometer, vacuum pump, sampling device, electronics, and an analog-to-digital converter. The instrumentation is within the present state-of-the-art. Based on current estimates, the flight instrument (exclusive of sample collection equipment) would weigh about 15 pounds and would occupy about 400 cubic inches. The power requirement is 15 watts, and the number of bits is between 5,000 and 10,000. A meaningful spectrogram involves the taking of at least 250 pieces of information.

The instrument would not require any special protection from the space environment other than that normally required for electronic instrumentation. Temperature, radiation, impact and vibration have no adverse effects.

There is serious doubt that the electronic components of this device will stand the presently recommended dry heat sterilization cycle of 135°C for 24 hours. The unit could be surface-sterilized with ethylene oxide. It may be possible to assemble the instrument under sterile conditions, but the interiors of the components would still be contaminated.

It must be pointed out that one of the most serious problems in the development of this instrument is that of sample acquisition, which has not been here considered in any detail.

Gas Chromatograph with Mass Spectrometer

A third way of obtaining chemical evidence of extraterrestrial life is the combination of the gas chromatograph with the mass spectrometer. Both instruments have been proposed as broad spectrum analyzers for planetary atmospheres and for the analysis of volatile or pyrolizable materials in planetary and lunar soils. Each instrument has inherent strengths and weaknesses, and each is a powerful analytical device in its own right. Recently, a technique has been developed that permits the combination of these two instruments into a package far more powerful than either instrument alone.

The mass spectrometer provides for most molecules an unequivocal determination of molecular weight and fragmentation products. For most relatively simple mixtures the mass spectrum provides quantitative determination of each component. However, there are many complications in the interpretation of mass spectra. One example of such a complication is the problem of mass doublets. Components such as ethylene, nitrogen, and carbon dioxide, each having a mass to charge ratio of 28, fall on top of each other in portions of their spectra. If large enough amounts of each component are present, a rough quantitative estimation of each may be made on the basis of fragmentation products, but this technique is difficult and inexact. Another complication arises in the analysis of high molecular weight organic compounds of biochemical interest. In such compounds the probability of fragmentation is much greater than the probability of ionization of whole molecules; thus, many different compounds give the same fragmentation products and make the resolution of mixtures extremely difficult.

The gas chromatograph in general separates complex mixtures cleanly into individual components. The identification of the individual components is usually inferred from their retention time in the column. This technique is suitable for laboratory application given some *a priori* knowledge of the input sample and given the availability of each component in the pure state for calibration. For extraterrestrial application it is at once apparent that identification by retention time is much less positive, and the probability of obtaining a completely unknown and unidentifiable constituent in the sample is quite high.

The technique of separating complex mixtures by gas chromatography and analyzing the effluent stream by mass spectrometry has been applied in many laboratories here and abroad. The principle difficulty in this technique is that a large volume of carrier gas must be introduced into the mass spectrometer along with the sample. Extreme sensitivity is required, since the mass spectrometer must be held at pressures on the order of 10^{-5} torr and the material of interest comprises only a very small fraction of this total. Within recent months a technique has been developed for the separation of the sample from the carrier gas by use of a pseudo-molecular beam device. Advantage is taken of the momentum of the heavier molecules flowing from the column to enhance their concentration by differential pumping to a level at least a hundred higher than in the original mixture. Submicrogram samples have been completely resolved and analyzed.

Development of instrumentation of this sort will be carried out at the Jet Propulsion Laboratory with the assistance of S. R. Lipsky of Yale University and K. Biemann of MIT. It is anticipated that an instrument package capable of atmospheric analysis during parachute descent and subsequent analysis of the pyrolytic products of surface materials may result from this developmental program.

Optical Shifts in Dye Complexes

A fourth approach of obtaining chemical evidence of extraterrestrial life involves an experiment called the "J-Band" and is being developed by R. E. Kay of the Aeronutronic Division of the Philco Corporation. It is intended, by visible spectrometry, to detect the shift of the absorption band of a dye (thiocarbocyanine) to one or two new wavelengths upon the interaction of the dye with certain organic macromolecules such as proteins and nucleic acids. As with most dye complexes, a high salt concentration can obviate the results.

The use of a pyrolyzed or oxidized soil sample extract is required as a control in the reference cell. Reference is obtained by dye samples in solution in both a test and a reference optical beam to determine a zero null. Alternately, a standard such as polyglutamic acid could be employed at the conclusion of the determination. The sensitivity is in the range of one gamma of biologically important macromolecules.

A single sample of soil which is processed by extraction, drying, and either pyrolysis or dialysis followed by a conductivity check is required. The sample acquisition mechanism needs much further development. One complete cycle is a minimum; however, recycling is planned to be internal to the experiment with the possibility of using two different temperatures. At the present time the experiment has been demonstrated only under laboratory conditions. No breadboard equipment has been constructed. The instrumentation required is a double-beam, optical-null spectrophotometer together with a light source, detector, amplifiers, and a sample processor. It is estimated that an appropriate instrument would weigh at least 5 pounds, use 3 watts of power, and have a data bit requirement of about

500. It would need protection against the low temperatures of the Martian night.

The ability of this instrument to tolerate the presently recommended heat sterilization cycle is unknown. The dye will have to be sterilized by a "cold" technique. Sterile assembly does not appear to be applicable to this instrument.

The main problem area in the laboratory feasibility study is to have more testing to determine finer distinction between classes of macromolecules and among specific molecules within a class.

Ultraviolet Spectroscopy

Detection of the absorptions near 1800Å that are due to peptide linkages has been proposed as a method for obtaining chemical evidence of the presence of living material. Experiments have been carried out on a wide variety of amino acids, dipeptides, tripeptides, polypeptides, and proteins. It was found that all substances containing peptide bonds exhibited an absorption maximum in the 185-190 millimicron region. Experiments with substances that might give false positive absorption showed that many non-peptides similarly absorbed in this region. However, it was observed that hydrolysis of the peptides resulted in a decrease in absorbancy, as did hydrolysis of the extracts of soil and sand. This effect might distinguish between peptides and non-peptides. However, a recent investigation by R. D. Johnson of the Ames Research Center showed that interference from non-peptide materials coupled with stray light errors would seriously compromise this approach to life detection. Interest is now centered in the possible incorporation of a refinement of this technique with the optical rotatory dispersion experiment described below.

Optical Activity

The sixth, and probably the most important, of the chemical approaches to detection of extraterrestrial life is that of optical rotatory activity. An instrument for this purpose is under development by Ira Blei and John Liskowitz of Melpar, Inc. It is designed to measure the optical rotation of plane polarized monochromatic light at 240-260 millimicrons when it is passed through a solution prepared from a soil sample. Depending on the nature of the extraction procedure, the source of such optical rotation would be either proteins, nucleic acids, or nucleotides produced as a result of biological asymmetric synthesis.

The control required for this experiment is a quartz plate of known optical rotation that will be introduced into the light path. This calibration will serve to establish a base line as well as to establish the functioning of the instrument. The sensitivity of this device, in terms of chemical compounds, is in the region of 1-10 micrograms. In terms of biological organisms, approximately 10^4 to 10^5 organisms would be required for a positive response.

No sampling method has yet been developed for this device. One sample per analysis is required. After collection, the sample will be extracted with an alkaline solution (probably sodium hydroxide); following extraction the solution would be clarified and then introduced into the chamber for observation.

The instrumentation is within the present state-of-the-art and it is estimated that a flight-sized instrument would weigh about 6 pounds and occupy a volume of 130 cubic inches. The power required is 2 watts, and the number of bits to be transmitted is approximately 20. The instrument is extremely durable and would need no protection from low temperatures.

There is doubt that the electronics of this device will tolerate the presently recommended dry heat sterilization cycle. Ethylene oxide can be used for surface sterilization. An instrument with sterile surfaces could also be achieved by means of sterile assembly.

The instrument is, at present, in the stage of engineering breadboard design.

PHYSIOLOGICAL EVIDENCE

Several instruments that depend on the detection of metabolic activities, growth, and reproduction are under development. These and other investigations that may lead to new instrumental designs are described below.

"Multivator"

This apparatus was devised by Joshua Lederberg of Stanford University, and is under development there. The principle experiment to be carried out with this device is the determination of the presence of specific catalysts, particularly phosphatase. However, the Multivator is a biochemical probe that could conduct a variety of biochemical or biological experiments on Mars. The variety of these experiments is limited only by those biological properties that can be measured by a photomultiplier tube as an output transducer. The device can be described as a group of cells or tubes in which samples are introduced and combined with appropriate reagents or biological materials. The resulting reactions are then detected with a photomultiplier. It has also been considered for use in the detection of biologically important macromolecules by fluorimetry, turbidimetry, nephelometry, absorption spectroscopy, or absorption spectral shifting in a test substrate. The basic elements of the instrument are a light source, followed by a filter, the sample under investigation, another filter centered at either the same wavelength as the excitation filter for colorimetry or light scattering, or at a different wavelength if fluorimetric observations are to be made, and finally, a light detector, usually a photomultiplier.

The most recent version of the Multivator consists of 15 modules ranged in a circle with an impeller in the center of the circle. Each of the modules comprises a reaction chamber, solvent storage chamber, tapered valve pin, explosive charge bellows motor, and a filtered light source. The entire solvent chamber is sealed prior to operation by means of a thin diaphragm placed in front of the pointed valve tip.

In operation, dust-bearing air is drawn through the impeller and in front of the reaction chambers. The impeller imparts sufficient velocity to particles larger than 10 microns in diameter to fling them into the reaction chambers, where they tend to settle. Upon completion of the particle-collecting operation, the bellows are operated electrically. Expansion of the bellows results in sealing of the reaction chambers and injection of the solvent. The substrate materials, which have been stored dry during flight in the reaction chambers, are dissolved and the reaction begins. After a pre-set reaction time, the excitation lamps are turned on sequentially and the light signal, or fluorescence level in the case of the phosphatase assay, is detected by the photomultiplier. This information is then reduced to digital form and transmitted. The only control required is a reference cell without a soil sample. Actually, the device contains three dummy chambers for control purposes. The biological sensitivity of the present apparatus in the phosphatase assay is approximately 10^5 organisms per milliliter, and the chemical sensitivity is in the microgram range. Live organisms are not required for this experiment.

At present the sample is obtained through the action of the impeller, which acts as a sort of vacuum cleaner.

With sample collection included, present estimates indicate a weight of about 3 pounds; a volume of about 90 cubic inches; and a power requirement of a maximum of 5 watts. The number of data bits required for this experiment is approximately 5,000. The present device is not affected by radiation, pressure, impact or vibration; but the temperature must exceed 0°C for the experiment to proceed.

Sterilization of the instrument is planned as a two-stage operation. First the Multivator, less substrate, will be sterilized by heating to 135°C for at least 24 hours. The sterile substrates are introduced into the instrument in a sterile glove box. It is possible that the instrument can be surface-sterilized with ethylene oxide gas. It is not known whether or not the instrument could be assembled under sterile conditions.

In the opinion of the experimenter, this device is almost ready for flight hardware development. However, a stable organic reagent for use in the phosphatase assay remains to be demonstrated. From this point of view the Multivator is still in the conceptual stage, and no hardware development will be undertaken until satisfactory dye reagents are developed for the phosphatase assay.

"Gulliver"

Gilbert Levin of Hazelton Laboratories and Norman Horowitz of the California Institute of Technology have designed an apparatus known as Gulliver. It is intended to detect bacterial growth by determining the formation of radioactive CO_2 from C^{14} labelled substrates. The present medium consists of basal salts fortified with soil extract and containing the organic C^{14} substrates as formate, glucose, lactate, and glycine. If the experiment were to function as planned, it would indicate the presence of a biota that could utilize the added sources of carbon and nitrogen for growth. If the production of carbon dioxide were exponential, as is characteristic of binary fission, growth would be indicated. If the production were not exponential, it would not be clear whether the carbon dioxide release were the result of exogenous enzymatic degradative metabolism in the absence of growth or chemical degradation of the radioactive substrate. The success of the experiment depends on being able to supply the appropriate environment for growth. The use of controls is also difficult because identical samples are not provided to both the test and control chambers. During present field tests, an inhibitor of bacterial growth is introduced into the growth chamber of one of the two units. This addition should result in a cessation of $C^{14}O_2$ formation. The number of organisms required to give a positive response has varied during these field trials; but it appears that the soil should contain approximately 10,000 organisms per gram if a positive response is to be obtained.

A single untreated sample is required. The sample is acquired on a length of chenille attached to the end of a line, which is ejected from the instrument. The line is dragged across the surface to collect soil particles, and these are introduced with the line and chenille into the growth chamber.

Recent estimates show a weight of 7 to 12 pounds; volume between 300 and 600 cubic inches; and power requirements of 3 watts average, and 5 watts peak, without heater (an additional 2½ watts is estimated for a heater). The total amount of data for this experiment is 700 bits.

The apparatus consists of a sample collecting mechanism, a main chamber containing a sample processing mechanism, a radiation counter, an electronic signal and data processing system, an electronic programmer, and a heater. All of these items are within the state-of-the-art. The instrument is not affected by temperature, radiation, pressure, impact or vibration. Incubation temperature will have to be kept above the freezing point of water.

It is not known whether the electronics of this system will stand a heat cycle of 135°C for 24 hours. The designers indicate that this heat cycle should present no serious problems. They also state that the instrument is suitable for sterile assembly.

At the present time the experiment can be considered in the status of an advanced flight-sized breadboard model. This experiment appears to be the farthest advanced in terms of engineering of all those now under development.

"Wolf Trap"

Measurement of microbiological growth is the functional basis of an instrument known as the Wolf Trap. The experimenters are Wolf Vishniac and C. R. Weston of the University of Rochester, and development is being carried out by Ball Brothers Corporation.

The experiment is designed to detect the growth of organisms by light scattering measurements and by change of pH. The relative concentration of microorganisms in a turbid culture can be estimated by measuring either the attenuation of a beam of light passing through the suspension, or the intensity of the light scattered by the organisms. The measurement of the scattered light (nephelometry) has been selected because of its inherently greater sensitivity.

The measurement of turbidity and pH has some drawbacks. If the sample introduced into the device contains large amounts of colloidal materials, the background scattering might obscure any changes in turbidity due to microbial growth. Furthermore, the presence of hydrophilic substances, which can swell, could produce light scattering without growth. If the sample contained highly buffered soil, changes in pH could be prevented; conversely, the slow release of relatively insoluble acidic or basic substance would give a change in pH without growth. With the present optical system in the two chambers of the engineering breadboard model, the Wolf Trap gives a reliable signal at approximately 10^3 bacteria per milliliter.

Two types of controls are planned: an inoculated blank (i.e., a non-nutrient medium, perhaps only water) and an inoculated replicate to which has been added some germicidal agent, such as formaldehyde.

The present two-chambered engineering breadboard of the Wolf Trap has been designed to be fully automatic, with the option of operating certain functions manually. The operation of the apparatus is controlled from a portable, battery-operated console that simulates the parent spacecraft. Upon command from the console, the sample pickup begins to operate, the collection nozzle is ejected and the gas flow initiated. Dust particles in the vicinity of the nozzle are sucked into the return line by a pressure drop across a venturi and carried by the gas into the culture chamber, where they are deposited. The pressure drop across the nozzle is adjusted, for test purposes, to a level that could be achieved at a 50 millibar Martian atmosphere. (Specifications for the present model were drawn up before it was known that the Martian atmosphere pressure was much lower than 50 mb). Trials have indicated that the present pickup design would, at best, operate marginally at a pressure of 10 millibars. Sample acquisition has turned out to be one of the most difficult aspects of the problem of designing a life detection probe. One sample is required for each chamber. Thirteen chambers, including controls, but not allowing for replication, are anticipated in the final model.

The instrumentation will include a gas pressure supply, a flexible tube with an enclosure shroud to be dropped to the surface, and a venturi nozzle which will provide a differential pressure.

A five-chamber system is estimated to weigh 5 pounds. The volume for five cells is about 200 cubic inches. Total power consumption is approximately 1 watt. The number of data bits is approximately 300.

The safe limits for experiments are the following:
1. Temperature: —50°F to 310°F. (Incubation chambers at 70–80°F.)
2. Radiation: total flux density of 1×10^7 roentgens.
3. Pressure: vacuum to several atmospheres.
4. Impact: the source lamp will limit shock loading to 2,000 g at 5 milliseconds.
5. Vibration: the unit will be designed to withstand the vibration normally encountered when boosters such as Atlas or Thor-Delta are used.

The sterilization requirement has already been met in the breadboard model; it can be repeatedly heated to 145°C for 24-hour cycles. The need for ethylene oxide sterilization is not anticipated. The unit is suitable for sterile assembly, but this method is rejected by the experimenter.

Development and construction of the breadboard model has been completed.

Detection of Photoautotrophy

Preliminary work has been done at the Hazelton Laboratories in an attempt to convert Gulliver to a device which can detect the presence of a photosynthetic organism. Experiments with *Chlorella pyrenoidosa* have indicated the feasibility of using Gulliver to detect photosynthetic metabolic responses. A urea salts medium containing DL-sodium lactate-1-C^{14} was found to be a suitable culture medium. Initial responses to light change were more pronounced when the inoculated chambers were started in the dark. A Mark III Gulliver has been modified for detection of photosynthesis by placing the light source directly in the culturing chamber. The unit is now being tested.

Detection of ATP

An experiment designed to detect microorganisms by determining the presence of adenosine triphosphate (ATP) is also under development at the Hazelton Laboratories. This development is being managed by the biological group at the Goddard Space Flight Center, who are interested in determining the vertical extent of the terrestrial biosphere. This system responds in fractions of a second to the introduction of organisms. There is no requirement for growth, nor is it required that the organisms be intact or alive. The ATP-luciferin system is well suited for use as a "real-time" life detection system in biological studies of the stratosphere. In terms of planetary exploration, this experiment may not require a landing vehicle since, potentially, it can be used on a probe if a high volume sampling of the planetary atmosphere can take place during descent of the spacecraft.

The reagents for this system contain luciferin, luciferase, magnesium ions and oxygen. The introduction of ATP brings about the emission of visible light. This system, in its present form, will detect approximately 10^{-4} micrograms of ATP. This amount of ATP can be derived from 4,000 yeast cells, 5,000 algae, or approximately 100,000 bacteria. It is hoped to increase the sensitivity by three or four orders of magnitude by use of cryogenics and synchronous detection. The control for this experiment is an uninoculated reagent mixture.

As indicated above, the sample can be obtained by high volume sampling of the atmosphere, or the sticky string device used in the Gulliver can be employed. The sample can be treated with methanol or another solvent to extract the intracellular ATP. A one- or two-minute extraction would probably increase the sensitivity.

The instrumentation would consist of a sample collection device, an extraction device, a processing device, and a photomultiplier tube. These components are commercially available. The power and bit requirements are undefined at present, but they should be in the same range as those of the Gulliver and Wolf Trap. The instrument would tolerate the Martian environment, but the enzymatic reaction would function slowly at freezing temperatures.

The instrument could probably be sterilized with the recommended dry heat cycle of 135°C for 24 hours, but the reagents would have to be sterilized by filtration. This experiment is the subject of a laboratory feasibility study, and a laboratory breadboard model of the instrumentation will be constructed.

Redox Potential

The observation that redox potential will change with metabolic activity is well established. It is common knowledge to the microbiologist that the development of bacteria in broth cultures brings about reducing conditions. In the field of dairy microbiology, various dye reduction tests (methylene blue, resazurin) have been used as indicators of microbial activity in milk.

The Marquardt Corporation has been engaged in the development of a biochemical fuel cell for another NASA group, and as a result of these activities made the suggestion that redox potential could be used to follow the metabolic activities of microorganisms in a planetary environment. Their present biodetector cells employ a calomel reference half-cell as the non-biological cathode and a platinum electrode as the biological anode.

Sensitivity of the technique appears to be low and the time for a detectable change in potential to occur is rather long (e.g., 10^7 to 10^8 organisms and 4 hours, respectively). Laboratory studies are in progress.

Isotopic Tracers

Another possible method of life detection is that of phosphorus incorporation into metabolizing cells. The original suggestion, by Harold Morowitz of Yale University, was to use a radioactive isotope of phosphorus as a tracer, but the half lives of the radioactive isotopes of phosphorus of interest are too short for the time span of a planetary mission. This problem can be obviated by use of phosphate labelled with O^{18}. If this phosphate is incorporated, H_2O^{18} would be formed and the process could be followed by monitoring the O^{16} to O^{18} ratio in water vapor samples.

In a related investigation, the Research Institute for Advanced Studies (RIAS) at Baltimore, has ascertained the laboratory feasibility of using isotopic oxygen anion exchange reactions as a means of life detection. Any living system based on water would, almost certainly, possess the ability to catalyze the exchange of oxygen between water and those oxygen anions that are important in metabolism. The availability of 90 atom per cent excess O^{18} and of water depleted in O^{18} would permit a high sensitivity in the detection of these exchange reactions. Such an assay for living systems can be accomplished, in principle, without knowing anything of the composition of the catalysts or the metabolism that the catalysts make possible. The assay is nothing more than an examination of the ability of aqueous extracts or homogenates of extraterrestrial surface material to catalyze the exchange of oxygen between water, phosphate, sulphate, silicate, RCOOH, and possibly, other oxygen anions at rates greater than those catalyzed by specified background conditions.

A closely related approach is based on the possibility that nitrogen plays a significant role in Martian life. If nitrogen is an important element in the build-up of living matter, or if nitrogen compounds are involved in energy transformations, one would expect gaseous nitrogen to be released and fixed in some parts of the biological cycle. The stable isotope N^{15} may be useful for detecting such reactions. Both of the approaches outlined above would require the use of mass spectrometric techniques that permit sampling of the aqueous solution during an incubation period.

Gas Exchange

Although the techniques now under study and development for the detection of life on other planets make the initial assumption that any existing biota may metabolize specific materials that are well known on Earth, several groups have suggested that it may be possible to detect extraterrestrial life as it exists on other planets without the introduction of foreign or extraneous substances. Terrestrial life requires the conversion of fuel to energy, and this is most likely to occur through an oxidation, or equivalent, process. Hence, in this process gases are usually exchanged. The chemistry of living organisms, while extremely complex, invariably shows a gas exchange. Such gas exchange would permit an inference that metabolizing organisms are present. This, coupled with the output of energy, would allow a determination of the presence of life. It is assumed that metabolism generates energy and liberates heat, that metabolism is a necessary indication of life, and that metabolism is common to all life. Thus, one could detect these activities by mixing the extraterrestrial soil with water to form a culture medium. This would be divided into two portions: one portion would be sterilized and used as a control, the second portion would be followed with devices to measure the production of heat and the ratio of N/CO_2 in the gas phase.

Automated Biological Laboratory

It has been recognized by many scientists associated with exobiology that it will eventually be necessary to place large, highly integrated laboratories of instruments on the surfaces of the planets in order to answer with assurance the question of the presence of life. The problems of design and function of such automated laboratories are under study.

POTENTIAL APPLICATION OF ELECTRON-OPTICAL METHODS TO STORAGE OF INFORMATION FOR DIRECT RETRIEVAL

H. Fernández-Morán

The basic problem limiting the information retrieval envisaged from Mars or any other planetary mission seems to be the limit to the bits of information obtainable, of the order of about 10^9 bits of information, that is given by inherent telemetry parameters. There is also a long time-interval involved. These limitations impose severe restrictions on the design of any type of system for the detection of extraterrestrial life.

It is therefore suggested that the development of a miniature microscope may also be of critical importance from the point of view of information condensation and retrieval. It has been demonstrated that the electron microscope cannot only be used to magnify but also to faithfully demagnify images several thousandfold [*Möllenstedt and Speidel,* 1960; *Fernández-Morán,* 1959]. In our case, we used a commercial electron microscope (Siemens Elmiskop) with a pointed filament source to produce very small microbeams of 100 to 1,000 Å diameter to write and print out letters and diagrams which were only a few microns to a few hundred Å in size (Figure 1). This printing was done on specially developed ultrafine grain films of silver halide (silver iodide and silver bromide with crystallites of the order of 100 Å; film thickness about 100-200 Å). Möllenstedt achieved the same results by a more complicated device involving modifications induced in a plastic film which were subsequently brought out by shadow casting. (Figure 2). This means that one could record any type of information

503

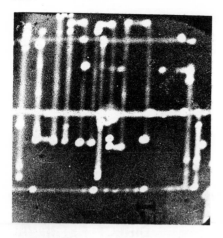

Figure 1.
Electron micrograph of ultraminiaturized circuit patterns produced by photoengraving with electron microbeam probes (500 to 1,000 Å diameter) on special ultrafine photographic film. ×10,000.

Figure 2.
Miniaturized letters (of less than 1 micron) engraved on thin collodion film using electron microbeam probes produced by demagnification in an electron microscope [*Möllenstedt and Speidel*, 1960]. ×20,000.

from letters to diagrams to oscilloscope signals, etc., in such a way that, in the optimal case, the contents of several million volumes of books can be condensed on an area of a single page size or its equivalent. . Therefore, this miniature microscope approach appears to be, in general, applicable to the whole problem of information collection, storage, and retrieval which is a critical bottleneck in extraterrestrial studies.

Specifically, it is proposed that all of the information obtained during the Mars missions and other extraterrestrial missions be considerably condensed by electron optical demagnification (ratio of demagnification, 1:1,000 to 1:50,000 or more). This would mean that bits of information, greater in number by several orders of magnitude, can be imprinted directly onto reels of special ultrathin tape by demagnification electron microscopy. The ultrathin tape of silver halide is about 100-200 Å thick and can be mounted on suitable resistant thin tapes of rhenium, tantalum, or other refractory material. The amount of information that could be recorded in a tape reel with a total area the size of a typewritten page varies from the content of a 1,000,000 volume library (each volume, 500 pages) to approximately a 10,000,000 volume library. A roll of this ultramicrotape after recording would be wound onto a bobbin of only a few cubic centimeters at most. This bobbin could be detached and provided with its own rocket propulsion (plasma or other type of propulsion that is practical and long-lived for such a small object) and with a radio beacon or other device to indicate and monitor its presence and trajectory. This "space courier pigeon" (in analogy to the earlier uses of microfilm transmission by pigeon courier post) would be programmed to "home," back to Earth, by making use of optimized navigational techniques. Once within the reach of our Earth or outer space retrieval capabilities, these microtape capsules could be directly retrieved and read-out in space. This is of particular importance in view of the possible contamination danger. Also, attempts to bring back the capsule would probably involve prohibitively large devices to prevent its burning up upon reentry. It is realized that the problem of retrieval is complex. However, many of these capsules could be sent, or many copies of the first one made immediately and distributed to enlarge the margin of retrievability through redundancy.

The problem of demagnification of the image could be approached in several possible ways:

(a) Either the vidicon image can be made to scan directly, using electron microbeams and electron optical demagnification through a permanently attached miniaturized electron microscope, operating in reverse, so as to print directly on the very fine photographic film which would be slowly unrolled from the tapes. It should be noted that from our experience, extending over more than five years, once printed, these silver halide films, which are of the direct print-out type and need no further development or fixation, are very stable to radiation and preserve detail of the order of about 100 Å quite clearly. This type of recording a television image onto an area only a few square microns in size would be ideal since the direct television image, with a larger number of bits than can be presently obtained, then can be read-out back on Earth or on space platforms with a converted electron microscope and image intensifier.

(b) The alternative would be to use the principle of advanced electron beam recording techniques such as those developed at General Electric by *Newberry* [1963] or some other type of ultraoscilloscope recording, not only for vidicon recording but for recording of all other types of information.

A critical analysis of this admittedly rather speculative proposal reveals that the main operational problem would be one of retrieval. It remains to be demonstrated that it is feasible that an object only a few cubic inches or a few cubic feet at most, if provided with sufficiently compact power supply and navigational aids, can navigate back to Earth with some measure of reliability. It might be asked whether it could escape first order perturbation influences on the way and be literally led "astray." Even if it approached Earth and could make a rendezvous with a space platform or with a large type of satellite, can the read-out mechanism function reliably enough that it can be automated? Many of these questions are outside of the domain of our present experience, but it is perhaps conceivable that by the time this concept is ready to be applied, we will be far enough advanced in our space technology to have space platforms which are manned. Under these conditions, retrieval of the space pigeon (alternative name: "Minicomp" or "Minicompo" system) becomes much more practical.

Actually, the main problem here resolves itself into the basic question, "Is the expected gain in information storage and retrieval worth the whole effort?" Here, the answer is undoubtedly, "Yes." First of all, there is no telemetry device that could conceivably carry this amount of information (of the order of 10^{15} to 10^{20} bits) and provide truly significant data retrieval with a sufficiently high signal-to-noise ratio in an economical and reliable fashion, as the described micro-recorded image. Even if manned space flights to Mars become feasible, the use of information packages of this type is just as necessary as in today's communication network. No amount of teletype, telephone, or even television, can replace the letter, the book, drawings, pictures, blueprints, etc.

This problem will become even more acute as the distances to other planets and surrounding perturbations (magnetic field, sunspots, etc.) make direct electromagnetic radio communications very long or actually impossible. Sooner or later, we will have to develop some type of compact, condensed, ultraminiaturized information storage and retrieval system. It will also be one of the safest ways of sampling alien environments with a minimum of cross-contamination, since a great deal of information can be recorded and transmitted without effecting actual bodily contact.

It should be noted that development of this idea on Earth is already of key significance in order to cope with the critical problem of information condensation and retrieval under the conditions of the present "information explosion." With all of these considerations in mind, it is suggested that this type of approach be given serious consideration and assigned a reasonably high priority since it merits a determined and concerted effort.

REFERENCES

Fernández-Morán, H. (1959), Studies of the Effects of Ionizing Radiation on the Ultrastructure of Developing Nervous Tissue as Revealed by Electron Microscopy. *Annual Rept. for U. S. Atomic Energy Comm. Res. Contract AT (30-1)-2278 for Period Nov. 1, 1958 to Oct. 31, 1959.*

Möllenstedt, G., and R. Speidel (1960), Elektronenoptischer Mikroschreiber unter Elektronenmikroskopischer Arbeitskontrolle. *Phys. Blät. 16,* 192-198.

Newberry, S. P., E. C. Buschmann and T. H. Klotz (1963), *Advanced Electron Beam Recording Techniques: Final Report.* RADC-TDR-63-234, Rome Air Development Center, Griffiss AFB, N. Y.

LIST OF PARTICIPANTS AND CONTRIBUTORS

Colin S. Pittendrigh, *Chairman,* Princeton University
Joshua Lederberg, *Co-chairman,* Stanford University

Steering Committee

Allan H. Brown, University of Pennsylvania
Melvin Calvin, University of California, Berkeley
N. H. Horowitz, California Institute of Technology
Harold P. Klein, Ames Research Center (NASA Observer)
Elliott C. Levinthal, Stanford University
Aaron Novick, University of Oregon
Donald G. Rea, University of California, Berkeley
Carl Sagan, Harvard University and Smithsonian Astrophysical
    Observatory
J. P. T. Pearman, National Academy of Sciences
E. A. Shneour, University of Utah

Working Group

James R. Arnold, University of California, San Diego
K. C. Atwood, University of Illinois
Robert M. Bock, University of Wisconsin
Von R. Eshleman, Stanford University
Humberto Fernández-Morán, University of Chicago
Sidney W. Fox, University of Miami

507

Hans Gaffron, The Florida State University
Donald A. Glaser, University of California, Berkeley
Jerome Gross, Massachusetts General Hospital
H. K. Hartline, The Rockefeller Institute
Thomas Jukes, University of California, Berkeley
Daniel Mazia, University of California, Berkeley
John McCarthy, Stanford University
A. D. McLaren, University of California, Berkeley
Stanley L. Miller, University of California, San Diego
Marvin Minsky, Massachusetts Institute of Technology
John Oró, University of Houston
George C. Pimentel, University of California, Berkeley
John R. Platt, University of Chicago
Ernest C. Pollard, The Pennsylvania State University
Alexander Rich, Massachusetts Institute of Technology
Drew Schwartz, Indiana University
Hyron Spinrad, University of California, Berkeley
Lubert Stryer, Stanford University
Wolf Vishniac, University of Rochester

NASA Representative—J. W. Haughey, NASA Headquarters

NASA Contributors

C. W. Bruch, NASA Headquarters
R. Davies, Jet Propulsion Laboratory
L. B. Hall, NASA Headquarters
P. Haurlan, Jet Propulsion Laboratory
D. Hearth, NASA Headquarters
U. Liddel, NASA Headquarters
F. H. Quimby, NASA Headquarters
O. E. Reynolds, NASA Headquarters
J. N. Smith, Marshall Spaceflight Center
H. J. Stewart, Jet Propulsion Laboratory
W. G. Stroud, Goddard Spaceflight Center

Secretariat

J. P. T. Pearman, Executive Director
E. A. Shneour
A. K. Grittner
E. A. Ottesen
R. A. Fisher
J. A. Durbin

Correspondents

I. Barshad, University of California, Berkeley
F. G. Beuf, General Electric Company
K. Biemann, Massachusetts Institute of Technology
D. F. Bradley, National Institutes of Health
R. E. Cameron, Jet Propulsion Laboratory
Sidney Coleman, Harvard University
R. Colwell, University of California, Berkeley
P. S. Conger, Smithsonian Institution
J. Conway, University of California, Berkeley
C. C. Delwiche, University of Californa, Davis
S. Q. Duntley, Scripps Institution of Oceanography
N. K. Freeman, University of California, Berkeley
K. Fredricksson, Smithsonian Institution
D. M. Gates, National Bureau of Standards
R. H. Gohlke, Dow Chemical Company
M. J. Johnson, University of Wisconsin
Amron Katz, Rand Corporation
S. R. Lipsky, Yale University
R. C. Lord, Massachusetts Institute of Technology
J. E. Lovelock, University of Houston
F. W. McLafferty, Purdue University
H. Mark, University of California, Lawrence Radiation Laboratory
W. G. Meinschein, Esso Research and Engineering Company
A. Metzger, Jet Propulsion Laboratory
Harold Masursky, U. S. Geological Survey
V. I. Oyama, Ames Research Center
R. Pepinsky, Florida Atlantic University
G. E. Pollock, Ames Research Center
J. D. Roberts, California Institute of Technology
R. Ryhage, Karolinska Institutet
C. D. Schrader, Aerospace Corporation
G. R. Shoemake, University of California, Berkeley
J. Shoolery, Varian Associates
F. J. Stephenson, University of Illinois
Verner Suomi, U. S. Weather Bureau
P. R. Swan, AVCO Corporation
H. C. Urey, University of California, San Diego
J. Waggoner, University of California, Lawrence Radiation Laboratory
Ralph Zirkind, Brooklyn Polytechnic Institute
A. Zlatkis, University of Houston

NOTE ON THE SPACE SCIENCE BOARD

The Space Science Board was established in 1958 by the President of the National Academy of Sciences to provide a focus for the interests of American science in the problems, opportunities, and implications of man's advance into space. It is advisory to government agencies charged by Congress with executive responsibilities in the field of space activity. It serves as a voice for the scientific community in this field and attempts to find ways to further a wise and vigorous national scientific program in the space sciences. The Board also serves as the national means, through the Academy, for cooperation with the international community as represented by the International Council of Scientific Unions (ICSU) and specifically, the Council's Committee on Space Research (COSPAR).

The membership of the Space Science Board presently consists of Harry H. Hess (Chairman), Luis W. Alvarez, Lloyd V. Berkner, Allan H. Brown, Loren D. Carlson, John W. Findlay, Herbert Friedman, William W. Kellogg, Gordon J. F. MacDonald, Nicholas U. Mayall, Courtland D. Perkins, Richard W. Porter, Bruno B. Rossi, Leonard I. Schiff, John A. Simpson, James A. Van Allen, George P. Woollard, and Martin A. Pomerantz (ex-officio); Hugh Odishaw (Executive Director), and George A. Derbyshire (Secretary).

Past and present members of the Space Science Board and its committees are:

W. Ross Adey, University of California, Los Angeles
Edward W. Allen, Federal Communications Commission
Lawrence H. Aller, University of California, Los Angeles
Luis W. Alvarez, University of California, Berkeley
Kinsey Anderson, University of California, Berkeley

Gould Andrews, Oak Ridge Institute of Nuclear Research
Kimball C. Atwood, University of Illinois
H. J. aufm Kampe, U.S. Army Signal Research & Development Laboratory

Horace W. Babcock, Mt. Wilson Observatory
Nathaniel F. Barr, Atomic Energy Commission
Charles C. Bates, Office of Naval Research
George Benton, Johns Hopkins University
Paul Berg, Stanford University
Lloyd V. Berkner, Southwest Center for Advanced Studies
Warren W. Berning, Army Ballistic Research Laboratories
John Billingham, NASA Manned Spacecraft Center
W. V. Blockley, Webb Associates, Inc.
Lawrence Bogorad, University of Chicago
George F. Bond, U.S. Naval Submarine Base, New London
Henry G. Booker, Cornell University
Sidney A. Bowhill, University of Illinois
John H. Browe, New York State Department of Health
Allan H. Brown, University of Pennsylvania
Harrison S. Brown, California Institute of Technology
Konrad J. K. Buettner, University of Washington
Theodore H. Bullock, University of California, Los Angeles
Elsworth R. Buskirk, National Institutes of Health

Melvin Calvin, University of California, Berkeley
Loren D. Carlson, University of Kentucky
Joseph W. Chamberlain, Kitt Peak National Observatory
C. O. Chichester, University of California, Davis
Hans G. Clamann, USAF School of Aerospace Medicine
Sydney P. Clark, Jr., Yale University
Gerald M. Clemence, Yale University
A. D. Code, Washburn Observatory
Paul J. Coleman, Jr., University of California, Los Angeles
Gerald F. Combs, University of Maryland
Julius H. Comroe, University of California, San Francisco
Robert A. Conard, Brookhaven National Laboratory
E. M. Cortright, NASA
Andre F. Cournand, Bellevue Hospital
Harmon Craig, University of California, San Diego
James F. Crow, University of Wisconsin
Howard J. Curtis, Brookhaven National Laboratory

William J. Darby, Vanderbilt University
Richard Davies, Jet Propulsion Laboratory
L. F. Dietlein, Manned Spacecraft Center, NASA
Thomas M. Donahue, University of Pittsburgh

Earl G. Droessler, National Science Foundation
*Hugh L. Dryden, NASA
A. B. DuBois, University of Pennsylvania

Richard V. Ebert, University of Arkansas
Mac Edds, Jr., Brown University
W. W. Elam, Office of Naval Research
John V. Evans, MIT Lincoln Laboratory
John W. Evans, Jr., Sacramento Peak Observatory

L. E. Farr, Brookhaven National Laboratory
Wallace O. Fenn, University of Rochester
John W. Findlay, National Radio Astronomy Observatory
William A. Fleming, NASA
Gilbert H. Fletcher, University of Texas
Robert D. Fletcher, Air Weather Service
Elizabeth F. Focht, Cornell Medical Center
Robert E. Forster, University of Pennsylvania
Leo Fox, NASA
Thomas Francis, University of Michigan
Herbert Friedman, U.S. Naval Research Laboratory
Sigmund Fritz, U.S. Weather Bureau
Arnold W. Frutkin, NASA

Robert Galambos, Yale University
Roger Gallet, National Bureau of Standards
Thomas Gold, Cornell University
Leo Goldberg, Harvard College Observatory
W. I. Goldburg, Pennsylvania State University
Nicholas E. Golovin, President's Science Advisory Committee
Solon A. Gordon, Argonne National Laboratory
Douglas Grahn, Argonne National Laboratory
Ashton Graybiel, U.S. Naval Aviation Medical Center
Stanley M. Greenfield, The Rand Corporation
E. Peter Geiduscheck, University of Chicago

Frederick T. Haddock, University of Michigan
Franz Halberg, University of Minnesota
Albert C. Hall, Directorate of Defense Research & Engineering
H. O. Halvorson, University of Illinois
James D. Hardy, John B. Pierce Foundation
H. Keffer Hartline, The Rockefeller Institute
Hollis D. Hedberg, Princeton University
D. M. Hegsted, Harvard University
G. L. Hekhuis, Defense Atomic Support Agency
Carl G. Heller, Pacific Northwest Research Foundation

* Deceased.

J. H. Heller, New England Institute for Medical Research
James Henry, University of Southern California
G. H. Herbig, Lick Observatory
Charles M. Herzfeld, DOD Advanced Research Projects Agency
Harry H. Hess, Princeton University
Rufus R. Hessberg, NASA Manned Spacecraft Center
A. R. Hibbs, Jet Propulsion Laboratory
Samuel P. Hicks, University of Michigan
Raymond Hide, Massachusetts Institute of Technology
Donald F. Hornig, President's Director of Science & Technology
Norman Horowitz, California Institute of Technology
Franklin Hutchinson, Yale University

Mark Inghram, University of Chicago

Robert Jastrow, Goddard Institute for Space Studies
John C. Jamieson, University of Chicago
William A. Jenson, University of California, Berkeley
R. K. C. Johns, Space Technology Laboratory
David S. Johnson, U.S. Weather Bureau
Leslie M. Jones, University of Michigan

William M. Kaula, University of California, Los Angeles
Geoffrey Keller, National Science Foundation
J. W. Keller, NASA
William W. Kellogg, National Center for Atmospheric Research
R. Kilkson, Yale University
Eugene B. Konecci, National Aeronautics Space Council
Zdenek Kopal, University of Manchester (UK)
William Kraushaar, Massachusetts Institute of Technology
Gunnar Kullerud, Geophysical Laboratory

Vincent E. Lally, National Center for Atmospheric Research
Christian J. Lambertsen, University of Pennsylvania
Wright H. Langham, Los Alamos Scientific Laboratory
D. A. Lautman, Smithsonian Astrophysical Observatory
Richard Lawton, General Electric Company
Joshua Lederberg, Stanford University
George V. LeRoy, University of Chicago
Gilbert Leveille, Fitzsimons General Hospital
William Liller, Harvard College Observatory
Donald L. Lindsley, Oak Ridge National Laboratory
C. Gordon Little, National Bureau of Standards
Robert Livingston, National Institutes of Health
*W. Randolph Lovelace II, Lovelace Foundation
Salvador E. Luria, Massachusetts Institute of Technology
* Deceased.

C. C. Lushbaugh, Oak Ridge Institute of Nuclear Studies

Gordon J. F. MacDonald, University of California, Los Angeles
E. F. MacNichol, Johns Hopkins University
Laurence A. Manning, Stanford University
William Markowitz, U.S. Naval Observatory
A. G. Marr, University of California, Davis
John E. Masterson, Pacific Missile Range
Nicholas U. Mayall, Kit Peak National Observatory
Daniel Mazia, University of California, Berkeley
G. M. McDonnel, University of Californa, Los Angeles
Carl E. McIlwain, University of California, San Diego
J. E. McKee, California Institute of Technology
E. J. McLaughlin, NASA
George R. Merriam, Jr., Institute of Ophthalmology
Charles Metz, Florida State University
David Minard, National Naval Medical Center
Philip Morrison, Cornell University
Emil M. Mrak, University of California, Davis
Gerard F. W. Mulders, National Science Foundation
Bruce C. Murray, California Institute of Technology
Jack Myers, University of Texas

Norton Nelson, New York University Medical Center
W. F. Neuman, University of Rochester
Homer E. Newell, NASA
E. P. Ney, University of Minnesota
James J. Nickson, Memorial Sloan-Kettering Center
Aaron Novick, University of Oregon
W. A. Noyes, Jr., University of Texas

W. J. O'Sullivan, NASA Langley Research Center

Nello Pace, University of California, Berkeley
Robert F. Packard, Department of State
Eugene M. Parker, University of Chicago
Courtland D. Perkins, Princeton University
Gordon H. Pettengill, Arecibo Ionospheric Laboratory
Norman Phillips, Massachusetts Institute of Technology
Robert A. Phinney, Princeton University
John E. Pickering, USAF School of Aerospace Medicine
Colin S. Pittendrigh, Princeton University
E. C. Pollard, Pennsylvania State University
Martin A. Pomerantz, Bartol Research Foundation
Richard W. Porter, General Electric Company
Frank Press, California Institute of Technology

C. Ladd Prosser, University of Illinois

Hermann Rahn, State University of New York, Buffalo
Arthur Reetz, NASA
John H. Reynolds, University of California, Berkeley
Donald A. Rice, U.S. Coast and Geodetic Survey
Dickinson W. Richards, Columbia University
Richard L. Riley, Johns Hopkins Hospital
Walter Orr Roberts, National Center for Atmospheric Research
Howard P. Robertson, California Institute of Technology
Randal M. Robertson, National Science Foundation
Bruno B. Rossi, Massachusetts Institute of Technology
Edmund C. Rowan, National Academy of Sciences

Carl Sagan, Harvard University and Smithsonian Astrophysical Observatory
Hermann J. Schaefer, U.S. Naval School of Aviation Medicine
Karl E. Schaefer, U.S. Naval Submarine Base, New London
L. I. Schiff, Stanford University
Hellmut Schmid, Aberdeen Ballistics Research Laboratory
Otto H. Schmitt, University of Minnesota
John H. Schulte, Department of Navy
G. K. Schwan, University of Pennsylvania
Martin Schwarzschild, Princeton Observatory
N. S. Scrimshaw, Massachusetts Institute of Technology
John W. Senders, Bolt, Beranek & Newman, Inc.
Alan H. Shapley, National Bureau of Standards
Eugene M. Shoemaker, U.S. Geological Survey
John A. Simpson, University of Chicago
William M. Sinton, Lowell Observatory
George Smith, Manned Spacecraft Center
Lawrence B. Smith, Sandia Corporation
James Snodgrass, Scripps Institution of Oceanography
Charles A. Sondhaus, University of California, Berkeley
Lyman Spitzer, Princeton Observatory
Leo Steg, General Electric Company
C. G. Stergis, Air Force Cambridge Research Laboratories
John K. Sterrett, North American Air Defense Command
S. S. Stevens, Harvard University
G. K. Strother, Pennsylvania State University
Ernst Stuhlinger, Marshall Space Flight Center
Otto Struve, National Radio Astronomy Observatory (deceased)
Verner E. Suomi, University of Wisconsin
Herman D. Suit, University of Texas
George H. Sutton, Lamont Geological Observatory

Edward L. Tatum, Rockefeller Institute

Kenneth Thimann, Harvard University
John Thomson, Argonne National Laboratory
C. A. Tobias, University of California, Berkeley
Irwin M. Tobin, President's Science Advisory Committee
Paul C. Tompkins, Federal Radiation Council
John W. Townsend, NASA Goddard Space Flight Center
John Torrey, Harvard University

Harold C. Urey, University of California, San Diego

James A. Van Allen, University of Iowa
C. B. van Niel, Stanford University
G. de Vaucouleurs, University of Texas
James H. Veghte, Arctic Aeromedical Laboratory
E. H. Vestine, The Rand Corporation
O. G. Villard, Stanford University
Wolf Vishniac, University of Rochester
William S. von Arx, Massachusetts Institute of Technology
Frank Voris, Office of Naval Research

Shields Warren, New England Deaconess Hospital
G. J. Wasserburg, California Institute of Technology
Arthur H. Waynick, Pennsylvania State University
Harold F. Weaver, University of California, Berkeley
James E. Webb, NASA
Willis L. Webb, U.S. Army White Sands Missile Range
Albert Weinstein, Directorate of Defense Research & Engineering
Billy E. Welch, USAF School of Aerospace Medicine
Frits Went, Missouri Botanical Garden
*Harry Wexler, U.S. Weather Bureau
Fred L. Whipple, Smithsonian Astrophysical Observatory
Charles Whitten, U.S. Coast and Geodetic Survey
William K. Widger, Jr., NASA
Karl Wilbur, Duke University
R. H. Wilhelm, Princeton University
John Winckler, University of Minnesota
Sheldon Wolff, Oak Ridge National Laboratory
Earl H. Wood, Mayo Clinic
John A. Wood, University of Chicago
George P. Woollard, University of Hawaii

Herbert F. York, University of California, San Diego

* Deceased.